D0271568

Drainage and Sanitation

Blake's Drainage and Sanitation

B. T. BATSFORD LTD. LONDON

Twelfth Edition 1962
Thirteenth Edition 1965

Twelfth Edition revised by
Sydney Webster,
Dip. Arch., Dip. T.P. (Hons), A.R.I.B.A.
Thirteenth Edition revised by
Stanley Jennings,
C.G.I.A., F.I.P.H.E., M.R.S.H.

MADE AND PRINTED BY OFFSET IN GREAT BRITAIN
BY WILLIAM CLOWES AND SONS LTD, LONDON AND BECCLES
FOR THE PUBLISHERS
B. T. BATSFORD LTD
4 FITZHARDINGE STREET, PORTMAN SQUARE, LONDON, W.1

Preface to Twelfth Edition

In the many previous editions of *Drainage and Sanitation* by E. H. Blake, CBE, care has been taken to preserve the character and scope of the original publication and without what have now become its "historical" aspects "Blake" would inevitably lose in value. Although the aim has been to preserve this value in the present edition much of the text has been re-written and re-arranged and many of the diagrams added to or modified to bring the information now presented into line with recent developments in the use of materials and with current sanitary practice.

I feel sure that "Blake" will continue to fulfil its established role as hand-book and guide to those approaching the study of sanitation for the first time and as a valuable and effective reference book on all sanitary matters.

Without references to official publications or the willingly given help by manufacturers of sanitary materials and equipment and by their Development Associations the preparation of this edition would have been vastly more difficult and I thank sincerely all those who have helped in lightening the task.

Official copies of the complete British Standards and Codes of Practice referred to may be purchased from The British Standards Institution, 2 Park Street, London, W.1.

Fig. 26 is taken from Fig. 6 of the *Building Research Station Technical Paper* No. 28 "Protractors for the Computation of Daylight Factors" by kind permission of the Controller of Her Majesty's Stationery Office.

LONDON
November 1961

S. WEBSTER

Preface to Thirteenth Edition

In this latest revision the opportunity has been taken to make corrections rendered necessary by changing legislation and information on results of research. An effort has also been made to define more clearly those sections which are included for their historical significance.

It is regretted that Building Regulations, to be made under the provisions of the Public Health Act 1961, have not been published, hence all references to local byelaws should be checked against the requirements of the Building Regulations when they are issued.

LONDON
Summer 1965

S. JENNINGS

Note: For the word "gulley" read "gully" throughout, and "byelaw" as "bylaw". Byelaw is the word used in official documents but most dictionaries give "bylaw".

Contents

1

The Building—its Environment

Geographical location and the consequent differences in climatic conditions in their wider sense have long been recognised as major influences on development of both mental and physical characteristics in human beings. Site selection nowadays, however, is more often determined by considerations other than those of local climate variations. In fact, selection of a site, even within a closely defined locality, is a much less frequent service demanded of architect or surveyor than that of assessing the relative merits of two or perhaps three alternative sites—or of simply advising on the best ways of exploitation of a given site to the best advantage by planning and/or physical means.

A number of factors will demand careful consideration whenever observations are called for, whether the service required is the selection of a site or advising on the detailed siting and construction of buildings and site works.

Climate. Even local variations in climate can be substantial and where sufficient latitude in selecting a site is allowed, rainfall, temperature variations and perhaps sunshine records should be investigated and compared for different locations. It is, for example, well known that in the west of England, Wales and Scotland, rainfall is substantially greater than in east and south-east England, and that temperatures vary sufficiently from place to place for design bases for heating installations to vary considerably.[1] General Meteorological details for a large number of places in the British Isles are published[2] and Table 1 is a summary of the information available for a few selected places. Alternatively, information of similar character is available from Public Relations services and some Local Authorities.

Aspect. The aspect of a site, i.e. the compatibility of its orientation with the demands on the orientation of buildings to be erected upon it, is perhaps the major single factor in determining the planning of a building. Although individual requirements will inevitably vary, satisfactory planning

[1] This aspect is fully dealt with in Chapter 4.

[2] *The Book of Normals*, published by the Meteorological Office: "Averages of Humidity".

TABLE 1

	Temperature				*Rainfall*
	Average for year °F.	Maximum recorded °F	Minimum recorded °F	Average days with ground frost	Average annual fall
Aberdeen	46·3	86	4	151	29·5
Glasgow	47·3	85	7	79	37·0
Cambridge	48·4	89	10	111	24·5
Southport	48·4	89	2	83	32·0
London	50·1	100	4	101	23·5
Southampton	50·8	92	11	61	23·5
Falmouth	50·9	83	20	48	31·0
Holyhead	49·5	86	17	not recorded	35·0
Dublin	50·0	87	13	35	43·5
North Shields	47·2	88	6	132	24·4

will require suitable aspect and prospect for at least the principal rooms. On the disposition of rooms relative to the points of access to the site, to each other and to service mains, will depend the general economy of the planning and the efficiency of the internal circulation.

Entry of sunlight into buildings is a primary consideration and any methods of predicting the extent of sunlight penetration into rooms of proposed buildings have been evolved. The diagrams in Figs 1 and 2 enable both the periods during which the sun will enter a room of known aspect at any time of the year and the extent to which it will penetrate the room to be worked out relatively simply.

---

1 *and* **2** *Sunlight penetration*

Fig. 1 is a plan on which are plotted sunrise and sunset times for each month of the year relative to the points of the compass. (Times are Greenwich Mean Time and sunrise and sunset times taken are for the fifteenth day of each month. Thus in mid-December the sun is shown to rise in the S.E. at 8.30 a.m. and sets in the S.W. at 3.30 p.m.)

Periods during which sunshine may penetrate a building's windows can be determined by placing a plan of the building, on tracing paper, over the diagram, as indicated by the dotted lines, the building plan being first marked with lines at right angles to the building faces through the centres of the windows—aspect lines—and with lines showing the limits of reception of the windows—limit lines. (These lines are marked for the sample plan shown on the diagram.)

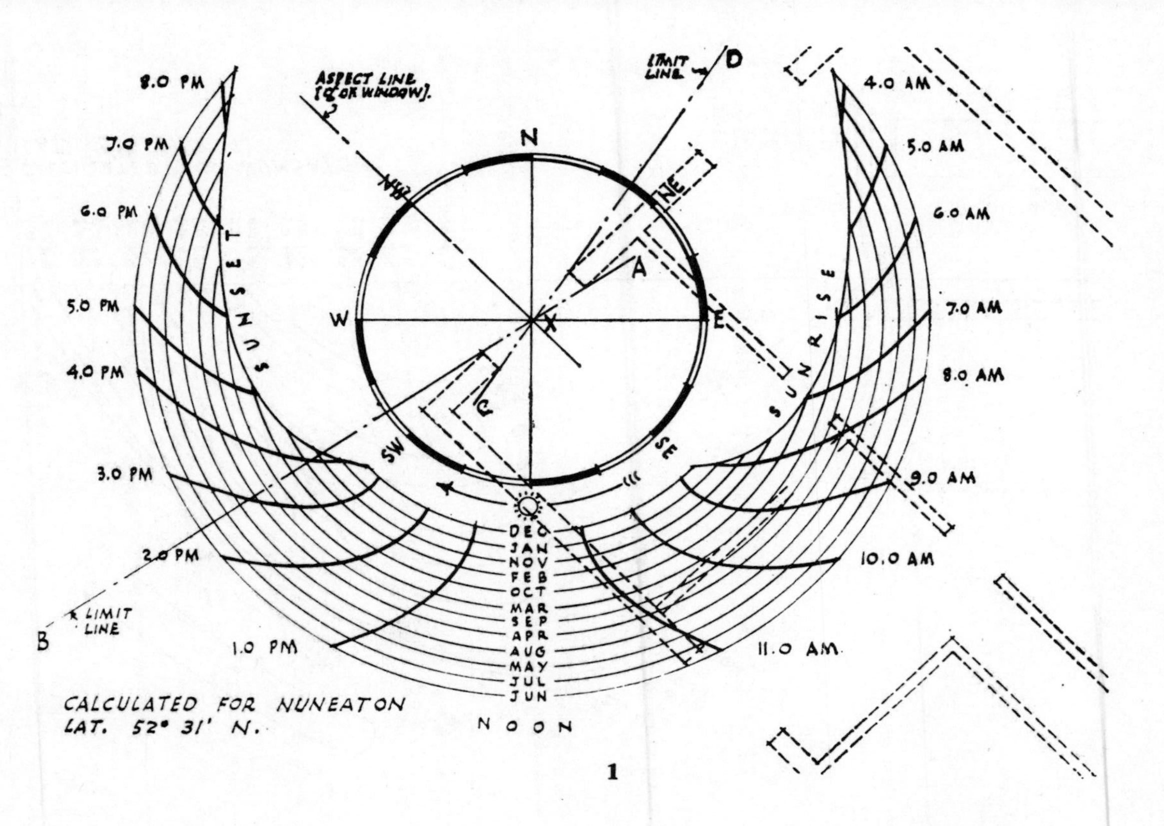
8.0 PM
7.0 PM
6.0 PM
5.0 PM
4.0 PM
3.0 PM
2.0 PM
1.0 PM
ASPECT LINE (℄ OF WINDOW).
LIMIT LINE
D
N
NW
NE
W
E
SW
SE
A
C
X
SUNSET
SUNRISE
4.0 AM
5.0 AM
6.0 AM
7.0 AM
8.0 AM
9.0 AM
10.0 AM
11.0 AM
DEC
JAN
NOV
FEB
OCT
MAR
SEP
APR
AUG
MAY
JUL
JUN
NOON
LIMIT LINE
B
CALCULATED FOR NUNEATON
LAT. 52° 31′ N.

1

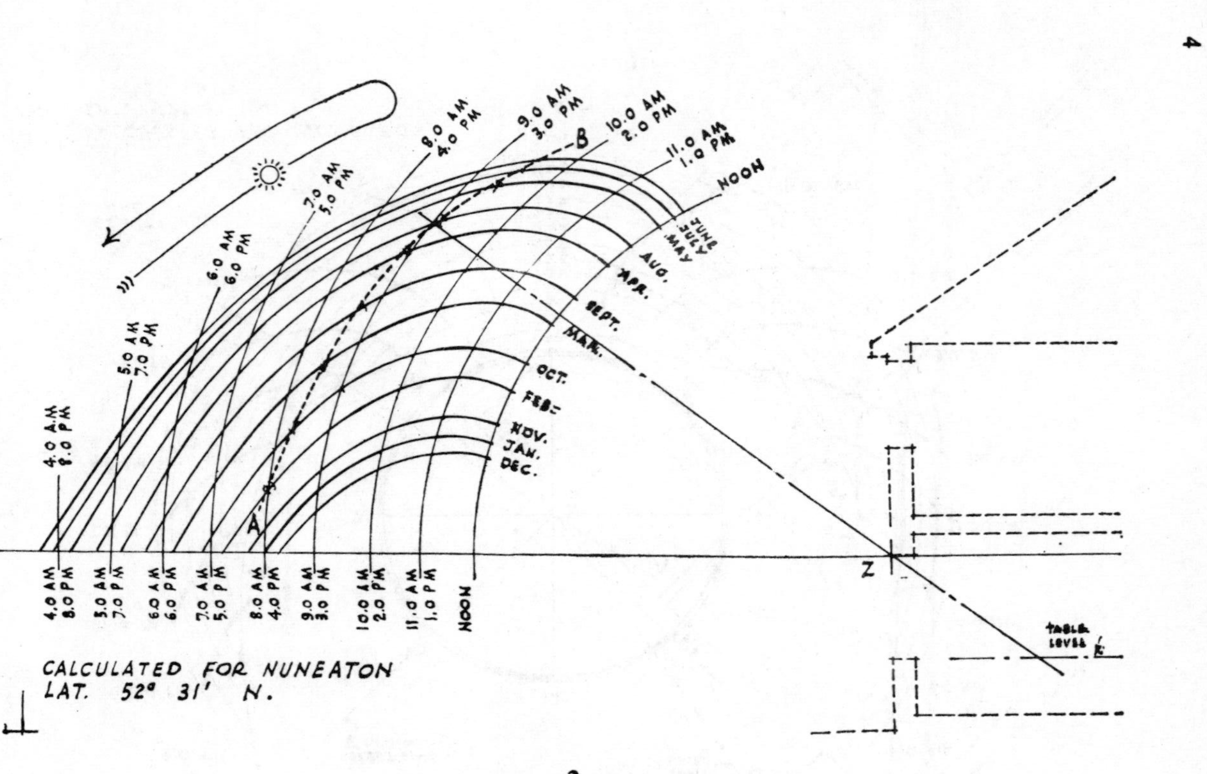
8.0 AM
4.0 PM
9.0 AM
3.0 PM
10.0 AM
2.0 PM
11.0 AM
1.0 PM
NOON
7.0 AM
5.0 PM
6.0 AM
6.0 PM
5.0 AM
7.0 PM
4.0 AM
8.0 PM
B
A
JUNE
JULY
MAY
AUG.
APR.
SEPT.
MAR.
OCT.
FEB.
NOV.
JAN.
DEC.
Z
TABLE LEVEL
CALCULATED FOR NUNEATON
LAT. 52° 31' N.

2

Public services. The availability of public supplies of water and electricity or gas, or of a public system of sewage disposal, will clearly influence choice of site or the economic development of a given site. When public services are not available the practicability and cost of providing private services will demand careful consideration. When public services are available, the positions of mains and positions and depths of sewers relative to the site will often have a direct influence on the positioning and/or the arrangement of buildings and the accommodation they contain. Information concerning service mains is obtainable from the statutory undertakings concerned (the offices of the Local Water, Electricity or Gas Board), and information concerning sewers from the Local Authority (the office of the Rural or Urban District or City Council).

Nuisances. The proximity of existing or foreseeable future nuisance to a site under examination will inevitably modify its desirability. Industrial development, sewage works, refuse disposal centres are obviously undesirable neighbours. Their presence in an area should be considered in conjunction with prevailing winds and the prospect of the site. Any source of noise, e.g. from aircraft, road traffic or railways, is usually regarded as disadvantageous,

---

Point *X*, the intersection of the limit lines *AB* and *CD*, is placed on the compass centre of the diagram.

In the example shown the aspect of the window being examined is N.W. and sun cannot enter the window until limit line *AB* has been passed—from 2·0 p.m. to sunset in June, from about 4·0 p.m. to sunset in February and not at all in December and January. By rotating the plan about the point *X* the effect of different aspects of the window can be readily determined. E.g. it can be seen that if the aspect were South both limit lines would become operative, *AB* determining when the sun first entered the window and *CD* determining when the sun's travel would have carried it past the window.

Although this diagram shows the direction and the periods during which sun may enter a window it gives no indication of the extent of penetration into the building. Fig. 2 is a section on which is plotted the sun's altitude at different times of the day and for each month of the year relative to a given point *Z*. By placing a section of the building, as shown by the dotted lines, with the window head on *Z* the extent of penetration can be seen for any time of day and year for a room directly facing the sun. For the diagram to be of value, however, penetration must be related to aspect. This is done by plotting on the section the times at which the sun can enter the window under consideration as shown by the limit lines on the plan diagram. (The dotted line *AB* is a plotting of the times indicated by the limit line *AB* on the plan diagram and the line through *Z* shows the extent of penetration into the room at 3·0 p.m. in August—the time when the sun first enters the N.W. aspect window chosen as an example. N.B.—If both limit lines were operative both would need to be plotted on the section diagram to determine penetrations at different times.)

and nearness to cemeteries and even to cinemas or dance halls is objected to by most people. On the other hand, attractive views from a site are often considered adequate compensation for disadvantages or shortcomings in other directions. Final decisions can often only be made by a client himself after all the facts have been placed before him.

Local topography. Although such general information as that concerning climate, aspect, etc., is invaluable in establishing preference for locality and in designing buildings in detail, the relationship of a site to surrounding physical features also demands careful consideration from other view points, and may be vital in fact in deciding whether a site can be recommended or not. Relative humidity[1] of the atmosphere is directly related to the openness of the site. Low lying or sites surrounded by higher ground or lying near to open water or marshy ground are clearly undesirable. Proneness of an area to mists and fogs[2] is related in no small degree to humidity levels and local topography. On a site at the base of a hill, ground will be damp because of water drainage down the slope and whilst sites on sloping ground are in general desirable because they are well drained, considerations of aspect and prospect will have far-reaching effects on a site's capacity for satisfactory development (see below).

Soil character must be thoroughly investigated. A sloping site will not necessarily dispose of drainage problems. It may in fact intensify them, if they are not foreseen, whenever impervious strata lie at or near the surface by preventing or retarding the percolation of rain into the ground. Figs. 3 and 4 illustrate diagrammatically the kind of problems which may arise and their possible solutions.

On more level sites, ground formation may result in a permanently high water table or the building up of lingering ground water after rain, either of

[1] *Relative humidity* is the measure of the amount of water vapour carried by the atmosphere and is expressed as a percentage of the greatest amount the atmosphere is capable of carrying. Air is capable of carrying more water vapour at higher temperatures so that if its carrying capacity is reduced, by a fall in temperature, when its relative humidity is high, some of the vapour carried is dropped in the form of dew or rain.

In the same way, air of high relative humidity deposits some of the vapour it is carrying when it comes into contact with a cooler surface. In areas where high relative humidities permanently obtain, conditions are generally damp and unhealthy. Such areas are commonly associated with complaints such as rheumatism, colds, etc.

[2] *Fogs*. The atmosphere contains an infinite number of minute particles of solid matter and fog or mist results when vapour dropped by the atmosphere condenses around these particles. This may occur whenever air temperatures drop suddenly or when air of high humidity meets colder air. Thus fogs result when air movement carries it over areas of different temperatures. At sea or where air is clean, fogs are "white" but where air is polluted industrially, "yellow" or "black" fogs result.

So-called "Scotch Mist" results when rising air meets colder layers of air above it, which is a phenomenon more often encountered on high ground.

which would be liable to produce unhealthy humid conditions. In these circumstances subsoil drainage is often resorted to as a means of lowering the water table or of speeding up the rate of drainage.

Subsoil drains. These are laid below the surface of the ground and constructed so that water in the ground can readily enter them for collection. Usual practice is to position them 2 ft to 3 ft below the surface and to set them at sufficiently close intervals to ensure percolation from all the ground between them. Distance between drains will obviously reflect the degree of permeability of the ground to be drained and the general arrangement of main and subsidiary collecting pipes will depend on the site's general contours and disposition. Fig. 4 illustrates typical arrangements and suitable spacings for pipes in different types of soil.

Unglazed clay pipes (field drain pipes) are the traditional material for subsoil drains. Second quality glazed stoneware drain pipes laid with open joints are an alternative sometimes used, particularly in lighter soils. A recent method used pipes of porous concrete (the bottom third of the pipe as laid being impervious) but the still more recent introduction of pitch fibre pipes, supplied with holes drilled at frequent intervals specifically for use as land drainage pipes seems likely to supersede previous forms of land drains.

In heavy clayey soils laying is often avoided by forming "mole drains". These are formed by pulling a "mole plough" behind a tractor.[1] Mole drains should be formed when the soil is moist and plastic, i.e. in winter or early spring and will generally remain effective for ten to fifteen years.

Control. That benefits do accrue from planning control is now acknowledged by the vast majority of people. To overlook the possibility of limitation or refusal of permission to develop a site under examination is unforgivable and could even be the basis for an action for damages. Information concerning the existence of any planning restrictions is obtained from Planning Authorities. These are in almost all cases County Councils who in turn almost invariably delegate local administration of their powers to Local Authorities at whose office Development Plans can be examined. These show the character and density of development permitted in particular areas, restrictions on heights of buildings, and similar information.

[1] *Mole drains.* Mole drains are formed by means of a torpedo shaped "mole", which may be from 2 in. to 6 in. in diameter, kept at the required depth and forced through the ground by means of a steel blade to which it is firmly attached. The blade is in turn connected to a steel beam attached to supporting wheels which maintain the beam's position relative to the ground. A "grid" layout for the drains (4) is essential and drain gradients are necessarily the ground gradients. Main and collecting drains are trenched drains or the grid discharges to an open ditch.

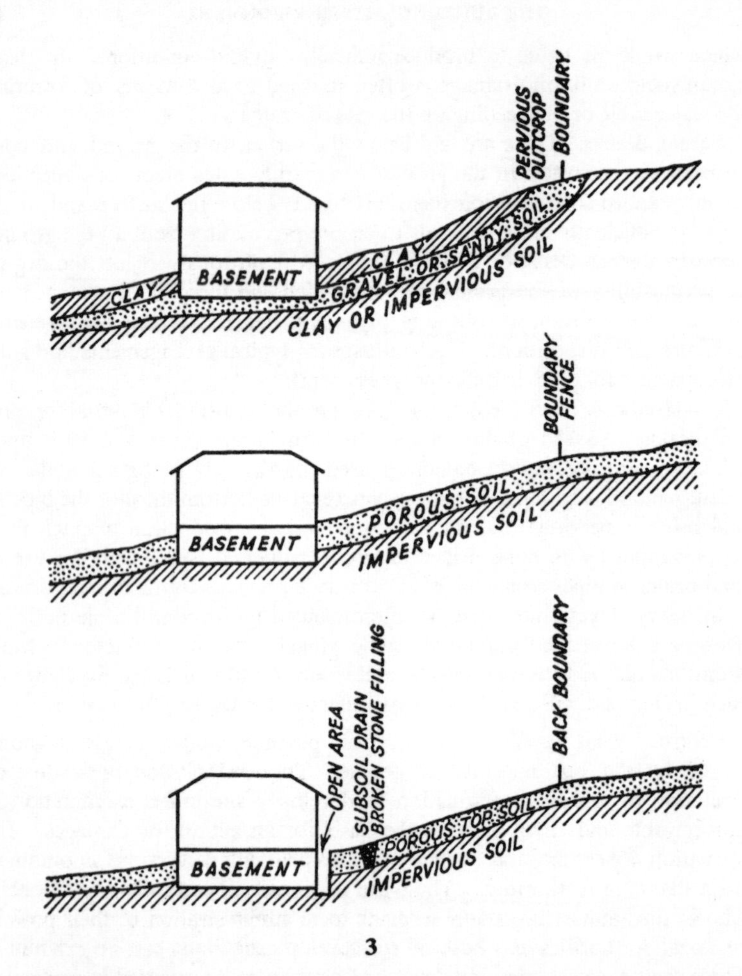

3

3 *Damp prevention*

In the ground formation shown (*top*) the outcropping of the sand or gravel stratum allows water to enter it at high level. This, because of the clay below it, would result in a stream of underground water running around the house basement. The surface clay nearer the house by preventing rain penetration would result in water running around the house walls at ground level.

In the ground formation shown (*centre*) rain penetrating the porous surface stratum would be concentrated around and against the basement walls because of the impervious soil underlying it.

Water could be prevented from penetrating the house walls by making them impervious[1] but a better method where circumstances allow its application is shown (*bottom*). The open area, which would be paved and drained, prevents water from reaching the house walls and the subsoil drain above it diverts the bulk of the subsoil water from the back of the area wall.

This diverting drain, usually called a "French Drain", consists of porous pipes, laid with open joints at the base of the trench which is back-filled with broken stone, gravel or clinker graded in size from coarse material at the bottom to fine material at the surface, the filling being usually topped with a layer of soil at the ground surface.

[1] This is more usual where basements are very deep or open areas are undesirable as may be the case in heavily built up areas of towns. The most usual way of achieving impermeability is to "tank" the basement with asphalt. This is discussed in Chapter 2.

---

4 *Drain arrangement* (see over)

(*Top*) Arrangement of open areas and french drain relative to a house sited on sloping ground (see caption to Fig. 3).

The proximity of a stream or ditch makes disposal of collected water a simple matter but in other circumstances the construction of soakaways may be necessary or alternatively connection to existing surface water drains may be possible (see Chapter 8).

SUBSOIL DRAINS

(*centre, left*) Parallel drain runs discharging to a common collecting drain or ditch.

(*Centre, right*) Drains arranged in "herringbone" pattern. N.B.—Layout of branch and collecting drains will be influenced by ground falls. A simple grid (*centre, left*) is suitable for ground with a regular gradient. The angle of branches to gradient is adjusted to produce a suitable fall in the branch drains with a constant drain depth, e.g. as required for "Mole Drains" (see text). Herringbone layouts are more used on flatter ground, or where drains must be laid against a ground fall. The relatively short branch drains reduce the overall amount of digging needed for the installation.

(*Below*) Arrangement of unglazed clayware pipes. Pipes are available in 2-, 3-, 4-, 5- and 6-in. diameters all in standard lengths of 12 in. The gap between pipes assists in water collection and the cover tiles prevent entry of silt and stones. (Cover tiles as shown are available from some manufacturers or more commonly pieces of broken pipe or tile are used as a substitute.)

The trench section shows the use of clinker or rubble as a surround to the drains. This is good standard practice ensuring efficient collection and also helping to prevent infiltration of silt.

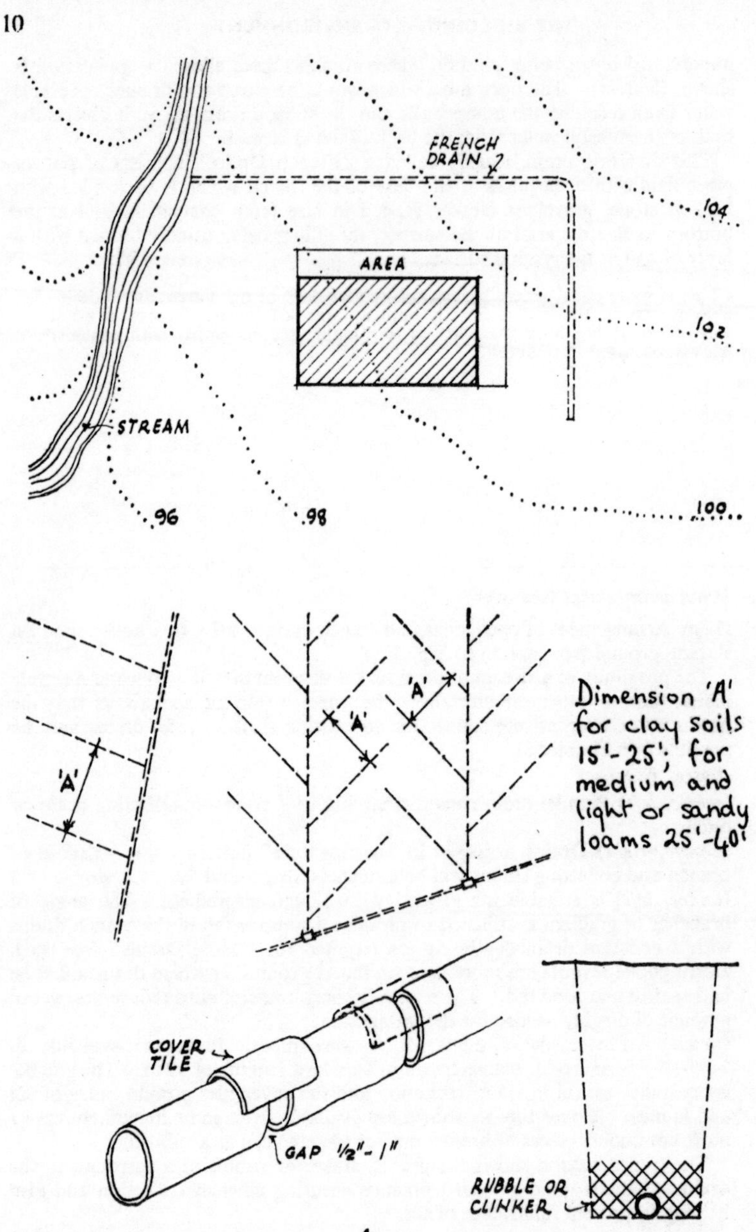
FRENCH DRAIN
AREA
104
102
100
98
96
STREAM
'A'
'A'
'A'
Dimension 'A' for clay soils 15'-25'; for medium and light or sandy loams 25'-40'
COVER TILE
GAP 1/2"- 1"
RUBBLE OR CLINKER

4

2

The Building—its Construction and Arrangement

The efficient construction and arrangement of buildings involves the solution of a great number of problems. Important amongst these because of their paramount importance in creating healthy and hygienic conditions[1] are those of excluding dampness. Methods of preventing water or moisture penetration are well established but choice varies with requirements and with materials and construction chosen for the building's structure.

Moisture penetration into a building may result in a number of ways:

(i) By dampness rising from the ground—through the material of the structure or through the air in contact with the ground below the building.

(ii) By penetration of rain through the surfaces of walls or roofs exposed to it.

(iii) By penetration of water through items of the building's construction which are improperly constructed or which have become defective—roofs, gutters, pipework or sanitary appliances.

Damp-proof courses. Most building materials are to some degree porous, i.e. will absorb moisture and allow it to travel through them by virtue of the capillary attraction[2] created by the minute voids and passages within the material. Because of this walls and floors in contact with the ground would convey moisture from it into the building unless prevented from doing so. Damp-proof courses are layers of impervious material inserted across walls or floors to prevent this movement of water from the ground. (Damp-proof courses are required in other positions in buildings. These are referred to later in this chapter.)

A number of materials possess the physical properties required of damp-proof courses. Choice of material will depend on cost and on the position a damp-proof course is to occupy.

[1] This aspect is stressed in this chapter but the disfigurement and general deterioration of building materials and structures resulting from dampness are also of vital importance and their avoidance is equally essential in good building.

[2] Almost all materials used in building are to some degree porous and water is drawn into the small air passages in the material by what is called *capillary attraction* whenever the opportunity is presented.

In the case of walls suitable materials include sheet metals (lead, copper and aluminium); bitumen or asphalt, placed in position whilst hot and molten, or bitumen in strip or sheet form; bitumen (or pitch), mounted on a flexible base and marketed in rolls of wall width.

Sheet metals have the advantages of flexibility and ease of laying but the disadvantage of being easily penetrated by stones or other obstruction during laying. Metal, and other strip damp-proof courses, require a smooth and level bed on which to be laid. The usual thicknesses in which metals are used are 3–5 lb/sq. ft for lead, 26 gauge (= 0·018 in.) for copper and 18 gauge (=0·05 in.) for aluminium. Lead, the traditional damp-proof material, is the most expensive, is subject to attack by active cement and lime, but is, in general, along with copper and aluminium considered permanent. Zinc, sometimes used in a similar way, in strip of 14 zinc-gauge thickness, is however considered to be of limited life.

Hot bitumen forms an excellent, permanent damp-proof course but application is costly and nowadays is normally reserved for "tanking" work or in situations where vertical damp-proof membranes are required (see later in this chapter). The usual practice in forming damp-proof courses in bitumen is to lay it in two layers of $\frac{3}{8}$ in. thickness, any joints in the two layers being staggered.

The most widely used materials for damp-proof courses are, however, built up bituminous strip. Some of these now incorporate a metal foil which, whilst imparting permanent impermeability, is protected from chemical attack and from physical damage during handling and laying by the bituminous covering. Strips built up with asbestos fibres as the reinforcing medium are to be preferred to those built up with a base of hessian or fibre.[1]

Damp-proof courses formed of slates, laid in cement mortar in two courses with the joints in each course staggered, are still preferred by many people. Although unquestionably permanent and an excellent water barrier, slates are brittle and are often objected to on the grounds that any differential settlement in the building may result in their cracking.

Damp-proof courses in floors. In floors, because of the large areas involved, many of the materials used for wall damp-proof courses are uneconomic. Bituminous felts in wide rolls have been used successfully but continuous overfloor membranes formed by a double brushed-on layer of hot bitumen or a cold-setting bituminous emulsion are nowadays more usual. Some of the latter contain rubber which imparts flexibility and a capacity for adhesion.

[1] B.S. 743 specifies minimum weights for the base and coating and minimum overall weights for rolls of 8 yards × 36 in. wide for different types of plain and cored damp-proof courses.

It has often been found adequate on dry sites to make the ground-floor slab function as a damp-proof membrane by adding waterproofing media to the concrete of which it is formed. These are usually proprietary materials added to the concrete matrix as a dry powder or dissolved in the water used to mix the concrete.

More recently thin sheets of plastic have been successfully used as the damp-proof membrane.

Damp-proof membranes of all kinds need to be laid on level and reasonably smooth surfaces and to be protected from damage. This is sometimes achieved by laying the floor slab in two layers with the membrane between them but more often by laying the membrane on the slab surface and over-laying it with the cement screed used to produce the true and level surface necessary to the laying of most solid floor finishes.

Damp-proof membranes in floors must of course be continuously linked with the damp-proof courses in the walls they abut. This presents no difficulty when walls are of cavity construction but may sometimes involve the formation of steps in the wall damp-proof course when walls are of solid construction (5).

Tanking. When floors are some distance below ground level the providing of continuity in wall and floor damp-proof courses calls for more elaborate construction. The vertical and horizontal surfaces of the membranes form in effect a waterproof box or tank within which the building sits. Work of this kind is called "tanking". The insertion of any length of vertical damp-proofing within a wall's thickness is a difficult and complex operation calling for a complete intermingling of bricklaying and asphalting operations. More usually the tanking is placed outside the building structure—and protected from damage by a second non-structural wall (5).

Placing the tanking on the outside of the building's walls ensures that water pressure which may build up around the building, and which would be transmitted through the wall once this had become saturated, cannot dislodge the tanking layer. This it could more readily do if it were on the inner side of the wall.

The protective covering to the tanking layer is more usually built after tanking is complete to protect it from damage during backfilling of the excavation. Alternatively the protective wall is built first, which enables all asphalting to be carried out in a single operation.

Dry areas. Dampness can be avoided in rooms below ground level without the use of tanking by forming what are known as "dry areas". This was the usual method before the widespread use of asphalt and such areas require, in effect, the extension of the building laterally at basement level.

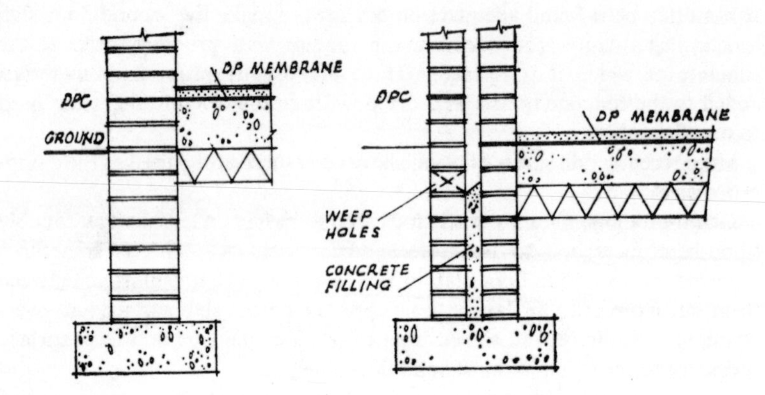
DP MEMBRANE
DPC
GROUND
DPC
DP MEMBRANE
WEEP
HOLES
CONCRETE
FILLING

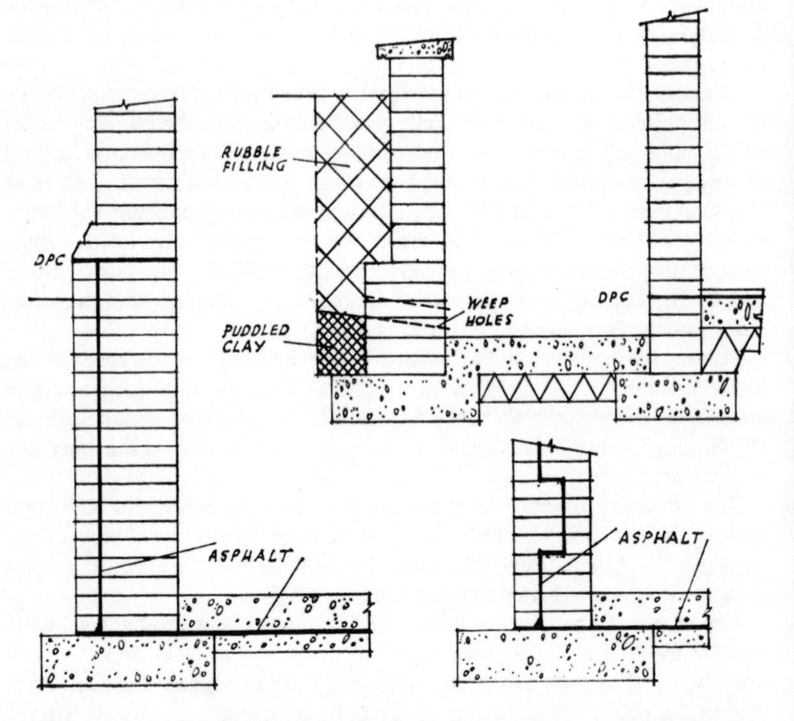
RUBBLE
FILLING
DPC
WEEP
HOLES
PUDDLED
CLAY
DPC
ASPHALT
ASPHALT

5

Although in some circumstances dry areas have advantages—e.g. in allowing exit at floor level from the lower floors of buildings on steeply sloping sites (the area being on the higher side of the building only), and in permitting windows in the walls of the basement they are more costly to construct and generally have the disadvantage of being difficult to keep clean and in some cases of creating drainage difficulties.

Suspended floors. Even when ground floors are not placed directly in contact with the ground the ground below them needs sealing off to prevent the rise of ground moisture. Air within a building, by virtue of its higher temperature (the building being heated or simply occupied), rises so that air from or in contact with the ground below the building is drawn upwards into the building carrying moisture vapour from the ground with it. Although other methods have been tried,[1] some with success, the method almost

[1] E.g. covering the ground with asphaltic material or compounding the ground surface with bitumen.

---

5 *Damp-proofing of walls* (1)

(*Above*) Floor membranes in conjunction with damp-proof courses in a solid wall (*left*) and a cavity wall (*right*). Wall and floor membranes are linked so as to be continuous and the level of the wall damp-proof course should be at least 6 in. above the ground outside. When solid walls are used achieving this may entail stepping the damp-proof course vertically within the walls' thickness but presents no problem in cavity walls where the cavity makes a link between the damp-proof courses in the two leaves of the wall unneceessary.

Note how water which penetrates into or condenses within the cavity is allowed to escape. Weep-holes are open perpends in the brickwork at about 3 ft centres and set below the damp-proof course level.

(*Centre, right*) Building wall below ground kept dry by a dry area, normal damp-proofing only being required. The rubble filling behind and the weep holes through the area wall (short lengths of stoneware pipe are commonly used) prevent its disfigurement to some extent and prevent water pressure building up behind it. The area itself would require to be drained.

(*Below*) Asphalt tanking to walls below ground. At left the asphalt is shown applied to the outside of the wall and then protected from physical damage by an additional thin wall. This is the simplest way although it requires that the inner wall alone must resist overturning pressure from the earth and is usually preferred to the method shown at right which although making full use of all the brickwork in resisting overturning complicates the asphalt placing considerably.

Asphalt for tanking should be applied in three layers, to a total thickness of ¾ in. and 1⅛ in. on vertical and horizontal surfaces respectively, junctions between areas of laying being staggered in successive layers. Note how asphalt is made to oversail at changes in plane and how junctions of asphalt in different planes are reinforced by fillets. As shown, tanking should always end at a through wall damp-proof course.

invariably used to seal the ground surface is to cover it with a layer of concrete, site concrete, which in addition to reducing the emanation of water vapour from the ground also prevents plant growth beneath the building. Suspended ground floors, by no means as popular nowadays as formerly, are traditionally of timber construction. Timber which is damp becomes susceptible to attack by fungus, "dry rot",[1] which by feeding on the cellulose in the timber eventually destroys it. To ensure that the level of moisture in the timber is kept below the level at which dry rot fungus is sustained not only must wall damp-proof courses be placed below all timbers in contact with the structure but the space between the site concrete and the floor timbers must be ventilated.[2] This is achieved by gratings, or perforated bricks, air bricks, built into the wall below floor level. These are carefully placed to ensure ventilation of all parts of the underfloor space, any intermediate supporting walls to the floor[3] being of "honeycomb" construction to allow air to pass freely through them.

When solid floors adjoin suspended floors providing for the cross ventilation below the suspended portion is more difficult. (The situation often arises when a living room adjoins a kitchen where a solid completely waterproof floor is often required.) The formation of ducts below the solid floor to carry air from an external wall to the areas below the suspended floors which would otherwise be by-passed by the air circulation is shown (6).[4]

In favour of suspended floors it is said that their greater resilience gives greater comfort to users and makes floors less tiring and that the illusion of warmth because of the non-conducting character of the surface itself outweighs the actual reduced heat loss of solid floors which feel cold to the touch. Wood surfacing can and often is applied to surfaces of solid floors however.

Water penetration through walls of bricks or blocks. Most bricks or blocks are to some degree absorbent. Those selected for external facings of build-

[1] Dry rot is not the only fungus which attacks timber but is the most virulent and the one to which timber is most readily susceptible and in the prevention of which conditions of timber installation play a critical part.

[2] In this country adequate ventilation—i.e. free circulation of air—is sufficient to keep the moisture content of timber below the critical content required to support dry rot, about 20 per cent of the dry weight.

[3] These are called "sleeper walls" and are arranged to reduce the distance the suspended ground floor's joists are required to span. The comparatively small loads they are required to carry enables them to be built off the site concrete without other foundation, and makes their honeycomb construction of adequate strength.

[4] On reasonably level sites solid floors are less costly both in themselves and in overall height of the building they require to accommodate them. The increase in their use during and since the Second World War is often correctly attributed to the shortage and high cost of timber during that period. Their continuing popularity springs from their greater efficiency in preventing heat losses from the building and from the development of a wide selection of low cost, long lasting surfacing materials of good appearance.

ings because of requirements of appearance, or perhaps cost, are almost invariably so. Solid walls generally resist penetration in depth. Rain which beats on to the external surface is partially absorbed and slowly penetrates, the depth of penetration being proportional in part to the duration of the rain and in part to the volume of voids in the bricks which may help to reduce penetration by virtue of their capacity to hold water.[1] Walls give up their moisture content by evaporation when the rain stops. Thus in periods of continuous rain even solid walls of considerable thickness may allow water to penetrate them.

Even when bricks are impervious joints are vulnerable and these are in any case subject to cracking due to movement or shrinkage and so liable to destroy the wall's efficiency as a water excluder. Thus in many cases walls amply thick enough to support the structure and its loads are not capable of safely excluding rain. In domestic buildings 9 in. thick walls have been extensively used, often with the addition of a protective coat of cement rendering externally. This can be and often has proved effective[2] in excluding water but the real reason for its use has often been to cover the low cost bricks used in the construction. Rendering is associated with this purpose in the minds of many people. It is now generally accepted that cavity walls are essential in any but the most sheltered situations if water is to be safely excluded without excessive material. In addition cavity walls possess far greater resistance to the passage of heat through them and so produce conditions of greater comfort within buildings and economy of fuel in heating them.

Cavity walls. Cavity walls are double walls built with a small space between them. Water penetrating the outer leaf of the wall, which it may often do quite easily, cannot reach the inner leaf of the wall and the interior of the building because of the cavity. For cavity walls to be economic in material both leaves of the wall must contribute to the support of the building and to ensure this the two leaves are linked by wall ties sufficiently closely spaced to

[1] Walls of very porous bricks, i.e. which have a high proportion of voids in their structure, often prove efficient water excluders simply because of their capacity to hold large quantities of water.

[2] Rendering for best results should be porous so that water penetrating its surface can later emerge through the external surface. If rendered surfaces crack and this is always likely because of the shrinkage which occurs in cement when it sets, water readily enters the cracks to become trapped behind its surface—increasing the likelihood of penetration through the wall or of the loosening and eventual dislodgement of the rendering particularly if trapped water becomes frozen.

A sound practice is to include lime in the mix of the rendering to impart "flexibility", (1: 1: 6 and 1: 2: 9 are widely used mixes), and to finish the rendering with a rough or textured surface. "Spatterdash" finishes are now widely used and these like the traditional "pebble dash" finish have the advantage of creating very large numbers of natural paths along which the rendering can crack. This "direction" of cracking produces large numbers of "invisible" cracks avoiding both the damaging large cracks and the disfiguring crazing often associated with smooth surfaced rendering.

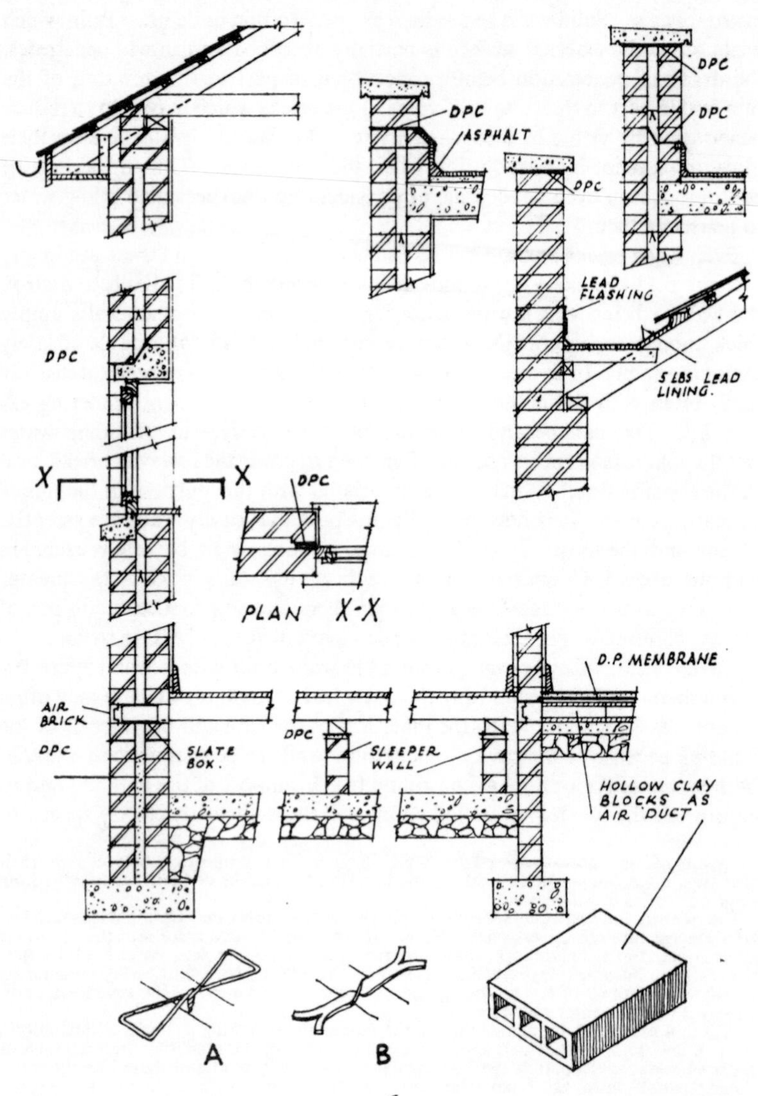
DPC
ASPHALT
DPC
DPC
DPC
LEAD
FLASHING
5 LBS LEAD
LINING.
DPC
X
X
DPC
PLAN X-X
D.P. MEMBRANE
AIR
BRICK
DPC
SLATE
BOX.
DPC
SLEEPER
WALL
HOLLOW CLAY
BLOCKS AS
AIR DUCT
A
B

6

6 *Damp-proofing of walls* (2)

(*Left*) The section shows the eaves to a pitched slate roof. The eaves overhang and the gutter protect the upper part of the wall. The diagram shows the arrangements of head-nailed slates. The double layer of slates required to make roof watertight and a straight edge are maintained by making the lowest slate the shorter (see also caption to Fig. 7). Note the bridging of the cavity by brick-work. This prevents ventilation of the cavity and makes sure the roof load is shared by both leaves of the wall.

Penetration through the solid areas necessary around openings through cavity walls is prevented at the head by the use of a damp-proof membrane arranged to direct penetrating water to the outer leaf. (The cavity is often drained at this point as at the main cavity base—see Fig. 5.) To be effective the membrane should oversail the lintel at each end.

Penetration at the cill is prevented by the use of a cill of water-proof material weathered and formed to throw water clear of the wall. When cills are built up of say bricks, or sometimes to insure against cracking, cills are laid over a damp-proof course.

Penetration at jambs of openings is prevented by the insertion of a damp-proof course in the thickness of the bridging. This may be of slate, as shown on plan *X–X*, or of other damp-proof material.

Ventilation inlets to space below suspended floors must be sealed off to prevent them from ventilating the cavity. To prevent water reaching the inner leaf of the wall the top and bottom of the slate box shown slope towards the outer leaf. Within the building, circulation of air below the floor is ensured by outlets on the opposite face and by supporting walls to the floor being of honeycomb construction. The floor shown adjoins an area of solid floor and to secure the necessary cross-ventilation of the under-floor area air is brought to it by means of ducts set in the thickness of the solid floor.

For the two leaves of cavity walls to function as a unit they must be effectively tied together. Model bylaws call for ties at not greater intervals than 18 in. vertically and 3 ft horizontally. Two typical forms of tie are shown. A is a tie of twisted wire, made of galvanised steel or copper. B is a flat twisted galvanised steel tie which has somewhat greater stiffness and for this reason is preferred by some authorities.

(*Above, right*) Prevention of penetration through parapet walls calls for damp-proof courses. These should be placed immediately beneath copings to prevent penetration through the top of the wall from disfiguring or disrupting the wall by water movement through it. Where parapets are of cavity construction they should be placed across the cavity immediately above roof level.

When parapet walls are high, as shown at the right, both faces are inevitably exposed to weather and this inevitably results in different weathering and earlier deterioration of this part of the wall. The advantage of cavity construction in this situation is in ensuring that the whole of the outer face of the wall is exposed to exactly similar weathering conditions and that variations in appearance do not occur. (Note the arrangement of the damp-proof course at roof level to prevent penetration through the "inner" leaf from reaching the "outer" leaf.)

ensure that the two leaves function as a structural unit (6). Ties which are of steel protected from corrosion by galvanising, or of non-ferrous metal, are shaped and arranged to prevent water which penetrates the outer leaf of the wall from running across them to reach the inner leaf (6).

The fact that water may easily penetrate the thin outer leaf of the wall makes it necessary to provide for its escape. This provision is in the form of "weep-holes", small outlet points, in the outer leaf which are positioned below the two damp-proof courses at the bases of the wall.

Openings in cavity walls. If cavity walls are to be efficient the necessary bridging of the cavity wherever openings are made through the wall must be carried out in a way which will prevent water penetration through the solid areas of the bridging. This is done by local damp-proof courses set in the bridging itself, as at the jambs of openings, or arranged to direct any penetrating water back to the outer leaf of the wall, as above openings through the walls (6).

Thermal value of cavity walls. In addition to forming an effective barrier to water penetration the cavity also forms an efficient barrier to the passage of heat through the wall. This is due to the fact that in addition to the resistance offered by a material to the conductance of heat through it additional resistance is set up by the surfaces of the material to its entry and egress. These surface resistances are not dependent on the thickness of the material and the greater insulating value of cavity walls arises from two additional surfaces of the cavity. The resistance to heat flow from surfaces is greatly reduced if air is allowed to move across them and so carry away heat by convection,[1] thus full efficiency in terms of insulation is only obtained when circulation of air through cavities of cavity walls is prevented. Cavities should be unventilated.[2] Care should also be taken to close off cavities at the top and to restrict air entry at the bottom to the weep-holes referred to above.

When suspended floors are used in conjunction with cavity walls ventilation of the underfloor space requires care. The problems of avoiding cavity ventilation and of preventing the transfer of water across the cavity are met by forming imperforate sleeves between the air bricks set in the inner and outer leaves of the wall. Sleeves are built of cut slate, the top and base being set to fall towards the outer leaf (6).

[1] This aspect is dealt with more fully in Chapter 4.

[2] When cavity walls were first introduced it was thought that circulation of air through the cavity was desirable to help dry up any moisture penetrating the outer skin and circulation was promoted by the introduction of air bricks at the base and head of cavities. Time has shown this ventilation to be an unnecessary precaution and in addition that it substantially reduces the resistance of the wall to loss of heat through it.

Parapet walls. Whenever tops of walls are exposed, penetration by rain from above is much more likely than through vertical surfaces. All such walls should have an impervious capping (6). When parapet walls are high enough to create the possibility of penetration by water at high level or, in the case of cavity walls by water penetrating the "inner" skin at high level, additional damp-proof courses are necessary to protect the interior of the building from dampness. If the wall immediately below the coping is not to suffer in appearance or stability from the action of water penetrating the coping[1] this must be made impervious—usually by means of a damp-proof course immediately beneath it.

Roof coverings. Prevention of water penetration through roofs is effected with a variety of different materials. Design and application of each is well established by experience and tradition. Coverings can be divided into two main types. Rigid materials which exclude water by overlaps made in the direction of a slope and laterally between separate pieces; (these range from tiles and slates to sheets of corrugated metal or asbestos cement as much as 10 ft in length), and flexible materials which are laid virtually flat and exclude water by raised and manipulated joints or by laying as an unbroken membrane. The latter type includes sheet metals, impregnated felts and asphalt. A full consideration of roofing methods and materials cannot be attempted in the space available here but brief consideration is given below to some of the principles involved so that the problems which are raised in the effective exclusion of water from buildings can be defined.

Slates and tiles. Exactly similar principles are applied in arranging slates and plain tiles. Overlapping of the tiles or slates in the direction of slope needs to be sufficient to ensure that water penetrating joints between adjacent tiles or slates upper surfaces falls on to a solid tile or slate in the course below and also runs sufficiently directly down the roof slope not to spread to adjacent joints in that course (7). This need and the fact that overlapping of tiles or slates reduces their slope relative to the slope of the supporting roof timbers calls for varying pitches for roofs covered with tiles and slates of different thicknesses and different size. Suitable pitches range from 40° for plain tiles and from 26°–40° for largest and smallest slates in common use respectively (7).

Unlike slates, tiles which are manufactured from clay or concrete can be moulded to different shapes and a large variety of tiles are made to interlock or "hook" along their side meetings, so eliminating the need for complete

[1] Water penetrating copings may dissolve chemicals present in bricks or mortar and by transferring these to the point at which the water leaves the wall by evaporation cause at least disfiguring efflorescence or at worst expansion and disruption of the jointing and eventual destruction of the wall itself.

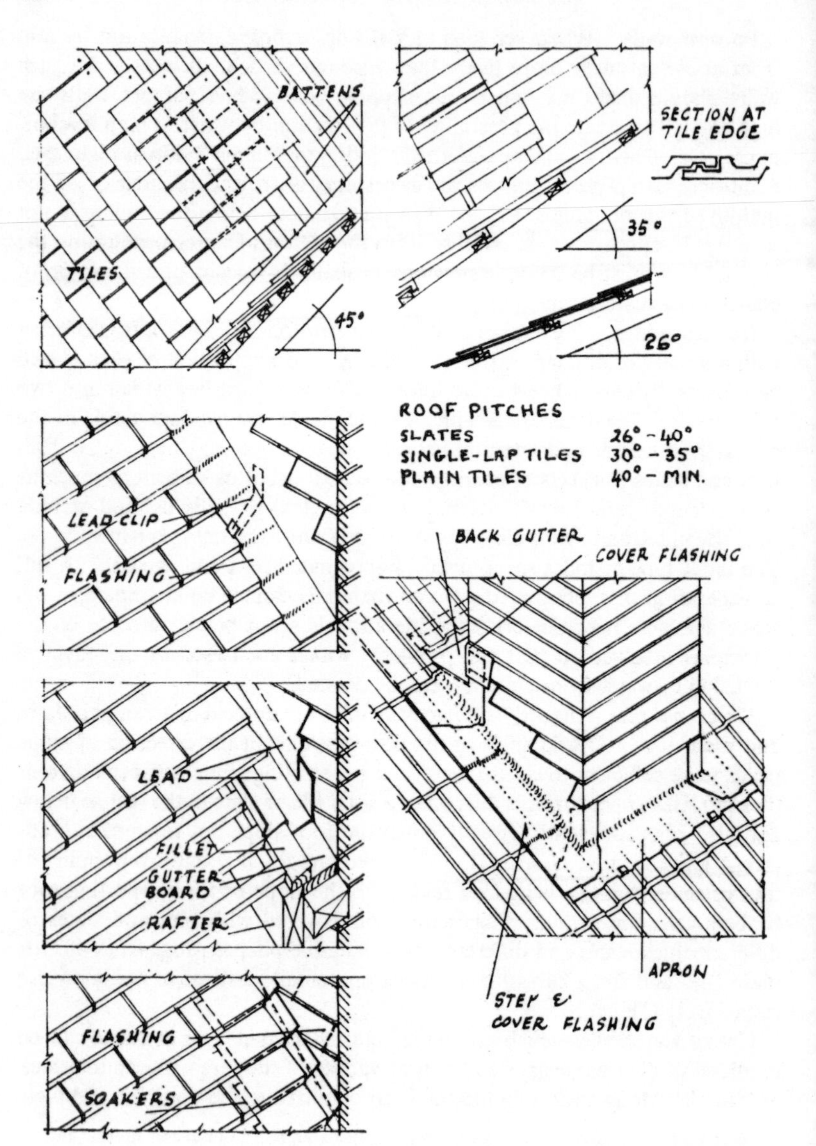
BATTENS
TILES
45°
SECTION AT
TILE EDGE
35°
26°
ROOF PITCHES
SLATES 26° - 40°
SINGLE-LAP TILES 30° - 35°
PLAIN TILES 40° - MIN.
LEAD CLIP
FLASHING
BACK GUTTER
COVER FLASHING
LEAD
FILLET
GUTTER
BOARD
RAFTER
APRON
STEP &
COVER FLASHING
FLASHING
SOAKERS

7

7 *Pitched Roof-Coverings: Flashings*

(*Top, left*) Part section and projected plan showing the arrangement of plain tiles, the staggering of joints between tiles in successive courses and the lapping of each course beyond the top edges of the tiles in the course next but one below it. The lap can be seen in section and by following the broken lines on plan. Tiles are laid from the eaves upwards in a similar way to the arrangement shown in the diagram and are prevented from sliding down the roof slope by "nibs", projections on the tacks of tiles, which hook over the batten edges. All tiles have two nail holes but it is usual to nail only every fourth course. Nails of non-ferrous composition, which resist corrosion, should be used.

The double coverage of tiles over the roofed area is maintained and brought to straight bounding edges by the use of shorter tiles at the eaves (6), and at the ridges and by wider tiles at verges. Tiles along eaves and verge are bedded in mortar and the gaps at meetings of two roof slopes at the ridge are made watertight by V or half-round capping or ridge tiles, also firmly bedded in position in mortar.

"Valleys" or "hips" formed by the meeting of two sloping surfaces are made watertight by the use of standard special valley and hip tiles, moulded in one piece, which extend along both the meeting surfaces or by pieces of sheet metal shaped and bent to extend along both surfaces and inserted between the tiles in successive courses ("soakers").

Ridges and hips were formerly often formed by a strip of sheet metal, usually lead, dressed over a wooden "roll", set along the hip or ridge, and down on to each slope of the roof.

Valleys are also often made watertight by means of valley gutters—metal linings set beneath the tile in a similar way to the secret gutter described below.

The standard size of plain tiles is 10½″ × 6½″, of eaves and ridge tiles 7½″ × 6½″, of verge tiles 10½″ × 9¾″. Tiles should be laid to a "lap" of at least 2½″ which calls for battens at 4 in. centres. Tiles are slightly curved, "cambered", in both directions to enable air to circulate between them and dry them quickly after rain.

(*Top, right*) Section and part plan showing concrete single-lap interlocking tiles (*above*), and a section showing slates centre nailed (*below*).

Interlocking of the tiles edges (shown *right*) enables coverage generally to be limited to one layer of material and the larger size allows the roof pitch to be shallower. Standard size of single lap tiles is 15″ × 9″ and the usual lap is 3 in.

Centre nailing of slates has the advantage of giving more resistance to lifting of slates by wind and of allowing a greater coverage by similar sized slates. In head nailing the narrow width of slate above the nail holes does no useful work in excluding water. N.B.—All forms of tiles and slates should be laid over a continuous layer of bituminous felt which is laid over the rafters before battens are fixed. This prevents penetration by water blown upwards between tiles and slates and also increases thermal value of the roof by excluding wind from the roof space.

(*Below, left*) A lead step and cover flashing (*above*), a secret gutter (*centre*), and soakers (*bottom*) used as abutment flashings to a tiled roof.

The cover flashing is formed from one strip, one edge "stepped" to enable it to be turned ¾ in. into brick joints and wedged to secure it. Clips, cut

side lap and reducing the coverage of the roof generally to one layer of material instead of two as required for plain tiles and slates (7).

With roof coverings of all these types prevention of water penetration calls for specialised detailing at abutments of roofs against walls, chimney stacks and other penetrations of the roof covering. Materials capable of arrangement to bridge the gap between the vertical surfaces and the roof

---

from heavier sheet and also secured by wedging, are set at about 2 ft centres to stiffen and prevent the free edge from lifting. This is the simplest form of flashing but must be of soft metal, lead or aluminium, to prevent damage to the roof covering when dressing to close contact with the surface.

The secret gutter may be in one piece but two, as shown, are more usual. The stepped cover flashing is secured as described above and the gutter piece by copper nails along the back edge of the fillet.

Secret gutters can be satisfactorily formed in lead, aluminium and copper sheet.

Soakers as shown are in effect bent tiles which are inserted between tiles and form a vertical extension of the tile against the wall face which is covered by the stepped hanging flashing. Because of the small amount of manipulation required, the soaker method is used when zinc sheet is the flashing material used. Flashings in lead should be of 4 or 5 lb sheet and gutter 5 or 6 lb sheet. Flashings and gutter linings of aluminium and copper should be of 20 gauge and 22–26 gauge respectively. Flashings and soakers of zinc should not be thinner than 14 zinc gauge.

(*Below, right*) Flashing to a chimney stack penetration in lead using step and cover flashings. These protect the abutments between roof and sides of chimney and are similar in arrangement to the abutment flashing described above. The junction between the back of the chimney and the roof is protected by a back gutter formed from one sheet of lead which extends beyond the stack width as far as the side cover flashings and is dressed along the upper edge to run up the roof slope and under the tiles and to turn up against the back face of the stack along the lower edge where it is overhung by a hanging flashing strip. This strip and the ends of the gutter sheet are dressed to return on the stack sides, as shown, to overlay the upper ends of the side flashings.

The junction between the front of the stack and the roof is protected by a one-piece apron. This is dressed to the stack face and down the roof slope and to return on the stack sides. The lower ends of the side flashings are dressed to overlap the ends of the apron as shown.

Soakers and secret gutters have the advantage of being far less obtrusive than cover flashings and both are for this reason often used in preference to them for the side flashings to stacks when lead or aluminium are used. (Treatment at back and front of stacks remain the same.) There is a trend nowadays to reduce the labour and skill required in stack flashing by building up the gutter and apron pieces by lead burning in the case of lead or by welding or welting in the case of aluminium. When copper or zinc are being used similar limitations to those described above apply to the back gutters and aprons, being invariably built up by welting, welding or brazing in the case of copper or by soldering in the case of zinc.

surfaces are necessary. Sheet metals are the materials almost invariably used—lead, copper, zinc and aluminium. Similar principles are applied in each case, details varying to suit differences in malleability and similar physical properties of each metal.

Flashings. Metals are used in strips or in pieces cut to size from sheet. Junctions with wall surfaces are made by tucking their upper edges into grooves or joints in the wall face, securely fixing them by wedging, and "dressing" the free edges across the gap to be bridged. When flashings are required to follow a sloping surface the slope is negotiated along the upper edge of the flashings by stepping it to meet the joints in the wall face when these are closely spaced, as in the case of brickwork, or by cutting a groove parallel to the slope when joints are widely spaced, as in the case of stonework.

Stepped flashings formed in one piece as described above are called "step and cover flashings" (7), and have the disadvantage that the whole of the flashing is exposed to view. This can be avoided by modifying the arrangement to produce what are called "secret gutters" or by the use of "soakers" (7).

Step and cover flashings are equally suitable for tile and slate coverings but can only readily be carried out in the softer metals. Secret gutters are also equally suitable for both types of covering and may be formed in one piece or more usually in two pieces as shown (7).

Flat roofs. Flat roofs are made watertight by forming a continuous impervious membrane over the whole surface of the roof. Asphalt,[1] which is applied in a plastic state whilst hot sets to form such a membrane in fact, impervious felts and metals, applied in the form of preformed sheets, must be arranged to ensure that joints between sheets are watertight.

Asphalt and felt. Apart from nominal falls to allow the roof to drain, roofs may be flat, i.e. any joints are made in the plane of the covering. Asphalt is laid in two continuous layers, the junctions between laying areas in the two layers being staggered. Abutments as at parapet walls or chimney or other penetrations are made by turning the asphalt up the vertical wall face as a skirting and tucking its top edge into a horizontal chase in the wall face (6).

In the case of parapet walls asphalt should be tucked into the wall at or near the level of the damp-proof course. In the case of cavity walls a damp-proof course is required at the asphalt level.

[1] Asphalt is used for roof coverings. It consists of asphaltic bitumen, bitumen extracted from naturally occurring asphalt, compounded with finely ground and graded limestone aggregate or with finely ground and graded natural rock asphalt. Standards of composition and performance of the two forms are covered by B.S. 988 and 1162 respectively. Asphalt is trowelled into position whilst hot and plastic.

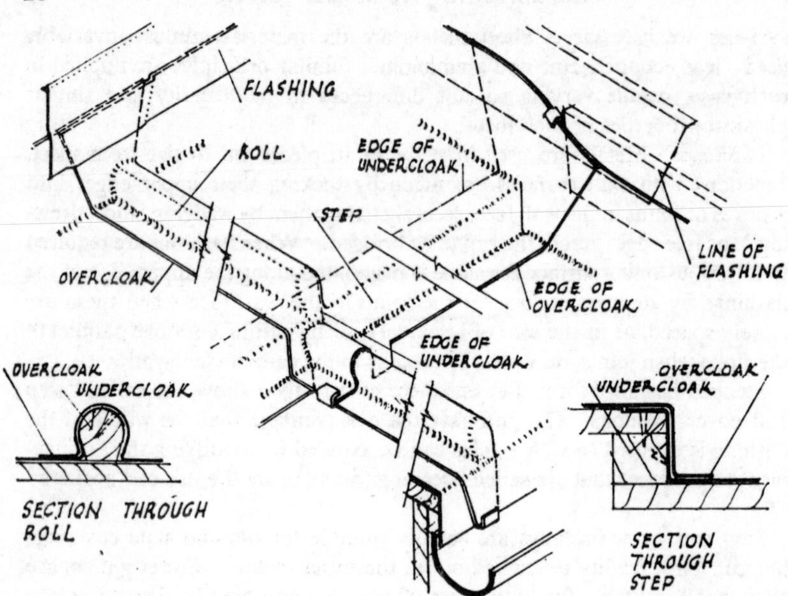
FLASHING
ROLL
EDGE OF UNDERCLOAK
STEP
OVERCLOAK
LINE OF FLASHING
EDGE OF OVERCLOAK
EDGE OF UNDERCLOAK
OVERCLOAK
UNDERCLOAK
SECTION THROUGH ROLL
OVERCLOAK
UNDERCLOAK
SECTION THROUGH STEP

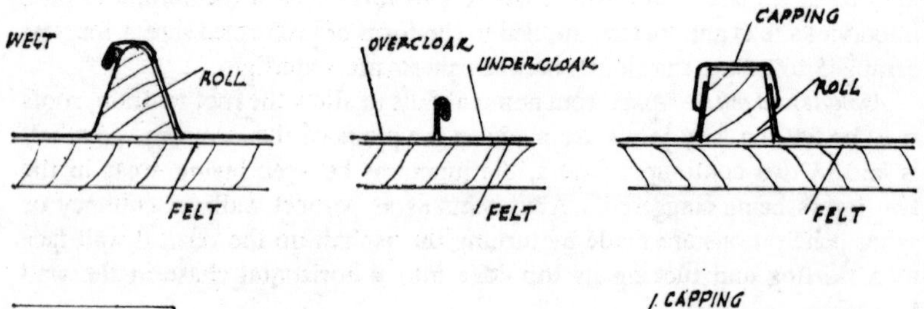
WELT
ROLL
FELT
OVERCLOAK
UNDERCLOAK
FELT
CAPPING
ROLL
FELT

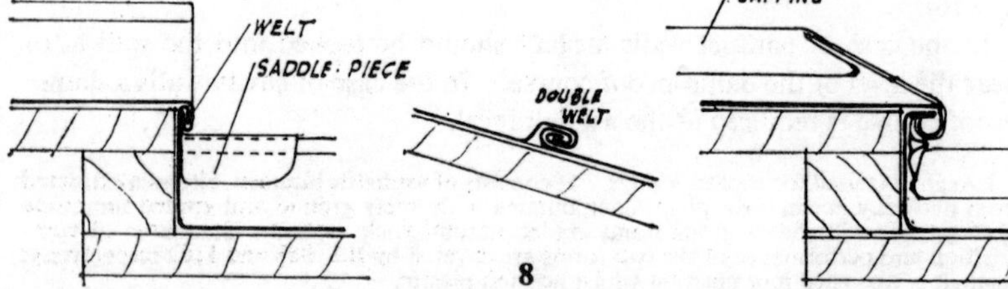
WELT
SADDLE PIECE
DOUBLE WELT
CAPPING

8

8 *Metal covered roofs*

(*Above*) LEAD COVERINGS. The roll section shows how joints parallel to the slope are made by overlapping sheet edges over timber "rolls". The "undercloak" only is copper nailed to the crown of the roll before the "overcloak" is placed, the dressing of about 2 in. of the edge of the latter flat to the roof surface retains it in position. The step section shows a joint at right angles to the slope. Note how the step surface is rebated to receive the nailed edge of the lower sheet, the "undercloak", and how about 2 in. of the edge of the "overcloak" is dressed flat to the roof surface below the step to retain it in position.

Rolls are cut from timbers 2 in. high and 1¾ in. wide. Steps should be 2½ in. high. The "undercloak" is sometimes dressed into a groove cut in the face of the step (shown in broken line), to prevent capillary movement of water between the sheets. The projection shows typical parts of the general arrangement of a roof.

At the eaves both undercloak and overcloak are bossed to fit the splayed end of the roll and to overhang the gutter as shown. The undercloak is cut to enable the two to be clipped together as shown.

At the step the "bossing" of the overcloak to the upper level over the roll to the step below increases the sheet length which produces the extension along the roll shown. N.B.—The upper edges of the sheets to the lower level run beneath the ends of the rolls on the upper level. The undercloak to the upper roll is cut back (shown broken line) to avoid ridges beneath the overcloak.

At the wall abutment sheet ends are bossed to fit the roll and wall junction as shown and the upper edges of both covered by the wall flashing.

At the step ends the upstands to the sides of undercloak and overcloak are dressed to the wall and step profile and then trimmed as shown to be overhung by the wall cover flashings. Undercloaks are often cut with projections, as shown, which can be turned over to clip undercloak and overcloak together.

(*Below*) COPPER AND ZINC COVERINGS

(*Left*) Sections through "conical" roll and step of a copper covered roof. Note how the simple welts at crown of roll and drip are positioned to shed water. Roll ends are negotiated by means of pre-formed saddle pieces, seen in side view on the step section, which sit on the roll top and have an upstand cut to the shape of the roll end so that the welt on the upper edge of the step can run continuously around the profile of the end of the roll.

Where rolls abut walls the saddle piece upstands are covered by a wall flashing.

(*Centre*) Sections through the standing seams and cross welts used on pitched copper roofs. The cross welt is drawn to show its arrangement. In practice welts are dressed tight to enable them to be incorporated within the standing seams and to make this easier cross welts should be staggered between seams. Roofs are finished at eaves by aprons welted to roof sheets as at step edges and set to overhang the gutter,

(*Right*) Sections through roll and step forms used on zinc covered roofs. Where upstands to rolls and steps meet simple dog-ear folds are made to tuck between the ends of rolls and the face of the step. The pre-formed cappings to rolls are kept in position by clips, folded from sheet and nailed to the rolls. Step and wall abutments are negotiated by simple folding and flattening

Laid over timber roof structures, which are susceptible to movement, asphalt should be laid on top of a layer of felt to prevent adhesion between it and the timber which could result in cracking of the asphalt. Edge skirting must also be arranged to allow freedom of movement as between the asphalt and the wall (8).

Bituminous felt is laid in a minimum of two layers, three layers being generally regarded as desirable. Layers are laid with joints staggered and each layer is set in hot bitumen or a cold-setting bituminous solution.

To reduce the effect of the sun, to reduce damage by walking over the roof and to improve the roof's appearance, flat roofs are often finished with a covering of chippings—e.g. of marble or mineralite, etc. Self-finished felts, felts with the mineralite or other chippings firmly attached to their surface, are now widely used for the top layer. When roofs are required to take foot traffic complete covering of felt roofs with cement paving, tiles or asphalt is generally considered advisable.

Felt and asphalt roofs are usually laid to falls sufficient to drain the roof (1¼ in. in 10 ft for asphalt; 2 in.–3 in. in 10 ft for felt), although standing water is not considered harmful to either material. Many asphalt roofs are deliberately laid flat—any resulting standing water being considered helpful in maintaining the asphalt in good condition. There have been a number of buildings erected on which up to 6 in. of standing water is permanently maintained on the roof. (This improves the insulation value of the roof and reduces risk of fire but adds considerably to the weight carried by the roof.)

Metal covered roofs. Arrangements of sheet metal to form a continuous roof membrane are governed by three principal factors. The need to attach the metal to the supporting surface without piercing it. The need to prevent damage by movements of the metal caused by alternate expansion and contraction of the metal between the points of fixing. The need to handle and position sheets with reasonable effort and without damage.

The necessary junctions or overlaps between sheets on "flat" roofs are made to upstand above roof level in the direction of the fall—i.e. where they offer no obstruction to the movement of water from the roof. Junctions between sheets at right angles to the fall are made by means of steps so that sheets can overlap without risk of water penetration and without obstruction to water movement over the surface.

---

of the capping ends which are then formed to the same profile as the sheets to the lower bay at steps or overhung by flashings at walls. Ends of rolls are splayed and covered by cappings folded and flattened to "stop ends" which enable them to be bent to follow the profile of the sheet above the step.

Detailed arrangements of joints reflect the different degrees of malleability of metals used whilst lead, and to a slightly less extent aluminium, can be "bossed"[1] to shape. Zinc, and also copper unless preventive measures are taken, rapidly harden and become brittle when worked.[2]

Pitched roofs in metal. Metal coverings can of course be satisfactorily used on sloping surfaces. Steps become unnecessary at joints at right angles to the fall and resistance to crushing at joints parallel to the fall becomes of secondary importance.

Cross joints in lead are made by plain overlaps of sheets—the amount of overlap varying with the steepness of the slope—the under sheet being secured by a double row of flat headed copper nails set at 3 in. centres. This is necessary to prevent distortion of the sheet's upper edge caused by creep under the weight of the sheet below. Joints with the fall may be made over timber rolls as described above, by means of hollow rolls, rolls made without the timber supporting core, or by double welts as described below for copper.

In the case of copper, joints across the fall are made by double welts, flattened to reduce obstruction to water flow, and joints parallel to the fall by "standing seams", i.e. welts made to stand clear of the roof surface.

In the case of zinc, the production of metal of very soft temper has recently enabled zinc to be applied in an exactly similar way to that described for copper. Both copper and soft temper zinc are marketed in rolls and the latest technique for economy in pitched metal coverings is to use these long sheets without cross joints.

[1] *Bossing*. By well directed blows from a wooden tool metal can be made to "flow" from one part of a sheet to another so that when the operation is skilfully performed sheets can be moulded to relatively complicated profiles, the original sheet thickness being maintained at all parts. An extreme example is the bossing of pipe sleeves and slates (used to flash the penetrations of pipes through pitched roof surfaces) from flat sheet. In current lead practice complicated bossing is often avoided by building up the forms required by cutting and leadburning.

[2] Zinc if bent rapidly hardens and becomes brittle and sheet junctions and flashings are designed to keep manipulation to a minimum to reduce fatigue and fracture during placing (8). Complicated formations in zinc when required are built up by cutting and soldering. Copper has the capacity of annealing easily and readily when heated. Where manipulation is heavy the metal can be softened by playing a blow-lamp over the worked areas and work carried out in stages without damage to the metal. By skilful annealing copper can be bossed as effectively as say lead but the heavier beating and greater time involved make it essentially a workshop process. Complicated formations on copper are almost invariably built up by welding.

3

The Building—its Ventilation

Relatively small changes in the composition of air produce conditions of unpleasantness, discomfort and/or conditions injurious to the health of persons breathing it. The need for ventilation—the replacement of contaminated or "vitiated" air by fresh air—has long been recognised and the design and arrangement of provisions for the ventilation of buildings, particularly larger buildings and buildings of specialised use, is nowadays often a matter for specialising engineers. Standards of ventilation appropriate to buildings' use and density of occupation are in many cases directly required by law and minimum provision for ventilation is ensured for all habitable buildings by means of building bylaws.

Some consideration of air and its behaviour is necessary to an appreciation of ventilation methods and standards.

Composition of Air. Air is a mixture of gases,[1] that is a mechanical combination of gases. Oxygen, making up about one fifth of its volume, is essential to all animal life and is the most important constituent. In breathing, oxygen is removed from the air and converted in part to carbon dioxide and in part to water which are returned to the air, the latter in the form of water vapour.

Carbon dioxide (CO_2). Carbon dioxide is always present in very small quantity (3 or 4 parts in 10,000) in the open air.[2] This amount increases

[1] The composition of dry air is given by Humphrey as follows:

Percentages by Volume

Nitrogen	78·03	Krypton	0·0001
Oxygen	20·99	Helium	0·0005
CO_2	0·03	Xenon	0·000009
Argon	0·9323	Ozone	0·00006
Neon	0·0018	Hydrogen	0·01

Amounts of the different constituents do vary slightly. Oxygen content for example decreases very slightly towards the equator. Nitrogen, together with the very small quantities of Argon, Neon, Krypton, Helium and Neon, act as diluting agents without which oxygen would quite quickly destroy the body's tissues.

[2] Carbon dioxide is essential to plant life. Plants, with the help of sunlight, absorb carbon dioxide and in exchange release oxygen, thus playing a major part in stabilising the balance between oxygen and carbon dioxide content of the atmosphere.

with respiration within buildings and, although not poisonous in itself as is sometimes mistakenly believed, increase in its amount dilutes the oxygen to produce a disproportionate reduction in the effectiveness of air breathed. (An atmosphere containing 10 per cent of carbon dioxide would cause loss of consciousness and much smaller amounts make greatly increased rates of breathing necessary and result in great discomfort—300 parts in 10,000 doubles the normal rate of breathing.)

Increase in carbon dioxide content as a direct result of respiration is an indication of the extent to which the oxygen content of air has been exhausted and measurement of increases of this kind are sometimes used as a means of determining the efficiency of ventilation systems. The maximum increase which it is generally considered can be tolerated for long periods without injurious effect is to 6 parts in 10,000. Within this limit however it has been shown conclusively that carbon dioxide content is of relatively minor importance in determining conditions of comfort compared with the creation of conditions in which production of body heat and its removal are properly balanced. Movement of air is a much more important factor.

Carbon monoxide, etc. Carbon monoxide can result from partial combustion of carbon and is likely to be produced by coal or coke burning appliances. It is a dangerous poison of cumulative effect[1] and its removal must be ensured. There are of course a great many other gases and vapours which are poisonous or dangerous. These are however associated mainly with industrial processes or particular trades and are specially catered for when their presence is known.

Odours. Odours are particularly important in determining satisfactory conditions of ventilation. Their effects may be largely or even entirely psychological but none the less are real enough to constitute the basis on which the effectiveness of ventilation is most often judged. The human body is the commonest source of odours and although not in themselves harmful elimination of body odours is a major factor in determining ventilation standards.

Any odours, e.g. from cooking, furniture, clothing, etc. give the illusion of lack of ventilation and are generally objected to although ventilation may be adequate in fact.

Smoke and dust. Smoke and dust are present in large quantities in the air of towns and cities—soot and ash particles from chimneys alone result in deposits amounting to many tons in industrial areas.

[1] 40 parts in 10,000 is rapidly fatal and 1 part in 10,000 is the maximum amount which people can tolerate over long periods. As little as 15 parts in 10,000 would be dangerous if breathed for more than half an hour.

Some industrial processes produce dust in large quantities. To prevent it being breathed, it is often necessary, as for example in wood-working workshops, to prevent its general diffusion by means of hoods and extract ducting independently of ventilation generally.

Where large volumes of air are drawn into buildings for ventilating purposes considerable damage to decorations results if dust and dirt are not removed from the air. Filtering of incoming air is common in larger schemes of ventilation (p. 52).

Water vapour. Water vapour is always present in the atmosphere and is referred to as humidity. The amount of vapour present will vary with weather conditions and local surroundings, the amount of vapour the air is capable of "carrying" being directly dependent on its temperature. If air contains the maximum amount of vapour it is capable of sustaining at a given temperature it is said to be saturated.

If the temperature of air which is saturated is lowered, i.e. its carrying capacity is reduced, some of the water vapour content condenses and is deposited as condensation or dew. To qualify the humidity of air the amount of water vapour present in it is expressed as a percentage of the maximum amount it would be capable of sustaining at that temperature. This percentage is termed the *relative humidity* of the air. When the temperature of air is lowered the vapour it contains comes nearer to saturating it at the new temperature, i.e. its relative humidity increases. If the temperature is reduced sufficiently air will first become saturated and then begin to deposit the water it contains as dew. The temperature at which this condensation begins is called the *Dew Point*—a value which will vary with relative humidity.

By determining the dew point of a given sample of air it is possible to calculate its relative humidity.[1]

Hygrometers are instruments designed to simulate dew point conditions so that with the help of reference tables the relative humidity of given samples of air as well as other information essential to designers of controlled ventilation systems (see p. 47), can be quickly determined.[2]

If air which is unsaturated is brought into contact with water it will take up water vapour until such time as it becomes saturated. In doing so its temperature drops due to the fact that the latent heat[3] absorbed in turning

[1] Methods of calculation involve principles of behaviour of gases and are intentionally omitted as irrelevant to the present discussion.

[2] E.g.—tables published by the Institute of Heating and Ventilating Engineers (*I.H.V.E. Guide*), relate wet and dry bulb temperatures to dew point vapour pressure, weight and volume of water vapour per pound of dry air, the total heat content of air and vapour together as well as to relative humidity.

[3] *Latent heat*. Heat, i.e. energy, is absorbed in making the physical change from liquid to vapour, there being no difference between the temperature of the vapour and the liquid

the water to water vapour is taken from the air. The usual forms of hygrometer comprise two thermometers, the bulb of one of these, the "wet bulb", being covered by fabric kept continuously damp by dipping its end in water. The other bulb, the "dry bulb", is exposed in the normal way. The saturation of the air in the immediate vicinity of the wet bulb lowers its temperature, the amount of lowering relative to the temperature recorded on the dry bulb being an indication of the amount of moisture taken up—i.e. of the amount of moisture originally contained.

To obtain accurate wet bulb readings effects of radiation from surroundings and conduction of heat from the body of the thermometer must be avoided. Better instruments have their bulbs shielded against radiation and a pumping bulb to blow air across the wet bulb and so produce the necessary air saturation as speedily as possible.

Conditions of comfort. The human body generates heat in relatively large quantities[1] but requires to maintain itself at a constant temperature. The balancing of the amount of heat produced to meet changes in surrounding conditions is achieved by the body in a number of ways—variations in blood supply to the different parts of the body, perspiration, etc.—and although capable of maintaining the necessary balance over a wide range of conditions it does so in adverse conditions at the expense of comfort and of bodily efficiency.

Heat is given up by the body by radiation, convection, via the movement of air over the body's surface, and by evaporation of perspiration. Loss of heat by radiation is directly dependent on the temperature of surrounding surfaces. Thus in winter when wall and window surfaces are cold and loss by radiation tends to be high, high air temperatures which reduce convection losses, are required for comfort. In summer low air temperatures are needed to compensate for the reduction in radiation due to the higher temperature of surrounding surfaces.

Loss of heat by convection depends on air movement, the changing of the air in contact with the skin. Too rapid a movement increases the rate of loss by evaporation as well as by convection, and conditions of discomfort are readily produced by too rapid movements of air, draughts, particularly if the air is cool or cold.

---

from which it is produced. In the circumstances under consideration this heat is drawn from the air. It follows from this that the total heat content of a volume of air cooled by the addition of water vapour, e.g. by washing, remains unchanged, a fact of some importance in air conditioning calculations (see p. 53).

[1] An adult body indoors in average conditions gives up about 400 btu/hr. When engaged in heavy physical effort up to 550 btu/hr. (Heat is lost partly as sensible heat and partly as latent heat in evaporation of perspiration.)

Loss of heat by evaporation is dependent on air temperature and to some extent on the relative humidity of the air. When the air is very dry higher temperatures are necessary to maintain comfort because of increased evaporation from the body surfaces and when humidities are very high otherwise acceptable temperatures produce conscious perspiration and discomfort through feelings of clamminess.[1]

TABLE 2

Room or Building	Recommended Air Changes per Hour
Schools:[2]	
Classrooms	6
Assembly Halls	4
Gymnasia	4
Common Rooms	4
Lavatories	10
Laboratories	8
Boiler Houses	15
Garages	*See below*
Hospitals:	
Wards—Winter	6
—Summer	10
Operating Theatres	10
Lavatories and bathrooms	10
Laundries	15
Public Buildings	
Assembly Halls	4
Dining halls, canteens, restaurants, etc. above ground	10

Table of recommended air changes for different types of buildings. Ventilation of garages will vary with position, size and probability of running motors. Local licensing authorities exercise control but in circumstances where the only requirement is to avoid risk of explosion 6 changes per hour is considered adequate.

(Figures taken from *I.H.V.E. Guide*)

As the foregoing shows both well-being and comfort are dependent on the maintenance of the quality of air in rooms. In general this is achieved by providing for the continual replacement of used air by fresh air. Standards for the amount of replacement necessary are firmly established, in terms of a

[1] N.B.—Relatively wide variations in humidity can be compensated for by small variations in dry bulb temperatures and over a wide range of humidities accurate humidity control is not essential to the creation of comfortable conditions.

[2] Reference should be made to the School Premises Regulations 1959 made under provisions of Education Act 1944.

number of complete changes of air in the room or building per hour or sometimes in terms of volume of "fresh air" to be introduced per occupant per hour.

The use to which buildings are put may be a sufficient guide to the amount of ventilation they require. In buildings of domestic character where the number of occupants rarely varies and where the volume of air within the building is large relative to the number of occupants, or in some factories, where noxious fumes may be produced and the extraction of these demands air removal far in excess of that used by the occupants[1] standards are expressed in terms of number of complete air changes.

In densely populated buildings where the number of occupants is much more likely to vary and the volume relative to number of occupants is small standards may be expressed in terms of quantity of air to be provided for each occupant. L.C.C. regulations in respect of Places of Public Entertainment for example call for a supply of 1000 cu. ft per person per hour. Table 2 sets out standards of air change required for a wide range of building types.

Table 3 shows the amount of natural air change which is usually allowed for in different types of building when heating requirements are being assessed and when no specific provision for ventilation is made.

Natural ventilation is the term used to describe ventilation achieved by harnessing the natural movements of air—the upward movement of warmed air and the more or less continuous movement of the atmosphere. Domestic buildings for example rely almost exclusively on natural ventilation.

Everybody is familiar with the strong through air currents created when doors on two sides of a building are opened at the same time. The existence of a wind inevitably creates a "lee" side—an area of reduced air pressure on one side of a building. This promotes, whenever openings exist, a movement of air from the building on the lee side and into the building on the windward side. This effect is enhanced or reduced by opening or closing windows (9 and 10). Alternatively permanent openings through external walls with or without means of closing them will promote ventilation (10).

[1] The Factories Act whilst calling for adequate ventilation does not make specific demands. Actual needs will vary with the type of work carried out, number of occupants and the volume of space per person. For general use, to allow for these factors, the need for ventilation to be effective in all parts of the building and the fact that natural infiltration of air occurs often in excess of requirements the *I.H.V.E. Guide* recommends an allowance of 1000 cu. ft per person per hour be made when assessing heat requirements (see Chapter 3). It is worth noting that in most buildings air enters "accidentally", through doors when opened and through gaps around doors and windows. The amount of this uncontrolled air entry will vary in different buildings and in many cases may be sufficient to make contrived inlets unnecessary. In smaller buildings where the areas of windows and doors are large relative to the building's volume accidental air change is likely to be large. In larger buildings, particularly those like cinemas where openings are few, accidental air change is likely to be small.

TABLE 3

Room or Building	Temperature °F	Air Changes Per Hour
Flats and Residences:		
Living Rooms	65	1 – 1½
Bed-sitting Rooms	65	1½ – 2
Bedrooms	50	1 – 1½
Service Rooms	60	1
Store Rooms	50	½
Foyers	60	2
Gymnasia	55	1½
Halls:		
For Assembly, Lectures, Meetings and General Purposes	60	1½
Hotels:		
Public Rooms	65	2
Dining Rooms	65	2
Ballrooms	65	2
Bedrooms	60	1 – 1½
Bed-sitting Rooms	65	1½ – 2
Sitting Rooms	65	1½ – 2
Lavatories	60	2
Bathrooms	60	1
Offices:		
General Offices	65	2
Private Offices	65	1½ – 2
Stores	50	½

Air changes which result naturally by infiltration when the suitable internal temperatures as listed, are maintained. N.B.—Heating calculations include for warming this quantity of air when no mechanical ventilation is provided.

(Figures from *I.H.V.E. Guide*)

Openings properly disposed on one side only of a building will promote air change even when through ventilation is prevented or restricted by internal walls or closed doors.

The natural upwards movement of air is fully harnessed when a coal or gas fire is used to heat a room. Hot gases and smoke produced by the fire in escaping up the flue provided for this purpose draw with them large

9 ***Windows as ventilators***

Casement windows, apart from the simplicity of their construction, offer by variation in the position and extent of their openings excellent control over

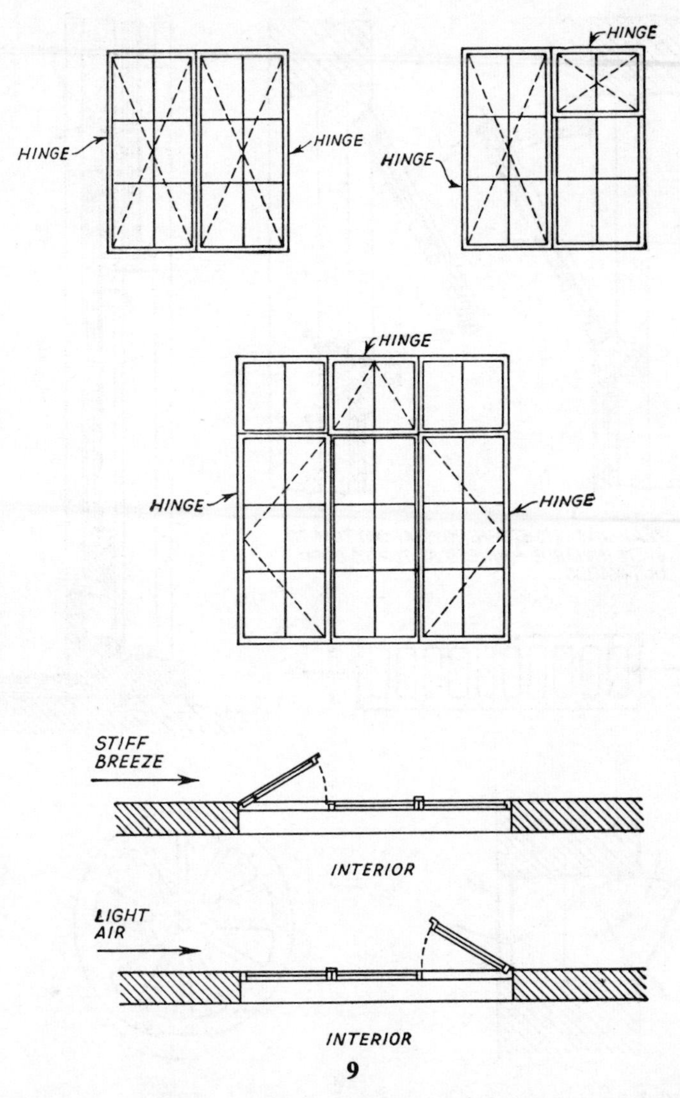

9

ventilation. Different direction of opening of different parts in one window (*top left*, and *centre*) give a choice in increasing or decreasing the wind action as shown by the plans. The outward opening top-hinged sections allow escape of air from high level in the room whilst excluding rain.

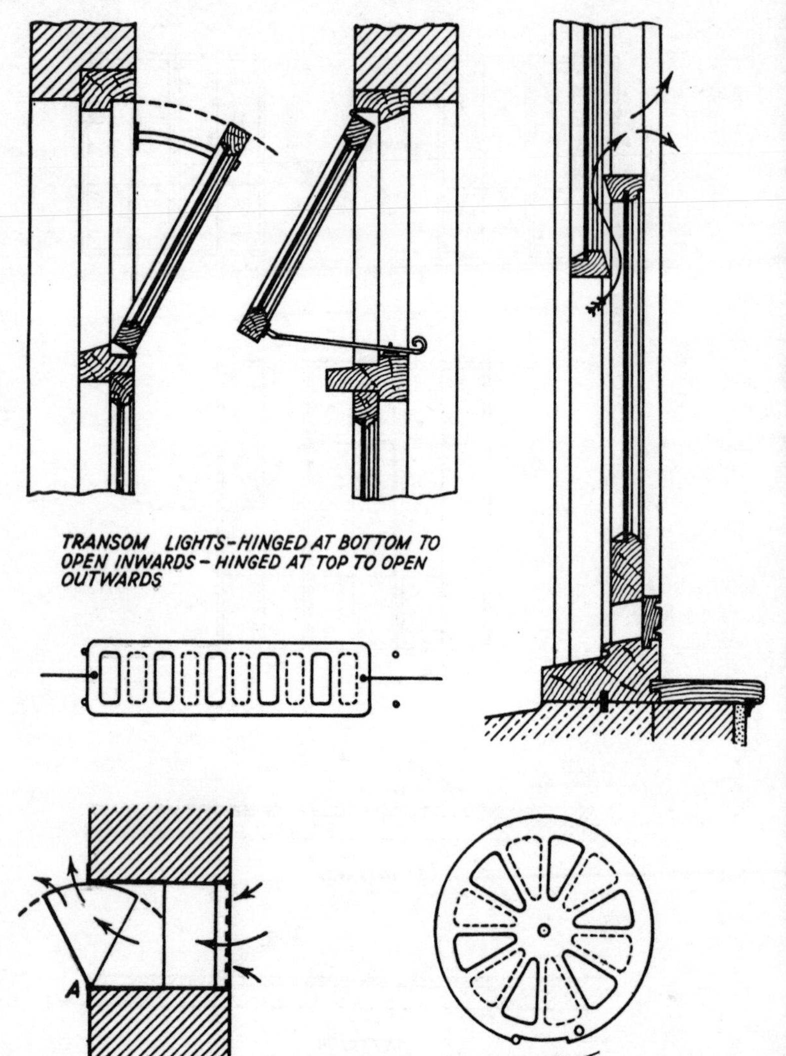

10

10 *Windows as ventilators*

(*Top, left*) Alternative hinging of transom lights, "ventilators". The bottom hinged type is useful when the window is out of reach. Kept in the closed position by a "ring spring catch" it can be opened and closed by means of a

quantities of unused air from the room. In domestic buildings where density of occupation is low, air enters the room to replace that drawn into the flue at a much faster rate than it is required by the occupants. In doing so—through open windows and gaps below doors or around doors and windows—it often creates unpleasant draughts and consequent discomfort for occupants. Recent years have seen a greatly increased use of solid fuel burning appliances designed to limit the amount of air drawn from the room by the fire. Slow combustion stoves do this by positive control over the amount of air admitted to the space below the fire and by preventing air from being drawn over the surface of the fire (and often by virtue of their need for a smaller than usual flue). Stoves and some recent open fires also make more efficient use of the fuel burnt and more efficient use of the heat produced by warming and circulating the air which remains in the room (16, p. 66).

A variety of open fires are now marketed in which the ventilating effect is reduced by means of specially constructed "air-tight" fronts which make it possible to control the amount of air admitted below the fire. Others are designed to draw the air required for combustion directly from outside the building by means of underfloor ducts. Proper control of this air saves fuel directly as well as indirectly by reducing the ventilation effect of the fire. Alternatively the provision of ducts to discharge air in the immediate vicinity of the fireplace will often successfully avoid the draughts set up by an open fire.

The effectiveness of a flue as a means of ventilation is considerable even when no fire is burning. Air in the room and in the flue is warmer than that

---

pole and hook. Both forms illustrated can be arranged for remote opening by cords and pulleys operating a worm gear set against a toothed opening arm. Bottom hinged and top hinged ventilators set in low and high positions on oposite sides of a room induce very effective cross ventilation.

N.B.—Bottom hinging of windows makes rain exclusion difficult. In the example shown, penetration would occur unless a weather board were fitted to the bottom frame member.

(*Top, right*) A sliding sash showing the fine degree of control possible over the opening area. Air enters, as shown, above nuisance level and escapes at the top of the window. Air is prevented from entering at the bottom by the "deep bead" or "draught board" fitted inside the window.

(*Below*) Control of ventilation through openings in walls achieved (*centre* and *bottom, right*) by "hit and miss" plates. Two perforated plates, one fixed and one movable, can be set so that holes are in alignment or not as required. (The circular form is sometimes called "Cooper's" ventilator.) The Sheringham Valve (*bottom, left*) controls inlet by means of a hinged cover flap with segmental side wings which together direct incoming air upwards.

outside so that air movement similar to but of less intensity than that set up by a fire takes place—air moves upwards in the flue and loss from the room is made good by infiltration of fresh air from outside it.

It is worth noting that the burning of an uncontrolled fire will on average promote four[1] or more complete changes of air per hour in the room heated (1–1½ changes would be adequate in living rooms). It is also almost invariably the case that flues from different rooms rise to high level in a group so that the ventilating effect of all is enhanced by the warming effect of a fire served by only one of them. This can sometimes be harnessed by forming a flue with a controlled inlet from a room requiring ventilation independently of a fireplace. It is strongly recommended for example that a flue or duct terminating internally in a hood or canopy set over the cooker in a kitchen be provided to prevent dissemination of smells.

Bylaw requirements. In setting standards which ensure that buildings are capable of adequate natural ventilation bylaws have always accepted the presence of a flue to a habitable room as adequate provision for permanent ventilation. Until recently alternative permanent openings for such rooms were required whenever a flue was not provided. (Permanent ventilation to all habitable rooms is still required by some bylaws—notably in the L.C.C. area.) Bylaws also require provision of permanent openings for ventilation of bathrooms and lavatories and for larders. Minimum standards are set for the size of windows to habitable rooms. These are required to total one tenth of the room's floor area exclusive of main framework, of which at least one half are arranged to open.

Minima are also set for heights of habitable rooms to ensure that adequate air volume is provided—in domestic buildings not less than 8 ft generally or less than 7 ft 6 in. on the topmost floor. (Equivalent figures for office buildings where denser occupation is expected are 8 ft 6 in. and 8 ft respectively.)

To ensure that air can reach the outside surface of buildings bylaws also call for minimum provisions of space around buildings—a clear depth of not less than 24 ft between a building's frontage and a facing building and an area of not less than 150 sq. ft belonging exclusively to it at the rear. (N.B.—these provisions are very much less than those normally made in the great majority of cases and in many the meeting of other requirements automatically produces much higher standards, e.g. positioning of buildings behind building lines, limitations on density of development of sites and requirements to build within angles set from opposing frontages.) Natural ventilation is not of course limited in application to domestic buildings. The differences between internal and external air temperatures resulting from the

[1] The number of air changes depends on the size of the room and height of chimney. In an average room, with 30 ft of chimney height, it may be nearer to 10 air changes per hour.

occupation or heating of buildings is effectively harnessed in a great many types of building to promote more efficient ventilation.

Buildings arranged so that windows or openings can be placed on opposite sides of rooms to produce cross ventilation, e.g. the great majority of school buildings harness natural movements of the atmosphere as well as the internal air movements resulting from occupation or heating. Disadvantages are associated however with any natural ventilation arrangements. These are the tendency for draughts to be created; the lack of control over either amount or condition of air admitted; the accumulation of disfiguring dirt deposits in the vicinity of inlets and outlets. To reduce the tendency towards producing draughts numbers of devices have been used from time to time, air inlets which can be controlled if conditions make them too active (11), varying from simple manually operated "hit and miss" covers to self-adjusting louvres (10 and 11). Placing of inlets behind radiators ensures that air entering rooms is warmed and the likelihood of draughts arising from its movement is reduced. (These latter are effective but increase the tendency to accumulate dirt and, if not controlled, may impair the economy of the heating installation by over-ventilation (11).

Deposits of disfiguring dirt near inlets can only be avoided by filtration, and this can only reasonably be effected in mechanical systems.

Fig. 11 also illustrates a device still encountered in some older buildings which is intended to harness upward air currents, position the air inlet point to eliminate draughts and to remove dirt and grime by filtering (the Tobin Tube).

Single storey buildings, particularly those of pitched roof construction, are eminently suitable for the application of natural ventilation and a wide variety of ventilators designed for use in this type of building are marketed. These may simply provide outlets at the apex of the roof, exploiting to the maximum the upward movement of air within the building, or may be designed to both prevent reversal of the outward air movement in adverse wind conditions and also to harness any wind to increase their rate of extraction. Both types should of course be used in conjunction with inlets so disposed as to promote air movements between them and the outlets which will ensure transfer of air from all parts. Fig. 12 illustrates typical examples of ventilators of these types.

Cowl type ventilators illustrated in Fig. 12 will function in any suitable position and are often used to extract air through a series of remote outlets linked by ducts in a similar way to that illustrated (13) for mechanical systems.

In designing for ventilation of this kind the arrangement for air inlet is of vital importance. Infiltration, if relied upon, is likely to produce draughts and

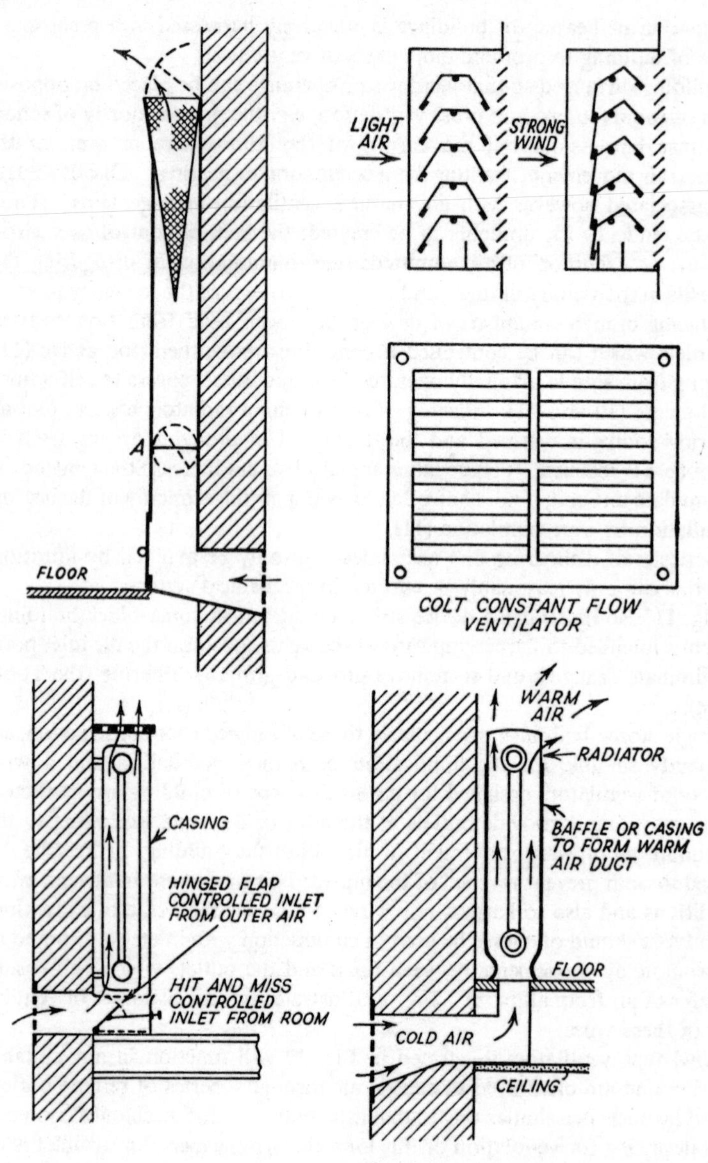
LIGHT AIR
STRONG WIND
A
FLOOR
COLT CONSTANT FLOW VENTILATOR
CASING
HINGED FLAP CONTROLLED INLET FROM OUTER AIR
HIT AND MISS CONTROLLED INLET FROM ROOM
WARM AIR
RADIATOR
BAFFLE OR CASING TO FORM WARM AIR DUCT
FLOOR
COLD AIR
CEILING

11

if ventilation is to be effective in all areas positioning of inlets to ensure proper cross movements of air is necessary (e.g. widely dispersed and at low level when ridge outlets are employed). To avoid excessive air movement at inlets these should be considerably larger in total area than the outlets where speed of air movement is often in the region of 5 or 6 ft/sec.[1] Inlets giving at least twice the amount of free area as outlets are generally considered necessary.

By proper relationship between the size of inlets and the capacity of ventilators some degree of predetermination of the amount of ventilation secured is possible. Given knowledge of conditions calculations can be made but these invariably depend on factors which vary so much that predictions in respect of natural ventilating schemes can never be regarded as more than approximations.

[1] When air is warmed it expands, its density is reduced and it rises. The speed of its upward movement will depend on the effect of gravity, on cooler air replacing it and on the resistance offered to its movement by surrounding surfaces. Below is a formula in its simplest form relating these factors: $V = C\sqrt{\frac{HT}{8}}$, where V = velocity of air in feet per second; H = the height in feet from inlet to outlet of tube or flue; C = the coefficient of friction of the duct or flue surface (0·5–0·75 according to sectional form, number of bends and roughness of the duct surface); T = temperature difference between inlet and outlet.

Velocity multiplied by duct area will give its capacity in air volume per second. Ducts are most efficient when circular in section and changes of direction made by easy curves. Right-angled bends reduce velocity drastically. One such bend will halve the velocity and a second halve it again.

N.B.—Some manufacturers publish tables of capacities of roof ventilators which relate these to wind velocity, temperature difference inside and outside the building and height of the ventilators above the inlet.

---

11 *Inlets*

(*Above, right*) A self-adjusting louvred inlet. The lightly pivoted plates are depressed, as shown on the sections, to reduce the open area of the ventilator when wind velocity increases. The elevation (*below*) shows an internal view of the ventilator. (Colt's "Constant Flow" ventilator.)

(*Below*) Alternative arrangements of radiator inlets. The arrangement on the left ensures that incoming air is warmed but that the quantity of air drawn from outside or from inside the room and recirculated can be controlled. The arrangement on the right whilst warming incoming air makes no provision for control over the quantity drawn into the room by the convection action of the radiator.

(*Above, left*) THE TOBIN TUBE. The amount of air admitted is controlled by the diaphragm plate at *A*, access for cleaning being provided by the plate at floor level. The diagram also shows a muslin filter at the outlet although these call for maintenance and were often omitted. The lid is in the form of a protective grill or in some cases is solid and used to control the ventilating action. The air inlet position can be varied by varying the length of the tube. Tobin Tubes suffered from their obvious susceptibility to fouling.

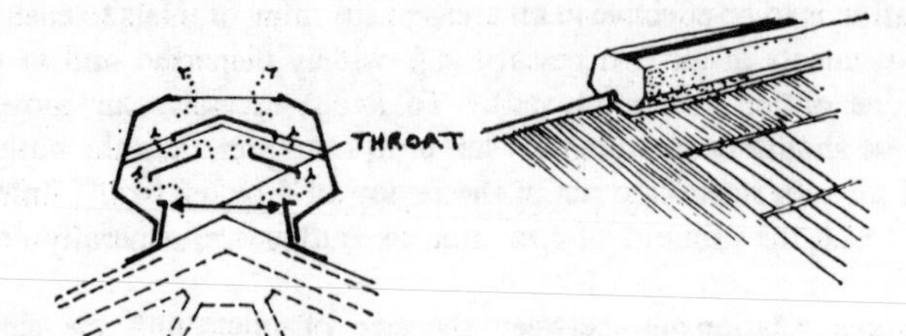

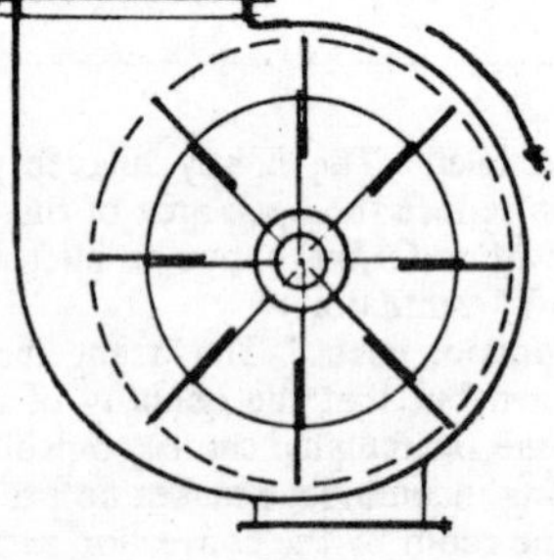

12

12 *Ventilators*

(*Top*) A typical ridge ventilator in section and perspective view. These are designed to be fitted at the apex of a pitched roof and are available in any length or to run, if required, continuously the full length of the ridge.

The arrangement of the internal baffles diverts rain to the sides of the ventilator to escape onto the roof surfaces. The outer casing protects the upward movement of air from wind interference. Ventilators are available with different

Mechanical ventilation. In its simplest form mechanical ventilation is merely the substitution of a fan, the capacity of which is known and controllable, for the uncertainties of air movements resulting from natural agencies. Extract or vacuum systems are the simplest and may, for example, follow closely the general principles described above with the fan or fans positioned in place of cowls. In conjunction with ducts for conveying air, power extraction has the enormous advantage over natural extraction of enabling equally effective ventilation to be secured in any part of a building and giving at the same time complete freedom in positioning the fan (13), Efficiency of ventilators of the cowl type is often assured by embodying fans in them when, to avoid the likelihood of creating draughts due to increased accidental air entry powered inlets may also be used. These ensure that sufficient controlled air input occurs. Where circumstances warrant it these incorporate heating units and filters as well as fans.

Plenum is a term now loosely used to cover ventilation systems which produce a positive air pressure inside the building thus eliminating incoming draughts by ensuring that any leakage of air is necessarily outwards. Heating of the incoming air is implied and a true plenum system is generally taken as one in which the heating of the air is the only heating provided for the building.

Unit heaters, self-contained units which comprise heating batteries over which air is drawn by a fan, are now much used in factories and similar buildings. They generally heat and circulate the air within the building and

---

"throat" sizes and manufacturers list extract capacities for different operating conditions. Ventilators can be fitted with fixed or adjustable dampers. Similar forms are made suitable for fitting in sloping surface of roof (Hills "Hillridge").
(*Centre*) A typical cowl ventilator in section and perspective view. Baffles, arranged to prevent rain penetration, and the outer casings arrangement prevents wind interference and assists upwards flow from the cowl. Exhaust capacities for different sizes of cowl are listed by manufacturers (Robertson Thain Limited). Ventilators of these types are manufactured from galvanised sheet steel, sheet aluminium or protected metal. Similar forms are available in asbestos cement.
(*Below*) A centrifugal air fan in section and perspective view. Air enters the fan casing at one side, in a direction parallel to the axis of the spindle. The rotary movement of the blades pushes the air to the outlet. Centrifugal fans are manufactured with great variety of arrangement of the impeller blades. Curvature inclination, etc., of these has a marked influence on the power, quietness and efficiency of the fans and actual selection in given circumstances calls for expert knowledge.

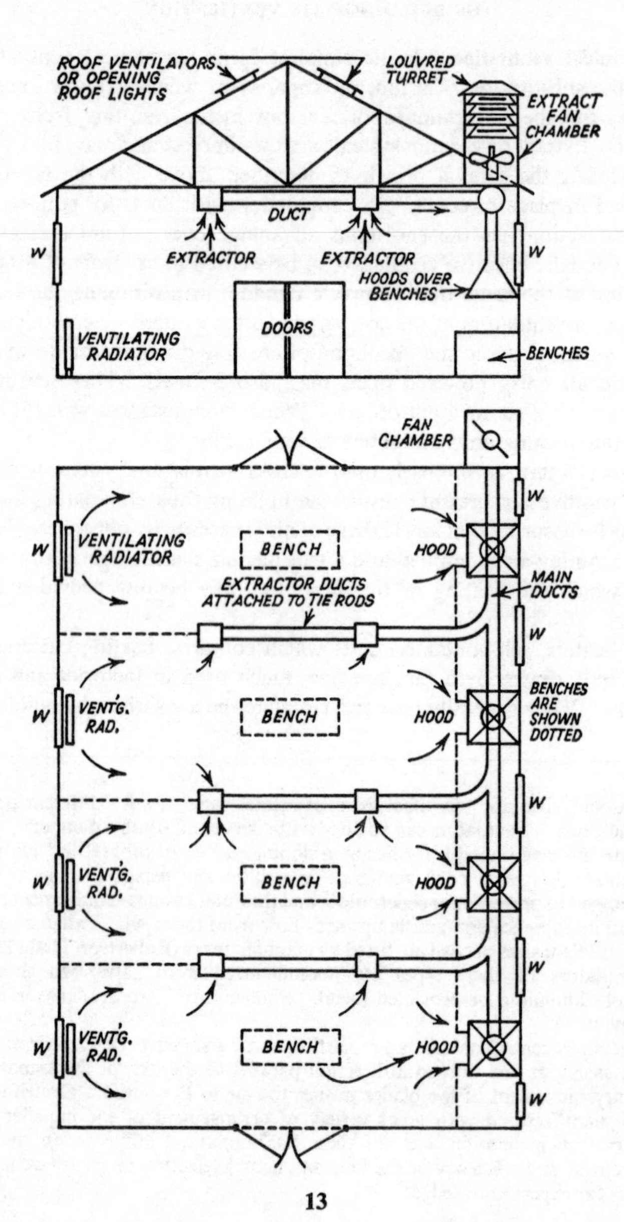
ROOF VENTILATORS OR OPENING ROOF LIGHTS
LOUVRED TURRET
EXTRACT FAN CHAMBER
DUCT
W
EXTRACTOR
EXTRACTOR
W
HOODS OVER BENCHES
DOORS
VENTILATING RADIATOR
BENCHES
FAN CHAMBER
W
W
VENTILATING RADIATOR
BENCH
HOOD
MAIN DUCTS
EXTRACTOR DUCTS ATTACHED TO TIE RODS
W
W
VENT'G. RAD.
BENCH
HOOD
BENCHES ARE SHOWN DOTTED
W
W
VENT'G. RAD.
BENCH
HOOD
W
W
VENT'G. RAD.
BENCH
HOOD
W

13

have the advantage that their output stream can be directed to give proper distribution of warmed air. By arranging some or all of the heaters with intakes of air from outside the building the equivalent of a plenum system is produced at much lower cost. Heaters are fitted with dampers so that air to be heated can be drawn from outside or inside the building as conditions require.

In ducted systems positioning of inlets, the control of the speed of air movement and its temperature and the arrangement and accomodation of the duct work are problems requiring early consideration.

Nowadays in systems of this kind both input and extract of air are almost invariably carried out mechanically, lower power and slightly reduced ductwork on the extract side ensuring a slight positive pressure within the building. Filtering of the air as well as heating it is essential and in bigger installations recirculation of part of the air extracted from the building is common to save heating and other costs. Recirculation of air is in turn usually associated with additional treatment.

Air conditioning is a term which by general usage is taken to imply a higher than usual degree of conditioning, i.e. conditioning which includes washing, control of humidity, refrigeration, etc., as well as filtration and heating. Fig. 14 shows diagramatically the arrangement of air conditioning in a cinema or theatre. Below is a brief consideration of the items of equipment and controls used in air-conditioning installations.

Fans. Fans are of three principal types; propeller fans; axial flow fans and cased or centrifugal fans. Simple propeller fans will move air satisfactorily only when resistance to its movement is small, e.g. when fans form part of a self-contained extractor cowl or when the length of ducts through which air is to be pushed or drawn is small. This is because movement of the propeller blades, and the thrust they impart is much smaller at the centre of

---

13 *An extract system of ventilation*

The plan and section illustrate diagrammatically the arrangement and ducting to a small workshop where it is assumed that vapour and/or dust is produced at the work benches.

Air enters behind the radiators, see Fig. 11, to circulate partly by convection due to warming by contact with the radiators' surfaces, and partly by virtue of the extract pull from the fan.

Direct extraction from hoods close to the work benches prevents general dissemination of dust and fumes. (A similar arrangement of hoods over cooking equipment is used in large kitchens.) The high level extractor grilles remove any dust escaping the hoods and used air rising from the remaining parts of the building. Ridge ventilators or roof lights, if fitted, would enable air or dust by-passing these grilles to escape.

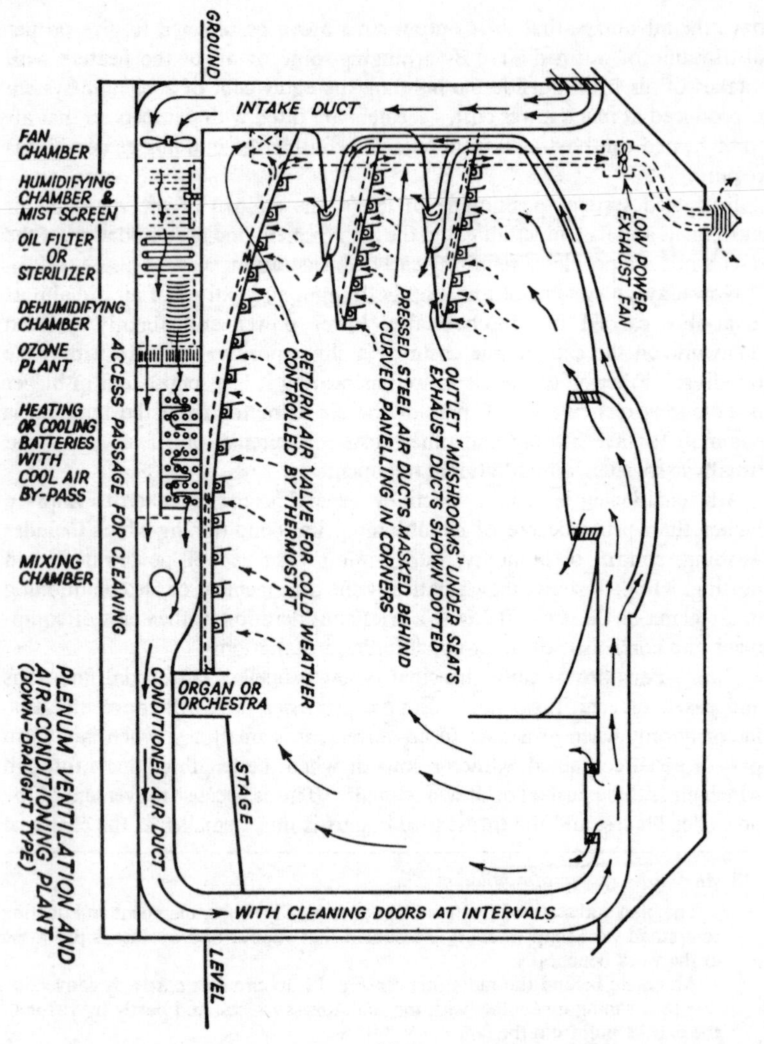

14

14 *Air conditioning*

A section showing diagrammatically the arrangement of air conditioning installation for a cinema or theatre. Air inlets are at high levels relative to each section of the auditorium and the incoming conditioned air is distributed

the fan than at the perimeter and when resistance to air flow is high the air drawn through at the perimeter tends to return through the fan centre.

Flow of air through a propeller fan is axial but fans described as axial flow fans overcome the deficiency of propeller fans by an enclosing rim and often by means of enlarged hubs which reduce the tendency to reverse flow at the fan's centre, so enabling them to work satisfactorily against resistance. Axial flow fans have the advantage of space saving and easier connection to ducting than centrifugal fans (cased fans). These consist of blades set radially around a hub which revolves within a casing of "scroll" or "volute" form. Air enters on the axis of the fan, through the sides of the casing, and is discharged at right angles to the axis (12).

Quietness in operation is the most important factor in choosing fans. Noise must be kept to a level which, relative to buildings' use, will cause no nuisance. Transmission of vibration through ducting is avoided by flexible canvas connections between fan and duct and by placing fan motors on resilient mountings. Noise is also created, however, by the fan blades, the speed of the blades' tips being a very important factor in the amount of noise produced. Propeller type fans are in general relatively noisy in operation.

Fans of similar types but of different sizes and operating at different speeds will give the same capacity for air movement. Bigger capacity fans operating at lower speeds should in general be chosen. Fan manufacturers publish tables or graphs relating fan sizes to speed of rotation and speed and volume of delivery against various resistances (expressed as static pressure in inches water gauge), but actual selection is a matter for the specialist.

Duct work. Although other materials are used, sheet metal is almost invariably the material chosen for ducting. Noise in ducts is produced by turbulence and friction between air and tube surfaces and projections. Sizes

---

and pulled downwards by the outlets positioned below the seating. To prevent a general movement of air from the proscenium opening to the audience, outlets at the sides and rear of the stage would also be provided. In many installations, lowering of the safety curtain (automatic in the event of fire), separates the ventilation ducting to the stage and auditorium to prevent spread of fire from the former to the latter.

Downward circulation of air has the advantage of ensuring that movement of conditioned air is gradual, the air becoming stratified and falling naturally as it cools, so that occupants get maximum benefit from it. In upward circulations the tendency for conditioned air to rise before occupants benefit from it can be corrected by large numbers of small inlets at floor level. Where seating is fixed, and these can be easily provided, as in cinemas, theatres, council chambers, etc., upward circulations prove equally as satisfactory as downward circulations.

of main and branch ducts are determined by the engineer on a basis of speeds of air movement that can be tolerated from the points of view of noise and speed of air movement at inlets. The *I.H.V.E. Guide* recommends that air velocity in ducts, in installations for public buildings, offices, hotels, etc., should not exceed 1000 ft/min at outside intake and discharge points, 1500 ft/min in main ducts and 700 ft/min in terminal branch ducts. For quiet inlet of air to rooms it recommends the limiting of speed through mesh type inlets to 300 ft/min and through smooth louvred inlets to 700 ft/min. (Somewhat less stringent standards are set for industrial buildings where higher noise levels can be tolerated.)

Noise apart, the speed of air at inlets will depend on their position and direction of air movement. As a general guide horizontal inlets set several feet above head level with air speed not in excess of 350 ft/min avoid troubles from draughts. (Movement at head level itself should not be more than about 60 ft/min.)

It is resistance to air movement offered by the ducting and the conditioning equipment which determines the fan power required for an installation. Duct resistance is dependent on volume of air passed, air density, i.e. temperature, and on the size of duct. Elaborate tables relating volume of air passed and air velocity to resistance to flow in ducts of different cross section are used by ventilating engineers in selecting the most suitable combinations of duct size, fan size and air velocity. In general circular ducts offer least resistance. Changes in direction, branches and restrictions in ducts all increase their resistance to flow. (These are usually converted to straight length equivalents before reference to tables.)

Recent developments in air conditioning techniques have been towards greatly increased air speeds within ducts. Duct speeds are reduced to acceptable limits at inlets to rooms by local-pressure reducing "boxes". High air speeds give advantages in reducing duct size and in giving systems the capacity for very close and local control. (See "Control of systems" below.)

Filters. Removal of dirt from air is effected in three ways. By screening, passing the air through material fine enough to trap the dirt particles; by adhesion, causing the air to impinge upon oil coated surfaces to which the dirt particles adhere, by electric precipitation, by imparting an electric charge to the dirt particles so that they are attracted by, i.e. precipitated on, plates holding an opposite electric charge.

Screen filters are generally made of two layers of fine fabric, usually cotton, between which is sandwiched, say, cotton wool. This fabric is then built up in zig-zag manner to present as large a surface as possible and so reduce the air velocity through it (15). Filters of this kind create resistance to air movement through them and this increases as the filter becomes clogged. Filters are changed when resistance reaches a predetermined maximum level.

Oil coated filters comprise a series of closely spaced corrugated metal plates set in frames or of packings of metal shavings, or glass fibres, contained between layers of expanded metal or other porous material. Units of the filter may be coated with oil by dipping or may be kept oiled by a continuous flow of oil over them or by arranging the filter units as an endless moving belt with the lower end dipping into an oil reservoir. The former type involves the great disadvantage of periodic cleaning of the filter units or alternatively the use of "throw-away" units—nowadays much more usual, particularly in smaller installations. Continuous oiling filters have the advantage of being self-cleaning except for periodic changing of the oil in the reservoir.

Electric precipitation filters are the most efficient form of air filter. Air is first passed through an electric field, so that all solid particles in the air acquire an electrical charge, and then between series of closely spaced plates between which a second electrical field is set up. The charged dirt particles are driven by this field on to the earthed plates in this series, to which they adhere; periodic washing removes the collected dirt (15). Electric precipitators in addition to their simple operation are superior in that they remove smoke, bacteria and fungi—particles too fine to be trapped by mechanical filters.

Air washers. These consist of finely atomised water sprays arranged to produce a "mist" through which the air is drawn on to "scrubber plates", plates over which water is continuously run to trap the dirt. Washers do help to clean air by removing dirt and soluble gases but their major function is that of controlling the humidity of air. Air leaving the washer is saturated with water vapour and variations in the amount of subsequent heating will produce variations in its relative humidity. Control of the air temperature when it leaves the washer relative to its final temperature enables it to be circulated at predetermined humidity (see footnote on p. 33).

Air heating is effected by passing the air over heated surfaces usually in the form of tubes, which may be plain or "gilled", arranged in series of staggered rows. Tubes may be heated by hot water or steam and their surface temperature and the area of heating surface they present will depend on the volume of air to be heated and its velocity—matters of calculation by the engineer designer.

Control of Systems. In air conditioning systems both efficiency and economy in operation depend on proper control and larger installations are controlled automatically. In buildings in which large numbers of people are

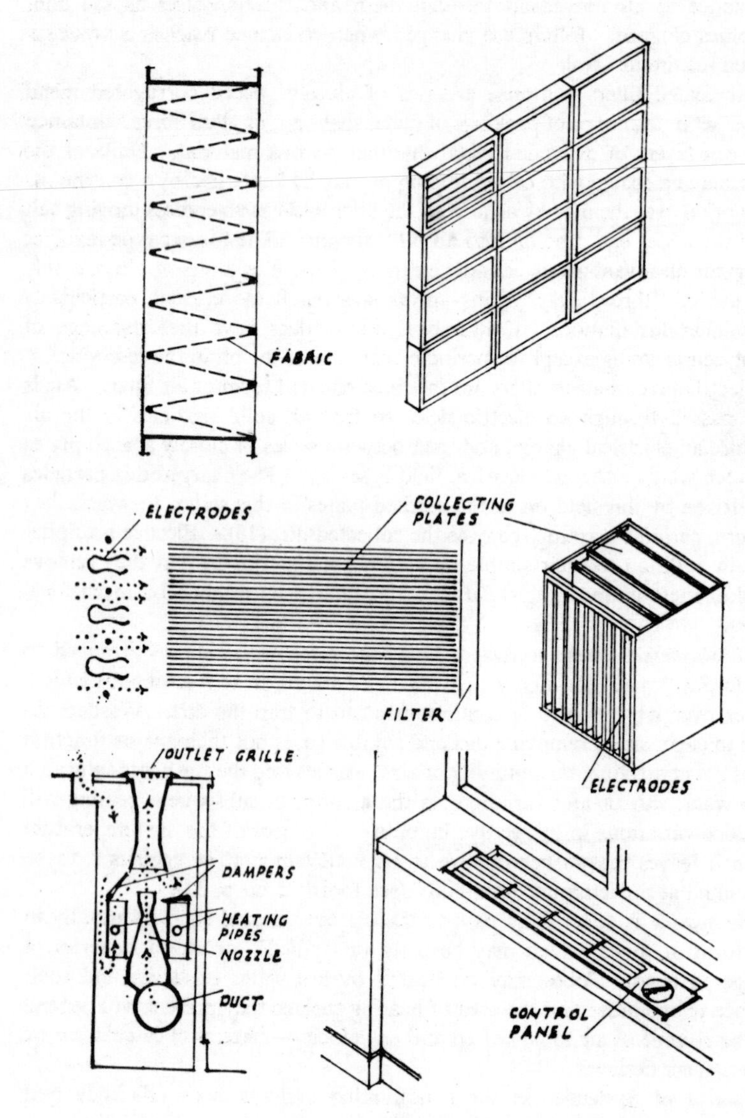
FABRIC
ELECTRODES
COLLECTING PLATES
FILTER
ELECTRODES
OUTLET GRILLE
DAMPERS
HEATING PIPES
NOZZLE
DUCT
CONTROL PANEL

15

accommodated the problem becomes largely one of dissipating heat and humidity produced by the occupants[1] without creating discomfort by introducing air at too low a temperature.[2]

When temperatures outside the building are low, heating of air before circulation and cooling after circulation will be necessary but when outside temperatures are high heating of outside air will not be required. In some cases cooling before circulation may be desirable. Control of humidity, the level of which will be raised by occupants is effected by the air washers. Air drawn from outside the building becomes saturated during washing and its temperature lowered by the loss of heat from the air in the turning of water to water vapour (see notes on humidity on p. 32). The raising of the temperature of the saturated air leaving the washer lowers its relative humidity. By stabilising the temperature of the air leaving the washer the relative humidity of the circulated air is also stabilised.

Constant after-washing temperature is secured by means of a thermostat which activates a motorised mixing valve controlling the temperature of

[1] An average adult emits sensible heat in the region of 300 btu/hr when at rest and when the surrounding temperature is 65°F.

[2] The difference between air temperatures at inlet and extract if discomfort is to be avoided should not exceed 15°F. Thus if other heat losses or gains are discounted the simple removal of heat emitted by each occupant would require the circulation of $300/(15 \times 0.019)$, about 1050 cu. ft of air per hour (0.019 btu is the amount of heat required to raise 1 cu. ft of air 1°F).

---

15 *Air conditioning*

(*Above*) A section showing diagrammatically the arrangement of a fabric screen filter. The zig-zag arrangement of the fabric presents maximum surface for contact with the moving air. Filters are built up from sections to sizes required as shown at *right*.

(*Centre*) Part plan and general view of an electronic filtering unit. Current passed through wires positioned between the curved electrodes sets up an ionising field which charges particles of dust in the air passing through it. These charged particles are then attracted to, and deposited on, the collecting plates between which a second electrical field is set up. The dry filter set behind the collecting plates ensures that air flow through the unit is even and prevents escape of water during the washing of the plates and also acts as a filter in the event of power failure. Filters of any size required may be made up by a number of units. (Manwood Miller Limited. Hi-C Electronic Air Cleaner.)

(*Below*) A high velocity inlet unit. Outlet of air from the delivery duct flows upward through the nozzle where its high speed induces entrainment of additional air at the inlet to the casing to the outlet grille.

The settings of the two dampers determine whether this additional air comes directly from the room via the inlet slot at cill level, or is first drawn wholly or partly over one or other of the heating or cooling pipes flanking the nozzle. ("Velovent" Air Control Installations Ltd.)

water fed to the washer. This thermostat also usually activates an electric motor powering the dampers which determine the proportion of air from the building to be recirculated. (When after washing temperature falls more air is recirculated and/or the temperature of the washing water raised.)

Variations in conditions inside the building, e.g. an increase or decrease in number of occupants, may also be catered for by means of a thermostat within the building. Temperature changes are sometimes made to activate a motorised mixing valve controlling the supply of water or steam to the air heaters. By means of a humidistat changes in relative humidity are made to vary the setting of a thermostat controlling the after-washing temperature. In summer conditions particularly when the humidity of the external air is high, depression of the air's temperature by washing is small and subsequent reheating often leaves relative humidity too high. To depress the temperature of saturated air leaving the washer sufficiently for suitable relative humidity to be produced by re-heating to circulating temperature often calls for refrigeration plant. Chilled water is used in the washer which by reducing the air's temperature reduces the amount of water carried by it from the washer. Raising the air's temperature then results in low relative humidity in the circulated air. Where a refrigerating plant is not installed the washer and of course the heater are simply dispensed with in summer conditions and air from outside the building is filtered and circulated.

4

The Building—its Warming and Lighting

Introductory

Although the origin of fire is uncertain it has undoubtedly been one of the major factors in early human development in all fields. In producing heat a wide range of very different fuels has been used. More recently with the growth of population and its industrialisation, timber was replaced by coal as a fuel and at the present time a trend towards replacement of coal by oil and electricity is discernible in both industrial and domestic heating. Demands for fuel of all kinds are now so great and are increasing so rapidly that its conservation in all forms and control over nuisance it creates in use, have become matters of national and international concern.[1]

Heat measurement. All materials have the capacity for absorbing and giving up energy in the form of heat. This energy they give up to or receive from materials around them, according to whether surroundings are hotter or colder than they are and in the absence of other influences the process continues until a state of balance results.[2]

Relative hotness or coldness is expressed comparatively in terms of temperature scales. These are divided into degrees, there being two principal scales in wide use. The Fahrenheit scale, used almost exclusively for general heat reference and heating design and calculation in this country, sets the boiling temperature of water at 212°F and its freezing point at 32°F, the

[1] Recent legislation in Great Britain requires the maintenance of minimum standards of insulation in new factory buildings. Bylaws set minimum standards of insulation for other buildings. Planning law has for a long time aimed at control of the industrial smoke nuisance by restricting the siting of industrial development and more recently legislation has been introduced to limit the amount of smoke emitted from chimneys of all kinds. The production of "smokeless" fuels from coal and design of appliances to burn them are sponsored by the government. (Free advice and information is placed at the disposal of the public and designers by the Coal Utilisation Council.) Choice of fuel, method and design of heating for any buildings, however small, has now become a matter in which knowledge of the principles involved is essential.

[2] Heat is always being permanently lost by radiation into space and of course replaced by radiation from the sun and the release of energy by chemical activity such as burning.

difference between being divided into 180 equal degrees (see Table 4). The Centigrade scale, used almost exclusively on the continent, and throughout the world in scientific fields, sets the boiling point of water at 100°C and its freezing point at 0°C (Table 4). When materials absorb heat or lose heat

TABLE 4

°F	°C
0	— 17·8
10	— 12·2
20	— 6·7
30	— 1·1
32	0 Freezing point of water
40	4·4
50	10·0
60	15·6
70	21·1
100	37·8
150	65·6
200	93·3
212	100·0 Boiling point of water

Comparison of Fahrenheit and Centigrade scales of temperature

To convert °F to °C: $°F = \frac{9}{5}°C + 32$

To convert °C to °F: $°C = \frac{5}{9}(°F - 32)$

then temperatures are raised or lowered. Materials vary greatly in the amount of heat they need to absorb or lose for similar changes in their temperature to be effected. These variations are defined in terms of Specific Heat—an expression of the amount of heat required to produce unit change in temperature in unit weight of a material compared with the amount of heat required to produce unit change in temperature in unit weight of water (Table 5).

Quantity of heat is measured in units which are defined as the quantity of heat required to raise the temperature of a given quantity of water one degree in temperature. Thus the British Thermal Unit, abbreviated to btu, is the amount of heat required to raise 1 lb of water 1°F. This is the unit used exclusively in presenting heating data and in the design of heating installations in this and *many other countries.*[1]

[1] The Centigrade equivalents are the large calorie, the amount of heat required to raise 1 kilogramme of water 1°C, and the small calorie, the amount of heat required to raise 1 gramme of water 1°C. The former is used on the continent in heating work and the latter in laboratory work throughout the world.

TABLE 5

Water	1·00	
Brick	0·19	
Stone	·21	
Concrete	·20	
Timber	·45	(average softwood)
Iron	·112	
Aluminium	·21	
Copper	·092	

Specific heat of common building materials—the amount of heat in btu's required to raise 1 lb of the material 1°F. or the amount of heat given up by 1 lb of the material in falling 1°F.

The value of water as a heat storing or carrying medium is immediately apparent.

Latent Heat. Many materials change their physical form with changes in temperature—from solid to liquid and from liquid to gas or vice versa. When these changes in form occur heat is given up and absorbed by the material which does not produce a change in its temperature, i.e. is absorbed or released by the physical change. This heat is known as Latent Heat. Thus in changing from ice at 32°F to water at the same temperature 142 btu's of heat are released for each pound of water formed and conversely 142 btu's of heat are absorbed in changing 1 lb of water at 32°F to ice at the same temperature. The changing of 1 lb of water to steam absorbs 998 btu's and the condensing of steam to water releases 998 btu's for each pound of water formed. This phenomenon is harnessed in some heating systems in which steam is circulated to radiators to warm buildings by means of the heat released when it condenses (see later in this chapter).

Transfer of Heat. Heat is transferred from one body to another in three ways. By conduction; by convection; by radiation.

Conduction is the transfer of heat absorbed by one part of a body to other parts of the same body, or to other bodies in contact with it. This capacity to conduct, "conductivity", is different in different materials. Metals generally and dense materials such as stone, brick and concrete are good, i.e. efficient, conductors of heat and light materials such as cork, timber and air are poor conductors of heat. In maintaining temperatures within buildings economically it is the capacity of materials to resist the conduction of heat through them, their "resistivity", which is of significance. Materials of high resistivity are known as insulators.

Conductivity, which is indicated by the symbol *K*, is measured as the heat in btu's transferred in 1 hour through 1 sq. ft of 1 in. thick material when the temperatures at the two faces differ by 1°F. The resistivity is the reciprocal of the conductivity (Table 6).

TABLE 6

Material	Conductivity K	Resistivity $1/K$
Brick	8·0	·125
Stone (average)	10·0	·10
Glass	7·5	·13
Plaster	3·3	·30
Tiles:		
Concrete	8·0	·125
Clay	5·8	·17
Timber	·87	1·15
Fibreboard	·5	2·0
Wood-wool (20 lb density)	·55	1·82
Cork	·28	3·57
Concrete:		
1: 2: 4 mix	10·0	·10
Foamed slag	1·7	·59
Cellular (40 lb density)	1·0	1·0

Conductivity and Resistivity of selected building materials

Conductivity is measured in btu's transferred through 1 in. thickness of material when temperatures at the two faces differ by 1°F.

Resistivity, the reciprocal of these values, is the measure of the material's resistance to heat transfer.

Convection is the transfer of heat by the movement of parts of liquids or gases. Localised heating and the consequent local expansion and reduction in density of, say, water results in the displacement of the heated portion by denser unheated water which in turn is heated and then displaced in the same way. Thus in a pan of water over a gas flame or fire, circulation is set up by warmed water rising from the bottom of the pan to the surface and water from the sides falling to the bottom of the pan to take its place. Water reaching the surface loses heat. The circulation thus continues so long as the pan remains over the heat. This phenomenon is harnessed in transferring water heated in a boiler to radiators or a storage tank, circulation being directed through the system of pipework. Circulation of air in a room is produced in a similar way by a radiator. Air in contact with the radiator is warmed and rises constantly across its surface to be replaced by colder, heavier air, heat from the radiator being transferred to all parts of the room by the movement of the air.

Radiation. All warm bodies emit heat in the form of energy waves which are absorbed or reflected by other bodies lying in the path of these waves. Heat waves although invisible are similar in character to light waves. They travel in straight lines and their intensity reduces in proportion to the square of the distance travelled from their source. When heat sources are radiant and localised in character they require to be of high temperature so that after rapid dispersal and reduction in intensity heat reaching persons is still effective (e.g. open fires and electric and gas fires). If of low temperature radiant sources require to be extensive in area (e.g. radiant wall and ceiling panels). The extent to which heat is emitted and replaced is greatly influenced by the nature of a body's surface. Matt surfaces have high capacity for emission and absorption and little capacity for reflection of heat waves. Polished metal surfaces have high capacity for reflection but very low capacity to emit or absorb heat. This explains why a highly polished kettle or teapot maintains its contents at high temperatures over long periods and why aluminium foil, a good conductor of heat, can be made to function as a good insulator. The capacity for emission is termed emissivity and is expressed relative to the emissivity of a surface coated with lamp black (Table 7).

TABLE 7

Matt black surface	1·00
Brick, tiles, etc.	0·90
Cast iron	0·80
Bright polished metals	0·04
Wood	0·90
Plaster	0·91
Painted surfaces	0·95
Aluminium paint	0·40–0·70

Emissivities of various materials relative to that of a matt black surface taken as 1·00 btu/sq. ft/hr.

Heat loss. Heat is lost from buildings in two ways: by the exchange of air warmed within the building for cooler air from outside and by conduction of heat from inner to outer surfaces of enclosing surfaces—to be then lost by radiation or convection due to the movement of air across them. The more sparsely occupied a building is, i.e. the less the heat lost by air change, the more important is control of heat loss through the building's surfaces, which has a direct influence on the cost of heating installations. Heat lost must be continually replaced if internal temperatures necessary for comfort are to be maintained, so that when heat losses are large more fuel must be burned and running costs are higher. To produce the greater amounts of heat heating appliances must be larger as must distributing pipework, radiators, etc., where these are used, so that installation costs are also greater. The resistance of materials to heat loss through them, their insulation value, is dependent on their thickness and resistivity and on the resistance to heat entry and egress at their surfaces. Heat transmission coefficients, referred to generally as *U* values,[1] are evaluations of overall resistance to heat transmission of materials or combinations of materials when thicknesses and surface resistances are taken into account. They are expressed in btu/sq. ft/hr/1°F difference at inner and outer surfaces. The value of *U* for a given construction varies to some extent with the degree of exposure of the outer surface which will influence the rate at which heat is lost from it by convection. The values for typical constructions given in Table 8 take account of this.

CALCULATION OF HEAT LOSS. Given the transmittance coefficients of the

[1] The *U* value of a given construction is determined from the formula

$$U = \frac{1}{RS_1 + (r_1 \times t_1) + (r_2 \times t_2) \ldots + RS_2}$$

where RS_1 = resistance of the internal surface,
RS_2 = resistance of the outer surface,
t_1, t_2 = thickness,
r_1, r_2, r_3 = resistivities of materials in the construction.

Example. Calculation of *U* value of a 9 in. brick wall plastered internally:

RS_1		= 0·70
$t_1 \times r_1$ (plaster)	= $\frac{3}{4} \times 0{\cdot}25$	= 0·18
$t_2 \times r_2$ (brick)	= $9 \times 0{\cdot}125$	= 1·125
RS_2		= 0·30
	Total	= 2·305

$U = 1/2{\cdot}305 = 0{\cdot}43$ btu/sq. ft/hr/°F

Surface resistance of internal surfaces of walls is 0·70 and of flat or sloping roof surfaces is 0·60. For general use surface resistance of external wall surfaces may be taken as 0·30 and of roof surfaces as 0·25 (these are their values in "Normal" exposure).

N.B.—Cavity constructions have enhanced *U* values because of the two additional surfaces presented by the cavity—an additional resistance of 1·0. Thus *U* value for a cavity wall is determined

RS_1		= 0·70
plaster	= $\frac{3}{4} \times 0{\cdot}25$	= 0·18
brick	= $4\frac{1}{2} \times 0{\cdot}125$	= 0·5625
cavity		= 1·0
brick	= $4\frac{1}{2} \times 0{\cdot}125$	= 0·5625
RS_2		= 0·30
	Total	= 3·3050

$U = 1/3{\cdot}3 = 0{\cdot}30$ btu/sq. ft/hr/°F

TABLE 8

Element of Construction	Exposure		
	Sheltered	Normal	Severe
Solid Walls			
Brick 4½ in.	0·49	0·53	0·57
Brick 9 in.	0·38	0·41	0·43
Cavity Walls			
4½ in. brick/4½ in. brick	0·28	0·29	0·30
4½ in. brick/4 in. clinker	0·25	0·26	0·27
4½ in. brick/4 in. hollow clinker block	0·21	0·21	0·22
Single window	0·79	0·88	1·00
Double window	0·44	0·47	0·50
Roofs			
Asphalt on 6 in. concrete	0·51	0·55	0·61
Ditto, lined 1 in. wood wool and plastered	0·22	0·24	0·25
Plaster ceiling with tiles, battens and felt above	0·40	0·43	0·46
Ditto, with 1 in. glass quilt over ceiling joists	0·15	0·17	0·19
Partitions			
3 in. breeze block plastered		0·42	
Stud partition plastered		0·38	
Door		0·50	
Internal Floors			
Timber		0·26	
Concrete		0·27	
Floors			
Hollow timber, ventilated		0·40	
Ditto, with lino		0·35	
Ditto, with ¾ in. glass quilt over joists		0·16	
5 in. concrete on 4 in. hardcore		0·20	
Ditto, finished lino or plastic tile		0·19	
Ditto, finished woodblock		0·15	

U values for different elements of construction in btu's/sq. ft/hour/°F. difference at surfaces.

Exposure is "Sheltered" for the first two storeys of buildings in towns; "Normal" for third to fifth storeys of buildings in towns and most suburban and country buildings; "Severe" for buildings on coastal and similar sites and storeys above fifth of buildings in towns.

Orientation of buildings slightly affects the values quoted which are correct for W., S.W. and S.E. orientations. (When orientation is S. decrease values by 10 per cent; when N.W. increase values by 10 per cent; when N., N.E. or E. increase values by 20 per cent.)

different constructions which make up the enclosing surfaces of a space to be heated, the total heat which will be transmitted through them can be calculated if the temperatures inside and outside are known. This amount of heat is of course the amount of heat which the heating appliances within the space must provide if the inside temperature is to be maintained. Calculations are necessary to enable heating appliances of the right capacity to be selected and they are made in advance by the engineer so that radiators and boiler, or other provisions to be made, can be sized to meet the most severe conditions likely to arise, i.e. to maintain a predetermined inside temperature when the outside temperature is at its lowest. Inside temperatures suitable for different kinds of occupation are well established (e.g. living rooms 65–70°F; bedrooms, kitchens, corridors, stairs, lavatories, etc., 50–55°F) and in England it is usual to take 30°F as the lowest outside temperature likely to be maintained for any length of time. When considering heat loss through walls and floors within a building this will be determined by the difference in temperature proposed for the adjoining rooms if any. Table 9 shows the usual method of tabulating heat losses when calculations are made.

TABLE 9

Surface	Area	*U*	Temperature Difference	Heat Loss
Living Room				
External walls	300	0·29	35	3,045
Window	100	1·00	35	3,500
Floor	280	0·35	35	3,430
Ceiling	280	0·26	10	728
Internal walls	380	0·42	10	1,596
Door	20	0·5	10	100
			Total	12,799

Typical setting out of heat loss calculations. In many cases losses between rooms within buildings are completely ignored.

N.B.—Only losses through external surfaces are of consequence in determining boiler capacities (see later).

APPROXIMATIONS. Calculations of the kind described are lengthy and often involved but nevertheless are essential in bigger installations where small margins of error over a large number of rooms would entail substantial difference in the size of, say, a centralised boiler. For preliminary investigations or other occasions when small degrees of error are of limited significance various methods of approximating heat losses are in common use. Typical of these is to allow for domestic buildings 3·66 and 4·43 btu's/cu. ft of volume when temperature rises of 30°F and 35°F are required. (This assumes 11 in. cavity walls or equal.)

UNIT APPLIANCES FOR HEATING

Heat is produced in unit appliances by burning one or other of a number of fuels or by the conversion of electrical energy to heat by passing it through elements of high resistance.

Open fires burning solid fuel, the oldest form of heating, have a long history of development but only recently has reasonable control over their output and performance been a general objective of design. This presents a number of problems: the effective distribution of the heat they produce; control over the degree of ventilation they induce; control over their rate of burning fuel. All these requirements are aimed at economy of fuel through higher efficiency in performance.

Design principles which have remained basically unchanged up to the present day were formulated early in the last century but it is only fairly recently that conscious efforts to apply them efficiently have been made.

Development of the open grate. Mention of iron grates for burning coal occurs in inventories of the early sixteenth century, and at the end of that century we know that the depth and width of the hearth recess was much reduced and the mouth of the flue contracted. An Italian architect, Scammozzi, writing at that time, also says that, in England, a door of iron is used to partly close the flue after the fire is well lighted, this being the first mention of the register plate.

About 1624 a French architect, Savot, further reduced the height and width of the fireplace opening and introduced the iron back and covings, together with the perforated base plate of the ordinary grate still in use. About 1738 came the use of fixed canopies, adjustable registers and the insulation of the grate by means of air spaces behind it. In the same century the well-known Bath fireplace was in vogue, consisting of a hobbed grate with an iron plate front, having an arched opening in it. It has great draught-creating powers, carrying off all the air in the vicinity. An old English writer, in commenting on it, says, "whoever, impelled by the merciless severity of the frost, comes near the grate, will find his front fried and his rear frozen".

At the beginning of the nineteenth century, Count Rumford, a versatile American, at various times shop-boy, soldier, diplomatist, financier, scientist, and founder of the Royal Institution in our own country, did more to improve the fireplace than anyone up to that time. He it was who brought the fire grate forward, the mantel lower, emphasised the importance of forming a "throat" to the flue, and introduced the diverging sides and covings to obtain greater radiation of the heat into the room. He pointed out that the bars should not be too far apart, ensuring brightness of the exposed surface of the fuel and increasing the radiation of the heat, and that dull, rough, iron covings were better radiators of heat than polished surfaces.

Dr Teale's experiments. Later in the nineteenth century, valuable experimental work was done in connection with the improvement of fireplaces by Dr Teale, F.R.S., who embodied his conclusions in a paper read before the Royal Institution in 1886, on "The Economy of Fuel in House Fires". The chief conclusion obtained by Dr Teale was that slow and efficient combustion depends on there being no current of air up through the grate, and he accordingly introduced what is known as the economiser, shutting in the space below the grate. He also laid down a series of rules for the design of fireplaces, the principal of which are:

1 Use as little iron as possible, making both back and sides of fire-brick.
2 The fire-brick back should lean over the fire; and
3 The greatest efficiency is obtained from the covings when they are inclined at an angle of 60° to one another.

To these might be added the need for a controlled draught, a throated flue and a good chimney capped by a clean-cut pot, clear of obstructions and free from the blanketing effect of high buildings or trees in the vicinity, which might cause a back pressure or down draught.

The sunk or well type. Later investigators have held that it is important that the air should not pass through the face of the fire, and so have designed fireplaces of what is known as the sunk type with raised hearths in front and ventilating fenders communicating with a hot-air chamber below the grating at the base of the fire, practically the whole thing being formed of fire-brick. In some examples the base of the grate is formed with reinforced fireclay bars to prevent the absorption of heat by the iron.

Other experts hold that there is no necessity to supply air to the lower side of the fire and that a grated base with an ash-pit under is a superfluity. It has been fairly well demonstrated that a good fire can be obtained without any supply other than that passing over the top of the fire; that more perfect combustion is thereby attained with economy of fuel; and that much less draught is caused in the room owing to the demand for air being far less than in the older types of grate.

It should be pointed out, however, that, in almost all types, ashes will accumulate and require removal. The grated base allows for the removal of the ashes without letting out the fire, which is a point not to be overlooked in the case of a sick-room where a fire is constantly required, while another advantage is that the fire, when newly ignited, can be "drawn up" more quickly if air is allowed to pass through the burning fuel. As soon as the fire has burnt up sufficiently, the damper (if one is provided) can be closed and the fuel will then burn more slowly with the air supply from the top only.

It should be noted, in passing, that logs burn best in their own ash, so they should be burnt on a flat hearth or in one of the sunk type, but coal does not burn so well in these conditions, and better control is obtained if a fretted stool is used through which the ash can fall for easy removal. The air supply can then pass under or over the fuel according to the rate of burning desired.

Care must be taken that open grates of this type are not placed on a hearth with timbers under or in too close proximity.

Modern grates. General principles of design may be summarised. Fireboxes are shaped on plan and in section to disperse the radiated heat over as wide an area as possible. Control over the amount of air and heat carried up the flue is effected by restricting its area at the inlet to it above the fire. The restriction and the proper shaping of this inlet to the flue, "the throat", also impart, because of the so-called venturi phenomenon, an initial velocity to the upward moving gases from the fire, so helping to overcome temporary resistances set up in the flue which might otherwise result in smoke escape into the room (16). Some recent grates also have arrangements by means of which the throat area can be varied. The most advanced of open fires include two further developments designed to increase efficiency in terms of useful heat output relative to rate of fuel consumption. Control over rate of burning is in many modern fire grates effected positively by an air-tight enclosure of the space below the fire inlet, entry of air for combustion to which can be accurately controlled by a damper. There are different ways of doing this:

(1) Air for combustion is ducted directly from points outside the building to the area below the grate, the rate of inlet being controlled by a damper operated from within the room. This, by reducing the amount of air drawn from the room, reduces heat lost from the room so that the demand that is made on the fire is less.

(2) The firebox and grate are constructed as a unit, usually of cast iron, around which an enclosed air space is constructed. (In some models there is a second enclosing casing which is an integral part of the unit.) Air within this space is warmed by contact with the outside of the firebox.

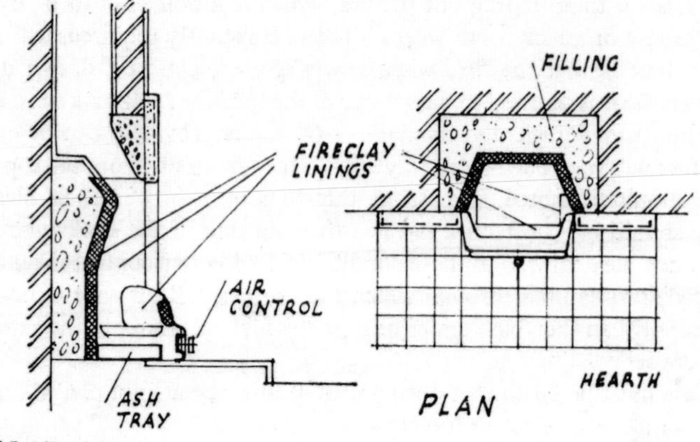

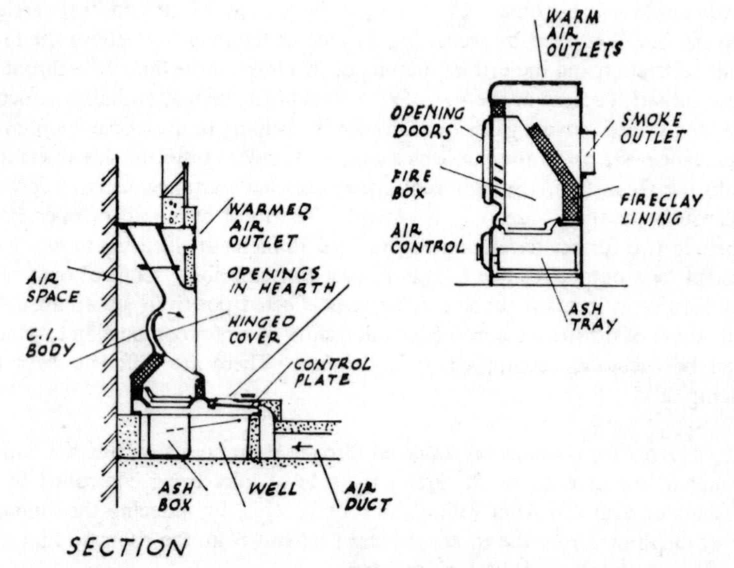

16

16 *Fires and Stoves*

(*Above*) A typical modern open fire. The fireclay back sloping above the fire increases fire temperature and radiates heat downwards into the room. The splayed fireclay sides radiate heat laterally into the room. The throat set

Suitably placed inlets and outlets cause air from the room to circulate through this space and so contribute by convection to the heat given off by the fire by radiation. In the period immediately after the Second World War a number of fires were designed in which air warmed in a space around the firebox was distributed by ducts leading from it to adjoining rooms or rooms on upper floors. It seems to have been found that heat dissipated in this way does in general place too great a demand on a reasonably sized fire and such convection circulation of air is now usually restricted to air taken from and returned to the room in which the fire is burning.

Other notable advances in fireplace design are the arrangement of large

---

directly above the fire is narrow but shaped to give smooth air and smoke flow through it.

The fire front is shaped to give a deep fire-box, lined at front and sides with fireclay, which enables the fire to burn smokeless fuels as well as soft coal. The front is sealed with fire cement along its lines of contact with the hearth and surround opening to exclude air from the space below the fire so that burning rate can be positively controlled by the air inlet control set in the fire front.

The filling behind the fireclay lining may be weak concrete or hardcore, the latter having the advantage of additional insulating value.

(*Centre*) A typical openable stove. The opening doors and the open bars behind give a view of the fire when desired. The double body around the fire-box promotes warming and circulation of air in the room.

When the doors are closed, air entering the appliance, i.e. drawn from the room, is limited to that allowed to enter the space below the fire through the front air control.

Stoves can be installed free standing or inset with fronts flush with a chimney breast in emulation of an open fire, but circulation of air warmed by contact with the body of the stove is an essential part of efficiency.

(*Below*) Section through a convector fire with underfloor air supply. The fire consists of cast iron body which is seated on the edges of a sunken well of the same size as the fire base. Air can thus only enter the space below the fire through a slot along the front edge of the fire base. The raising or lowering of the control plate, which is hinged along its back edge, allows air passing through this slot to reach the under fire space or diverts it to openings set in the hearth as desired. A gap left around walls to the well allows air from outside to reach the space behind the fire body to be warmed. In the example shown this warmed air is released through an opening over the fire.

Areas in the vicinity of the fire are lined with fireclay slabs and the fire has a hinged lid which is lowered for overnight burning. The rate of the fire's burning is closely controlled and whether air supply is over or under the fire it comes from outside so that draughts and excessive ventilation are eliminated.

The output of heat from fires and stoves of the types and sizes described, are quoted in btu's per hour by manufacturers so that proper selection from a knowledge of heat losses is a simple matter.

ash-collecting boxes set below the fire. These reduce the need for cleaning in some cases to as infrequently as once a week. Most models with air-tight fronts will burn satisfactorily overnight, some incorporate hinged covers which can be lowered to cover the fire and exclude air from the top of the fire for overnight burning (16).

Stoves. The design of closed stoves and stoves which can be closed has greatly improved in recent years and much of the prejudice against earlier models, arising from overheating, drying of the air and consequent production of smells due to roasting of organic matter in the air, has been dissipated. In closed stoves the major portion of the heating output is by convection. Air is warmed by circulating between the stove and an outer perforated casing in the case of freestanding stoves (16), or behind the stove in built-in models.

The complete enclosure of the fire enables precise control over the air for combustion whether below the fire or above and below as in the case of openable stoves. The very slow rates of burning which can be achieved provide obvious opportunity for economy and the predominantly convection character results in greater efficiency[1] than can be effected by open fires.

Unit appliances which burn gas, electricity or oil in place of solid fuels are widely used as alternatives to solid fuel appliances and relative to these offer the advantages of labour saving and cleanliness and availability for intermittent use, the reduction or elimination of the need to store fuel and direct and immediate control over their heat output. A brief review of some of these is given below.

Gas appliances. The most familiar of these is the radiant fire in which gas flames raise ceramic elements to radiant temperature and for which flues are essential to carry away products of combustion. In addition to the general advantages referred to such flued appliances have the advantage that whilst promoting ventilation this is not excessive as is the case with conventional open fires. It is also established that the radiant heat distribution is better than from an open solid fuel fire—a greater proportion of the heat being thrown out in a horizontal or downward direction—a factor which has a direct bearing on comfort conditions produced.

As with solid fuel appliances combination of heat transfer by radiation and convection increases efficiency. Convector/radiant gas fires which circulate air warmed by circulation through cavities in the body of the fire give 25 per cent more heat output than purely radiant fires (17). Although effective as long period heaters the main use of gas fires, particularly "radiant only" forms, is for short period heating where comfort conditions need to be

[1] I.e. useful heat produced relative to heat content of the fuel.

achieved at short notice and maintained for limited periods, e.g. in domestic dining-rooms and bedrooms. Used continuously over long periods they are distinctly less economic than solid fuel appliances.

Gas fires produce products of combustion which may contain carbon monoxide but in spite of this and the fact that carbon monoxide is a cumulative poison numbers of gas appliances are designed for safe operation without flues. These flueless heaters, many of which are portable, transfer heat almost entirely by convection and achieve very high efficiency as none of their heat is lost by flue induced ventilation. They are however limited in capacity and limits are advised for period of use and position. Gas convectors for use in hallways are familiar examples as also are portable bar-type gas fires intended for use as short period auxiliaries to more continuous heating. For continuous heating without the need for conventional flues "balanced flue" heaters offer advantages of freedom in positioning and individual control. These are convector heaters which draw air for combustion and discharge combustion products directly through an opening in an outside wall behind them (17). They are obvious equivalents to hot water radiators and whilst dispensing with the need for pipework or boiler installation, offer greater flexibility in use because of their capacity for individual control. Running costs are however considerably higher than conventional central heating (see later).

Gas as a fuel generally is discussed later in this chapter.

Oil appliances. Oil burning appliances are still, rightly in many cases, associated with fumes but improvements in design of appliances and quality of fuel have led to a widely increased use of oil burning unit appliances which are claimed and generally accepted as odourless. These burn paraffin as fuel and their popularity is undoubtedly due to their portability and complete independence of supply installations such as are required for gas or electric equipment. Appliances include simple air heaters in which an oil flame heats and circulates air passing through it; water filled containers, "radiators", which warm the air in the room by convection over the water filled radiator surfaces; radiant heaters in which an oil flame is used to heat a metal grille to incandescence the radiant heat from which is distributed by means of a highly polished reflector (17).

In spite of popular belief oil heaters are not economic for continuous heating relative to solid fuel appliances and need careful attention in refilling and wick trimming and adjustment if freedom from odours is to be maintained and fouling of decorations, unavoidable to some degree, is not to be excessive.

Oil as a fuel generally is discussed below.

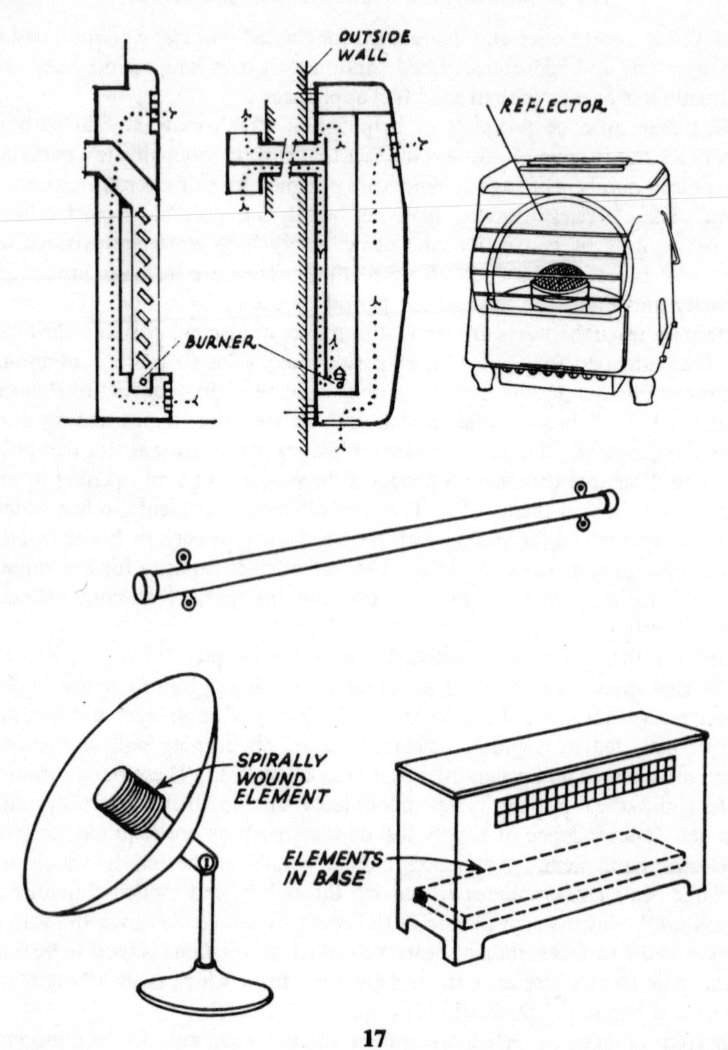

17

17 *Heaters*

(*Above, left*) Diagrammatic section of gas convector/radiant heater. The ceramic element and backing above the burner become incandescent and radiate heat into the room. At the same time air is drawn from the room below the burner, and after warming by passage through the hollow casing around

Electric appliances. Electricity is converted to heat by passing current through elements of high resistance, usually of wire wound around a fireclay or similar core, different temperatures and output being achieved by varying size and resistance of the elements to produce a number of different forms of heater.

Radiant heaters are the commonest form of electric unit heaters. In these, elements rapidly attain and then maintain red heat which is radiated, usually with assistance from highly polished metal reflectors. Heaters of this type are available with a wide range of outputs and design—for installation as fixed inset panels, as semi-portable items designed as substitutes for open fires and as completely portable items (17). For psychological reasons radiant elements are often combined with low powered lamps set behind coloured transparent material arranged in imitation of burning coals.

In spite of their undoubted convenience and cleanliness and extreme simplicity in installation running costs are high enough to limit the use of this type of heater to short period intermittent heating where the need is to quickly reach maximum output which can be dispensed with at short notice.

Convector heaters which consist essentially of a heating element within a casing arranged to direct air from the room over it are much more effective

---

the radiant fire, emerges above it. (About 60 per cent of the total heat produced is released in the room, as against about 45 per cent in the case of purely radiant fires.)

(*Above, centre*) Diagrammatic section through a "balance flue" heater. As shown, air for combustion is drawn from outside and products of combustion released outside by means of a single terminal fitting. This and the air passages from it are arranged to ensure that heat wastage is a minimum. Only air actually required for the combustion is circulated through the heater.
Air from inside the room is warmed by circulation around the burner container as shown.

(*Above, right*) A paraffin-burning radiant heater. The flame below the metal grille heats this to radiant temperature, heat being distributed by the reflector behind it. Only paraffin oil heaters in accordance with B.S. 3300, 1963 should be used.

(*Centre*) An electric tubular heater. Surface temperature of the exposed casing is maintained at a safe level and heat transfer is almost entirely by air convection over the tube surface. Current consumption is usually about 80–100W per ft length.

(*Below, left*) An electric bowl radiant fire. Heat from the incandescent element and its ceramic core is "beamed" by the reflector as required. Similar arrangements of reflector and "bar" elements are available in wide variety designed for directional adjustment or for fixed positions (see text).

(*Below, right*) Diagram showing the essentials of electric convector heaters. The casing form can and is varied greatly in the large number of proprietary models now marketed.

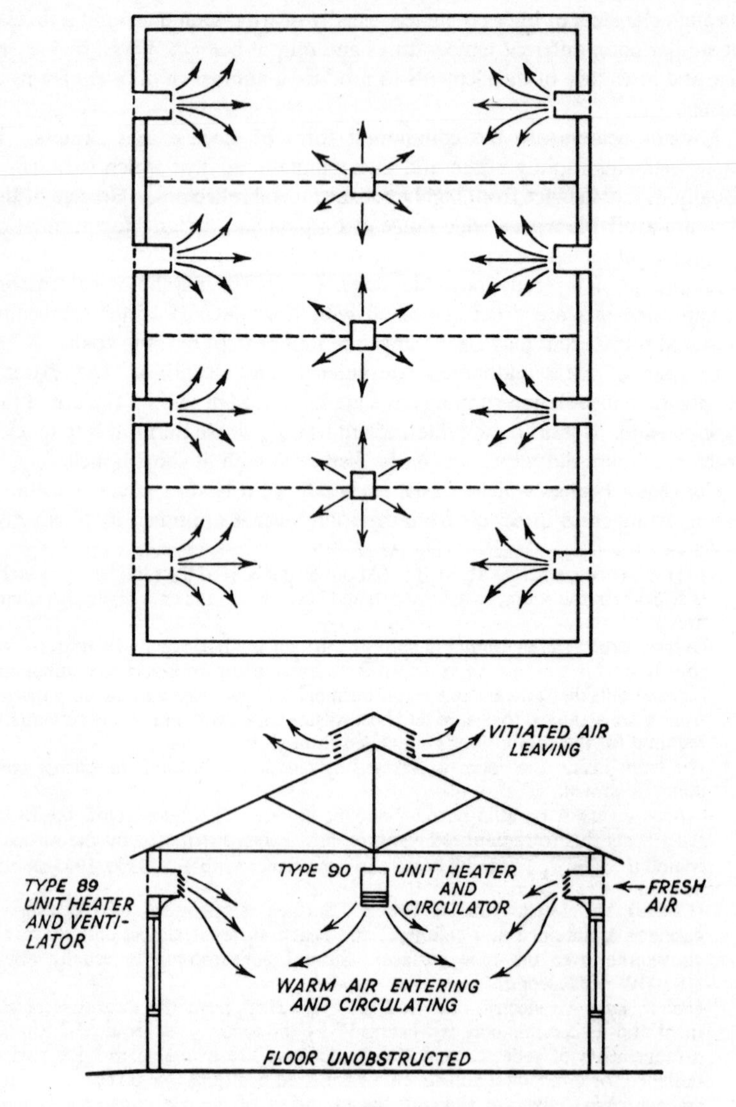
VITIATED AIR
LEAVING
TYPE 90 UNIT HEATER
AND
CIRCULATOR
TYPE 89
UNIT HEATER
AND VENTI-
LATOR
FRESH
AIR
WARM AIR ENTERING
AND CIRCULATING
FLOOR UNOBSTRUCTED

18

for continuous heating whether as the only heat source or auxiliary to, say, an open fire (17). Convector cabinets vary widely in design and in many economy in running is greatly assisted by the incorporation of thermostats, operated by air temperature in the room, which switch on and off the supply of electricity to the heating element to maintain air temperature at a predetermined level. Others also combine convector cabinets with radiant elements and most incorporate lighting which assists psychologically in the sensation of warmth as well as enhancing appearance when the heater is in operation. Freedom in shaping convectors is almost complete and body shapes include "traditional" box forms as well as panel forms for positions against walls, circular forms designed for "island" positioning, and skirting height fittings designed to be part of the permanent furnishing of rooms. An early form of radiator-simulating fitting was the tubular heater (17)—a low powered continuous element within a metal protective casing. Available in almost any length, these enable heat transfer surface to be inconspicuously distributed over a wide area or positioned to provide local warmth in small quantities—below glass areas to discourage down-draught and condensation or to heat cupboards.

Convectors which incorporate fans enable output to be directed for more efficient distribution and allow concentration of heating elements to produce smaller and more portable units. These are identical in action to "unit" heaters referred to briefly in Chapter 3 (p. 45). These are illustrated diagrammatically in Fig. 19 and a simple typical arrangement in Fig. 18. Convector heaters of course produce somewhat similar results to radiators warmed from a central heat source but these are more exactly emulated by electric radiators. These closely resemble in form the hot water radiators described later in this chapter. The better types of these are oil filled, the oil being heated by means of an element set within the radiator. Thermostatic control is the rule rather than the exception in the case of radiators, control being arranged to maintain a constant temperature for the radiator filling or alternatively for the surrounding air. Many models incorporate automatic time switches which completely turn off the supply to the radiators during periods when heating is not required. The ease with which thermostatic control can be applied to electrical equipment does much to limit running

---

18 *Arrangement of unit heaters*

Plan and section showing diagrammatically the arrangement of unit heaters to heat and ventilate a small workshop.

The wall units can be set to partly recirculate air within the building, i.e. to control the extent of the ventilation, if required. (See also Chapter 3, p. 45.)

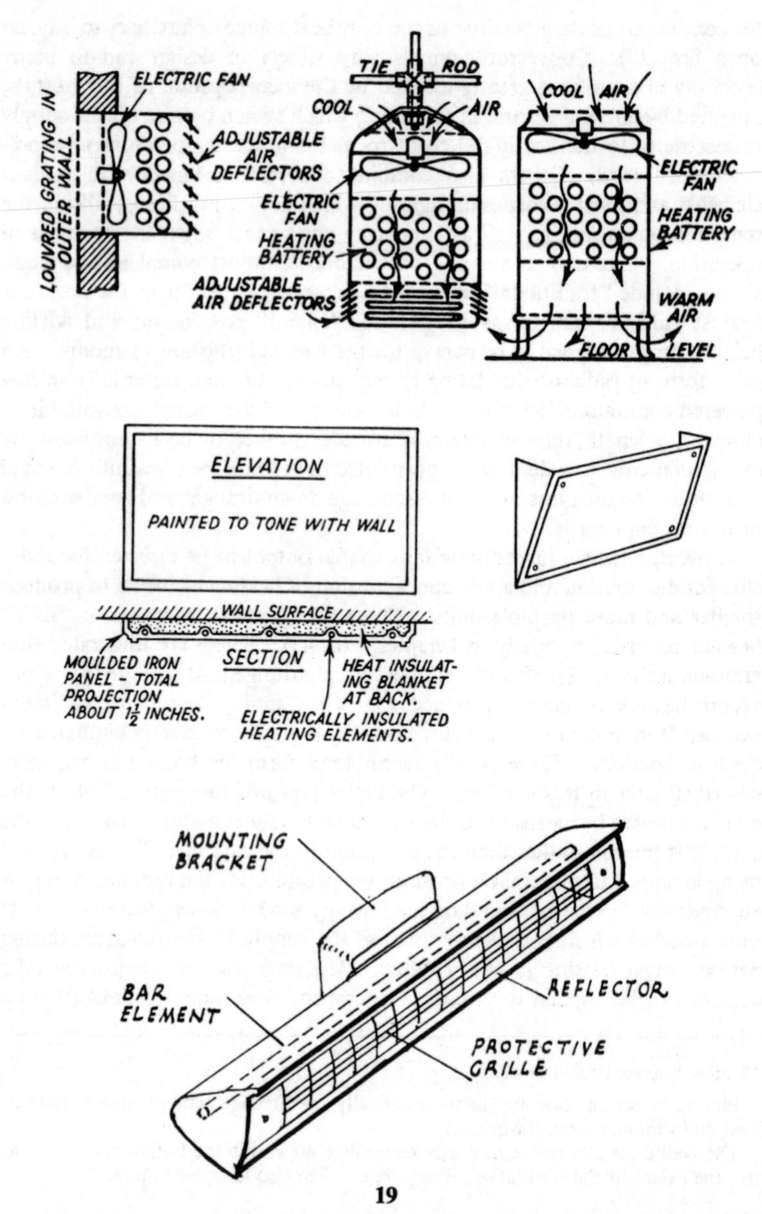
LOUVRED GRATING IN OUTER WALL
ELECTRIC FAN
ADJUSTABLE AIR DEFLECTORS
TIE ROD
COOL AIR
ELECTRIC FAN
HEATING BATTERY
ADJUSTABLE AIR DEFLECTORS
COOL AIR
ELECTRIC FAN
HEATING BATTERY
WARM AIR
FLOOR LEVEL
ELEVATION
PAINTED TO TONE WITH WALL
WALL SURFACE
SECTION
MOULDED IRON PANEL - TOTAL PROJECTION ABOUT 1½ INCHES.
HEAT INSULATING BLANKET AT BACK.
ELECTRICALLY INSULATED HEATING ELEMENTS.
MOUNTING BRACKET
REFLECTOR
BAR ELEMENT
PROTECTIVE GRILLE

19

costs but heating by electric convectors or radiators is more costly than heating by solid fuel appliances or heating by hot water radiators supplied from a central boiler (see "Central heating" below). Installation and pipe work costs are however completely eliminated and it is often justly pointed out that not only are superior comfort conditions created by electric radiators but that a number of years' complete running costs is represented by savings in installation. Optimists go so far as to suggest that by the time this benefit is used the cost of electricity will be low enough to make their running cost at least competitive.

The use of electricity as fuel for central heating is discussed later in this chapter.

Electric radiant heaters are produced to meet similar conditions. These may comprise heating elements arranged to raise the temperature of a panel surface of high emissivity. Direction of radiation from these on to occupants maintains comfort to some extent independently of high rates of air change which may be necessary or unavoidable (19).

More recently elements have been produced which emit infra-red radiations (heat radiations), in large quantities for relatively small consumption of electricity. Such infra-red heaters (19) provide radiant heating much more economically than the high temperature panels described above and the use of reflectors makes direction of radiation much easier and more effective. The use of domestic models, e.g. for wall mounting in kitchens and bathrooms, is also increasing.

Central heating. The heating appliances described above may be referred to collectively as unit heaters—each being self-contained and capable of independent use—as opposed to *central heating*, a term implying the circulation of heat to a number of transfer points from a central source. In this

---

19 *Unit heaters*

(*Above, left*) Diagrammatic arrangements of unit heaters designed for mounting on external walls; (*centre*) suspension overhead; (*right*) floor mounting. The heating batteries in the units can be and often are heated by hot water or steam from a central boiler.

(*Centre, left*) A low temperature electric radiant panel. These are designed for radiation at relatively close quarters from wall or ceiling and surface temperature is kept in the region of 100°F. Similar items which are portable are also produced.

(*Centre, right*) A high temperature electric radiant panel intended for longer range radiation, mounted on ceiling or above head-height on walls.

(*Below*) An infra-red heater. The highly polished reflector makes accurate direction simple. Current consumption is low and almost entirely converted to radiation.

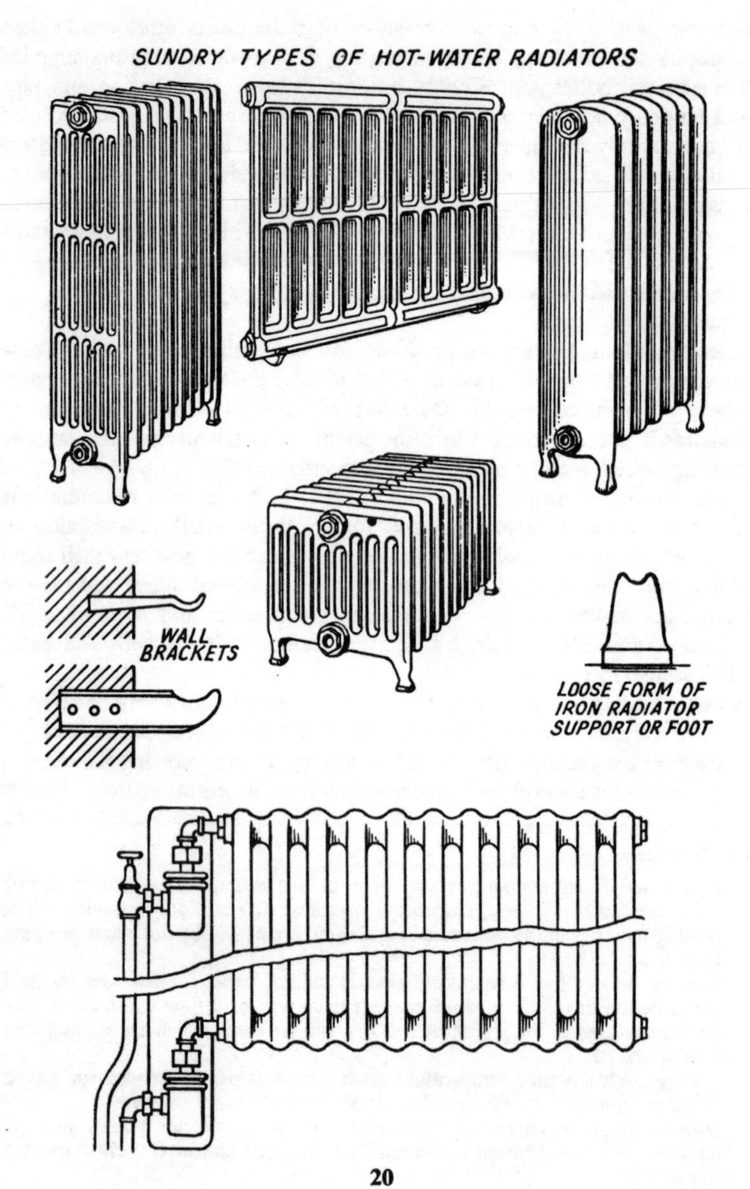
SUNDRY TYPES OF HOT-WATER RADIATORS
WALL BRACKETS
LOOSE FORM OF IRON RADIATOR SUPPORT OR FOOT

20

sense the air circulation systems described in the last chapter are central heating systems but by far the most widely used circulating medium for such systems is hot water. Water heated by a conveniently situated boiler is circulated to selected points to give up heat by cooling before return to the boiler for re-heating—proportioning and concentration of this heat transfer, necessary to control over heat distribution, is effected by radiators earliest forms of which were simply concentrations of additional pipe length in the form of coils. Heat is transferred from radiators mainly by convection currents set up by the warming of air in contact with them (see p. 58) and the amount of heat transferred is dependent on a number of factors. The difference between temperature and the radiator surface, i.e. the water temperature and that of the surrounding air; the area of contact between the radiator surface and the air; the amount of obstruction offered to the free circulation of air around the radiator (e.g. placing radiators too close to the wall surface behind; placing a shelf above a radiator or enclosing radiators within recesses or casings).

Heat transfer is quicker when temperature difference is greater so that installations are designed to circulate water at as high a temperature as is reasonable and in sufficient quantity to deliver the amount of heat required in falling through a small temperature drop. (In so-called Gravity Systems of circulation, described later, it is the increase in density of the water due to

---

20 *Radiators*

Design is aimed principally at presenting as great a surface of contact between radiator surface and air as possible for a given water content. Radiators of all types are assessed in terms of square feet of surface.

Radiators of equal surface area have approximately equal rates of heat transfer—about 150 btu/sq. ft/hr when air to radiator difference is 90°F.

Multi-column types (*top, left*) are highly efficient in this respect and patterns vary from 2 to 6 columns in depth and 18 in. to 36 in. in height, but some surfaces are difficult to reach for cleaning. This is overcome in the wall type (*top, centre*) and the "hospital" type (*top, right*), but both present less surface for equivalent space requirements. Both types can be wall-mounted by means of brackets (*centre, left*), in which case feet are omitted. The window seat type (*centre*) has 9 columns and is made in one height, 13 in.

Wall types are also available to fit tightly against walls and have a flat smooth surface (*not illustrated*). These panels transfer a higher proportion of their heat by radiation than conventional radiators.

Radiators are also produced with skirting profiles, behind which air is circulated and warmed, giving advantages of better heat distribution and avoiding space and appearance demands.

The hinged radiator (*below*), designed to make back surfaces accessible, is rarely encountered nowadays. (Hinging arrangements are a weak point and vacuum cleaners make their use unwarranted.)

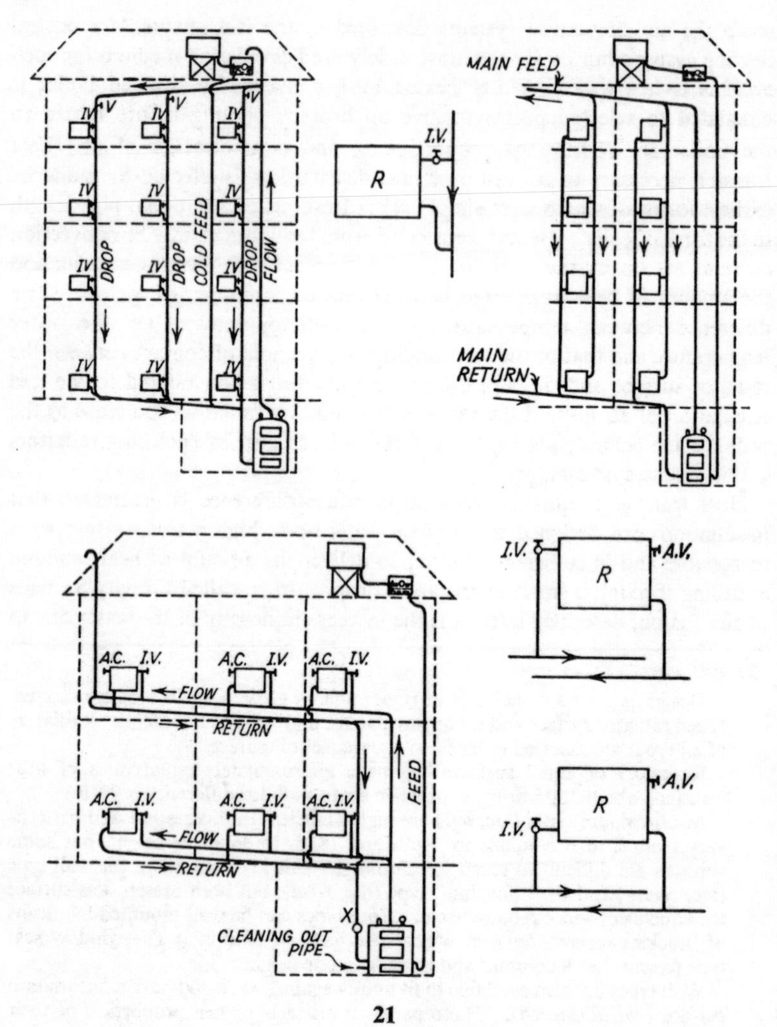

21

21 *Gravity circulations*

(*Above*) DROP SYSTEMS in which hot water from the boiler is apportioned at high level between a number of drop pipes. Temperature fall between first and last radiators is evenly distributed and the majority of pipes are small, e.g. relative to long horizontal circulations. The details show the method of connecting radiators (see notes following).

cooling which promotes its circulation through the pipework and the designer's aim is to achieve the circulation of sufficient water with a relatively small difference between the temperature of water when it leaves the boiler and when it returns to it.) Fig. 20 illustrates and describes a number of common forms of radiator.

Gravity systems. The expansion of water due to heating and the consequent reduction in its density are enough for the pressure difference at the feet of similar columns of hot and cold water to provide the motive power for the circulation of water through pipework against the friction resistance of the pipes. Installations designed to operate by virtue of this naturally

---

The two-pipe arrangment (*right*) has the advantage, relative to the one-pipe arrangement (*left*), of separately returning direct to the boiler all water that has once passed through a radiator. Except for minor losses from pipes all radiators will be at the same temperature instead of being progressively cooler further from the boiler.

The diagrams show alternative methods of feeding cold water to the system; by a connection to the return at low level (*left*) and by separate drop pipe direct to the boiler, the method generally preferred. Cold feed tanks must of course be separate from main storage tanks, although often fed from them as shown, to avoid possible contamination of the water supply. They should be large enough to accommodate overflow due to expansion when the open expansion pipe is turned over them.

RISER SYSTEMS (*not illustrated*) are similar in arrangement but the flow pipe is run at low level, water rising from it to radiator inlets and returning to it, or to a return pipe in two-pipe circulations, via "risers".

(*Below*) TWO-PIPE RING SYSTEM. As in the two-pipe drop system, water which has passed through radiators is turned directly into a return pipe and not mixed with water flowing to more distant radiators (see detail diagrams). N.B.—Inlet and outlet to radiators are best made at opposite corners, but neater bottom connections can be made by blanking off the bottom connection of the end column.

In all layouts, pipes rise to and fall from the highest point in the system from which is run an open ended expansion pipe. In addition to relieving pressure and allowing increase in volume of water in the system to escape this allows any air trapped in the pipes or released from the water in them to escape. If any intermediate high points are formed in the circulation, outlets for trapped air from these must be provided. Thus the air cocks (marked A.C.) in the lower system are necessary to release air which would inevitably collect at the tops of radiators and prevent circulation if not released.

In addition to the inlet valves shown (marked I.V.), which enable the radiator to be turned off or down, it is usual for second regulating valves (marked R.V.) to be fitted at the outlet from each radiator. These, operated only by key, are permanently set to ensure that flow through each radiator is what was intended by the designer, i.e. to ensure the exact apportioning of the total flow from the boiler which is not possible by variations in pipe sizes alone.

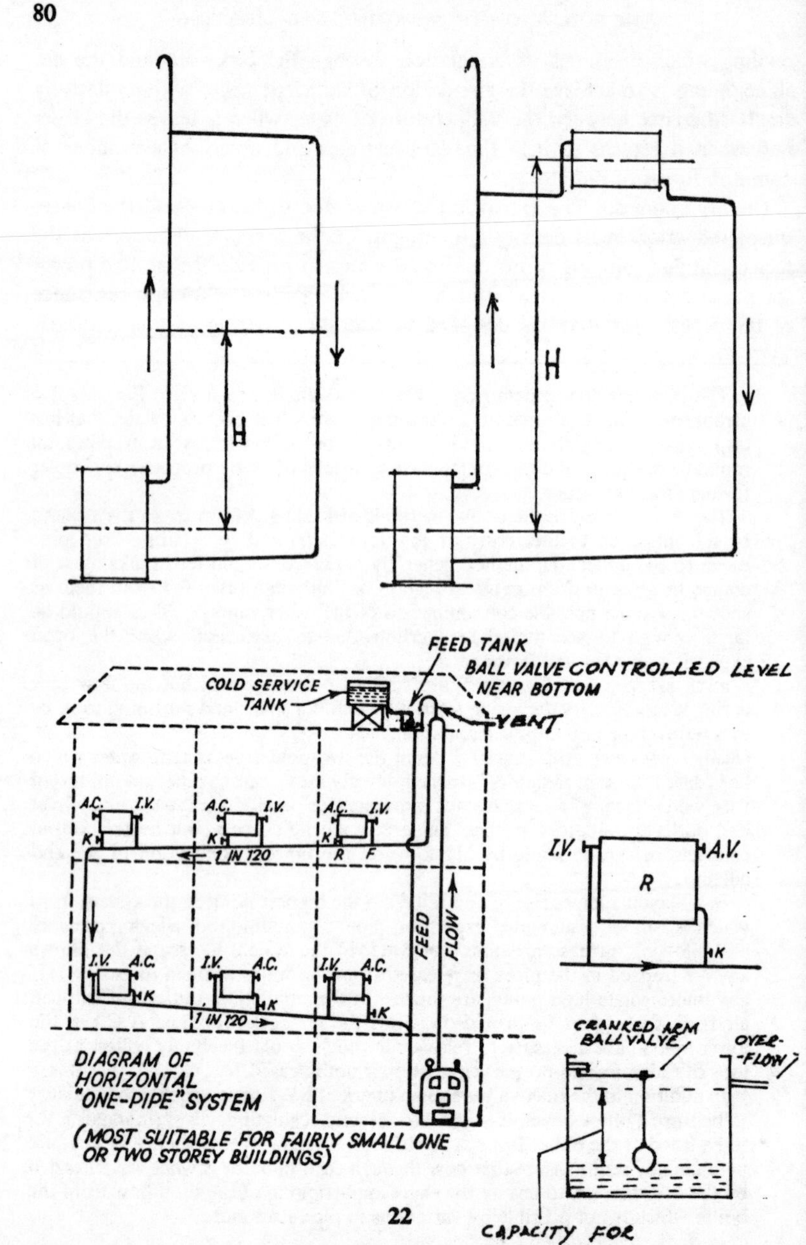
H
H
FEED TANK
BALL VALVE CONTROLLED LEVEL
NEAR BOTTOM
COLD SERVICE
TANK
VENT
A.C.
I.V.
K
R
F
1 IN 120
FEED
FLOW
1 IN 120
I.V.
A.V.
R
K
DIAGRAM OF
HORIZONTAL
"ONE-PIPE" SYSTEM
(MOST SUITABLE FOR FAIRLY SMALL ONE
OR TWO STOREY BUILDINGS)
CRANKED ARM
BALLVALVE
OVER-
-FLOW
CAPACITY FOR
EXPANSION

22

created movement are termed gravity systems and have the obvious advantage of being completely independent of outside assistance in operation. The diagrams in Figs 21 and 22 illustrate and describe typical layouts for gravity systems of circulation.

Design of Installations

In determining the total demand to be made on a heating installation the amount of heat carried from the building by air displaced in its ventilation must be added to that lost through its enclosing surfaces (see pp. 59). The extent of ventilation being decided (see pp. 34 and 35), the amount of heat required is that which will be used in raising the air leaving the building from its temperature at entry, usually taken as 30°F, to the temperature maintained within the building. The heat required to raise 1 cu. ft of air 1°F being 0·019 btu the number of btu's per hour required to make up for ventilation losses is thus:

(Volume of the room or building) × (the number of air changes per hour)
× (the difference between inside and outside temperatures) × 0·019 btu's

---

22 *Circulating head*

(*Above, left*) The circulating head *H* in the simple loop is half the height of the circulation (measured to centre of boiler).
(*Above, right*) The radiator in the circulation ensures that the whole of the temperature drop will occur, for practical purposes, whilst water is in the radiator and the circulating head is measured to the centre of the radiator.

N.B.—When there are a number of radiators the circulating height will be somewhere between the radiators (midway when radiator areas at upper and lower levels are equal in area), proportionally as their areas differ on other occasions (see sample calculation in Fig. 24.)

RING LAYOUT
(*Below*) A one-pipe ring layout most commonly used in smaller buildings. The change over from "flow" to "return" is made as high as possible to increase the relative circulating head. However, the principal temperature drop is at the radiators and if cooling in the length of return column above the upper radiators is necessary to the creation of adequate circulating head, water circulated to radiators will be at lower temperature than usual, i.e. the installation is not well designed.

Deliberate dissipation of heat is sometimes necessary to promote circulation, e.g. in a single storey building when all radiators are at or near boiler level, a high level loop (usually in the roof space), is often used to cool water sufficiently to create a circulating head before water reaches the radiators. In this case it is usual to design pipe sizes to promote the required water circulation under the circulating pressure created by a difference of 10°F in the flow and return columns. (Radiator emissions are then calculated for an average temperature, 5°F lower than usual.)
(*Below, right*) Expansion and feed tank. See page 89.

The amount of radiator surface required to transfer the heat can now be determined by dividing the heat demand by the transmission rate of the radiators to be used assuming them to be adequately supplied with heated water. To determine the radiators' transmission rate and the amount of water it will be necessary to circulate to them, the operating temperatures of the radiators, i.e. how much the radiators are to be allowed to cool in transferring the heat, must be known. This temperature drop must produce a change in water density large enough to promote circulation and yet be limited as far as possible so that average temperatures of radiators and heat transmission from them are kept as high as possible. Flow and return temperatures of 180°F and 140°F respectively for water, leaving and returning to the boiler, i.e. a drop in temperature across radiators of 40°F, are the most generally suitable working temperatures.[1]

Thus the average temperature of radiators will be 160°F and if the normal temperature of 65°F is maintained the radiator to air difference will be 95°F and the radiator transmission 160 btu/sq. ft/hr. The amount of water which will give up this amount of heat in cooling through 40°F is 160 divided by 40, i.e. 4 lb, the amount of water to be supplied per hour per sq. ft of radiator surface (1 btu = heat given up by 1 lb of water in falling 1°F). Additional water will have to be circulated to provide the heat transmitted by the pipe surfaces in the installation but the amount cannot be determined exactly until pipe sizes are known. These in turn cannot be determined until the total amount of water to be circulated is known. This problem is resolved by estimating the amount of additional water required to provide the heat lost by pipes so that their sizes can be determined. The working of the system is then checked with these provisional pipe sizes and adjustments made if necessary. At the usual design temperature difference between pipe and air (95°F) heat lost from 1 ft lengths of steel pipes is 104, 92, 75, 66 and 52 btu/hr for diameters of 1½, 1¼, 1, ¾ and ½ in. respectively.

The allowance to cover heat loss from pipes before sizes are fixed is usually taken as half the radiator loss and the total amount of water to be circulated to cover both pipe and radiator emission assessed at the rate of 6 lb/sq. ft of radiator surface.

Circulating pressure. The pressure set up at their bases by two columns of water of similar height but of different temperatures, i.e. densities, will clearly differ in direct proportion to their height and difference in temperature. In hot water heating circulations two such columns of water are

[1] A bigger temperature drop would call for larger radiators—their average temperature and their rate of heat transfer would be lower. A smaller drop would reduce the circulating pressure created by the increase in density of the water by cooling and this would call for bigger pipework. The latter applies to single pipe circulations as shown in Fig. 22 where returns from radiators enter the same pipe.

in effect created but the difference in their temperatures varies progressively. In the case of a simple single return pipe (22) density increase over that of water in the flow column will be nil at the top and maximum at the bottom. For convenience this column of varying density is expressed as an equivalent column of maximum density throughout—in this case a column of height *H* as shown. This equivalent height, called the circulating head, varies with the way in which heat is given up by the return circulation and must be determined relative to particular arrangements of circulations before their circulating pressures can be determined. When flow and return temperatures of 180°F and 140°F respectively are used a circulating pressure of 0·163 in. water head is created by each foot of circulating height. This being determined the circulating pressure created by the circulation can now be determined. Pipes are sized so that this pressure will circulate the necessary quantity of water against their frictional resistance to its flow.

Pipe sizing. Frictional resistance offered to the flow of water through pipes varies with the amount of water flowing, the length of the pipe and the size of the pipe (23). Additional resistance is offered by bends, valves and radiators and in determining overall resistance in a circulation from tables the resistances all of such items are expressed as equivalent lengths of straight pipe and added to the total length of the circulation.[1] Sizes of pipes are then selected which will pass the amount of water required through their total length without offering a resistance greater than the circulating pressure created by the system. A simple example design is given in Fig. 24.

The principal disadvantages associated with Gravity Systems are:

1 The relatively long period required for the installation to attain an effective operating temperature; in buildings of occasional occupation boilers have to be lit a day or more in advance. In, say, office buildings boilers have to run continuously overnight and most of the weekend to maintain temperatures for daytime occupation.
2 The tendency for radiators to be cooler at the end of a circulation due to the fall in temperature of the water necessary to promote circulation. This can be compensated for by progressive increase in radiator size—i.e. reduction in economy of the system or is overcome in some systems by the use of two pipe circulations—see Fig. 21.
3 The slow response to adjustments made to meet variations in weather conditions. The bulk of water in the installation and the relatively slow rate of its movement result in a long time-lag between ad-

[1] More approximately the amount of straight pipe in a circulation is increased by, say 25 per cent to allow for all bends, valves, etc., in the circulation.

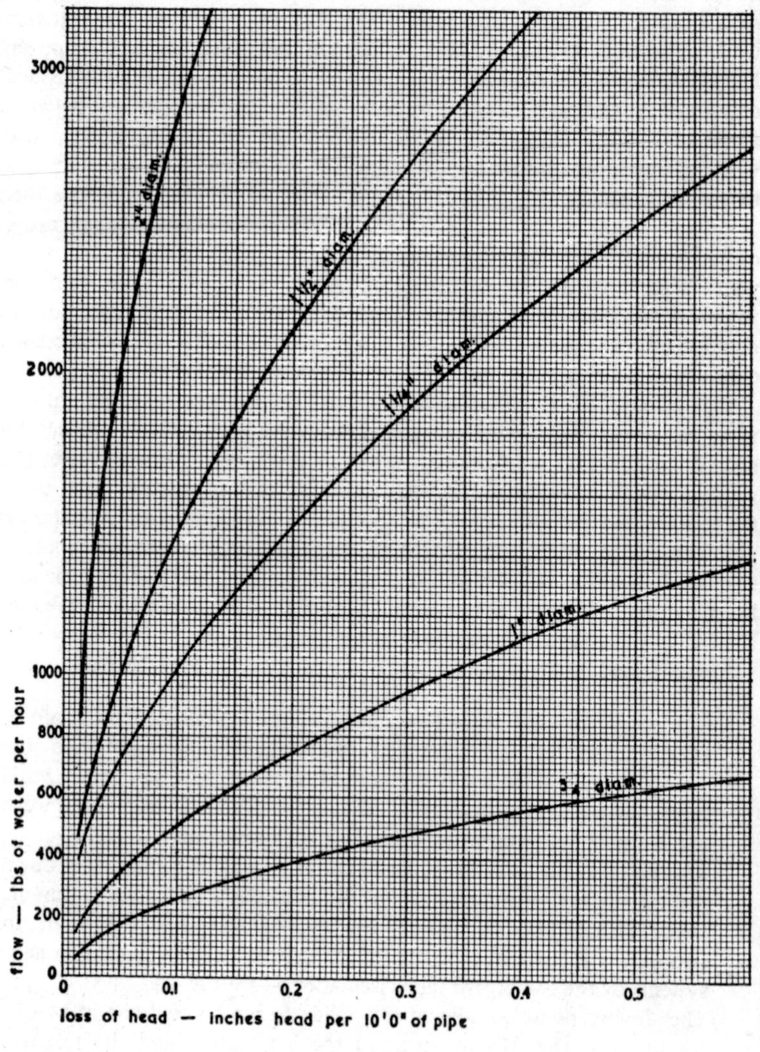

23

23 *Friction*

Head lost to friction by flow of water through steel pipes of different diameters.

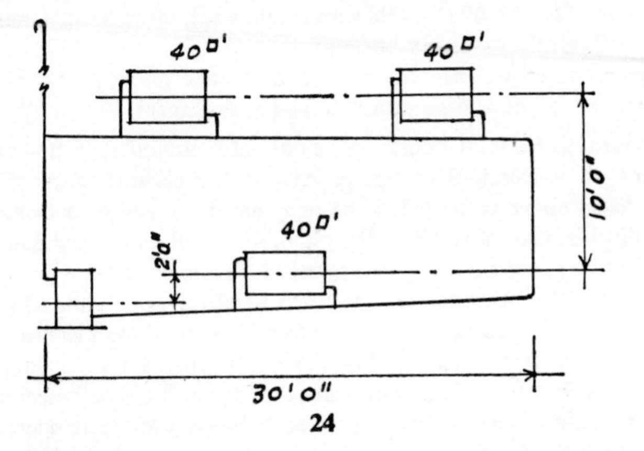

24

24 *Design calculations*

Circulating head. If areas of radiators at upper and lower levels were equal, the circulating height would be half the height between their centres (see Fig. 22), but in this case is determined as follows:

$$\left(\begin{matrix}\text{circulating}\\ \text{head}\end{matrix} \times \begin{matrix}\text{total}\\ \text{radiator area}\end{matrix}\right) = \left(\begin{matrix}\text{height above}\\ \text{boiler}\end{matrix} \times \begin{matrix}\text{radiator area}\\ \text{at high level}\end{matrix}\right) + \left(\begin{matrix}\text{height above}\\ \text{boiler}\end{matrix} \times \begin{matrix}\text{radiator area}\\ \text{at high level}\end{matrix}\right)$$

$$H \times (40+40+40) = 12 \times (40 + 40) + 2 \times 40$$

$$H = \mathbf{8{\cdot}66}\text{ ft}$$

Circulating pressure $P = 8{\cdot}66 \times 1{\cdot}63 = 1{\cdot}41$ in. (see text)

Length of circulation = 80 ft
Add 25 per cent for valves, etc. 20 ft
Total = 100 ft

$$\text{Circulating pressure per 10 ft of circulation}^{[1]} = \frac{1{\cdot}41}{10} = \mathbf{0{\cdot}141}\text{ in}$$

Amount to be circulated = $(40 + 40 + 40) \times 6$[2] = 720 lb/hr

From Fig. 23 a 1 in. diam. pipe will pass 600 lb/hr at the pressure available.

Checking the amount of water actually required if this size of pipe is used:

Heat loss from radiators = 160 (40 + 40 + 40) btu/hr
Heat loss from pipes = (75 × 80) btu/hr

$$\text{Amount of water required} = \frac{160\,(40 + 40 + 40) + (75 \times 80)}{40} = \mathbf{630}\text{ lb}$$

A 1 in. diam. pipe will probably be just adequate. (This is so because the provisional allowance for heat loss from pipes proved generous in this case.)

[1] This is found the most useful unit of pressure when tabulating pipe capacities (see Fig. 23).
[2] 6 lb is the usual provisional allowance to cover loss from pipes and each sq. ft of radiator surface (see p. 82).

justment at the boiler and its subsequent effect on radiator temperature (see "Control of systems" below).

4 The need to provide accommodation for relatively large pipe sizes and the accommodation of their rather limited arrangement.

Accelerated systems. Circulating the hot water through pipes and radiators by means of accelerators or pumps enables the disadvantages of gravity systems listed above to be overcome or reduced. Freed of dependence on natural displacement of water in the pipework circulation speed can be predetermined by assessing the system's resistance and selecting a pump of the right power. Thus the time taken to reach an effective operating temperature is reduced. Pipe sizes can also be reduced,[1] the resulting increase in resistance being accommodated by the pump. Because a fall in temperature through the system, and the resulting increase in density, is no longer essential to the circulation, water can be circulated at higher average temperatures so that transfer of heat from the radiators takes place at a higher rate and radiators can be smaller.

Because the difference between flow and return temperatures is limited drop in operating temperature of radiators at the end of the system is smaller. Response of systems to adjustments, e.g. to meet changes in demand, is also quicker because interruption of circulation is immediate via the pump and the reduced total mass of water in the system takes less time to cool or heat as the case may be (see also notes on "Control of systems" below).

In the design of accelerated systems heat requirements and radiator areas are determined as before and the water quantity it will be necessary to circulate them calculated on the basis of a 20°F drop (180°F to 160°F), between flow and return. Water allowance to cover loss from pipe surfaces is reduced to 25 per cent of the radiator requirements. Different pipe sizes and the resistance they create in passing the water to be circulated can now be examined and an appropriate pump capacity selected.

Theoretically there is no limit on pump size but in practice these are kept relatively small to reduce noise and ensure economy in their running. Usual practice is to design pipework to produce resistance in the region of $\frac{1}{10}$ in. per 10 ft length of circuit. Pumps are positioned on by-pass loops, off the main flow or return[2] pipes. The limiting of resistance allows some flow to take place in the event of pump failures.

[1] In addition to their space requirements and poor appearance larger pipes reduce an installation's efficiency by the amount of heat they dissipate in areas where heat is not required and in limiting to some extent the concentration of heat transfer in predetermined positions by the designer of the installation.

[2] When a pump is inserted in the main flow of a system its thrust is applied directly against the resistance of the system. If inserted in the return its thrust is also applied directly against the head of water in the vent pipe and/or the cold feed to the boiler, the ultimate effect depending on the point where vent is taken from system. (See alternative vent position, Fig. 21, bottom, left.)

Freedom from dependence on gravity for circulation allows greater latitude in positioning heat transfer surfaces in accelerated systems. Pipe coils embedded in ceiling, wall or floor surfaces[1] are readily possible. These in addition to completely hiding the radiators' pipework have the advantage of producing areas of surface which transfer heat mainly by radiation, desirable in some circumstances (see "Comfort conditions" below).

One recent development aimed at overcoming this disadvantage makes use of "gilled" pipes in place of radiators.[2] The gills are of thin metal and closely spaced along the pipes to give maximum heat transfer rate. Pipes are placed behind flat screening plates set with bottom edges clear of the floor to direct air flow over the heating tube. In addition to producing a much neater appearance than exposed or enclosed radiators the total bulk of water in the system is greatly reduced. The warming up period relative to radiator installations is short and response to control adjustments rapid.

Small pipe systems. Until fairly recently types and sizes of pump and control equipment available, and their cost, limited the economic application of pumped circulations and their attendant advantages to larger installations. The development of suitable pumps and control equipment, however, has led to a growing use of forced circulations in smaller and domestic installations.

A number of noiseless "glandless circulators" are now marketed. These electrically operated impellers are mounted in the main flow or return pipe and are water-lubricated. Minimum maintenance is required and impellers are constructed so that in most instances this can be carried out without emptying the installation. Acceleration of small installations in this way allows pipe sizes to be small enough for concealment to be unnecessary in addition to the advantages of lower costs of reduced radiator sizes and pipework. Systems are also responsive enough to permit substantial savings in running costs by effective control. Freedom in arrangement of pipework allows the employment of other than normal radiator systems.

Skirting radiators, which as the name implies are little more obtrusive than the normal skirting they replace, and underfloor coils have obvious

---

These often then need extension to ensure that the head of water they contain is greater than the working head of the pump in order to prevent overflow from the system through them.

[1] Panels comprise lengths of continuous pipe bent as necessary to run in parallel lengths at about 6 in. or 9 in. centres. These are fixed over insulating material to prevent heat loss through the back of the panel. Even in accelerated systems radiators and pipework hold considerable bulk of water so that although reaching of operation temperature is quicker than in gravity systems this does still involve considerable time lag and something less than immediate response to adjustments made to meet sudden changes in heat requirements.

[2] "Weatherfoil" heating systems.

advantages of invisibility and more effective distribution of heat (see "Comfort conditions" below). As in the case of pumps in larger installations circulators are positioned to avoid pump pressure causing overflow from the system.[1] Working heads however rarely exceed 6–8 ft and this problem is likely to arise in domestic installations only when pipes are run in the roof space or near feed tank level. Because of their construction circulators are best fitted in the return to the boiler where the temperature of water passing through them is lower.

In practice systems are designed around the circulators which, to keep noise and vibration and running costs within acceptable limits for domestic use, are limited in capacity.

Underfloor heating. The concealment of heating pipes within wall, floor and/or ceiling surfaces has been common practice for many years in larger buildings. The advantages of better distribution of heat and better comfort conditions so secured are, if anything, more desirable in domestic buildings than elsewhere but the necessity for circulation to be forced has, until recently, made these methods impractical in the domestic field. The development of the glandless circulators of low power and cost, referred to above, has made small-scale application of underfloor heating practical and economic.

Small bore pipes are arranged in continuous lengths far enough below the floor surface (with about 2 in. minimum cover), for the heat they emit to bring the whole surface to an even temperature.[2] This temperature is kept low (70–90°F) by controlling the temperature of the water circulated to an average temperature of 110–120°F.

Pipe coils are built up from continuous lengths of copper tube, which can be placed simply without joints, or by welding into continuous lengths from steel tubes. Circulations are subdivided into self-contained circuits all limited in frictional resistance to lie within the capacity of the circulator and all starting from a centralised control and regulating point near the boiler. Automatic control of the kind described below is generally considered essential.

Ceiling or wall coils can be applied on a domestic scale but the latter always create furniture placing problems and the former are likely to create comfort deficiencies (see "Comfort conditions" below).

Arrangement of systems. The expansion of water, in addition to making provision for release of pressure necessary via the open ended expansion pipe referred to earlier (see caption to Fig. 21), may also result in the for-

[1] This occurs only when there are two or more vents, one to allow the air to be drawn in to replace the water pumped out.

[2] Pipe spacing varies from 6 in. to 18 in. centres, closer spacing being usual below windows and along external walls where more heat is required to obviate downward air currents and where higher surface temperatures will not be inconvenient. The disadvantage of the system is the time lag in control. A sudden increase in atmospheric temperature requires dissipation of a lot of heat.

mation of air pockets at high points in the system whenever water in the system is allowed to cool. This is catered for in the pipework by inclining "horizontal" runs towards the vent outlet but in radiators, and upward pipe loops, provision for release of air (by means of key-operated air cocks)[1] is essential.

This cycle of expansion and contractions calls for provision to prevent loss of water through overflow having to be replaced by fresh water (air content increases corrosion potential and temporary hardness scale potential, apart from actual loss of water). It is done by the ball-valve controlled level of water being maintained so that the volume of the tank is retained to absorb expansion.[2]

Safety-valves. Although heating installations are protected by open-feed and vent pipes from the enormous pressures which would result from the expansion of water in them if it were confined, additional precaution against such build-up of pressure is required. This takes the form of a safety-valve fitted either directly on the top of the water jacket of the boiler or in the flow pipe close to the boiler. This is necessary because of the possibilities which do exist that one or other of the pipes connected to the boiler will become completely blocked by the building up of hardness deposits, or by dislodgement and subsequent accumulation of these at a critical point, or alternatively that some section of the pipework, e.g. the upper part of the vent pipe becomes frozen during a period when the boiler is shut down.

There are several kinds of such valve, including spring, lever, deadweight, diaphragm and fusible plug. In the case of the spring safety-valve, a cylindrical brass case has a valve at the bottom, and a screw cap at the top with a hole through it. Passing downwards through this hole is a vertical spindle with an enlarged conical point resting on the valve. Around the spindle, between a shoulder above the conical point and the underside of the screw cap, is a spiral spring, the strength of which can be regulated by screwing in or unscrewing the screw cap. This type of safety-valve is unreliable. As generally constructed, the surfaces in contact between the valve and its seating are too large and liable to become firmly stuck together.

The lever safety-valve is a regular item in connection with steam boilers, but it is cumbersome and unsightly in smaller hot-water installations. It consists of a valve held on its seating by a lever having an adjustable weight at its end.

The deadweight safety-valve is the most usual for hot-water installations. It is simple in construction, compact and efficient. In its usual form, the surfaces in contact are very small. The valve outlet is closed by a ball held down by a casing carrying a number of circular weights. From the smallness

1 In large systems automatic air relief valves are used on the unvented loops.
2 Water expands $\frac{1}{23}$ of its volume at 39°F when raised to 212°F.

of the surface in contact with the ball there is no danger of the valve sticking, whilst even if this did occur, the surfaces would break apart under far less pressure than would be necessary to burst the boiler or pipes. (A valve of this type is illustrated in Fig. 42, p. 180.)

The so-called diaphragm safety-valve is not really a valve at all. Between two short lengths of pipe or tube a sheet of mica, thin copper, or lead is placed, closing the outlet. The thickness of such sheet or diaphragm is such as to make it the weakest spot in the system, so that it gives way when there is danger of an explosion. In the case of the fusible plug safety device, which also is not a valve in the true sense of the word, a plug of fusible alloy is placed in a brass case, the plug being of such a nature that it melts at a temperature slightly above the boiling-point of water, and in this way affords relief to the dangerous pressure that would exist in the installation at such a temperature.

Regulation of systems. However well pipe sizes and resistances are selected to reflect the required division of the total flow to different sections of the system the infinite variety of circuit length, i.e. resistance, and quantity of flow which may be required makes other provision for regulating the flow of water through different parts of the installation necessary. The accurate "sharing out" of the total flow from the boiler to each section of the system, even to each radiator, is essential to the interpretation of the designers' calculations and predictions—i.e. the proper working of the system. In addition to a control valve on the inlet to each radiator which allows flow to it to be reduced by the room occupants, each radiator and each sub-circuit of an installation (e.g. each drop-pipe in Fig 21), is also fitted with a regulating valve. Before an installation is put into commission flow through all parts is regulated by means of these valves so that the correct temperature at each radiator is secured. Regulating valves are of lockshield pattern, operated by key only, so that regulation of the system is not subject to unauthorised disturbance.

Control of systems. If systems are to be run economically the amount of heat transferred first from the boiler and then from pipework and radiators must be varied to suit varying requirements by adjustments in the amount of heat produced by the boiler if wastage is not to occur from overheating or such methods of cooling as opening windows. In operation output of heat from heating systems can be controlled in a number of ways. The simple cutting off or reducing of the circulation to individual radiators by closing of valves may be satisfactory as a means of controlling temperature in rooms of intermittent use but adjustments of the output from an installation generally, such as are needed to meet changes in weather conditions, are best effected by modifications in the rate of burning of fuel in the boiler. The simplest way of doing this is by adjustment of the boiler control settings to regulate the temperature of water leaving the boiler. This can be done manually but skill and judgement are required as well as more or less constant attendance. Thermostatic control of the boiler's output temperature is now a feature of the majority of boilers, even those of small domestic type. Thermostats activated by changes in the temperature of water leaving the boiler modify its rate of burning by varying the amount of air supplied to the boiler or in the case of gas- or oil-fired boilers by varying the amount of gas supplied to the boiler or the rate or frequency of burning oil. Modifications of this kind are generally slow to take effect on circulations and means of regulating, i.e. stabilising, the temperature of water in the pipework more quickly and accurately have been developed. These embody the use of mixing or blending valves by means of which the amount of the outflow required from the boiler is varied by adding more or less of it to cooled returned water—the degree of cooling of which will depend on heat demand. By means of a by-pass link between flow and return pipes from the boiler, water from the return can be turned directly into the flow pipe without passing through the boiler, the setting of the valve controlling this being modified in different ways to meet changes in conditions.

A room thermostat, sited in a position most typical of the building's heat requirements, e.g. in the living-room of a dwelling, may be used to activate the electric motor operating the blending valve to adjust its setting to suit variations in the room's temperature. A much more reliable method, however, is to use a "compensator"[1] sited outside the building and which is designed to measure and relay via a thermostat to the valve any changes in climatic conditions.

Alternatively direct automatic control can be effected over the flow through each radiator by the use of specially designed valves which incorporate thermostats.[2] Manually set to the temperature required in the room these close and open the valve as the room temperature rises above or falls below the required level.

Boilers and fuels

Solid fuels, although offering the most economic supply of heat, are still associated with disadvantages relative to other fuels in spite of recent advances

[1] A form of combined compensator and blending valve has been marketed recently which is sufficiently low in cost for use in small scale installations. In these the valve is directly modulated by the expansion and contraction of liquid in a container placed outside the building. (The Satchwell BMT Valve—The Rheostatic Co. Ltd.)

[2] Danfoss Automatic Controls and Equipment.

in the design of equipment: storage and handling of fuel; need for boiler stoking and ash removal; lack of flexibility and control in boilers.

In the domestic field, improved boiler design has reduced the frequency of re-fuelling required for many types and the fitting of thermostats reduces the need for attendance by relating the rate of burning to demand automatically. Boiler thermostats are activated by changes in the temperature of the water leaving the boiler and adjust the boiler burning rate by means of a linkage with a diaphragm controlling the amount of air admitted below the boiler grate.

Fig. 25 shows diagrammatically a modern domestic boiler, a traditional sectional boiler and a gravity feed boiler.

In larger installations firing and ash removal is often automatic. In some boilers fuelling and ash removal is effected by gravity, fuel being carried to vertical magazines above them by conveyor belts and the ash pushed out below being carried away in the same manner. Others are designed to admit fuel below the fire, fuel being pushed continuously to this position by means of worm screws set within an enclosed tube. Fuel is fed to the worm by gravity from a hopper set above it. Alternatively, traditional boilers can be fired automatically by means of pre-burner units. These are positioned outside the boiler, fuel is burned in them and the heat produced forced or drawn into the fire-box of the boiler. The pre-burners themselves are arranged for automatic feed and ash removal.

Oil fuels of several types are used for boiler firing. The lightest and most volatile oils are used in vaporising burners of various kinds. Those which require wicks to conduct the oil to the point of burning are confined to use in portable stoves, but those in which a wick is used to heat perforated annular drums sufficiently to commence vaporisation and burning of oil between them are used in some small domestic boilers. Carburettor type burners are, however, more usual and more efficient. In these, air is drawn through perforations in the sides, sometimes also through the base of a carburettor in which oil is maintained at a constant level. The vaporised oil and air mixture burns above the oil pool, the lack of air near its surface preventing it igniting, the oil being vaporised by heat from the flame and air drawn into the carburettor by the updraught caused by the burning. Rate of oil vaporisation depends mainly on the heat from the oil flame, but the character of air and oil mixture, and its burning, depends on the rate at which air is drawn into the burner. For this reason flues to oil boilers of this kind must be fitted with draught stabilisers—plates set across openings in flue walls hung to swing to permit or prevent direct air entry to the flue with variations in chimney pull, the suction exerted on the flue below them so remaining constant.

Carburettor burners in which fans are used to increase vaporisation are used for slightly larger boilers. In these air is blown into the burner and by increasing vaporisation allows heavier grades of oil to be used, and also disperses carbon deposits, making cleaning less frequently necessary.

Oil burners of vaporising type must burn continuously with high or low flame according to demand relayed by the boiler thermostat, periodic cleaning cannot be avoided and the boiler must be lit and shut off by hand. In contrast, atomising burners in which oil and air are blown through one atomising nozzle, the mixture being electrically ignited, are fully automatic and have none of these disadvantages (see Fig. 25). They are more costly, however, and not available for the very smallest outputs. Greater efficiency arises from their intermittent burning, the burner only being ignited when the thermostat indicates demand. Methods of atomisation differ in different types of burner. The amount of noise produced varies as does the character of fuel required. Some larger burners incorporate arrangements for pre-heating the oil before atomisation to enable more viscous, i.e. cheaper, oil to be burnt.

Although highest efficiencies are achieved when boilers are designed for oil burning, oil burners can be and are widely used for converting solid fuel boilers to oil. Additional linings and flame deflectors within the boiler fire-box are usually required, the burner being placed outside the boiler, and its flame directed through the stoking door.

In designing for oil burning, precautions necessary in arranging fuel storage are important. In domestic installations tanks are generally sited outside the building proper and positioned so that oil feed to the boiler is by gravity. In larger installations where storage is necessarily inside, effective fireproof enclosure of the oil tank and prevention of oil spread in the event of tank leakage are required and usually the provision of a pipe-line to enable fire-extinguishing foam to be pumped into the fuel store from a point outside the building.

All oil storage tanks are required to be vented and contents indicators are usually regarded as essential.

Gas. Gas-fired boilers offer advantages of cleanliness and automatic control without the need to store fuel. They share with oil the flexibility of immediate response to demand and immediate shutting down of fuel consumption during periods of no demand. Running costs are high, in spite of the economies possible because of this flexibility and because of their capacity for easy predetermination of operation periods by clock controls.

Boiler size. Boiler output in terms of btu/hour for all types of boilers is published by manufacturers. These are calculated from the area of

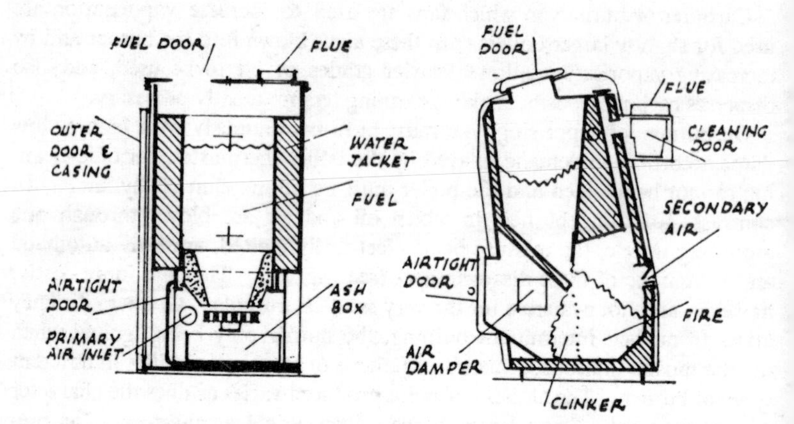

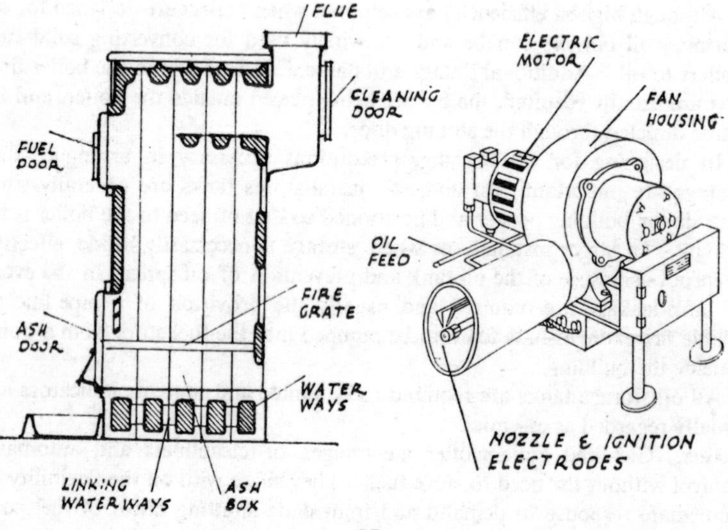

25

25 *Boilers*

(*Above, left*) A closed, solid fuel, domestic boiler. The water jacket is circular and acts as a fuel magazine, the fuel burning from the bottom on the fireclay lining. Ash falls through the grate, which can be shaken by a tool from the heating surface (area of water way presented to the fire), in simpler solid fuel forms like the domestic and sectional boilers, or established by test in more complicated forms. In selecting a boiler for a given load, however, it is usual to allow a margin, usually of about 20 per cent, to cover periods of extra demand, possible deficiencies in stoking and, in the case of solid fuel

---

front. Supply of air to the boiler is from below only and is controlled by means of a thermostat set in the flow from the boiler which is linked mechanically to a diaphragm over the primary air inlet. (Allied Ironfounders Ltd.)

(*Right*) A closed, solid fuel boiler designed for minimum attention and maximum economy. Note the intricate arrangement of the water jacket to provide a maximum of contact surface with both the fire and the hot gases produced. The fuel is gravity fed to the fire and selected fuel and method of burning produce a solid clinker which can be removed in one piece from the front. Main air supply is to below the fire and the controlling damper is opened and closed by an electro-magnet current which is switched on and off by a thermostat set in the boiler flow. The secondary air supply to above the fire is preheated to ensure complete burning of the fuel.

The fuel hopper holds fuel for 24 hours' burning and efficiency, i.e. the percentage of the total heat transferred to the water is 75–80 per cent. (Janitor Boilers Ltd.)

Similar types of boiler incorporate electric fans to provide the primary air and so produce rapid response to demand for heat.

(*Below, left*) A typical sectional boiler. Suitable for both domestic and bigger loads, these are low in cost and designed initially for hand-firing and for assembly of boilers of different capacities from standardised sections.

Whilst the domestic boilers illustrated above are finished with built-in casings and are designed to eliminate dirt in operation, sectional boilers were not designed for good appearance and are usually sited in boiler rooms with in-situ insulation applied after installation. They are, however, now available with streamlined out casings and automatic thermostat control.

Sectional boilers have the advantage of greater tolerance of variations in fuel and can be readily adapted to oil-firing by the addition of fire-brick protective linings and deflectors, an oil pressure burner being positioned in front of the ash door.

(*Right*) An oil pressure jet burner. The motor drives both an oil pump and an air fan which deliver a finely atomised oil and air mixture at the nozzle, this being automatically ignited by a high voltage spark across the electrodes. The burner is automatically switched on for short periods of burning only in response to demand by the thermostat in the boiler flow.

Other types of pressure burner are marketed, selection depending in particular circumstances on the type of fuel to be burned and the probable burning rate of the boiler.

Burners are generally available for use with any boiler designed or adapted for oil burning, but most manufacturers offer boilers specially designed for use with their burners. Higher efficiency, 80–85 per cent, is achieved by boilers designed for oil burning.

boilers, to enable general running to be well within the boiler's capacity which makes for economic operation.

Boiler space and flue size required will of course be influenced by boiler and equipment arrangement and are properly matters for the heating engineer. Provisional allowances are made fairly safely on a basis of heat requirements. Thus for outputs up to 150,000 btu's boiler space should be not less than 90–100 sq. ft and for outputs up to 500,000 and 1,000,000 btu's 150–160 sq. ft and 300–320 sq. ft respectively. (Two boilers are allowed for in the latter figure. Fuel storage and space for hot water supply equipment would be additional to the areas quoted.)

Flue size required varies with flue height as well as boiler size but in general flues of internal dimensions of 9″ × 9″ will be adequate for boilers up to say 150,000 btu's and flues 14″ × 9″ and 18″ × 14″ for boilers up to 250,000 and 500,000 btu's respectively.

Electrode boilers. These are containers in which water is heated by means of immersion heaters, or by passing electric current directly through the water. Water heated is transferred to storage cylinders and from these circulated to the heating system. Because of the way water stratifies (hot and cold water remain separated from each other), water at high temperature can continue to be drawn from the storage cylinders over a long period, i.e. heating of the water and its actual use can occur at different times. This enables electrode boilers to be used to heat water during night periods, when electricity can be supplied at low cost, ready in sufficient quantity for circulation in a heating system during the following day. Water from storage is fed gradually to the heating circulation to maintain its temperature and is replaced by water cooled by circulation which then awaits reheating during the ensuing night.

Electrode boilers reduce installation costs and eliminate the need for flues and fuel storage and the promise of reducing costs of electricity supply may well foreshadow an increase in their use. The space required for storage of large volumes of hot water is however a disadvantage.

Electric underfloor heating is a fairly recent development which can be applied on any scale. Wires of suitable resistance, set within tubular plastic sheaths to allow their withdrawal, should this be necessary, are arranged in continuous circuit below floors in a similar way to that described for pipes in underfloor water circulations. To allow for withdrawal and replacement of defective wires removable access covers are required, e.g. along one wall of a room to give access to each end loop in the heating coil.

Current for heating is used only during the "off-peak" night period, when cheap rates are available, the mass of the floor being raised in temperature during this period and allowed to cool and warm the building during the period when cheap electricity is not available. To form an effective heat reservoir, floors must be of concrete and of adequate thickness, and to ensure that heat is given up in the right directions their insulation may also be necessary. (The undersides of upper floors are often insulated; the outer perimeters of ground floor slabs are invariably insulated; the whole of ground floor slabs are sometimes insulated.)

This form of heating has the advantages of low installation costs—no boiler pipes, etc., are required—and is completely automatic in operation but is only economic on "off-peak" supply. Output obviously declines as the floor cools and "booster" periods during normal supply times are often necessary to maintain temperatures throughout the day.

Self-contained thermal storage units working on similar principles are also now available. These may be used to supplement underfloor heating or as independent heaters. The disadvantage with either system is the poor regulation of heat input.

Whole house warming. Another recent development in domestic heating is the circulation of warmed air for heating. Systems vary from a centrally placed air heater (from which air is released or forced by fan into two or three adjacent ground floor rooms and from there circulates to warm them and the remainder of the house) to fully duct conveyed distribution of air from and back to the heater.

Ducted air systems are efficient but expensive to install because of the cost of construction of ducts which must be insulated, but do have distinct advantages of quick response, great flexibility and easy local control. They achieve high comfort standards.

Heaters are specially designed to combine air heating with hot water supply. Control is by means of a furnace thermostat, which controls its rate of burning to maintain a constant temperature in the air heater, and a room thermostat which stops and starts the air circulator fan at the heater.

High pressure water heating. Water under higher than atmospheric pressure boils, i.e. turns to steam, at higher temperatures than normal, the boiling temperature depending on the increase in pressure. By preventing the free expansion of water in the boiler and circulating pipes (by eliminating the ventilation pipe and other pressure-relieving outlets provided at low pressure systems), water in a closed circuit can be heated to temperatures far above normal boiling-point without the formation of steam. Water circulated at increased temperatures gives greater efficiency in heat distribution and is an advantage in some industrial processes. Heat is transferred by pipe coils or through unit heaters, and pipes are dangerous to touch, being usually at temperatures in the region of 300°F. Boiler temperatures are usually much higher than this, constant pipe water temperature being maintained by means of a mixing valve which blends boiler and return water for circulation.

Pipes need to be of great strength, welded or high pressure joints being necessary, and provision for expansion is by a sealed vessel.[1] Installation and maintenance costs are high and the system is little used anywhere and never in domestic work.

Steam heating. By circulating steam to condense in radiators and so release its latent heat, far greater efficiency in heat distribution can be achieved. (1 lb of steam releases 966 btu's in condensing to water without fall in temperature.) Additional problems are raised, however, relative to water circulations. Higher standards in pipework are necessary and systems must be arranged to provide for the return of condensed water to the boiler. In some single pipe systems condensate runs back to the boiler in the pipes used for steam delivery, sometimes resulting in noise due to steam and water intermingling; water on occasion being driven to ends of pipes with loud "hammering" noises. A better arrangement is for "horizontal" flow pipes to fall away from the boiler, so that in these condensate and steam travel in the same direction, a second return horizontal then being required to carry condensate back to the boiler.

Two-pipe systems follow in general arrangement two-pipe riser systems of hot water circulation. The return pipes are deliberately placed below water level of the boiler so that they are part filled with water, which ensures that steam reaches the radiators only through the flow pipe.

Steam at high pressure is sometimes used for heating circulations but usually only where this is being produced for other purposes, e.g. the steam after exhaust from power machinery is used for heating.

Vacuum systems are those in which a vacuum pump is inserted in the main return. This prevents accumulation of air in the installation and helps in the return of condensate to the boiler.

Steam heating has advantages of quickly bringing transmission surfaces to operating temperature and of very quickly cooling when turned off. Radiator temperatures are high, however, and the roasting of organic matter in the air can cause unpleasant smells.

In high buildings the use of steam eliminates the high pressures created in pipe work and boilers by the head of water involved in water circulations.

District heating simply means the supply of heat to a number of independent buildings from a central source. By centralising water heating installations in this way substantial economies can be effected in both running costs and installation costs. Heat is circulated by means of external mains between the

[1] The vessel is part filled with air or nitrogen under pressure (nitrogen is not absorbed by water and obviates the corrosion potential of air).

boiler house and buildings served, its transfer to individual buildings being effected by branch mains and/or calorifiers.[1]

Even greater economies are possible when surplus or waste heat from industrial sources can be made available. The supply of heat as a service is implied so that the system is best applied to groups of buildings in the same ownership or where a standing charge can be made for supply of heating and hot water.

Comfort conditions. Creation of satisfactory conditions of comfort involves consideration of a number of influencing factors. These include the amount of air movement, changes in the air's temperature and humidity and changes in temperature of surrounding surfaces. Air temperature and its relative humidity affect the rate at which the body loses heat by convection movements over it and by evaporation of moisture from the body's surface. Air movement and temperature together determine whether or not occupants are conscious of draughts. Temperature of surroundings determines the rate at which the body will radiate heat to them. Cold surfaces, e.g. windows, may create convection currents in the air in contact with them of sufficient strength to constitute draughts. Relatively wide variations in any of these factors, however, can be compensated for by variations in one or more of the remainder.

To enable these varying factors to be allowed for when comfort standards are defined or assessed a scale of "Equivalent temperatures" is used. Equivalent temperatures are assessments of combinations of the factors affecting comfort as made, so far as can be determined, by the human body. Scales have been constructed by careful recording or large numbers of individual reactions to varying conditions[2] and more recently in this country by the use of an instrument called the *eupathescope*. This consists basically of a cylinder constructed so that when heated to appropriate temperature it loses heat by radiation and convection at similar rates to a clothed human being, i.e. it responds in a similar way to changes in temperature of the surrounding air and of surrounding surfaces and to air movements around it. Changes in humidity do not affect it. Except in fairly rare combinations of circumstances natural humidity levels in this country do not vary sufficiently to be a

[1] Calorifiers are closed tanks in which are arranged pipe coils through which hot water or steam is circulated. Water in the tank being heated by contact with the surfaces of the heated coil.

[2] E.g. Equivalent temperatures for living-rooms in dwellings recommended in the Egerton Report (PW.B.S. No. 19) were 62–66°F. These would be produced by air temperatures of 63–67°F and mean radiant temperatures of 66–70°F. In rooms heated by high temperature radiation, open fires or gas or electric bar fires, similar equivalent temperatures obtain when air temperatures at head level are 58–62°F and mean surface temperature of surroundings are 58–62°F.

serious factor in determining comfort—variations in humidity between 30 and 60 per cent having little or no effect on comfort at normal temperatures. However in a densely populated hall, particularly on moist warm days, lack of humidity control will produce sensations of clamminess and overheating (see p. 33). On cold, dry days the already low level of humidity will be further reduced by a rise in the temperature of the air and sometimes results in discomfort due to feelings of dryness in the throat in centrally heated buildings.

Conditions which will result in satisfactory comfort standards may be briefly summarised:

Air temperature should be no higher than necessary and should vary as little as possible. Appreciably higher temperatures at head level will produce discomfort. Hot water radiators, for example, produce higher temperatures at higher levels than at lower levels and although variations are not generally enough to cause awareness of discomfort this is one of the reasons that radiant wall panels and underfloor heating are considered more desirable. Low temperature ceiling panels in rooms lower than say 12 ft high are likely to be unsuccessful. The temperature of enclosing surfaces should not be appreciably lower than the air temperature in a room. Heating by low temperature radiant surfaces, when surface temperatures are higher than air-temperatures, produces excellent comfort conditions. In continuously heated buildings wall surfaces attain and hold temperatures just below air temperatures (unless insulation values are very low) and produce satisfactory conditions. Where heating is intermittent time taken to raise wall surface temperatures and produce comfort conditions invariably involves waste because of the need for pre-heating periods. Wall linings of high insulating value, which become warm quickly, have been used successfully in reducing this problem but in many cases these are unsuitable, e.g. fibre boards, or expensive, e.g. timber panelling.

There should be a reasonable amount of air movement but not enough to constitute draughts. Just perceptible air movement is stimulating and some movement is necessary to dissipation of body heat by convection. Movements of air of greater velocity than about 50 ft/min produce discomfort in the great majority of cases (see Chapter 3).

Lighting of buildings

Daylighting. Legislation calling directly for standards of daylight in buildings is limited to that setting minimum sizes of windows relative to rooms' floor area referred to in Chapter 3. It has long been recognised, however, that healthy and comfortable conditions cannot be dissociated from adequate standards of daylighting. Efficiency in almost every human activity is so dependent on adequate lighting that the provision of adequate natural light is regarded as an economic necessity in many buildings and has become a design requirement in government-sponsored schools and housing.

A great deal of research work has been carried out, with increasing intensity during and since the Second World War, to determine suitable standards and methods of predicting levels of daylight in buildings before their erection.

Measurement of daylighting. Conditions in which daylight is received, as well as the quality and intensity of daylight itself, vary widely. Differences in the state of cleanliness of windows, the possible presence of helpful reflecting surfaces and the quality of internal decorations are all factors which affect substantially the intensity of natural lighting within different buildings provided with similar sizes and positions of window openings. Whether the sky is cloudy or overcast, whether the sun is shining and, of course, variations in the sun's position will all affect the quality of light received.

To make direct comparisons possible, daylight is measured in terms of "sky factors"—the sky area visible from the position under consideration (i.e. the area of sky directly contributing to daylight received). Although this necessarily ignores the possible variations referred to above, the method interprets reasonably closely the conditions of an overcast sky, when the sun is obscured and all parts of the sky are equally bright and daylight intensity is low.

Methods of calculating sky factors consist of plotting the areas of sky visible through the window openings through which light is to be received and then expressing these areas as a percentage of the total sky hemisphere—the area which would contribute to the light received at a point completely open to the sky. It is this percentage which is termed the sky factor and although invaluable as a basis for comparison of daylight in different buildings and alternative designs, sky factors are not a complete solution to the problem of prediction. They take no account of light received by reflection from surfaces within or near buildings.

One method of determining sky factors on the drawing board is to plot by angular measurement the openings as seen from the reference point directly on to a chart which represents the sky divided into areas of equal effectiveness[1] —an angular projection on to one place of the half hemisphere of sky visible

[1] Waldron diagrams. See *BRS Digest No. 80.*

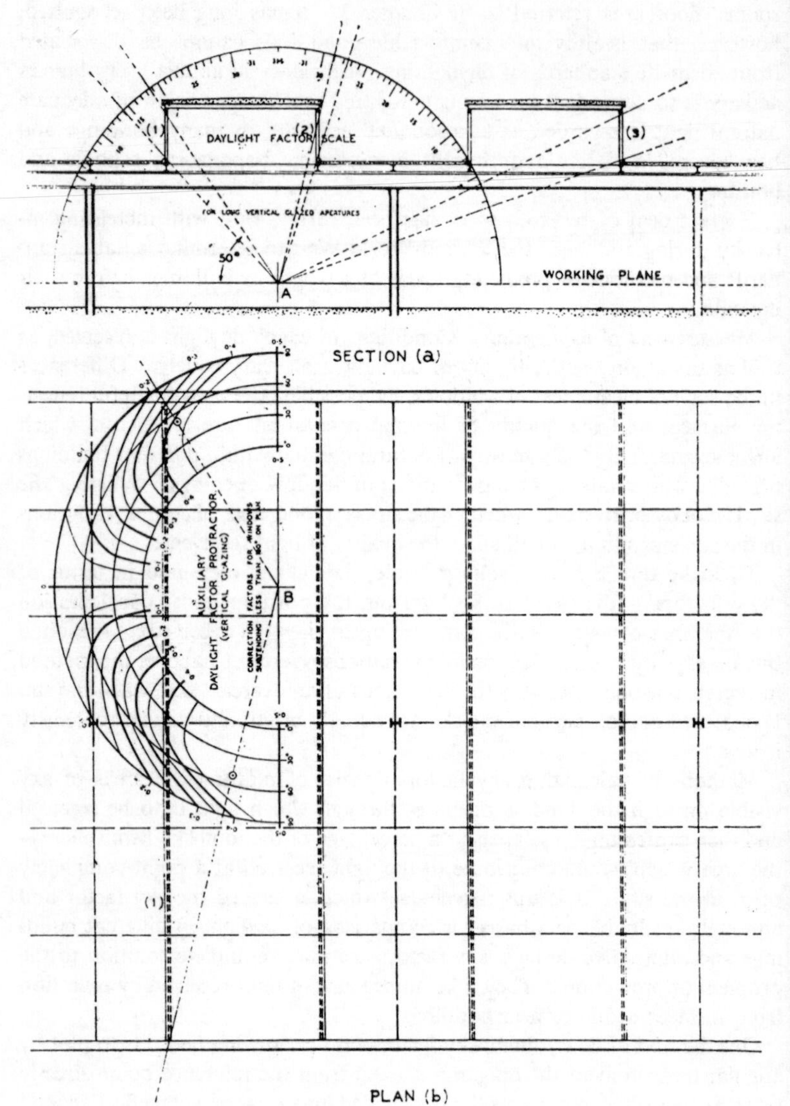
DAYLIGHT FACTOR SCALE
FOR LONG VERTICAL GLAZED APATURES
(1)
(2)
(3)
50°
A
WORKING PLANE
SECTION (a)
AUXILIARY DAYLIGHT FACTOR PROTRACTOR (VERTICAL GLAZING)
CORRECTION FACTORS FOR WINDOWS SUBTENDING LESS THAN 180° ON PLAN
B
(1)
PLAN (b)

26

from one side of a building. Variations in angle of reception of light both vertically and horizontally are thus allowed for and after plotting the openings, and any obstructions outside them, the contributing area can be determined by counting.

The most usual way of predicting daylight factors on the drawing board is to use the special protractors developed for the purpose by the Building Research Station. These convert angular readings directly to daylight factors—see Fig. 26.

Alternatively, areas of specific daylight intensity and depth of penetration relative to window openings of known height and width may be tabulated for direct reference. Thus British Standards Code of Practice CP 3 (Daylight in Dwellings and Schools) recommends minimum sky factors, depth of penetration and daylight area (the superficial area measured on the working plane which is illuminated to at least the recommended level) for domestic buildings. The Code includes comprehensive tables of daylight areas and penetration depth for sky factors of 0·5, 1 and 2 per cent for a large range of window heights and widths. From these tables daylight contours can be

---

26 *The use of B.R.S. protractors in computing sky factors*

Measurements are made on section relative to a selected point at working level point *A* on the "working plane" on section (a)—by means of one of the protractors of the appropriate pair[1]—the Daylight Factor scale.[2] As shown, contributions from three windows, indicated by the number of divisions on the protractor contained by the receiving angles, are 4·6, 1·5 and 1·8 from windows 1, 2 and 3 respectively.

Each of these readings is modified in accordance with measurements on the plan, made with the second protractor of the pair, to determine the lateral restriction to light entry created by the sides of openings. Sight lines are drawn from the opening boundaries to the point under consideration, and the protractor placed in position as shown. It will be seen from the section that the average altitude of window (1) is 50°, and readings are taken at the points where the sight lines cut the 50° altitude scale on the protractor as indicated. These readings, 0·41 and 0·48, are added together to give a correction factor by which readings on section are multiplied. The true sky factor reading for window (1) is thus 4·6 × (0·41 + 0·48) = 4·1 per cent.

The procedure is repeated for each window and the corrected values added to give the true sky factor.

By similar examination of a number of points within a room contours showing variation in Sky Factor can be set up or daylight curves shown as illustrated in Fig. 27.

[1] In this case the pair for vertically glazed openings.
[2] When these protractors were introduced, Daylight Factor was the term less accurately and loosely used for Sky Factor.

constructed for windows of given sizes from direct readings from the tables.[1]

Desirable standards of daylighting have been established for a number of different types of building and the effects of designing to achieve these on the buildings' form and arrangement have been thoroughly analysed. Notable results have been achieved in the design of schools, factories and hospitals.

In addition to the provision of light in quantity, effective daylighting requires consideration of such problems as its even distribution, its adequate penetration into buildings, the avoidance of glare and control of the direction from which light is received. In illustrating predictions of distribution and level of daylight buildings sections at typical positions, on which light intensities at a number of points are plotted to produce a daylight curve, have been found most useful. Results of analyses and comparisons of alternative results are usually presented this way. Figs 27 and 28 illustrate the application of this method and examples of the results of designing for daylight in different building types.

[1] It has been recently recommended that sky factors obtained by use of diagrams and protractors be modified to allow for variations in the brightness of the sky (*BRS Digest No. 80*), and that to get an accurate evaluation of daylight received at points under consideration allowance also be made both for light reflected from outside surfaces and for light reflected by internal surfaces. This is undoubtedly worthwhile when some estimate of actual light to be received is required but the methods described above are usually adequate in determining general building form.

---

27 *Natural lighting*

(*Left*) A much used school classroom arrangement shown in plan and section. The upper canopy or roof projection excludes summer sun (and eliminates the accompanying glare), the lower canopy reduces the daylight received in the immediate vicinity of the window and helps, by light reflected from its upper surface, to brighten the ceiling and light the rear of the room. The overall result is to produce approximately even illumination throughout the depth of the room. This is achieved with light from one side only and classroom sections of this type have superseded those in which the light was taken from two sides—usually through or over an adjoining corridor.

The baffles, dividing the continuous windows on plan, eliminate the glare which results from contrast between brightness of surfaces within the room and direct views of the sky.

The arrangement, one of several developed since the Second World War, meets the Ministry of Education light recommendations without excessive height of rooms.

N.B.—The curves are built up from daylight factors calculated for different points on the section at working level. These are plotted on a logarithmic scale which interprets more accurately the response of the human eye to changes in light intensity. (To produce equal observable increases in illumination, actual intensity of light has to be increased in geometric progression, e.g. increases of 2, 4, 8 and 16 per cent daylight factors are registered by the eye as equal improvements in illumination.)

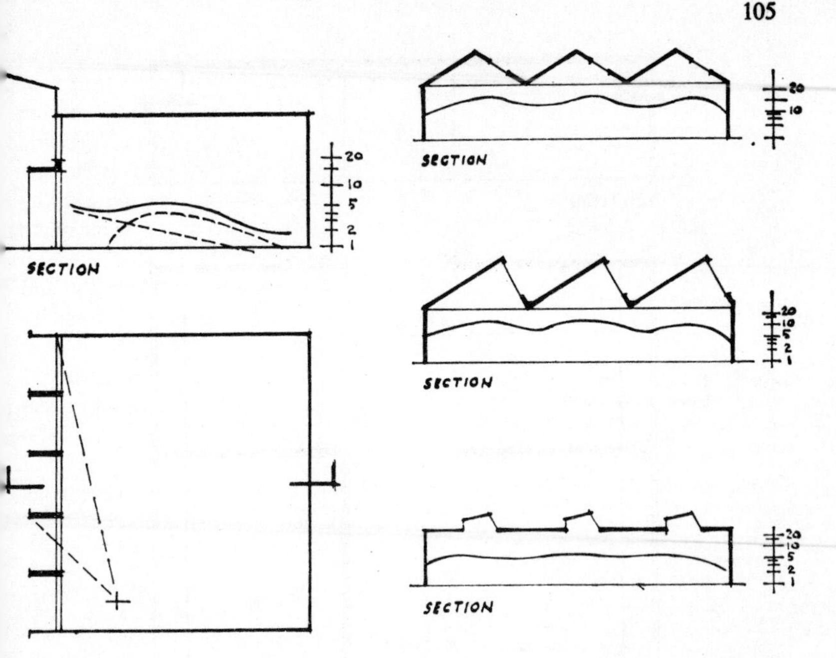

27

(*Right*) Traditional factory roof forms compared with the more recently developed "Monitor" section.

The traditional forms produce considerable variation in light intensity, which is avoided by the monitor form. In the north light form the essentially one-directional character of the light is often undesirable, although essential in some industries such as precision instrument manufacture.

Monitor lighting also has the advantage of being received to a large degree laterally, which avoids the creation of undesirable hard "under-shadows" associated with overhead lighting. It shares with north lighting the advantage of avoiding the glare which often results from strong contrast between glass areas and their immediately adjacent surfaces. In monitor and north light forms these surfaces are brightly lit.

Monitor forms enable glass to be easily cleaned on both sides from the flat roof surface whilst the internal glass areas of other forms are difficult, sometimes almost impossible, of access.

The fact that internal surfaces of glass accumulate dirt about three times as rapidly as external surfaces makes this of vital importance in practice.

N.B.—The sections compared are of similar heights of eaves, i.e. the monitor form encloses a somewhat less volume of air, and in each case the total area of glass is the same. Both these factors are of great importance in determining heating requirements and heating costs.

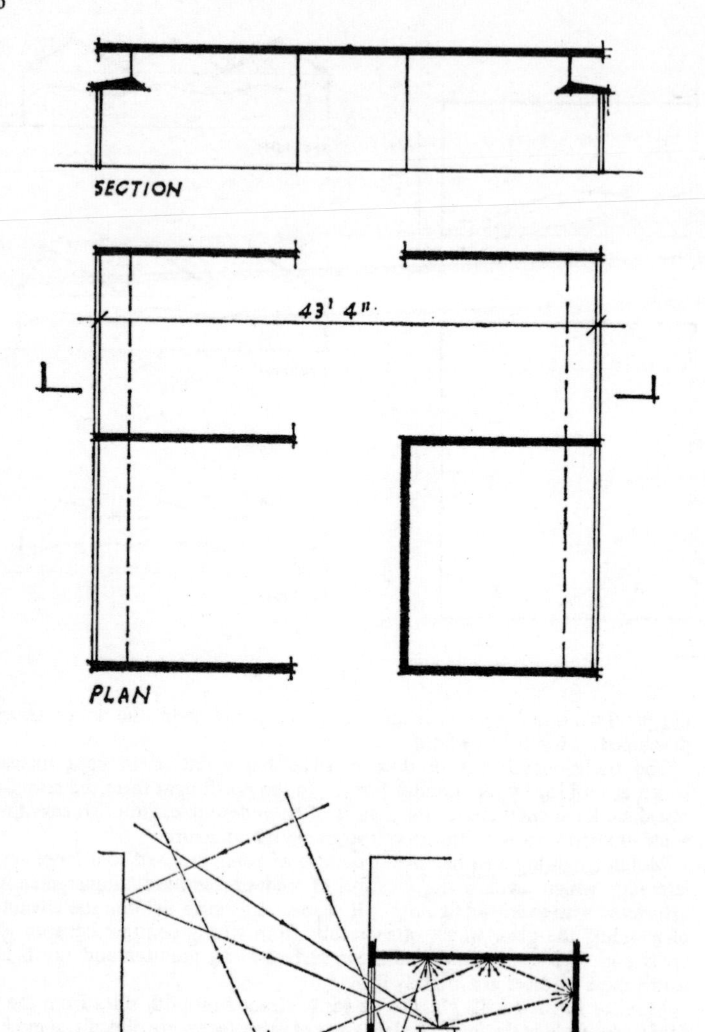

28 *Natural lighting*

(*Above*) THE "RIGBY" HOSPITAL SECTION. An arrangement of hospital ward designed to produce efficient daylight distribution and economy in hospital construction. Research carried out by the Nuffield Investigation showed that

Planning considerations. A major factor in determining daylight levels in buildings is the extent to which daylight reception is obstructed by the building's surroundings. The need for consideration of this problem when placing buildings relative to each other is obvious, particularly when density of building is high, as in towns and cities.

Limiting of buildings' heights and control of angles they subtend from opposing frontages have long been part of planning control. It has been conclusively demonstrated, however, that buildings can be arranged to produce development densities permitted by current planning controls but with far less mutual obstruction of daylight than that resulting from the application of present height and angle limits whenever the areas to be developed are of reasonable size.[1] The layout of buildings to ensure specific limits to their obstruction of each other's daylight is essentially a matter of trial and error but in practice this is made relatively simple and speedy by the use of diagrams which enable maximum acceptable obstructions to be defined at a glance from the layout plan only. These diagrams are prepared on the basis of a minimum sky factor acceptable for the building in question. From a selected point inside the building the minimum area of sky which needs to be visible to produce this factor is first defined in terms of vertical and horizontal angles. By comparison of this area with the total area of sky visible through windows of suitable size for the building in question the proportion of the window area which can be obscured by obstructions outside the building can be similarly defined in terms of angular height and width (29). The diagrams illustrated in Fig. 29 are in fact definitions in terms of height and angular width of different obstructions which would produce similar interruptions of light received at a given point.

The provision of minimum sky factors is now in fact being used as the basis of planning control for a number of areas of comprehensive development. The methods used are briefly described in Fig. 29.

[1] It has been shown that densities without reduced daylight standards can be increased above normal when sites are of one acre or larger.

---

daylight fully adequate for both staff and patients' activities could be achieved in all areas of the ward with a ceiling height of only 10 ft.

In this case findings took full account of light reflected from the upper surface of the inset canopies, the floor, walls, ceilings and outside ground surfaces. Investigations were made by means of scale models and specially developed photo-electric cells for direct measurements of light received.

(*Below*) A diagram showing the different ways in which light reaches a point inside a building. It shows clearly the importance of the floor and ceiling and the ground near the building as reflecting surfaces.

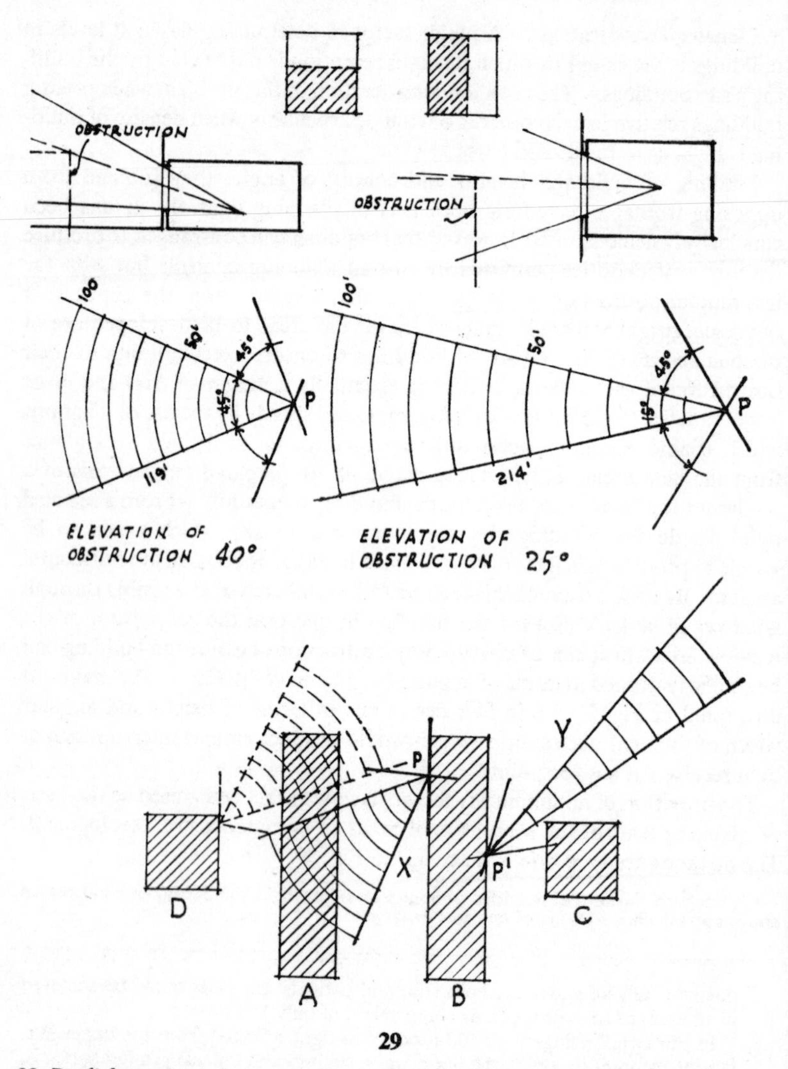

29

29 *Daylight testing indicators*

(*Above*) The section and plan show how the sky area seen from a given point within a building, i.e. the amount of light received at the point, may be the same when seen over or around obstructions of different forms. By assuming fixed window heights and widths (typical of and appropriate to particular types of

ARTIFICIAL LIGHTING. The almost universal availability of electricity[1] now makes the standard of artificial lighting to be provided in buildings, for

[1] The development of the electrical grid system has extended the advantages of electricity to remote parts of the country. The presence of a grid line will, however, not always make a supply available in its vicinity at a reasonable cost. Grid lines carry current at a high voltage, to diminish losses in transmission. It would be unsafe to supply houses at a high voltage. Consequently the installation of a transformer is necessary to make the supply available locally, and the cost of this, and of the low-tension cables, will be justified only where a considerable number of consumers will take a supply.

---

buildings) the angular widths and heights of alternative sky areas which must remain visible to permit a predetermined amount of daylight to reach a given point within the building are specified. From these alternative angular widths and heights of maximum obstructions which can be tolerated are specified. N.B.—In doing this allowance is made for the fact that external faces of buildings will be tested at ground level.

(*Centre*) Typical test indicators constructed from angular definitions of permissible obstructions. Each diagram represents a light reception (plan) angle and the vertical angle subtended by the maximum obstruction which can be tolerated in conjunction with it. The two diagrams are interpretations of the same lighting standard,[1] the curves showing heights subtended by the relevant angle at different distances from the reference point. Thus the diagrams would show (*left*) that when the angle of reception is 45° an obstruction 100 ft high can be as close as 119 ft to the reference point but that when (*right*) the reception angle is only 15° a similar obstruction cannot be closer than 214 ft. Diagrams are drawn on transparent material to the same scale as plans to be examined.

(*Below*) Part of an imaginary building layout showing the indicators in use. The indicator *X* shows that the standard of light required will reach rooms at *P* on block B if block A is not more than 58 ft high. Indicator *Y* shows that light to rooms at *P′* on block B will not be obstructed by block C whatever its height.

All points of the building's perimeter are tested and in use the indicators must not be turned beyond the point at which the "wing" lines coincide with the building face—light received more obliquely than this would not penetrate rooms sufficiently.

The indicator positioned in broken line shows that light to rooms in block D would be obstructed if block A were more than 39 ft high.

N.B.—Indicators shown are for tests relative to buildings on the same site. A second range of indicators is used to check obstruction by a proposed development, of adjoining buildings by similar testing along plot boundaries and along the centre lines of surrounding roads. These are less exacting than the tests between buildings within the site as similar tests are carried out from the other sides of boundaries and roads.

For fuller details of applying this method of Planning Control the reader is referred to the *Redevelopment of Central Areas* published by H.M.S.O.

[1] Two from the range of indicators evolved by the Ministry of Town and Country Planning for testing building layouts for Central Development Areas. (A sky factor of 1 per cent at a point 12 ft within the building is set as the minimum standard.)

all practical purposes, a matter of choice. Other forms of lighting are still used in some areas, e.g. where a supply of electric current is either not available or the supplanting of earlier gas supplies by electricity is not yet complete. Brief mention of these alternatives is made below.

Oil lamps. Oil lamps are still used where electricity and gas are not available. For efficiency good construction and careful attention are essential. Complete combustion and freedom from smell are dependent on means of regulating the air supply to the flame, and the use of a chimney of proper height. There are risks in use in that if the receptacle for oil should be allowed to get quite empty an explosive mixture of air and oil vapour may be formed, or if the receptacle should be filled too full the oil may run out and be set alight.

Paraffin lamps are of two principal types, those which produce a blue flame to heat a ramie-thread mantle to incandescence and those which produce a white fish-tail or circular flame as the illuminant direct. Mantle lamps are far more efficient and produce less pollution for a given unit of illumination. In use, oil lamps give off impurities in the form of carbon dioxide, water vapour, free carbon and oily vapour.

Coal gas. Ordinary coal gas is still used a good deal for lighting streets and buildings. It can be said to consist of three classes of constituent: the illuminants, the diluents and the impurities. The power of illumination is derived from unsaturated hydrocarbons, which would cause smoke in the absence of diluents such as hydrogen, saturated hydrocarbons, such as methane, and carbon monoxide, etc. The impurities consist of small percentages of carbon dioxide, sulphur compounds not effectively removed in the process of purification, etc.

The impurities given off by the combustion of gas include carbon dioxide and monoxide, ammonia and sulphur compounds, and water vapour.

Coal gas is generally burnt, mixed with atmospheric air, in a heat-giving blue flame, in such a way as to heat an asbestos gauze or ramie-thread mantle to incandescence. The mantle may be upright or "inverted", the latter throwing less shadow downwards. The old-fashioned "batswing" or "fish-tail" burner is obsolete for coal gas, though an adaptation of it is still used for acetylene gas, which burns with a whiter flame. In the fish-tail burner, the main source of light was the burning, in the gas, of tiny particles of carbon which were carried along the pipes in suspension.

Calor gas. Calor gas has been referred to earlier. It is quite suitable for lighting in situations where neither electricity nor coal gas is available. As an alternative to electricity it does not seem to have the advantage of cheapness for lighting purposes that it has for heating and cooking.

Water gas. Water gas is produced by passing steam through incandescent coke or anthracite coal, vaporised mineral oil being added to the resulting product. The fittings and pipes should be thoroughly gas-tight if this gas is used, as it contains a large proportion of carbon monoxide, a very dangerous gas to breathe.

Acetylene gas. Acetylene gas is produced by the action of water on carbide of calcium. It gives a very brilliant light, making the mantle a superfluity. It is used for country houses without the advantage of public services such as gas and electricity, but is not in very general use owing to the extreme care required, and Calor gas is preferable in such cases. All pipes and fittings must be thoroughly gas-tight, as a mixture of a very small proportion of acetylene and air is explosive.

Air gas or Petrol gas. Opposite in nature to that just described is what is known as air gas, in reference to which it is claimed that a burner might be turned on all night, unlighted, in a bedroom without danger. Air gas is a mixture of air and petrol vapour, a very small percentage of the latter being sufficient to produce an illuminant. Small plants for producing air gas have been used as an alternative to small private electricity generating plants.

Electricity offers the obvious advantages of convenience, lack of combustion products and almost complete lack of unwanted heat production and the risk of fire which accompanies it. The variety of lamps available for converting electric current to light not only meet almost every imaginable requirement in light character but also make electric lighting by far the cheapest available.

Electric lamps. Electric current is converted to light in two basic ways: by passing it through an element or filament of high resistance (so bringing it to incandescence); by creating an electric discharge in a gas or vapour. Filament lamps with tungsten filaments are the most widely used for general purposes and although most convenient in use and in first cost they are less efficient and economic to run than discharge lamps.

Mercury and Sodium discharge lamps, in which light is produced by passing an electric discharge through metallic vapours of these elements, are the most efficient types of lamp but the light they produce gives marked distortion of colours seen in it. These lamps are widely used where colour distortion is of secondary importance, e.g. in street lighting and for some industrial processes. Discharge lamps have a disadvantage in that they require additional gear to control starting and running.

By blending the light from different sources, e.g. by using mercury vapour lamps and tungsten filament lamps together, some degree of colour correction can be effected—with some loss in overall efficiency.[1]

Fluorescent tubular lamps are mercury vapour discharge lamps in which the ultra-violet light from the discharge causes a coating on the walls of the lamp to fluoresce. Variations in the coating can be made to produce lamps giving light of different colours. So-called "hot-cathode tubes" need starting and running gear; cold cathode tubes resemble them closely but although requiring no starting and running gear do need a transformer to provide the higher than mains voltage they need for operation.

Observations are made below concerning the considerations involved in the arrangement of artificial lighting but for comparisons to be drawn or standards to be defined some reference to light measurement is necessary.

THE LUMEN. The lumen, formerly called the foot-candle, is the amount of light from one standard candle which falls on 1 sq. ft of surface set at a distance of 1 ft from it. Light intensities are expressed in lumens per sq. ft and Table 10 sets out established standards for the levels of illumination needed for the efficient performance of a number of different tasks.

TABLE 10

	lumens per sq. ft
Casual reading	7
Ordinary bench and machine work	15
Carpentry	15
Sustained reading	15
Sewing	20
Typing	20
Draughting	30
Fine assembly work	50

Levels of illumination recommended for satisfactory performance of different tasks. (*I.E.S. Code of Lighting*)

N.B.—Equivalent daylighting standards expressed as sky factors are for levels of 1·4/7, 3/15, 4/20, 6/30 and 10 per cent/50 lumens respectively.

[1] Efficiency of lamps is expressed as lumens produced for each watt of current consumed. Average figures are, for tungsten filament 12–15; for mercury vapour 34; for sodium vapour 65; for hot-cathode tubes 27–50 and for cold cathode tubes 20–28.

Economic lighting will depend on length of the lamps' life as well as on their efficiency. Average life in hours for vapour lamps, hot-cathode and cold-cathode lamps respectively are 4000, 5000 and 15,000 hours as compared to a life of 1000 hours for tungsten filament lamps.

THE FOOT-LAMBERT is the unit measure of brightness resulting from 1 lumen per sq. ft on a perfect matt white diffusing surface. (White paper which reflects 70–80 per cent of the light falling on it would thus have a brightness of 7–8 ft-lamberts if illuminated to a level of 10 lumens per sq. ft.)

Notwithstanding the foregoing, conditions of glare will arise whenever adjoining surfaces differ substantially in brightness. A view of a window or skylight for example will often create glare because of the relative darkness of the wall surfaces surrounding it, and sunlight falling on work will, in the majority of cases, produce glare discomfort by reflection from the work. The basic requirements for the avoidance of glare are to provide a general brightness of illumination for all areas by means of light sources of controlled brightness and area so that as far as possible they merge gradually into the surroundings. Table 11 relates general levels of illumination to acceptable brightness of light sources of different area, including windows.

TABLE 11

	Brightness of light source		
Intensity of illumination on the work	Windows or large skylights	Source area larger than 200 sq. in.	Source area less than 200 sq. in.
Under 15 lumens	250 ft-lamberts	500 ft-lamberts	1000 ft-lamberts
15–20 lumens	500 ft-lamberts	1000 ft-lamberts	1500 ft-lamberts
Over 50 lumens	1000 ft-lamberts	1500 ft-lamberts	—

Recommended maxima for brightness of light source when different levels of illumination are to be provided. (*B.R.S. Digest No. 70.*)

For ideal working conditions it is also recommended that there should be slightly greater intensity of illumination on work areas themselves and light sources should of course be chosen to give sufficiently accurate colour rendering for the task illuminated.

Economy and maintenance. In selecting the most suitable type of artificial lighting installation factors other than direct efficiency of lamps (see footnote on p. 112) need consideration. The proportion of the total occupation period of the building during which the artificial lighting will be required must be balanced against the capital cost of the lighting fittings required. Fluorescent and vapour discharge lamps and the auxiliary equipment needed for their

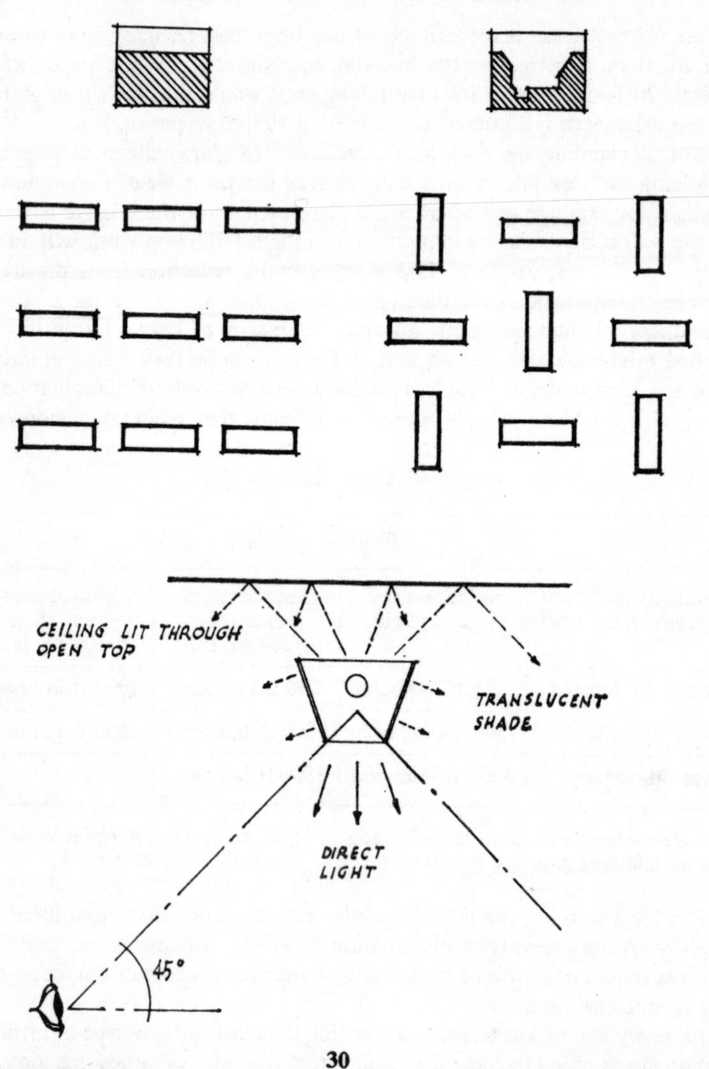

30 *Light arrangement*

(*Above*) DAYLIGHTING. Diagrammatic layout plans of buildings of similar size. The layout at right is typical of those producing high standards of daylighting, i.e. of the type likely to be produced using the methods of testing described in the text and Fig. 28. (*Continued on next page.*)

operation are high in first cost and in assessing overall economy this must be offset against their savings in current consumption.

It will be clear from this that where artificial lighting is required for only short periods (say in winter only), particularly where the level of illumination required is high and would call for large numbers of lamps—e.g. in school buildings for day-time use only, savings in running costs of say fluorescent lamps which could be offset against high installation costs would be small. Tungsten filament lighting is generally the correct choice in such circumstances.

Where artificial lighting is required continuously over long periods the situation described above is likely to be reversed, particularly if costs of electric current are high. Thus in industrial buildings, in use perhaps 24 hours a day, the amount of current consumed and the frequency with which lamps have to be replaced become the major factors in determining overall economy. Fluorescent or vapour discharge lamps become the obvious choice.

Particular requirements of appearance for example will, as in most fields, override the basic considerations outlined, e.g. in display lighting or lamps incorporated above illuminated ceilings.

Levels of illumination produced at work level will depend on distribution of light sources, their type and distance from the work position. Exact determination of the power and number of light sources required is a matter for specialists. An approximate indication of the relationship between overall magnitude of source and illumination level achieved in average conditions (ceiling heights in the region of 10 ft, decorations of moderate lightness and light source positioned about $\frac{1}{3}$rd down between ceiling and floor) can be obtained by an allowance of $\frac{1}{5}$th watt per lumen for filament lamps or $\frac{1}{15}$th watt per lumen for fluorescent lighting. Thus in a room of 600 sq. ft general level of illumination of 15 lumens per sq. ft would call for filament lamps totalling 1800 watts ($600 \times 15 \times \frac{1}{5}$) or fluorescent lamps totalling 600 watts ($600 \times 15 \times \frac{1}{15}$).

General considerations. Although the light intensity provided is of primary

---

The outlines above the layouts illustrate the sort of sky views through low-level windows which result within buildings in the two layouts.

(*Below*) ARTIFICIAL LIGHTING. Diagram of ceiling fitting which meets the general requirements referred to in the text (p. 116). General brightness of the shade surface should not exceed 1000 ft-lamberts, or be brighter than 1500 ft-lamberts at any point.

In some circumstances direct views of the light source may be prevented by structural elements, e.g. by truss members in a factory, making shades unnecessary. In others, a 45° angle may not be a steep enough angle, e.g. in hospitals where patients are lying down.

importance and must be adequate for the activity proposed, adequate intensity alone will not produce satisfactory lighting. It has been well established that working efficiency is impaired for example by lack of interest (i.e. lack of variation in light level), and by the existence of glare. Wholly indirect lighting, i.e. where all light reaches the work plane only after reflection from ceiling and/or wall surfaces, avoids the latter but as well as being wasteful, due to losses resulting from reflection, the light produced is "shadowless", an often undesirable characteristic because of the resulting lack of modelling in objects lit. Many people also find this form of lighting "soporific" and the ceiling, the brightest surface of a room, irritatingly distracting. Although design for maximum efficiency and economy, particularly in larger installations and those designed to meet specialised requirements, is nowadays the province of illuminating engineers, the conditions likely to produce comfortable and efficient lighting may be summarised in principle.

Light source. The human eye is automatically attracted by brightness and light so that a readily visible source of light becomes a distraction. If it is of a high order of brightness either in itself or in contrast to its immediate surroundings this will result in discomfort as well as reduced working efficiency due to glare. As almost every type of light source is too bright to be allowed within the field of direct vision, screening of light sources by shades which obscure or diffuse their light is recommended if these shortcomings are to be avoided. Light from lamps is also best arranged to illuminate nearby surfaces. Fig. 30 shows these principles applied to the arrangement of a notional ceiling fitting.

5

The Building—its Water Supply

Few things have been more instrumental in raising standards of living or of health and well-being than the provision of adequate and unpolluted supplies of water. Water without impurities of some kind does not occur naturally and, although many of these impurities are not harmful, but in fact desirable, water can rarely be distributed to consumers without some purifying treatment. Impurities are of various kinds.

Inorganic impurities. Inorganic matter is dissolved by water during its passage through the air and through or over soil or rocks, the nature and amount of such impurities depending on where and how far the water has travelled. They include mineral salts of many elements; bicarbonates and sulphates of calcium and magnesium being by far the most common, but salts of sodium, iron, and silica and other elements also often occur.

Contact of acid water, or water containing large amounts of nitrates and no carbonates, with lead or copper can result in salts of these metals occurring in solution. Salts of lead are poisonous, as little as 1 part in 700,000 being sufficient in some cases to cause lead poisoning.

Many salts in solution cause what is called "hardness" in water—discussed later in this chapter.

Inorganic substances not soluble in water are also picked up and are carried along in suspension. Particles of sand, chalk, soil, etc., which are undesirable, if not harmful, must be removed before water is ready for use. This is easily accomplished by filtration and/or sedimentation, described later in this chapter.

Organic impurities. Organic substances of animal or vegetable origin also occur both in solution and in suspension. Those of either vegetable or animal origin in solution may be harmful, the latter almost invariably so. These comprise ammonia compounds and products of putrefaction—their presence usually indicating sewage pollution. Vegetable contamination, however, is not necessarily harmful; e.g. waters from peaty collection areas are wholesome although through their acid character may raise problems. Organic matter in suspension—wood-fibre, pollen, fungus, etc., are typical of those of vegetable origin; dead insects, hairs, etc., typical of those of animal origin—is usually indicative of contamination by undesirable and disease-carrying bacteria.

Bacteria. Bacteria present in water may or may not be harmful. Classification, however, is difficult because of their minute size and as polluted waters abound in bacteria absence of all kinds is made an objective of water purification.

Water quality. From the foregoing, the requirements for good quality water can be summarised as freedom from organic pollution and bacteria, freedom from sediment, colour and smell. Water should also be sufficiently aerated to be pleasant to drink, should be soft to touch and dissolve soap readily.

Water testing. Water being considered as a possible supply should always be examined by analysts to determine whether its purification is possible or practical but there are a number of preliminary tests which can be usefully carried out.

Palatability. Palatability, a matter of taste and smell, may be tested as follows. Take a stoppered glass bottle of large size, e.g. a "Winchester quart", and holding about half a gallon. Wash out with a weak solution of sulphuric or hydrochloric acid and rinse repeatedly with the water to be tested. Immerse the bottle in the water to fill it to within about 2 in. of the neck, securely stopper it and expose to light and warmth for not less than twenty-four hours. Growth of vegetation will be visible or if putrefaction occurs, this will be discernible by smell. Either will indicate need for treatment.

Colour. If water is tinged with colour, it may be due to dissolved organic matter, such as peat or decayed leaves, or it may be due to iron. (In this case it is not necessarily bad water, although to be avoided if possible.) Colour cannot as a rule be judged merely from filling a tumbler. Two glass tubes, each about 24 in. high and 2 in. in diameter, are used, one filled with distilled water and the other with the water to be examined. If they are placed on a white tile or sheet of white paper, a comparison of colour can easily be made, when viewed from above and the tube lifted about 2 in. from the tile.

If found to be tinged with colour, a rough test can be made in order to see if the cause is organic matter. A drop of Condy's fluid added to a glass of the water should turn it pink. The presence of organic pollution is indicated by bleaching. The presence of chlorine (as chlorides) may be detected by adding a small quantity of nitrate of silver and dilute nitric acid. Small tabloids are obtainable for this purpose. If chlorides are present, the fact will be indicated by a haziness or by a more or less white precipitate (1 grain per gallon gives haziness, 10 grains per gallon a considerable precipitate). The presence of chlorides in considerable quantities is not sufficient in itself to condemn a water. They may be due to urine or other animal contamination, but may only have passed through or over rocks containing chlorides; they may also be due to sea-spray or to seaweed used as manure. Their origin should therefore be investigated as far as possible and perhaps a geologist consulted.

If the above rough tests clearly indicate serious pollution the source of supply will be abandoned if any other source is available; otherwise it would be necessary to install filtration and sterilisation apparatus which will be expensive.

Analytical and biological tests. If the water passes preliminary tests satisfactorily, it should be submitted to expert investigation by an analytical chemist and a bacteriologist. The manner of taking the samples is important.

For the chemist the sample should be of sufficient quantity and accompanied by the fullest particulars. A "Winchester quart" bottle should be obtained, cleaned and rinsed out as before described and filled to the neck, the stopper being firmly put in and covered by a strip of leather or cloth, which should be tied round and sealed. (If a glass stopper is unobtainable, a cork may be used, but it must be a clean, new one.) The bottle should be labelled with brief particulars and the date, and at once forwarded to the analyst with the fullest particulars, such as the nature of the source and reason for requiring the analysis. For example, if it is a case of illness, the nature of such illness. In the case of a supply from a well, the approximate depth, position in relation to drains and cesspools, if any, and any other possible source of pollution should be stated. The analysis should be commenced within forty-eight hours if possible. Small scale water supplies require examination from time to time. Occasional pollution may be due to a spell of heavy rainfall, bad condition of filters, or in the case of a house, defective cisterns and fittings.

For the bacteriologist a smaller bottle is used, generally of about 8 to 12 oz in capacity, fitted accurately with a ground glass stopper and thoroughly sterilised before use. The stoppered bottle should finally be made secure by a piece of aluminium foil over the stopper. It is also necessary that it should be kept very cold and examined with the least possible delay. Bacteriologists use special bottle cases for the transmission of samples. Bottles fit into a tin-lined receptacle, surrounded by another casing for holding ice, this in turn being surrounded by a layer of asbestos, and the whole fitting into a wooden box fitted with a lock.

If the sample is to be drawn from a pump or tap, the nozzle of the pump or tap must be thoroughly cleansed, and then flamed with a plumber's blow-lamp, or else flamed with a large wad of cotton wool, soaked in methylated spirit.

The chemist's report. The report of the chemist is sometimes rather too full of technicalities to be readily understood by the surveyor, but there are certain guiding points which may with advantage be referred to.

A large quantity of "albuminoid" ammonia, together with large amounts of "free" ammonia and chloride, points to sewage pollution. This will be confirmed if the bacteriologist finds large quantities of those bacteria which are characteristic of animal pollution.

A large quantity of "albuminoid" ammonia, with only a little "free" ammonia and a little chloride, points to vegetable contamination only. This will be confirmed if the bacteriologist finds few of the bacteria which are characteristic of animal pollution.

In addition to the ammonias and chlorides, nitrites and nitrates may be present. Nitrites and nitrates are always found in sewage effluents after treatment of the sewage in bacteria beds. Nitrites indicate that there has been a quantity of organic matter present, that this has been undergoing oxidation, but that the process is not yet complete. Nitrates indicate that oxidation of such organic material is complete. If a water contains nitrites and nitrates the report of the bacteriologist will again be of great interest, as the bacteria originally present may still be present in very large quantities.

The most useful information derived from a chemical analysis is that relating to the quantity of albuminoid ammonia present, and the amount of oxygen which will be absorbed by the water when kept at the standard temperature of 80°F for the standard time of 4 hours. Chemists will normally approve a water if it has not more than 1 or 1½ parts of albuminoid ammonia in ten million parts of water, and if it will, at the same time, not absorb more than one part of oxygen per million parts of water.

The bacteriologist's report. The report of the bacteriologist is even more technical in character than the chemist's: He is able to determine the presence of "pathogenic" (harmful) bacteria in a sample of water, and to estimate the quantity of both these and non-pathogenic varieties, and so draw conclusions as to the degree of pollution to which the water has been subjected. The normal procedure in water examination is to look for and count a group of bacteria known as "Bacillus Coli", an intestinal organism found in immense quantities in the excretions of all animals, healthy or otherwise, and which survives for long periods in water at ordinary tempera-tures. The importance of this group lies in the fact that its presence in a sample of water clearly indicates contamination from animal excretion and that all the water-borne diseases affecting man, such as cholera, typhoid, paratyphoid, dysentery, etc., are transmitted from the intestines of animals. To search for the specific bacilli of these diseases is too difficult an undertaking to be practical in routine water examination, though it might be attempted in special cases, as where a disease has broken out locally.

It may be taken as proved fact that a natural water which contains no Bacillus Coli cannot contain any dangerous number of disease-producing bacteria, and that a polluted water which has been so treated as to destroy all Bacillus Coli is as incapable of producing disease as the purest natural water.

It is usual to look for Bacillus Coli in samples of 0·1 c.c., 1 c.c., 10 c.c., 50 c.c., and 100 c.c. If the bacillus is present in 50 c.c. the water is viewed with suspicion; if present in 1 c.c. it would be regarded as dangerous.

Need for treatment. A water which is found not to comply with the above standards of chemical analysis and bacteriological examination would not necessarily be discarded. A careful examination of the source of the supply and its surroundings should be made with a view to the removal of sources of pollution, after which the water may be tested and examined again. If this proves fruitless, the water, if not hopelessly polluted, may be rendered safe by filtration, accompanied probably by sterilisation,[1] by methods which will be described later.

Quantity of water consumed. The quantity of water required per head of population per day depends on a variety of circumstances. In some rural areas it may be limited to that needed for cooking, drinking, clothes washing and house cleaning, and a small amount for waste. Water closets and bathrooms may be less general and there are no manufactories to be supplied with water for conversion to steam or for trade processes. The generalisation for rural areas must not however be too broad as in horticultural areas the water used for intensive growing of crops may exceed that of industrial areas. Thus demands may vary from 5 to 50 gals or more per head per day for rural areas, 30–35 gals per head per day for urban and suburban residential areas to 50 gals per head per day for large industrial centres with indications that these will all increase in the future.

Sources of supply

The original source of all available water is the rainfall. Part sinks into the ground to form underground supplies, part flows off the surface to form streams, and part evaporates. The amount of rainfall varies greatly in different places; thus on the east coast of England it averages about 20 in. per annum, on the south coast about 30 in. and in a few places in the Lake

[1] Sterilisation is not an accurate term as in many cases only harmful bacteria are killed. The term disinfection is now being used.

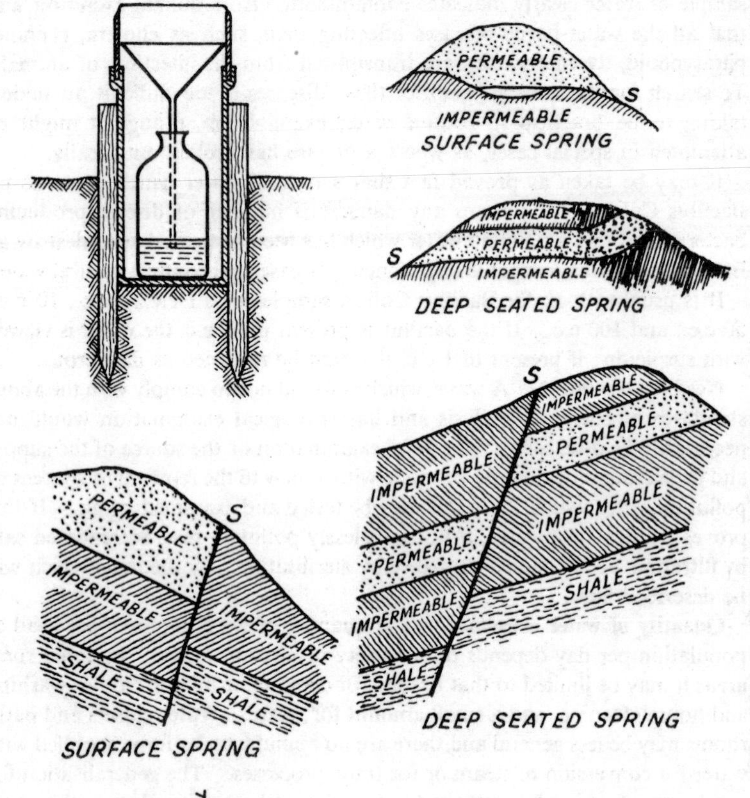
PERMEABLE
S
IMPERMEABLE
SURFACE SPRING
IMPERMEABLE
PERMEABLE
IMPERMEABLE
S
DEEP SEATED SPRING
S
IMPERMEABLE
PERMEABLE
IMPERMEABLE
IMPERMEABLE
PERMEABLE
SHALE
IMPERMEABLE
SHALE
DEEP SEATED SPRING
PERMEABLE
S
IMPERMEABLE
IMPERMEABLE
SHALE
SHALE
SURFACE SPRING

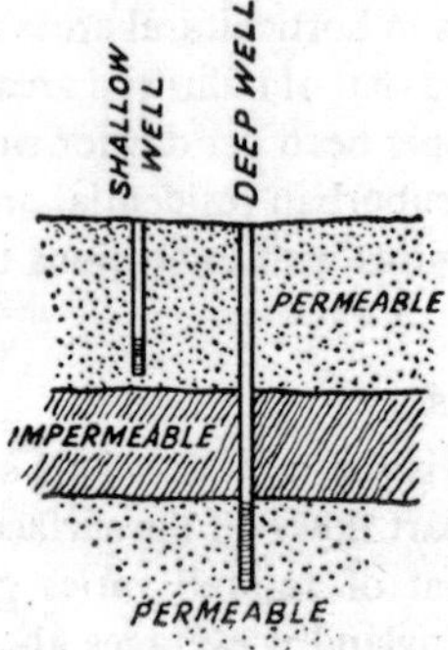
SHALLOW WELL
DEEP WELL
PERMEABLE
IMPERMEABLE
PERMEABLE

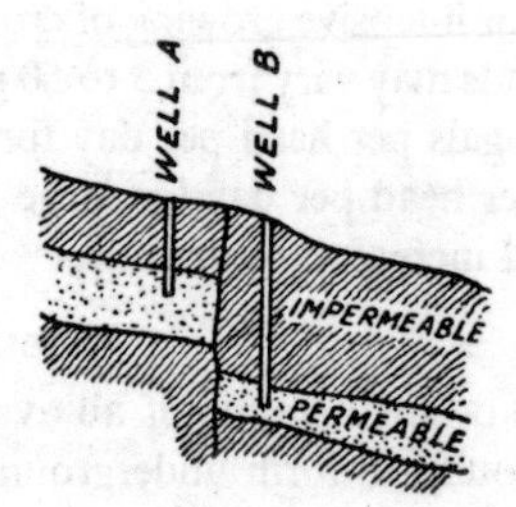
WELL A
WELL B
IMPERMEABLE
PERMEABLE

31

District it is over 100 in. per annum. For private and public supplies water is collected in a number of ways.

Springs. Springs are derived from that portion of the rainfall which has sunk into the soil. They are of two types, surface springs, and deep-seated springs.

Springs, when available, give a useful source of water supply for isolated houses in the country or small isolated blocks of cottages. The more deeply seated a spring is, the better, generally speaking, will the water be. From Fig. 31 it will be seen that the water is less liable to surface contamination in deep springs owing to its filtering through greater depths.

---

31 *Sources of water supply*

(*Top, left*) A RAIN GAUGE. As shown this comprises a screened collecting surface from which rain is diverted to an enclosed container. Rainfall is measured by pouring the collection into a measuring glass calibrated proportionally to the horizontal area offered by the collecting funnel.

The instrument is secured to the ground with small oak stakes and is fixed with its mouth about a foot above the ground, to prevent water splashing in. It is made of various diameters, but that in most general use has a diameter of 5 in. at the mouth. Rain gauges must be fixed in an open space, clear of any obstructions such as trees or anything likely to prevent the direct access of rain.

(*Top, right*) SPRINGS. Rain falling on the ground will percolate downwards until it is stopped by an impervious layer. It will then issue at the lowest point of the porous stratum, usually on the side of a hill or cliff, at point S in the upper diagram. In the diagram *below* a permeable stratum is shown between two which are impermeable, the former coming out to the surface, or outcropping, on either side of the hill. Surface water will pass over the upper impermeable layer, and with that collected on the exposed part of the permeable will percolate through the latter, issuing at the lowest point S. This is a deep-seated spring as opposed to a surface spring as described above.

(*Centre*) Where the continuity of the permeable stratum is interrupted by a fault water will collect in it and overflow in the form of a surface spring as shown left. In the diagram on the *right*, owing to a fault or dislocation of the strata, the water in the permeable stratum is obstructed in its downward flow and finds an outlet upwards through the line of fault, to produce a deep-seated spring.

In general water from surface springs is likely to be less pure than that from deep-seated springs.

(*Below*) WELLS. The diagram at *left* illustrates the terms "shallow" and" deep".

It is important to note that water will not always be obtained when a boring is made through an impermeable stratum to one which is permeable. In the circumstances shown in the diagram at *right* the fault, or dislocation of the strata, ensures water being collected so that well A is ensured a supply, but with the permeable stratum dipping downwards, as it does, there will be no certainty of supply to well B, which would probably be a dry or "dumb" well (see also Fig. 32).

Sometimes the spring outlet area is rather large, but this can be overcome by forming a channel, or a small gallery, in the hillside to tap the water as it reaches the surface.

Springs do not normally provide a sufficiently constant source for the supply of towns, but there are a few cases in which towns are supplied in this way, notably Bath, Malvern and Lancaster. A part of London's supply also comes from springs in Hertfordshire, a conduit about 40 miles long having been utilised by the New River Company for the purpose of conveying it.

In supplying houses in the country, a spring may sometimes be found at sufficient height to supply a storage tank by gravitation. Such tanks are usually made of sufficient size to contain from about three days' to one week's supply and if the spring is large, a ball-valve inlet is used to prevent overfilling. The tank should be covered and ventilated and provided with an overflow. Such tanks can be formed of concrete backed by clay puddle and rendered inside in cement mortar.

If the water is not of satisfactory quality it may be made to pass through a sand filter before reaching the tank, or, if it is not so filtered, pressure filters should be used on the taps supplying drinking water. (These filters will be fully described later.)

If the level of the available spring does not enable the storage tank to be filled by gravitation, water is pumped up to a storage tank situated in the highest part of the house.

Wells. Wells are holes sunk into the underground water to a level below that at which it would issue as springs. Wells are classed as shallow or deep, and it is important to note that these terms, as used in this connection, have no direct reference to depths in feet. A "shallow" well may have greater depth than a "deep" one, the term shallow meaning that the source of supply is the subsoil water, the supply for deep wells being derived from a water-bearing stratum lying beneath an impermeable one and often at great depth.

Geological considerations. As the foregoing shows, the presence of underground water is dependent on the geological formation of the area. Alluvial soils often overlie impervious strata and water trapped by these can be reached by sinking "shallow" wells, the impervious London clay forming the base for great numbers of such wells. Water in quantity and of much greater purity however is invariably obtained from permeable strata overlaid by or sandwiched between impermeable strata.

The so-called Bunter Sandstone, which extends over most of north-west England, provides vast quantities of water in Lancashire, Cheshire and Staffordshire. In the Manchester and Salford areas alone, wells yield

6,000,000 gallons per day. These wells are sited in built-up industrial areas and although much of the water reaching them undoubtedly originates from the rivers Irwell, Irk, and Medlock which traverse the strata and which are very foul, the water yielded by them is of high quality due to the filtering effect of the sandstone.

In the London Basin the chalk and "Greensand" strata which lie below the London clay provide reservoirs of high quality water which enters these strata where they are exposed on the surrounding downs. Well water makes a useful contribution to the enormous water demand met by the Metropolitan Water Board.

Shallow wells. The water from shallow wells is always open to suspicion, owing to the liability of pollution from defective drains and cesspools. Subsoil water is always moving, its lateral motion or its rise and fall in times of heavy rainfall or drought may place the water in a well in direct communication with contaminated soil. To avoid this a well must be as far as possible from any likely sources of contamination. The "dip" of the strata in which it lies should be towards any neighbouring cesspools and the well should be lined (or "steined") with brickwork (32), stone, concrete tubes, or iron cylinders, be covered over and have a permanent pump fixed. The old-fashioned "draw" or "dipping" well is not permissible under any circumstances, principally because of the possibility of polluting matters finding their way in at the top.

STEINING. There are many ways of steining a shallow well with brickwork.

If the ground is reasonably firm it should be possible to excavate successive depths of 3 ft or 3 ft 6 in. and then to timber each length immediately with poling boards, walings and struts, until a depth is reached several feet below the lowest level of the subsoil water, the excavation being kept dry by continuous pumping. When the bottom is reached a 6-in. diameter pipe is sunk vertically in a hole to act as a sump for the pump and around it is built a floor of concrete. The walls are then built up, timbering being removed as required. The brickwork for some distance up from the bottom will have open vertical joints, to allow water to enter the well; above this level it will be solidly built in cement mortar, with clay backing, to exclude surface water. At the top the diameter is reduced by corbelling to about 2 ft and the opening covered by a stone slab with lifting ring, the top of the slab being about 1 ft above the level of the ground, whose surface should be concreted around the cover. A permanent pump is fixed and the temporary sump in the floor concreted in.

A similar method, possible only when a reasonable depth of soil can be

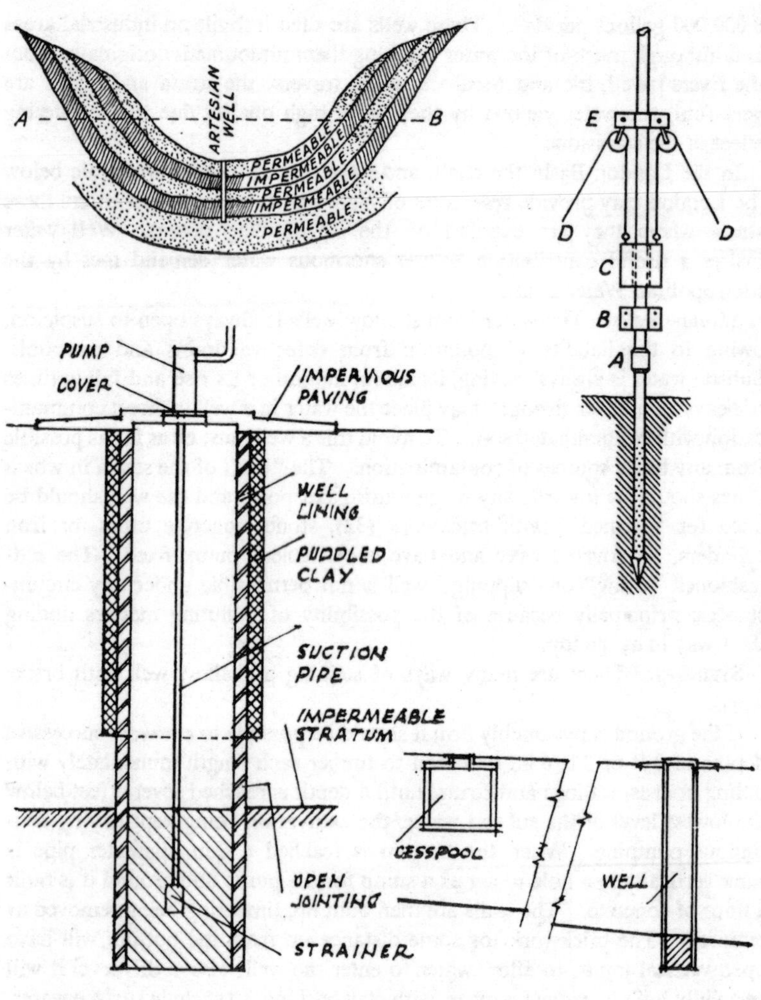

32

32 *Wells*

(*Top, left*) AN ARTESIAN WELL. Water enters the permeable strata, where these are exposed, to build up a reservoir of water beneath the impermeable strata. If the level of underground water is assumed to reach A–B it is clear that a well sunk at the bottom of the basin will produce water under considerable pressure. (*Top, right*) AN ABYSSINIAN TUBE WELL. The well is sunk by driving steel tubes

excavated without supporting timbering, is to excavate down as far as is safe and then place a circular kerb of oak or elm, 9 in. wide, to form a support for the wall. The wall is then built up in cement mortar on top of the kerb and backed with clay puddle, 6 in. thick. Holes are then dug in the ground below for the insertion below the kerb of inclined struts, for its temporary support, with their lower ends resting on solid wooden foot-blocks near the centre of the well and their upper ends wedged under the kerb. Excavation then proceeds down to the level of the foot-blocks, where another kerb is laid. Brickwork with clay backing is built upon it, as before, to a level as close as possible to the kerb above, the final gap being wedged tight with pieces of slate and cement mortar. In building the lower length gaps must be left around the inclined struts, but when the brickwork is sufficiently set to carry weight, the struts are removed and the remainder of the brickwork filled in. Successive lengths follow in similar manner, but the last length or two are built with open vertical joints and no clay backing.

---

fitted with a driving shoe into the ground. The first tube length is shown in the ground with the next length connected to it, A being the collar joint. At B two plates are firmly clamped to the upper length by means of bolts. At E is a similar clamp carrying two pulleys. Over these pulleys run ropes, marked D, attached to a heavy weight, or monkey, C. The monkey is pulled up by means of the cords and then allowed to fall, driving the tube in by its impact on the clamp B. An alternative way is to put a protecting cap over the upper end of the tube, with a separate rod above it carrying the monkey. In this case the impact comes on the cap, which avoids damaging the tube, which sometimes occurs with the clamp method. When the water is reached a pump is screwed on to the uppermost length; for a short time the water is muddy, due to the clearing of the earth out of the perforations and the forming of a cavity around the bottom of the tube, but once this has been done the water runs clear.

In any tube well, if the water level is not within 24 ft. of the pump valve, the valve must be taken down the tube to within such distance of the estimated lowest level of the water (see notes on pumps later in this chapter).

(*Below, left*) GENERAL ARRANGEMENT of a shallow well. The shaft penetrates the full depth of the subsoil and into the impermeable stratum. The upper length of the shaft is made impervious, in this case by a clay backing (Model bylaws require this to a depth of at least 6 ft), and the lower length is open or dry jointed to allow water entry. To prevent contamination via the wall top Model bylaws call for the shaft to extend at least 6 in. above ground level, to be covered and to be surrounded by an impervious paved area extending at least 4 ft in every direction.

(*Below, right*) A BADLY SITED WELL. The slope of the impermeable stratum would encourage contamination in the event of leakage or overflow from the cesspool. (Model bylaws require a well to be at least 60 ft from a cesspool and at least 40 ft from an earth closet.)

There are methods which can be used even where the soil is so insecure that it would not be possible to excavate any appreciable depth without timbering. They share the disadvantage that it is not possible to form a clay backing to the steining, so that percolation of surface water down the outside of the wall is more likely than where the methods described above are used. A circular iron kerb, with bevelled cutting edge below, is sunk a little way into the ground and carefully levelled. Brickwork is built upon it to a height of 3 or 4 ft and the ground within the kerb excavated to a depth of about 1 ft. Soil is then removed from under the cutting edge evenly all round, so that the kerb sinks under the weight of the wall above. Another foot of soil is then excavated and the lowering repeated, whilst the bricklayer continues to build up the wall. Very great care must be taken to keep the kerb quite level as, if the steining gets out of the vertical, it may become impossible to sink it further.

Whichever method of construction is used, the thickness of the walling will usually be 9 in., though occasionally it is more. The upper part, which is solidly built in cement mortar, is usually built of radiated bricks, but this is quite unnecessary for the lower part, which has open joints. The internal diameter of wells of this kind is generally about 4 ft.

When iron cylinders are used as steining they are made up of sections, with machined flanges which project internally. These are bolted together with their faces smeared with a mixture of iron filings and sal ammoniac. This form of steining can usually be sunk into position on a kerb. The lowest section has perforations to allow water to enter.

Wells of small diameter are sometimes lined with concrete tubes, the lowest one or two being perforated. Reinforced concrete is also sometimes used for steining, the thickness being about 4 in. with vertical and horizontal reinforcement.

Deep wells. Wells which are sunk to considerable depths are dug out to only a depth of about 4 or 5 ft. From that depth they are completed by boring (also called "drilling") with special tools. Diameters are usually much less than for shallow wells, although bores of quite large diameter are possible. The borehole is almost always lined with steel tubing, which serves the purposes of holding the subsoil in position and of excluding surface water. The lining does not of course extend to the bottom of the borehole.

The methods of drilling are of two distinct types, the Percussion System and the Rotary System.

In the Percussion System the breaking up of the rock or soil is done by a chisel bit, which is screwed to a vertical rod, suspended from a derrick set up over the borehole. As the work proceeds the rod is extended by screwing on additional lengths of rod. The rods and tool are raised by a winch and allowed to drop under their own weight, so that the chisel digs into the stratum. When 3 or 4 ft of soil has been penetrated the tool is brought to the surface and replaced by a shell-bucket, a contrivance for hauling out the debris after this has been softened by water. The chisel is afterwards substituted once more and drilling continued. The objection to this method is the time which is lost in raising the tools and changing them and in using the shell-bucket. To avoid this it is sometimes the practice to use hollow rods and a hollow chisel with oblique holes at its sides and to force water down inside these by a pump at the surface. The water carries to the surface (outside the rods) the cuttings or debris. These are settled in a settling tank and the water decanted for re-use. If this "hydraulic flushing" is used the drilling chisel has to be brought to the surface only when lining tubes have to be inserted.

In the Rotary System tubular boring rods, screwed together in 6-ft lengths, are suspended from a derrick and rotated by bevelled gearing at ground level. At the drill end the circumference of the rod has either saw-like teeth, fixed diamonds, or a serrated face resting on chilled steel shot. By these means a circular groove is cut in the bottom of the borehole and the core of the boring works up into the tubular boring rod and can be brought to the surface for an examination of the nature of the strata. To facilitate drilling, water is circulated down the interior of the rods as a lubricant and in some cases enough water is pumped down to wash loose debris to the surface on the outside of the rods.

As already stated, in boring through the upper formations it is usually necessary to line the borehole with steel tubing. Tube wall thickness is generally from $\frac{3}{8}$ to $\frac{3}{4}$ in., the tubes being 10 or 12 ft long with screwed ends, so that they can be fitted together to form watertight joints. The lowest tube length has a steel shoe with a cutting edge. Until some considerable depth is reached there will be no difficulty in lowering the lining into position, but at great depth it will need to be driven down with a ram or monkey. The lowering and driving is done in stages while drilling is suspended.

Artesian wells. A true artesian well is one formed in a valley or "basin" under conditions which ensure that water rises and discharges at the surface with some force. Fig. 32 shows the conditions favouring an artesian well. The name artesian is derived from the fact that the first such well was sunk in the province of Artois, in France. One of the earliest artesian wells in London was that sunk in 1844 to supply the fountains in Trafalgar Square. It goes down 393 ft to reach the upper chalk formation. Since the date of its construction, however, the water level of London's underground water has

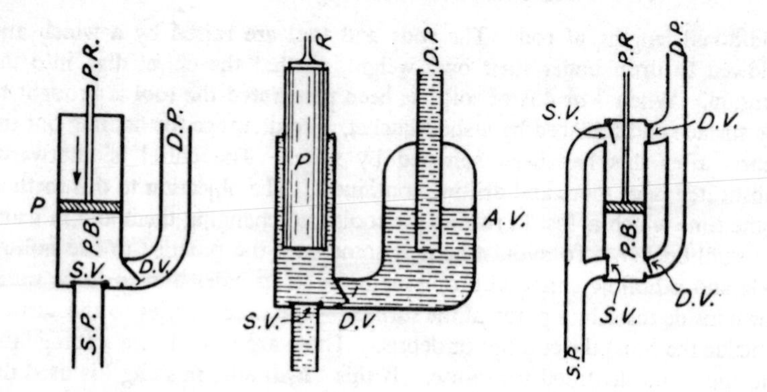

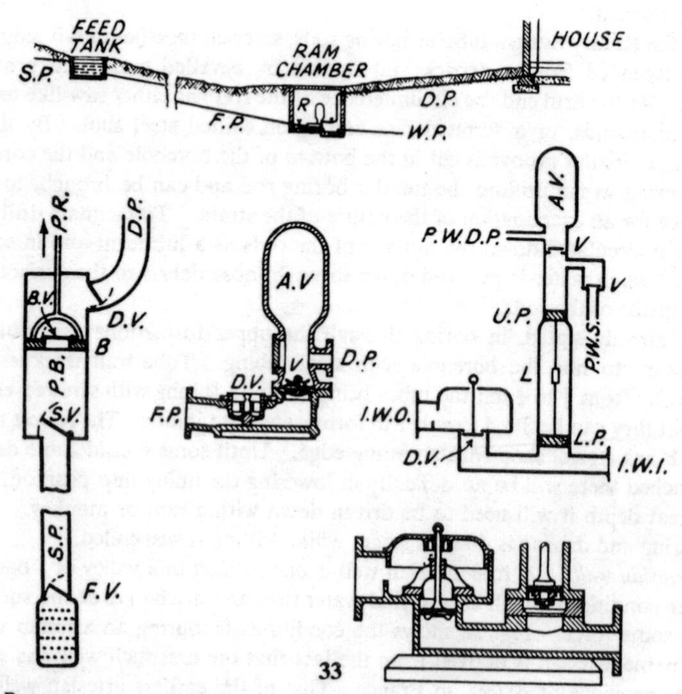

33 *Pumps*

(*Below, left*) A diagrammatic section through A LIFT PUMP. Passing down into the water of the well is a suction pipe, S.P., having at its foot a strainer or rose, the sum total of the areas of the holes in the strainer being equal to not less than twice the sectional area of the suction pipe. Above the suction pipe is the pump barrel, P.B., opening out of which is the delivery pipe, D.P. Working up and down in the barrel is a piston or bucket, B, controlled by a piston rod, P.R., the latter being actuated by a handle or a cranked axle. The bucket has a valve, B.V., and there are also valves at the upper end of the suction pipe, i.e. the suction valve, S.V., and at the lower end of the delivery pipe, i.e. the delivery valve, D.V.

A valve is also usually placed at the foot of the suction pipe, the foot valve, F.V. Its purpose is to prevent water running out of the suction pipe when the pump is not working, thus making it easier to start the pump again.

The action of the pump is as follows: As the bucket is raised, there is a tendency to cause a vacuum in the part of the pump barrel below it. The water under pressure of the atmosphere consequently forces open the suction valve and rises into the space below the piston. As the bucket descends, the pressure closes the suction valve and opens the bucket valve, allowing the water to pass to the upper side of the bucket. On the bucket again rising it lifts this water, which forces open the delivery valve and passes up the delivery pipe, the delivery valve closing again on the descent of the bucket. If the delivery is directly through a spout, no delivery valve is required.

Two pump barrels may be placed side by side, served by a common suction pipe, and serving a common delivery pipe, the bucket of the one going down as that of the other goes up.

(*Top, left*) A FORCE PUMP, sometimes termed a lift-and-force pump. The piston has no valve in it, and the entrance to the delivery pipe is at the bottom of the barrel. No water can pass to the upper side of the piston so that when the piston is descending the pressure will close the suction valve, open the delivery valve, and force water up the delivery pipe. On the piston rising, the weight of water in the delivery pipe will close the delivery valve, the suction valve will open and admit more water, and the whole process will be repeated.

(*Top, centre*) The foregoing notes show that the discharge of a pump would, unless means were taken to prevent it, occur in intermittent jerks, instead of a continuous supply. This is obviated in various ways. The diagram shows an air vessel, in the top of which air is imprisoned. This air acts as a cushion, being compressed as the water rises in the vessel when the delivery valve is open and expanding again when the delivery valve is closed to force a certain quantity of water up the delivery pipe when the plunger is not doing so and so make the supply more continuous. The air also absorbs shock. (The pump shown is a plunger pump—a force pump in which the piston is in the form of a solid plunger.)

Air vessels require to be carefully proportioned, and means for making good the loss of air, which occurs by the water absorbing it, are necessary. These take the form of either a valve of special form, a snifting valve, or two small taps, one at the top of the vessel to let air in and the other at the bottom to let water out.

(*Top, right*) A diagrammatic section of A DOUBLE-ACTING FORCE PUMP, the action of which is as follows: As the piston descends, the lower suction valve closes and the lower delivery valve opens, water being forced up the delivery pipe. At the same time water enters the pump barrel above the piston, through the upper suction valve, the upper delivery valve being closed. As the piston

steadily dropped, and the Trafalgar Square supply is no longer artesian. Actually a pumping chamber has been constructed well below the level of the Square and the fountains now play by mechanical power.

The water from artesian and deep wells is generally very even in tem-

---

(*continued from previous page*)
rises the upper delivery valve opens and the upper suction valve closes, water entering the barrel below the piston, to be displaced on its next descent.

N.B.—In large pumping plants, steady and continuous delivery is obtained by working three pumps, side by side, the plungers being worked from the same crankshaft by means of three cranks set at 120° to one another.

HYDRAULIC RAMS

(*Centre*) An outline section of a water-supply system in which A SINGLE-ACTING RAM is used. A feed tank (with a strainer and grit chamber) is fed by a supply pipe, S.P., from, say, a stream. From the feed tank a feed pipe or drive pipe, F.P., passes to the ram, R. The ram passes a small proportion of the water into the delivery pipe, D.P., but the bulk of it, used to drive the ram, into the waste pipe, W.P.

Below is a section through a typical ram. The water enters from the feed pipe at F.P. D.V. is a dash valve, whose weight is very little greater than the water pressure due to the head of water behind it; hence, when the water is at rest in the pipes, the valve falls and water flows out through the valve to waste. As its velocity increases, the impact of the water on the valve closes it, and the momentum then opens the valve, V, admitting water to the air vessel, A.V. There the air is compressed, and its reaction, in expanding, forces the water up the delivery pipe, D.P. When the momentum is expended the valve, V, will close, the water will surge back in the ram, causing the pressure in the ram to fall below that of the atmosphere, and the valve D.V. will open. Water again escapes at the dash valve and the whole cycle of events occurs again.

N.B.—The length of the feed pipe should not be less than the height it is desired to raise water above the ram. To prevent damage by shock it is essential to keep air in the air vessel. Air tends to be carried away in the delivery stroke, and a "snifting valve" should be fitted in the ram below valve V, to admit a small quantity of air when the rebound of the water causes pressure to fall below atmospheric.

(*Below, right*) A diagrammatic section of A DOUBLE-ACTING RAM—a combination of ram and pump. Pure water enters the supply pipe, P.W.S., and passes through a valve into the space above the upper piston, U.P. Impure water enters the lower part of the apparatus, through the pipe marked I.W.I. and passes on to the dash valve, D.V. This opens and closes as described above. When closed the impure water exerts pressure on the underside of the lower piston, forcing it up and so displacing the pure water into the delivery pipe. The upper and lower pistons are connected by means of a rigid rod, through which a weighted lever passes at L, to facilitate the downward movement after the pure water has been displaced.

N.B.—The pistons must be tight fitting to prevent the passage of impure water. *Below* is an enlarged section of the lower part of the apparatus, showing by a thick line the cup leather put to the pistons to ensure this.

perature summer and winter. In a true artesian well it sometimes happens that the natural lift is enough to carry water to the storage tanks without pumping.

Abyssinian tube wells. For a temporary supply, or very small demand, "Abyssinian" tube wells are useful. These are made up of strong mild steel tubes, driven into the soil, one length being screwed on to another or, in fairly soft ground, the joint is made by means of collars. The bottom length has a hardened steel spike and is perforated for a length of about 2 ft to let the water in.

INCREASING THE YIELD OF WELLS. When pumping is carried on from a well, water is drawn in from every direction, so that, if another well is sunk within the area from which the first well draws its supply, the yield of the latter will be affected. The exact area drained by wells is however an uncertain factor.

To increase the yield of a well, adits or tunnels are often driven horizontally at the bottom, a series of wells being sometimes connected in this way to concentrate the pumping arrangements in one well.

Suction pumps are designed to exploit atmospheric pressure in lifting water. At average barometer pressure the atmosphere is theoretically capable of supporting a column of water 34 ft in height and this capacity is harnessed to raise water to the body of a suction pump (also called a lift pump) positioned above it. Fig. 33 illustrates a number of pumps making use of this principle. In practice friction losses and variations in barometric pressure limit the height of the pump above lowest water level to 22–24 ft and in wells up to this depth the pump can be positioned at ground level. If water is to be raised further than this, pumps are sited within the well shaft and are more likely to be of the "force and lift" form than the suction or lift form (33).

Centrifugal pumps. Centrifugal pumps are entirely different in principle to those described, water being drawn by suction into the axis of a casing which is volute or spiral-shaped. Inside the casing is a wheel with blades fitted around its circumference which just clear the inside of the casing at that part of the spiral nearest to the centre, there being ample room for water elsewhere. The wheel is kept in rapid rotation, driving the water around with it and the centrifugal force, set up by the water's rotation, causes the water to pass up the delivery pipe, which is tangential to the spiral casing. Centrifugal pumps are very efficient for lifting large volumes of water through small lifts, but are less efficient for high lifts.

A point to note is that a centrifugal pump of ordinary type cannot be started unless it is full of water. To ensure that it remains full of water, when not in action, it is often submerged below water level. When this is not done a foot valve must be placed on the suction pipe to prevent the water running out of it. This valve must be kept in good condition or it will leak and trouble will then result. An additional precaution sometimes taken is to dip the delivery pipe from the pump below water level before taking it up the well; if this is done the apparatus will be kept full of water by siphonic action even if the foot valve is a little leaky. As in the case of other pumps with suction pipes the length of the suction should not exceed about 22 ft.

Certain improved types of centrifugal pump are now on the market, which are "self-priming" so that starting presents no difficulty, even when they become emptied.

Air-lift pumps. In this form of pump compressed air is forced into the annular space between two pipes of different diameters, set one within the other inside the well or borehole to reach well below water level—the outer pipe being somewhat longer than the inner pipe. The air depresses the level of the water between the pipes until it can escape up the inner central pipe carrying water with it. To ensure that sufficient pressure can be applied the end of the inner pipe should be a distance equal to one and a half times the required lift below water level. This appliance is inexpensive, simple in operation and reliable; it is, however, very inefficient as compared with many other forms of pump and this makes it unsuitable for work on a large scale. In view of the fact that it is not the best type of pump for either small or very large plants, it is not surprising that this form of pump is almost obsolete.

For small installations, such as those for a private house or group of smaller dwellings, or a farm, where skilled mechanics are not available and it is not economic to allot one man's time to caring for the plant, it is all-important to choose a pump which is simple in character and reliable in operation, efficiency being of less importance. For large installations, such as those of a public water authority, efficiency is the chief factor to be considered: there is always skilled labour in attendance for repacking glands, remedying leaky valves, etc.

POWER REQUIRED FOR PUMPS. The power required to pump water can be calculated as follows:

Assume that it is required, during the hours at which the pumps are to be worked, to raise 1500 gallons per hour through a height of 160 ft.

One gallon of water weighs 10 lb, so that the weight lifted per hour is 15,000 lb, and the weight lifted per minute is 15,000/60 = 250 lb.

Horsepower[1] output of pump = $Wh/33{,}000$, where W = weight in lb lifted per minute and h = lift in feet; so that in the present instance the horsepower output of pump

$$\frac{250 \times 160}{33{,}000} = \frac{40}{33} — 1\tfrac{1}{4} \text{ horsepower.}$$

The engine required to drive the pump must have more power than this, since the efficiency of small pumping plants seldom exceeds 60 per cent. Taking the efficiency in the present case as 40 per cent,

$$\text{Power output of pump} = \frac{40}{100} \times \text{horsepower of engine.}$$

$$\therefore \text{ Horsepower of engine} = \frac{100}{40} \times \text{power output of pump.}$$

$$= \frac{10}{4} \times 1\tfrac{1}{4} = 3\tfrac{1}{8} \text{ horsepower.}$$

In the above example it has been assumed that the delivery pipe is of ample diameter, so that the frictional resistance offered by it does not appreciably increase the head against which the pump has to work.

Hydraulic rams. Hydraulic rams are often used in connection with the supply of water to large country houses. The principle underlying their action is that of harnessing the momentum of a body of water falling through an inclined pipe to raise a smaller quantity of water through a greater height. There are both "single-acting" and "double-acting" hydraulic rams. In the former type the water lifted comes from the same source as the water utilised for driving the ram, whilst in the latter the water lifted is pure, and that used for driving the ram is usually of doubtful quality and from a different source. Fig. 33 illustrates and describes the arrangement and action of both types of ram.

The Hydrostat ram. An improvement on the hydraulic ram is the hydrostat, manufactured by Hydrautomat Ltd. In this there are two cylinders of widely different diameters, one vertically over the other, their pistons being on one common vertical piston-rod, so that movement of the one entails similar movement of the other.

In the large cylinder, "driving water" is admitted alternately above and below the piston and is exhausted from the other end to waste, or to some house or district situated at a lower level.

In the smaller cylinder, "driven water" is admitted, either from the same source or from another source of purer quality, and is forced to the high

[1] 1 horsepower = 33,000 ft lb/min.

level at which the supply is needed, either to a reservoir or direct to the consumers.

The entrance of the driving water to each end of the large cylinder, and its exhaust from the other end, are automatically controlled by an ingenious moving valve appliance. The entrance and exhaust of the driven water to and from the smaller cylinder are controlled by ordinary lift valves.

The superiority of the hydrostat over the hydraulic ram lies in the fact that it is noiseless in action, less liable to wear and tear, and more efficient.

Not only is it useful for lifting water from a stream for the supply of an isolated dwelling at a high level, but it is also much utilised for "boosting" up pressure in certain mains of public water supplies. The driving water in such a case is the water which is supplied to some low-lying district and is not run to waste, whilst the driven water is that which is needed for the supply of some district which is abnormally high in level.

The appliance is automatic in action, and will adjust its rate of working to the amount of driving water available and to the amount of driven water being consumed. It is unnecessary to provide a reservoir at the high level to receive the driven supply, unless the maximum rate of consumption at the high level exceeds the maximum rate at which the hydrostat will work, which of course depends upon the amount of driving water available.

Stored rainwater sometimes forms the only source of water supply when no other is available. It is more often used as a supplementary supply, being very soft and therefore good for cooking and washing. Although too soft to be very palatable it is somewhat improved by filtration. It is mainly in open country that this source is used and the question of the rain taking up impurities in its fall rarely arises.

The collecting area is generally the roofs of the buildings. Slate should be chosen as the roof covering, it being less absorbent than tiles. If the water is to be used for drinking purposes, there should be no lead gutters or flats because of the possible solvent action of the soft water. The gutters and rainwater pipes should be of iron, protected against corrosion preferably by the process introduced by Dr Angus Smith (consisting of dipping the articles, when hot, into a hot solution of bituminous composition).

Collecting grounds. If the roofs do not furnish a sufficient collecting area an additional collecting area may be formed. It should be carefully fenced in to guard it from pollution and may either consist of a sloping surface of concrete finished with cement or asphalt, falling to a collecting channel communicating with the storage tank; or a similar surface covered with special tiles to form a false floor supporting about a foot of earth covered with grass. The rainfall is partly filtered and purified by the earth and grass as it passes through to the collecting floor below and thence into the channel. Any such surface should be isolated by a channel sunk around it and to a lower level to prevent lateral pollution.

Rainwater separators. Where roofs are used as the collecting surface, gutters will be regularly cleansed but a rainwater separator should also be used. This is a device for diverting the first part of the flow, charged with the washings of the roofs and gutters, to waste. It then automatically directs the after-flow to the storage tank. An example is illustrated in Fig. 34.

In estimating the quantity of water that will be collected, allowance must be made for the quantity diverted to waste and for loss by absorption and by evaporation from the surface of the water in the storage tank. The proportion of rainfall available for actual supply is approximately as follows: with roofs and similar collecting surfaces, a separator being used, about 65 per cent; without a separator, about 85 per cent; with a grass-collecting surface (part of the rain being retained by the soil), about 60 per cent.

If the annual rainfall is known, the collecting area required to produce a given yield—or the yield from a given collecting area—can be simply calculated. 1 in. of rain will yield ½ gallon from each square foot of collecting area. (This is a gross yield and collecting areas, whether sloping or flat, should be measured horizontally.)

Rainwater storage tanks. The storage tank should preferably be capable of containing from 90 to 120 days' requirements, according to the annual rainfall of the district, though much smaller tanks are often used. The shape of the tank on plan is not important but it must be watertight, not only to keep the water in, but to keep impurities out.

Tanks may be constructed of brickwork or concrete, lined with cement mortar or asphalt. They should be enclosed but have means of access for cleaning and be ventilated—Fig. 34.

Filters. Rainwater should be filtered, particularly if it is the only source of supply. The filters are constructed of a bed of fine sand 1 ft 6 in. thick, supported by a bed of washed gravel 1 ft thick. Such filters will efficiently filter about 400 to 450 gallons per square yard per day; and one about 2 ft sq., the smallest size that could be constructed conveniently, would be of ample size for a domestic installation. To permit of cleansing, however, the filters should be in duplicate.

A common arrangement is to run water from storage through a filter to a clean water tank, usually holding about 3 days' supply. This has the advantage of allowing the stored water to clear by sedimentation but requires additional attention in periodic valve operation to control flow between the

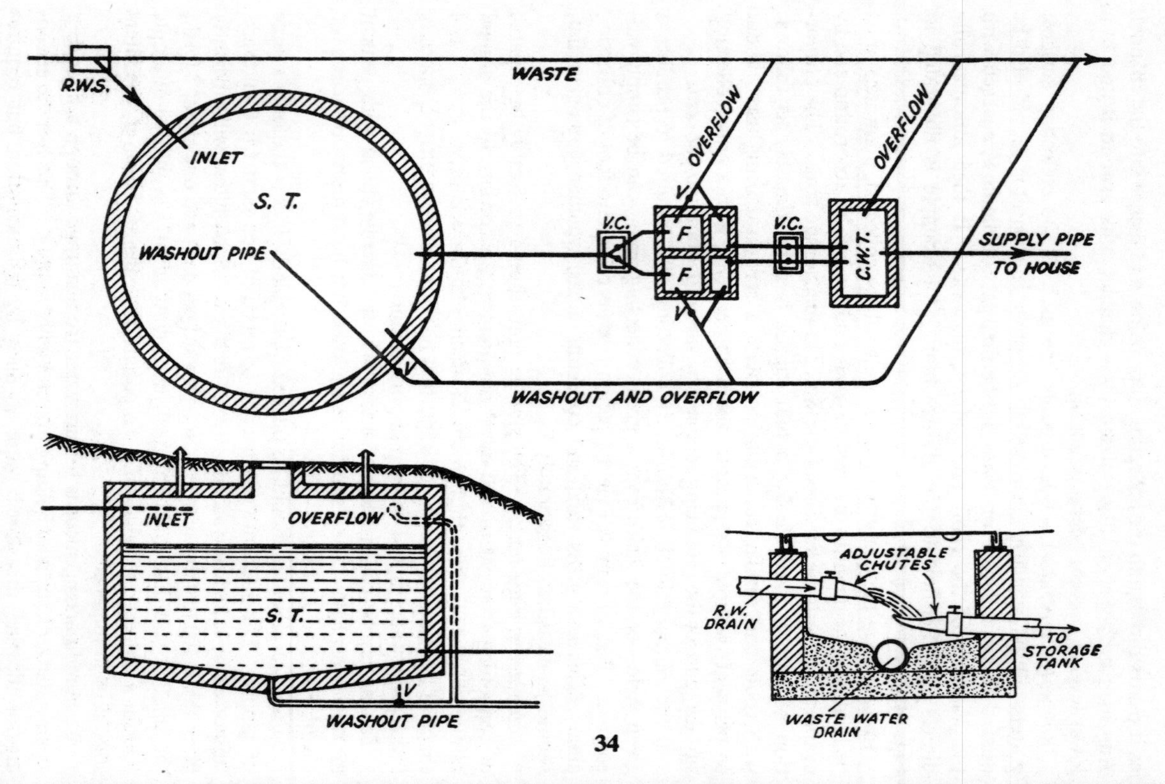
WASTE
R.W.S.
INLET
S. T.
WASHOUT PIPE
OVERFLOW
OVERFLOW
V
V
V.C.
F
F
V.C.
C.W.T.
SUPPLY PIPE
TO HOUSE
V
WASHOUT AND OVERFLOW
INLET
OVERFLOW
S. T.
V
WASHOUT PIPE
ADJUSTABLE
CHUTES
R.W.
DRAIN
TO
STORAGE
TANK
WASTE WATER
DRAIN

34

two tanks (see Fig. 34). It is perhaps more usual to place filters before the storage tank so that all water stored is clean and can be pumped directly to the high level cistern in the building as required.

Surface collection. The most important source of large-scale water supply is water collected directly from the ground surface in artificial or natural reservoirs. Water is impounded to create an artificial lake, usually by damming a stream and valley in upland or moorland areas, or drawn from natural upland lakes. Liverpool and Birmingham, for example, obtain water from reservoirs in the Welsh uplands, and Leicester, Derby, Nottingham and Sheffield from reservoirs in the Derwent Valley. Glasgow obtains water from Loch Katrine and Manchester obtains water from the lakes in Cumberland.

A "gathering ground", or catchment area, is generally at a high altitude. Thus, in the Derwent Valley scheme, referred to above, the catchment area forms part of the hilly country known as the Peak district, and for the most part is moorland. It has an area of nearly 32,000 acres, all over 580 ft above sea level; 26,800 acres are at a height of over 1000 ft and 11,600 acres are above 1500 ft.

The catchment area in such schemes is the area of land draining towards a stream or streams, and is bounded by the watershed line of the surrounding hills. The quantity of water available from such a source is estimated in

---

34 *Rainwater Storage*

(*Above*) A rainwater storage installation in plan and (*below, left*), a section through the storage tank. Rainwater collecting pipes lead to a separator, marked R.W.S., from which one pipe enters the storage tank and another goes on to waste. From the storage tank a supply pipe is taken to a pair of filters, either of which can be thrown out of use by valves in the valve-chamber, V.C., for the purpose of cleansing. Each filter has its own outlet pipe to the clean or filtered-water tank, C.W.T., from which the main supply pipe to the house is taken. Storage tank, S.T., filters, F., and filtered-water tank all have manholes for access, and are ventilated. All three should have overflow pipes, and the storage tank and filters should be provided with wash-out pipes at the bottom. The overflow pipe and wash-out pipes can be joined together outside the tank. The effective depth of the storage tank is the difference between the levels of the overflow and outlet, the floor being sloped to the wash-out pipe. Installations are most conveniently arranged on ground with a fall, but the various parts need not be so close together as shown, for convenience, in the diagram. (*Below, right*) A RAINWATER SEPARATOR. The first run-off from the collecting areas is sluggish and, having insufficient momentum to leap the gap between the two chutes, runs to waste. As the run-off becomes cleaner and momentum increases water leaps the gap and runs to storage. However, in long drizzling rain, water may not attain momentum to leap gap and so be lost. Other forms are available which operate on a tipper principle and overcome this by measuring the quantity run to waste.

either of two ways: by ascertaining the rainfall in the district, and calculating the quantity available after deducting a certain amount (approximately 12 to 15 in. per annum[1]) for loss by absorption and evaporation, the loss due to absorption depending, of course, on the nature of the geological formation; or by gauging the flow of the streams flowing from the valley for as long a period as possible, and, if a storage reservoir is to be formed, deducting a small amount to allow for evaporation. The methods of gauging the flow are numerous and include weirs, floats, current meters, Pitot tubes, and other contrivances. From a weir the flow can be calculated direct, but from the other methods the mean velocity is obtained, so that the flow can be readily calculated by determining the sectional area of the stream.

The flow in all years is not the same and is also greater in winter than in summer and reservoirs are made large enough to store up part of the winter supply, and the excess rainfall of wet years, in order to provide a supply in time of drought. The best site for a storage reservoir is a narrow part of the valley where a comparatively short embankment will form a reservoir of large capacity.

Compensation water. Where a reservoir is formed on a stream used by mill owners, farmers and manufacturers, a certain part of its flow must be preserved. Usually about one-fourth to one-third of the whole available supply is set aside as compensation water, sometimes stored in separate "compensation" reservoirs to enable a continuous flow to be arranged.

The available capacity of a reservoir is the volume contained between the highest and lowest working levels, and is less than the total capacity by a volume left for the collection of sediment. No hard-and-fast rule can be laid down for the amount of this, but in many good examples it amounts to about one-sixth of the greatest depth of water at the deepest part of the reservoir.

The storage capacities of impounding or storage reservoirs are very considerable. The two reservoirs which were constructed as a first instalment under the Derwent Valley scheme, for example, have a total capacity of 3940 million gallons.

River water. A large number of towns obtain their water supply from rivers although many have had to abandon this source owing to increasing pollution by sewage and refuse from manufactories. London is the most notable example of a town taking its main supply from a river. As the dry weather flow of the river may be insufficient, storage reservoirs are usually formed to impound the flood waters. In the case of London, two impounding reservoirs at Staines have a total area of 421 acres, with a capacity of 3300 million gallons, and reservoirs constructed at Chingford in Essex have a total area exceeding that of Hyde Park.

[1] In exceptional years losses up to 24 in. have been recorded by some Authorities.

Improved methods of purification and sterilisation have of late years made it possible to utilise rivers formerly regarded as unfit, so that there is no doubt that rivers will continue to afford a valuable source of supply for towns. Relative to supplies from rivers it is worth mentioning here the much-debated question of self-purification of rivers. It has been pointed out that water taken some miles below a source of pollution is purer than a sample taken nearer the source of pollution, and it has been estimated that a river flowing with a mean velocity of about 4 miles per hour will purify itself within a distance of about 16 miles from the point of pollution. Some authorities say that when pathogenic or disease-bearing bacteria pass into relatively pure water, they are in an unnatural medium and die off, others that sedimentation is the chief cause of self-purification. If this is so, there is no guarantee that harmful microbes will not be present and be carried down by the next flood which stirs up the river bed.

River water is usually softer than that derived from wells and springs. It seldom happens that the supply can be delivered by gravitation, but it is usually cheaper to pump the water than to bring it from a great distance by gravitation.

Water treatment. It is, of course, essential that water distributed by a water authority is absolutely safe for use when it reaches the consumer and a great deal of the water so distributed requires some degree of treatment to ensure this.

The principal methods of treatment are by sedimentation, filtration and sterilisation.

SEDIMENTATION

Sedimentation is effective in removing suspended matter and some bacteria; it is not by itself a sufficient treatment of water polluted by sewage, but is a useful first step in its purification. If water is kept in a quiet state for a sufficient time the heavier suspended matter will settle, carrying with them some of the bacteria, and the clarified upper part of the water can be decanted off; the deposited sludge must be periodically removed. The settling process is often aided by the use of sulphate of alumina; this combines with bicarbonates present in the water to form a cloudy precipitate which falls to the bottom, dragging suspended particles and bacteria with it. If there are no bicarbonates present in the water, lime or carbonate of lime is mixed with the aluminium sulphate.

FILTRATION

Sand filtration. Filtration on a large scale is carried out by passing water through sand, contained either in open beds or in closed tanks. The open "slow sand filter" is contained by walls and floor, usually formed of reinforced concrete (35).

The action of such a filter is partly mechanical and partly biological. The former action holds back the suspended matter which forms a film on the upper layer of sand; this film is charged with bacterial life which promotes nitrification of organic matter, and arrests the passage of further bacteria. Efficiency is due entirely to this surface film and until the film is formed bacterial life is not removed. After a time, however, it becomes so dense that, although its efficiency is increased, the passage of water through it, at a reasonable rate, becomes difficult. When this stage is reached a thin layer of sand is scraped off the filter surface and the process begun again, water being run to waste for about five days until the film has begun to form again. This necessitates there being at least two filters, but there are generally more.

The bed of sand should be at least 2 ft thick at first; this is gradually reduced by scraping, but is never allowed to get less than 1 ft in thickness. It is then restored to its original depth by the addition of more sand. The sand rests on two or three layers of gravel, graded in size, the largest at the bottom, the combined thickness of these layers being about 15 in. On the floor a network of drains is formed to receive the filtered water and conduct it away. They can be of open-jointed pipes, or of special stooled tiles. Correctly designed under-drainage is a most important factor in ensuring equal use of all parts of the filter. From the under-drains the water flows through a control valve and rises in an outlet well from which it passes over a weir to a pure water tank or channel.

Water should not be allowed to flow through a filter bed at a greater velocity than about 4 in. per hour, at which rate the filter will deal with 2 gallons per sq. ft per hour. This rate is secured by means of the control valve, referred to above, adjustment of which will alter the level of water in the outlet well and therefore will alter the "head" on the filter. Increase of head necessary to attain the desired rate of flow through increasing resistance at the surface of the sand indicates the need to scrape the surface.

Slow sand filters are not suitable for treating water heavily charged with suspended matter, as is the case with many rivers and streams, because of the expense and inconvenience of the frequent scraping and sand-washing that would be required. In such cases a preliminary settlement tank, and/or a series of "roughing" filters are placed before the slow filters.

Roughing filters usually take the form of rapid gravity filters described below.

Rapid gravity filters. Sometimes used as an alternative to slow sand filters when chemical precipitation and sedimentation are generally necessary.

These occupy far less space than slow sand filters and whereas the rate of flow through the latter does not usually exceed 4 in. per hour, or 2 gallons per sq. ft of surface per hour, in the "rapid" type the rate may be from 10 ft up to 16½ ft per hour, or 60 to 100 gallons per sq. ft per hour, according to the condition of the water to be treated.

The nature of the chemical treatment necessary will depend entirely upon the amount of bicarbonates present in the raw water. If entirely absent, chalk, hydrated lime or soda ash is added, after sulphate of alumina in solution has been introduced. This, combining with the carbonates, forms a cloudy precipitate or "floc". The success or otherwise of the process depends largely upon the nature and quantity of this "floc". In most instances far too much "floc" results, but this is all to the good of the process and the excess must be allowed to precipitate in a suitably designed sedimentation tank, through which the water travels slowly, usually in the space of two to four hours according to circumstances. Water reaches the filter, carrying sufficient "floc" to quickly fill up the spaces between the sand grains with this jelly-like material.

It has been stated above that in the "slow" process all mineral and vegetable solids in suspension, as well as bacteria, are caught in the surface film of the filter. This is not the case in the rapid type, where the efficiency in interception of bacteria is uncertain owing to the high velocity of the flow. As a consequence of the increased burden placed on the comparatively small area of filter, very frequent cleaning becomes necessary; generally speaking this will be once in every 24 hours. Need for cleaning is indicated by gauges showing the rate of filtration (which will drop as use of the filter proceeds), or by the difference of head on the filter at the inlet and outlet. When this amounts to 6 to 6½ ft it is time to wash the filter.

The washing of a rapid filter is done by reversal of the flow of water, accompanied by an agitation of the clogged filter by means of rakes or compressed air.

Bacteriological investigation is made in each case but normally the filter must be run to waste for 15 minutes on restarting after cleansing.

From the above it will be realised how the nature of the "floc" will affect the rate of efficient filtration, the frequency of washing, and the length of the period of running the early filtrate to waste.

"Rapid" filters are not as efficient as the "slow sand" process and require more constant supervision and investigation. With a raw water containing any large number of pathogenic organisms, they are not relied upon except with the subsequent use of a sterilising agent such as chlorine. This can be made an absolute safeguard to any supply, and is used in nearly all large municipal works (see later in this chapter).

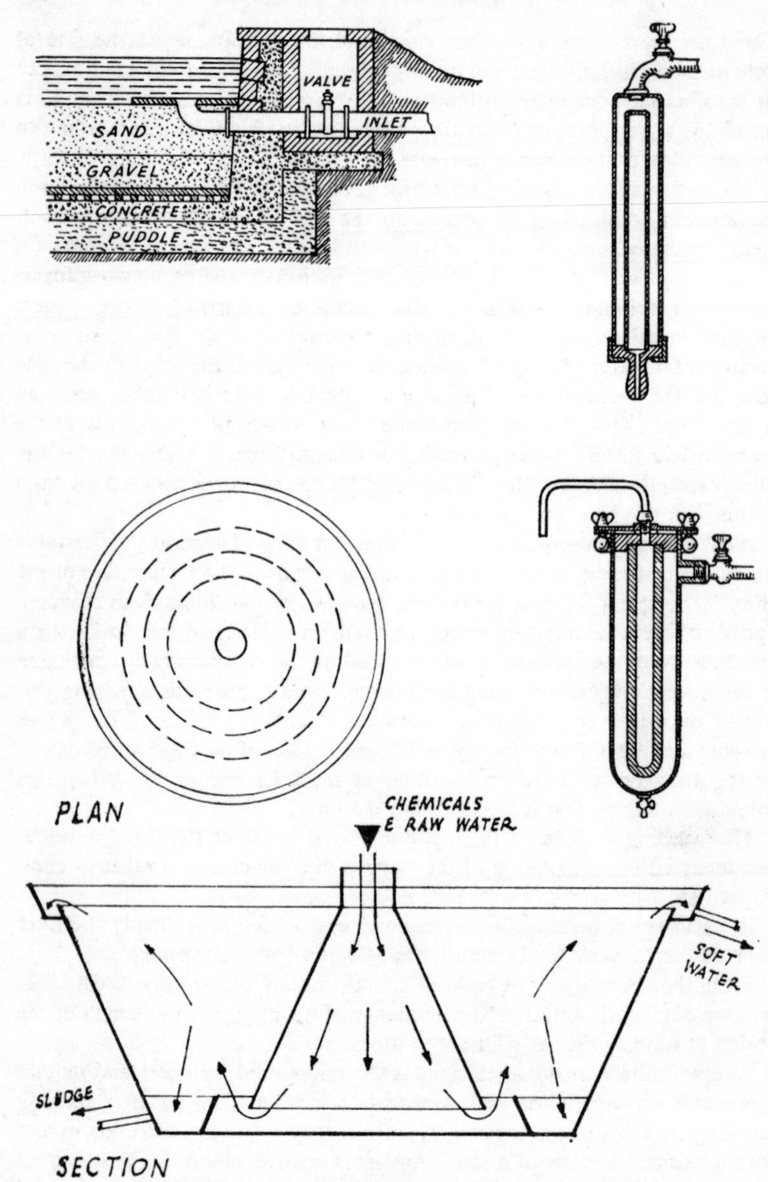
VALVE
INLET
SAND
GRAVEL
CONCRETE
PUDDLE
PLAN
CHEMICALS
E RAW WATER
SOFT WATER
SLUDGE
SECTION

35

At the Thames-side works of the Metropolitan Water Board, rapid gravity filters are being used without coagulants, merely as preparatory or roughing filters, and the result is that the water can afterwards be passed through slow sand filters at a greatly increased speed, with comparative safety; but even this double process of filtration is not permissible for Thames water without subsequent chlorination. It is particularly useful during those seasons when the raw water is heavily infested with "algae" (minute vegetable growths), under which condition the slow sand beds soon become quite unusable without the preliminary roughing filters.

Pressure filters. A "pressure" filter (often termed a "mechanical filter") consists of a cylindrical steel tank, at the bottom of which is a false perforated

---

35 *Water Treatment*

(*Above, left*) Part section through A SLOW SAND FILTER. Slow sand filtration, efficiently carried out, will remove all suspended matters, oxidise practically all the organic impurities and remove as large a proportion as 96 to 99 per cent of the bacteria. The diagram shows a section through the inlet end of a typical form of sand filter, the inlet taking the shape of a bell-mouthed bend, surrounded by a stone slab to prevent disturbance of the sand around it. Below the gravel is a layer of hollow perforated tiles, the floor falling to a sunk main drain in the middle. Such a drain would lead to a small chamber at one end, containing means of regulating the depths of water on the filter, according to the condition of the film on the surface of the filter, usually by raising a weir form of outlet. Leading up the walls, around the filter, from the hollow floor to a height of about a foot above the ground, is a series of ventilating pipes.

(*Above, right*) A PASTEUR-CHAMBERLAND FILTER. The metal case screws on to the tap, water reaching the glazed outlet nozzle by passing through the "candle" walls. The candle is removed for cleaning by unscrewing the collar immediately above it.

(*Centre, right*) A BERKEFELD FILTER. Similar in action but with the filtered water outlet and "candle" access at the top. The candle material is not so fine as in the Pasteur filter, being of baked fossil earth instead of earthenware, so that although quicker in action the Berkefeld filter is less efficient than the Pasteur filter.

(*Centre, left and below*) A plan and diagrammatic section of an automatic soda-line softening installation. This consists basically of a large conical tank with an inverted conical central compartment. Water and chemicals, introduced at the top of the central compartment, are mixed by mechanically operated "paddles" and flow downwards through this compartment and then upwards towards the outer collecting rim of the main tank as shown. The shaping of the tank ensures that the speed of movement of water flowing through it decreases progressively so that it becomes unable to carry the precipitates formed along with it. These fall out and sink to collect in the sludge channel at the base of the main tank. The head of water above the sludge in this channel enables it to be simply drawn off periodically by opening "sludge valves".

floor supporting the 3 or 4 ft of filtering material. In this floor are a large number of nozzles which serve the double purpose of collecting the filtered water, when the filter is in action, and of equally distributing the wash water when flow is reversed for cleansing. If compressed air is used to disturb the sand the same nozzles are available. In some types of filters compressed air is used at the same time as water, in others the operations succeed each other, pressures being so arranged that the sand is not washed out of the filter by an excessive flow of water or air. (The flow of the wash water must also be controlled for the same reason if disturbance is made by means of rotating rakes.)

Sand filtration methods can, of course, be applied on any scale, but a number of so-called domestic filters are available which filter water as it is drawn from the taps.[1] These are available for high or low pressure operation.

Candle filters. Candle filters take various forms, but the principle in all is the same. A metal case contains a hollow candle-shaped filter of fine unglazed earthenware. The water filters through from the outside to the inside of the candle, depositing a scum on the outside of it, which is readily removed by taking the candle out of the case and cleaning it. (Fig. 35 shows a section through the Pasteur-Chamberland form. A metal case contains the "candle" and is screwed on to the tap. At the bottom is a glazed nozzle outlet. By unscrewing the collar just above this, the candle is at once freed for cleaning purposes. Fig. 35 also shows the Berkefeld filter, which is of rather different construction. It has a thicker candle formed of baked fossil earth and filters more rapidly, but its efficiency is less. The water in this case is drawn from the top of the filter through the small pipe shown. The candle is removed by unscrewing the two wing nuts at the top. The small tap at the bottom is for the purpose of scouring out. The Berkefeld filter should be cleansed daily.) These filters all pass the water very slowly and are therefore often provided of larger size and in cases of batteries containing two or more candles. In the same way, several candles can be put into a filter of jar form for low-pressure filtration.

It is hardly necessary to point out that domestic filters of these types, needing, as they do, frequent cleansing, are mere makeshifts and not to be compared in efficiency with the scientifically managed purification works of a water authority. They may on occasion be the only appliances available.

It has already been pointed out that the number of bacteria present in a raw water is considerably reduced by sedimentation, and further reduced to

[1] Jar type filters filled with such materials as charcoal, manganous carbon, etc., are generally considered obsolete, being ineffective in removing bacteria.

quite a minute quantity by efficient filtration. With most water supplies these processes will be sufficient to render the water safe. Where, however, the raw water is highly polluted, even the removal of 99 per cent of the bacteria will not make it quite safe, especially as the bacteria which are still present will multiply rapidly in a short period. To make such waters safe the bacteria must be exterminated and this can only be done by sterilisation.

STERILISATION[1]

The science of sterilisation of water has made such progress in recent years that it has enabled authorities to take back into use old sources of supply which had been discarded owing to their polluted state. Many authorities, too, are able to use local river water and so avoid the expense of bringing water from great distances.

Ozone gas has been proved to be an effective sterilising agent, but the process has hitherto been too expensive for general use. It is becoming less expensive and it is quite possible that before many years are past the method will be in general use.

The use of "ultra-violet" light is also expensive, although effective, and needs clear water for its application. The two principal methods in use to-day are "chlorination" and the "excess lime" treatment; of these the former is in more general use.

Chlorination. Chlorine may be added to the water in a number of ways: As a solid, in the form of calcium hypochlorite ("bleaching powder"), this being dissolved in a small body of water before being added to the main supply. (The method, used for some years by the Metropolitan Water Board, was introduced to the armed forces in the first World War where its use saved many thousands of cases of sickness. It was retained to a large extent in the second World War because it provided the simplest and safest method of transporting chlorine, but the bulky plant required for obtaining large quantities of chlorine solution has rendered it obsolete for public water authorities.) As a liquid, sodium hypochlorite, in which form it may be convenient for small installations or in emergencies. As a gas, delivered under pressure in steel cylinders, this being the method in almost universal use to-day.

The chief difficulties met with in any chlorination process are that chlorine in the presence of moisture, or any strong solution of chlorine, corrodes metals and that the amount to be added to the water has to be adjusted with precision: if too much is added the taste will be unpleasant; if insufficient, sterilisation will not be complete, and the margin between these two extremes

[1] See footnote on page 121.

is narrow. Gas is put into solution in machines called chloronomes in which gas is introduced into a hemispherical glass dome and absorbed by water in the bottom of the dome. The rate at which chlorine is added and the level of water are carefully controlled. The chlorine solution is drawn off by a venturi tube which regulates the dose added according to the rate of water flow.

Chlorine in a free state, if added to a water still containing organic impurities, will first of all oxidise these, and chlorine so used will not be available for destroying bacteria. It is therefore necessary to add a little more than is required for such oxidation. Chlorination consequently almost invariably is done after filtration and not before it, so that the amount added shall be as small as possible. (The only circumstances in which it may be desirable to chlorinate before filtration is where it is necessary to destroy algae (minute vegetable growths), which would block the filters in a very short time.)

The explanation of the effectiveness of the process is that chlorine combines with hydrogen in the water and releases oxygen, "nascent oxygen", i.e. oxygen newly formed by a chemical process—a far more active agent than ordinary oxygen. The dose usually required for a filtered water is about ¼ to ½ part per million parts of water.

It is found with some waters that an effective dose of chlorine must be so large that the resulting taste of water will be most objectionable, especially when the water is boiled. Fortunately, objectionable taste can be prevented by ensuring that the water contains an excess of free ammonia, which may be done by the addition of a solution of ammonium sulphate, prior to the introduction of the chlorine. The substance thus formed, known as "chloramine", is a germicide. It was thought when it was introduced that the method would provide a solution to all the previous problems. It has however a number of disadvantages chief of which is the time taken for complete treatment (4–10 hours) and generally super chlorination (or over chlorination) followed by dechlorination is now followed by most water authorities.

Excess lime method. The "excess lime" method is usually rather more expensive than chlorination. Lime is also sometimes used to soften waters containing bicarbonates, and also to neutralise the acidity of waters containing acids (see later). If more lime is added than is required for either of these purposes it will be available for the destruction of bacteria. After sufficient time has been given for sterilisation, the excess lime is precipitated by blowing carbon dioxide through the water in a "carbonating chamber". The resulting carbonate of lime is removed, dried and heated, to drive off the carbon dioxide, so that the lime is recovered for re-use.

Removal of colour. Finely powdered "activated carbon" is now being largely used for the elimination of colour and taste from water that cannot otherwise be freed of them. This is the only method of getting rid of the very offensive taste which results from the decomposition of algae. It is not a costly process, but the carbon must afterwards be removed by filtration and this adds to the complication of the treatment works. It is now most effectively used at the Southend Water Works, where objectionable taste would otherwise result from the use of the river water.

Hardness in water. It was stated early in this chapter that the so-called "hardness" of many waters is due to inorganic matter in solution. Water is said to be hard if a curdy precipitate is produced when in contact with soap, instead of readily formed lather. Hardness of water is measured by its soap-destroying capacity.

Hardness is chiefly due to the presence of bicarbonates and sulphates of calcium and magnesium but also, sometimes, to their nitrates, nitrites and chlorides. It may be of a temporary or permanent form, temporary hardness being due to bicarbonates and permanent hardness chiefly to sulphates. Temporary hardness is so called because it can be removed by boiling. This converts the bicarbonates of calcium to carbonates, which are insoluble in water, and which are precipitated.[1] Hardness of this kind leads to the furring up of boilers and hot-water pipes and waste in laundry work.

Both hard and soft waters, however, have their uses. Thus, a very hard water is needed by the brewer for making pale ale, while for the darker beers a soft water is desirable. Soft water is also desirable for cooking purposes, a hard water making vegetables and meat, if cooked in it, harder and less palatable.

Generally speaking, surface waters are soft and subterranean waters hard, depending on the nature of the strata with which the water has come in contact. From calcareous strata hard waters result and from igneous strata soft ones.

Measurement of hardness. Hardness is measured in degrees, and a sample is said to have 1° of hardness on Clark's Scale when its soap-destroying power is equal to the effect of 1 grain of carbonate of lime in a gallon of water. Each degree of hardness in 1 gallon of water wastes from 8 to 9 grains of soap. A water having not more than 5° of hardness is classed as a soft water and one containing anything above 15° as a hard water.[2]

Softening hard water. In order to understand the various methods of

[1]The chemical formula for the reaction is:

$$Ca\,(HCO_3)_2 + \text{Heat} = Ca\,CO_3 + H_2O + CO_2$$

[2] Some of the Glasgow water supply has as little as 0·8° of hardness. The supply in Manchester has 2° hardness and the supplies in Halifax and Derby 5° and 3° respectively. London supplies range from 16–20° whilst in the Peterborough area hardness may be as high as 37°.

softening hard waters it is necessary to know that there are two "carbonates" of lime and magnesium. One is the true carbonate, of which hard limestones are a fairly pure example and chalk is a more impure form. This carbonate is practically insoluble in pure water. The other is the bicarbonate, which can be regarded as a combination of the carbonate with carbon dioxide. This bicarbonate is soluble in water.

Boiling a water which contains bicarbonate in solution results in the carbon dioxide becoming separated and driven off. Carbonate remains and this, being insoluble, is precipitated to form a "fur" on the containing vessel. This fur is very harmful in boilers and hot-water pipes, since it is a bad conductor of heat and progressively reduces the bore of pipes. This is one of the chief reasons for adopting some method of reducing hardness in a town supply, or in that part of it which is used for steam-raising.

Strange though it may seem, a usual method of reducing temporary hardness in water on a large scale is to add lime, or rather a solution of lime in water. When a solution of lime is added to water containing bicarbonates these combine to produce the full carbonate[1] which, being insoluble, is precipitated. This must be given time to settle, in tanks from which it can be periodically removed, to prevent it from being deposited in the water mains.

SODA ASH PROCESS. An effective softening treatment for a water which is "permanently" hard, i.e. which contains sulphates, is by the addition of sodium carbonate ("soda ash"). The result is that the calcium (or magnesium) sulphate and sodium carbonate become changed to calcium (or magnesium) carbonate and sodium sulphate.[2] The carbonates, being insoluble, are precipitated and removed; the sodium sulphate remains in solution, but is not detrimental if present in only reasonable quantities. The method of treatment is the same, whether it is desired to remove temporary and permanent hardness, or temporary hardness only.

Older installations involve separate settling tanks and sometimes filtration to remove the precipitated carbonates but latest installations are single process and automatic in action (35).

BASE EXCHANGE PROCESS. The above method of softening is generally most suited to use on a large scale, as on a town's supply. For use on a small scale it has disadvantages, notably the need to dispose periodically of the carbonate sludge. For domestic use the "Base Exchange" method is more often adopted. It removes both temporary and permanent hardness,

[1] The chemical formula for the reaction is:

$$Ca\,(HCO_3)_2 + Ca(OH)_2 = 2\,Ca\,CO_3 + 2H_2O$$

[2] The chemical formula for the reaction is:

$$Ca\,SO_4 + 2\,Na\,HCO_3 = Ca\,CO_3 + Na_2SO_4 + H_2O + CO_2$$

and can be adapted to both domestic and town supplies. In this process the water is passed through a bed of natural or synthetic sodium silicate (Zeolite). The bicarbonates and sulphates of lime and magnesium in the water are converted to bicarbonates and sulphates of sodium, which remain in solution but are not usually detrimental; the silicate of sodium becomes silicates of lime and of magnesium and these, being insoluble, remain in the filter. When a considerable part of the silicate has been changed in this manner the water is shut off from the bed and a solution of sodium chloride (common salt) is passed slowly through it; a chemical reaction[1] takes place by which the silicate returns to its original form of sodium silicate, whilst chlorides of lime and magnesium pass off in solution to waste. The bed of silicate is then ready for action once more.

N.B.—The base-exchange method is not suitable for a water containing iron, which causes deterioration of the silicate, and it is not suitable for a water containing suspended solids, unless these are first removed by filtration.

Soft and acid waters. It is seldom that natural waters are perfectly neutral in character, being nearly always either slightly acid or slightly alkaline. The student of chemistry, who has been taught to distinguish between acids and alkalis by the action of a sample on litmus paper or litmus solution, would not find this method of much use in examining natural waters. There are, however, a number of other "indicators" of a character similar to litmus, but more sensitive, by means of which a very accurate observation as to the condition of a water may be made. One may purchase a very useful "Universal" indicator solution which, added to a sample of the water, produces a distinct colour reaction, indicating the approximate degree of acidity or alkalinity of the sample within a fairly wide range on either side of the neutral. For a degree of accuracy needed in the control of chemical treatment of a public supply, other indicators are used and the resultant colours are compared with those of standard colour solutions, the most useful of these indicators being brom-thymol-blue, cresol-red and methyl-red. The result of such tests is expressed by the hydrogen-ion concentration in the water, also known as the *p*H value. To explain the meaning of this would involve an explanation of some of the principles of electro-chemistry. It will be sufficient to say here that neutral water has a *p*H value of 7, that water with a *p*H value greater than 7 is alkaline and that water with a value less than 7 is acid. The importance of this lies in the fact that acid water is

[1] Also called ion exchange. The formulae for the softening reaction may be written:

Calcium Sulphate + Sodium Zeolite = Sodium Sulphate + Calcium Zeolite

and the regeneration formula:

Calcium Zeolite + Sodium Chloride = Sodium Zeolite + Calcium Chloride.

liable to attack lead pipes and cisterns lined with lead, with the result that lead poisoning may result to consumers, and that acid waters lead to galvanic action when certain metals are in contact with each other in their presence. The most important instance of this in plumbing installations is when zinc (galvanised) items are placed in contact with non-ferrous items leading to greatly accelerated corrosion of the zinc (see also p. 413). Hard waters are generally alkaline, so that with them there is seldom any danger of "plumbo-solvency", as it is termed, although it is known that water which is hard because of sulphates, but contains little or no carbonate, may also be plumbo-solvent if it contains nitrates also.

The soft waters which come from moorlands are often acid and, when they are, there is a real danger of lead poisoning unless steps are taken to neutralise the acid. It is often erroneously stated that soft waters are plumbo-solvent; this is not necessarily the case, for a soft water may be quite neutral, i.e. neither acid nor alkaline; it is only when it is acid that danger arises.

In copper tubes non-acid water forms an oxidised film which prevents any harmful action. With acid water this protective coating is not formed, and a green tinge is acquired by the water. Although not harmful to health, this does lead to unsightly staining of sanitary fittings.

If a water is acid the usual remedy is to treat it with lime or carbonate of lime. The acids present are usually the result of bacterial action upon vegetation (including algae), and the chief one due to the presence of carbon dioxide is carbonic acid. This will combine with the lime, or the carbonate of lime, to form bicarbonate of lime, which remains in solution and, if sufficient be added, the water is now feebly alkaline and a little harder than it was, though it would still be classed as a soft water.

It may seem peculiar that lime should be used for two almost opposite purposes: to soften a hard water, which incidentally reduces its alkalinity, and to neutralise the acidity of an acid water, which incidentally hardens it. Any difficulty in understanding this will however disappear when it is realised that the only reason why it softens, and reduces the alkalinity of, a hard water is that carbonate is precipitated and then physically removed; if it were not removed the hardness and alkalinity would be even greater than before.

Iron salts in solution. It sometimes happens that water is discoloured by the presence of iron in solution. Much of this can be precipitated if the water is well aerated; this can be effected by exposing it to the air in open channels or, better still, by allowing it to fall in cascades down a series of steps, discharging it as a fountain into an open reservoir, or by any similar means. In extreme cases more drastic treatment may be required, such as by lime and compressed air.

Public distribution of water. There are many ways in which the elements of public water distribution are arranged. Much will depend on ground levels between source and distribution area in deciding the relationship between elements (36), which are considered in more detail below.

Impounding reservoirs. Impounding reservoirs are generally partly natural and partly artificial. The site must be such that a dam of comparatively short length will form a reservoir of large capacity. There must be an impervious bed under the whole site at a reasonable depth to ensure water tightness, and any cracks or fissures near the site of the dam must be sealed—usually they are filled by pumping cement grout under pressure into bore-holes. The slope of the bed must be fairly uniform and there should be few parts of shallow depth, as this encourages vegetation. Dams are built of masonry, concrete or reinforced concrete, or a mixture of concrete and masonry, in which the body of the dam is formed of very large rough blocks of stone embedded in concrete and the whole faced with prepared blocks of stone or pre-cast concrete blocks. Alternatively a dam may be an earthwork dam faced with stone setts and with a thick wall of clay puddle in the middle. The earth is usually sloped at about 3 to 1 on the side which will be submerged and about 2½ to 1 on the other side. In any case the foundations of the dam are carried well down into the impervious stratum.[1]

In all such schemes provision is made for overflow of flood waters; if the dam is of earth and puddle the overflow must be on solid ground around one end of the dam, but if the dam is of concrete or masonry the water may be allowed to overflow the dam itself. Occasionally a flood-water channel is constructed, so that turbid water after heavy rain may by-pass the reservoir instead of flowing through it. All timber should be removed and all vegetation should be burnt before the reservoir is filled, and there should be no houses left on the catchment area above the water level.

Capacity of impounding reservoirs. The capacity required for impounding reservoirs is usually determined by Hawksley's formula, $D = 1000/\sqrt{F}$; in which D is the number of days' supply to be stored, and F is $\frac{5}{6}$ of the average annual rainfall in inches. A normal capacity is about 180 days' supply.

Compensation reservoirs may be of the form just described, or entirely

[1] The Howden dam, in the Derwent Valley scheme, is 1080 ft long and of masonry, has a height of 117 ft, and is carried down below the ground to a depth of 125 ft, the bottom 55 ft taking the form of a watertight curtain wall about 6 ft thick. The greatest thickness of the dam is 176 ft and its entire weight is about half a million tons. It was afterwards found that the hill-sides up the reservoir were not absolutely watertight, and "wing" walls were constructed up each side of the valley for a distance of 3000 ft. In similar works executed to-day an attempt would be made to secure watertightness by pumping cement grout into boreholes in the fissured rock, a method of procedure which is far cheaper than that of constructing long wing walls.

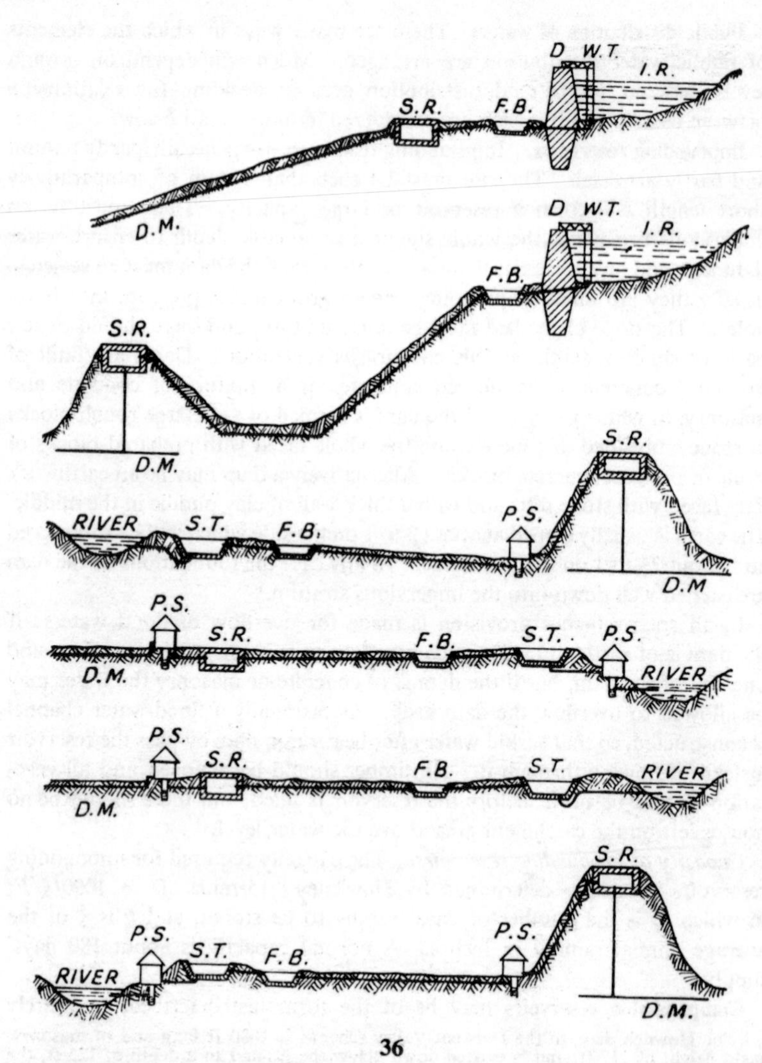

36 *Public Distribution of Water*

Arrangements are governed by ground levels between source of supply and point of distribution, i.e. may be either gravitation or pumping systems. The examples show some of the many cases that occur in practice and give an idea of the relative positions of the units forming such schemes.

artificial, having walls and floor of concrete, backed by clay puddle. Their capacity should be about one-fourth to one-third of that of the storage reservoirs.

Settling reservoirs are usually entirely artificial. The object of them is to provide for the settlement of the suspended matters at the least possible expense. In a perfect system four should be used, one filling, one settling, one discharging on to the filters, and one held in reserve. They are usually cleaned out about twice a year.

Humber's rule for the area of settling tanks is:

$$\text{Area in sq. ft} = \frac{\text{Demand in cu. ft per day}}{\text{Velocity of deposit in ft per day}},$$

the area being quite independent of the depth. This is usually from 10 to 15 ft, a lesser depth encouraging the growth of vegetation. Settling tanks

---

(*Above*) Diagrammatic sections through gravitation schemes. Thus in the uppermost diagram waters passing through a valley are held up by a dam, D., in an impounding reservoir, I.R., the outlet of which is controlled by a valve at the foot of a valve tower, W.T. It passes on to filter beds, F.B., and then into a service reservoir, S.R., from which the distributing mains, D.M., pass to supply the town. A somewhat similar arrangement is shown below, but the levels permit an elevated service reservoir nearer to the town, which is a better arrangement.

In the third section the supply is drawn from a river, and passes first into a settling or sedimentation reservoir, then to filter beds and a pumping station, P.S. From there it is pumped up to an elevated service reservoir, the height of which gives the necessary pressure in the distributing mains (a pressure ideally great enough to ensure the water being thrown over the tops of the houses in case of fire).

In the fourth section the levels are such that the water has to be pumped up into the settling reservoir, from which it flows by gravitation to the filter beds and on to the service reservoir, the pressure in the distributing mains is shown provided by a second pumping station. The fifth section is a similar case, but the levels permit water to reach the settling reservoir by gravitation.

The lowest section shows a somewhat similar case, but the filters discharge into a main, leading to pumps which raise the water to an elevated service reservoir, from which the distributing mains are run.

If the supply is from a well or borehole the general principles of pumped supplies apply but no sedimentation reservoirs are needed.

If a high site is available near the town the water is pumped direct from the well to the service reservoir, passing through pressure filters en route; and thence to town by gravity. If no such site is available the water will still be pumped to the service reservoir through pressure filters and pumped from there into the mains or into elevated tanks.

are not always worked on the intermittent principle described above. They are sometimes continuous in action, the water always flowing through them at a slow rate. In this case they should be long and narrow in order to ensure a uniform flow as opposed to a current through the middle.

Service reservoirs must be covered to exclude dust and light, but they must be ventilated. They may be formed entirely below ground, entirely above, or partly above and partly below ground. The daily demand for water varies, and the object of these reservoirs is to keep a reserve near at hand on a compensating basis. A usual capacity is half a day's supply if the source of supply is quite near, but if the water is to be brought from a distance, the capacity is greater, to act as a store, in case of accidents to the mains conveying the supply. It should be noted, however, that water which has been treated and improved in quality may deteriorate rapidly in service reservoirs, so that storage should not exceed 2 or 3 days' supply. Reservoirs may be of concrete, or reinforced concrete, now widely used, or even large iron or steel tanks elevated on a tower of stone, brick or steel to sufficient height to give the required pressure in the mains. They are placed as near the point of delivery as possible. Probably the largest service reservoirs in the world are those of the Metropolitan Water Board at Honor Oak, having a capacity of about 60 million gallons.

Distribution. Water is conveyed from its source to the point of distribution in a number of ways: by means of open channels, covered channels and tunnels, cast-iron, steel and reinforced concrete pipes.

Open channels. Open channels, which may be formed in concrete, brick or masonry, can only be used where the ground allows suitable slopes. (It is obvious that such channels cannot follow the undulations of the land and go up and down hills.) The objections to them are that water is deteriorated by exposure and wasted by evaporation, gets heated in summer whilst in winter expense is incurred in keeping the channel open during frost. The "New River", one of the conduits supplying London, is a well-known example of an open channel.

Covered channels. Covered channels are of somewhat similar construction to those just described, but roofed over. They may be either circular in section or with vertical sides and an arched top and base. Like the open channel, they fall continuously, i.e. cannot go up and down hills. In some cases, as in the Loch Katrine supply to Glasgow, the covered channel takes the form of a tunnel through rock. Covered channels should be adequately ventilated and have manholes at intervals for convenience of access. They overcome the objections given above for open channels, but still have the disadvantage that they cannot follow the undulations of the ground.

Pipe water mains. The advantage of using pipes is that the water can be conveyed at varying levels—up hill and down dale—within reasonable limits, so that pipes can be laid in a direct line, with a covering of 2½ to 3 ft of earth only. With rises and falls there will be accumulations of air at the "summits" and means for its escape must be provided to prevent air-locks and retarded flow, with a danger of bursting the pipes. Considerable rises in the pipe line are avoided. The imaginary line drawn from the level of the water in the reservoir to the point of discharge of the pipe is termed the hydraulic gradient, and pipes are usually not allowed to rise more than 25 ft above this line. When conditions allow they are kept wholly below this line.

Cast-iron pipes. Cast-iron pipes are cast vertically in sand moulds with the sockets downwards or "spun" by a method introduced in recent years, in which molten iron is introduced into a water-cooled steel mould, which is kept in rapid rotation so that the iron is forced against the mould walls by centrifugal force and solidifies there. These pipes are denser, so that they can be made thinner without loss of strength, whilst the interior is smoother and probably less liable to corrosion. "Spun" pipes are now largely used for the smaller sizes of main, but for large mains vertically cast pipes are still required. British Standard Specifications cover iron pipes—B.S. No. 78 for vertically cast and B.S. No. 1211 for those of spun iron.

Jointing water mains. Cast-iron pipes almost always have socket joints, though it is often convenient to use a flanged joint when a valve is to be inserted, to permit removal for repairs if needed. All such pipes need to be protected against corrosion by the Angus Smith[1] or other process, since not only does the rusting of the pipe reduce its strength, but it also makes the inside of the pipe rough and retards the flow, by increasing friction.

Cast-iron pipes are usually jointed with caulked lead, i.e. molten lead poured into the socket and consolidated by means of a caulking tool. In recent years a material called lead wool has been introduced as a substitute for molten lead. It consists of skeins of fine strands of lead and can be readily used for work under water or other positions in which molten lead would be difficult to use.

Flexible joints. There are now on the market a variety of flexible joints which are coming into general use. Their chief advantages are flexibility, rapidity of laying, and the fact that large excavations for joint-holes are unnecessary. These advantages are claimed to fully compensate for the extra cost of the joint. In addition their flexibility enables pipes to be laid to curved routes without special bends and reduces the danger of fracture in bad ground or from traffic vibration.

[1] Dipping pipes into hot bituminous liquid.

One of several satisfactory joints is the Stanton mechanical lead joint. A lead ring, in which a steel spring has been cast to distribute the pressure on the lead evenly, is placed over the spigot of one pipe, which is then pushed into the tapered socket of the next. Two half collars, fitted with two set screws each, are then tightened to compress the lead ring and make the joint watertight.

In the Stavely flexible joint the joint ring is of rubber, faced with lead, and this is pressed against a shoulder in the socket by a cast-iron ring, when the latter is tightened by bolts or wedges.

The Baxter pre-cast lead joint has lead rings cast in the inside of the sockets and the spigots are slightly tapered. When the spigot is forced home the lead is compressed and is finally caulked with tools.

The jointing material in the Stanton Cornelius joint is merely a rubber ring, placed initially on the end of the spigot by rolling it up a wooden cone fitted to it temporarily. When the spigot is pushed into a socket the rubber ring rolls relatively to both, so that it takes up its final position halfway down the socket, where there is a slight recess to receive it. This joint is very cheap and therefore suitable for rural supplies, where economy is of great importance. It cannot be expected to be as durable as the more expensive joints previously described, but a good quality rubber has a longer life than might be expected.

Steel water pipes. Steel pipes possess many advantages over cast iron. They are much thinner, so that their weight, for the same strength, is from one-third to one-fourth that of cast-iron pipes. They are obtainable in much greater lengths, so that the number of joints to be made is about halved. Their cost is less. They are especially suitable for use in ground liable to subsidence, on account of the greater elasticity of the metal.

Their chief disadvantage is that steel is more liable to corrode than is cast iron. As a protection they are treated by the Angus Smith method and are wrapped on the outside with hessian cloth, impregnated with bitumen, or covered on the outside with asphalt. These pipes have socket and spigot joints, which are filled in the same manner as those of cast iron. The British Standard Specification for steel pipes is B.S.S. 534.

"Lined" pipes. A comparatively recent development is the introduction of "linings" of concrete or asphalt on the interior of both cast-iron and steel pipes, the lining being "spun" in by centrifugal action. Such means of protection are very efficient in preventing corrosion, but are somewhat costly.

Reinforced concrete pipes are rarely used for water mains. The introduction of "spun" reinforced concrete pipes, however, has made them suitable and economic and their use is undoubtedly increasing. The main obstacle to their use is the difficulty of forming satisfactory joints at a reasonable cost.

Asbestos cement pipes are particularly useful for water which has a corrosive action on iron. These are made to withstand the same pressure as cast-iron pipes, but should not be used where settlement or vibration are to be feared, because of their lack of longitudinal strength. They have little resistance to impact, e.g. to a blow from a pick, which may easily occur when they are laid in roadways near other pipes. They are cheaper than cast-iron pipes, especially if the latter would have to be lined to resist corrosion, and are widely used for semi-temporary and rural supplies.

Pipes have no sockets. An asbestos-cement collar is threaded over one of the pipes to be jointed and a rubber ring is placed on each pipe in such positions that when the collar is moved to cover the joint it will roll the rubber rings to their proper places. The ends of the collar are usually pointed in cement-mortar to protect the rubber, unless the maximum degree of flexibility is desired, in which case the pointing is omitted. British Standard Specification 486 covers these pipes.

Distributing mains. The distributing mains from the service reservoirs are laid along the streets, and should have not less than 2 ft 6 in. to 3 ft of covering over them to protect them from frost and from injury from traffic vibration. They are usually of cast iron with caulked-lead or flexible joints, and often with flanged joints where valves occur. The main from the reservoir splits into two or more as soon as possible, in order to diminish the area affected by accidents, and secondary mains are arranged as circuits from the principal mains so that each can if necessary be fed from either of its connections to the principal main. Dead ends to mains are avoided, owing to the possibility of stagnation; sharp bends and junctions are avoided also, owing to the loss of pressure they cause.

Pressure in pipes. Pipes are tested to double the working pressure they will have to sustain. This is done in a hydraulic machine, the pressure being shown by a gauge. A few lengths of pipe are put together for testing, so as to test the joints as well.

The pressure in the mains should if possible be sufficient to serve the highest buildings in the district. A good working pressure is 80 lb per sq. in., which is equal to a "head" of about 180 ft, or a column of water about 180 ft high. In practice any head between 80 and 200 ft is considered reasonable.

Valves on water mains. Sluice valves are placed on the mains at distances of 800 to 1000 yards and at the commencement of each branch main (37). Cast-iron valves are used even if the pipes are of steel or asbestos cement. Their form and dimensions are covered by B.S. No. 1218.

Hydrants. Hydrants are placed on all mains at intervals of about 200

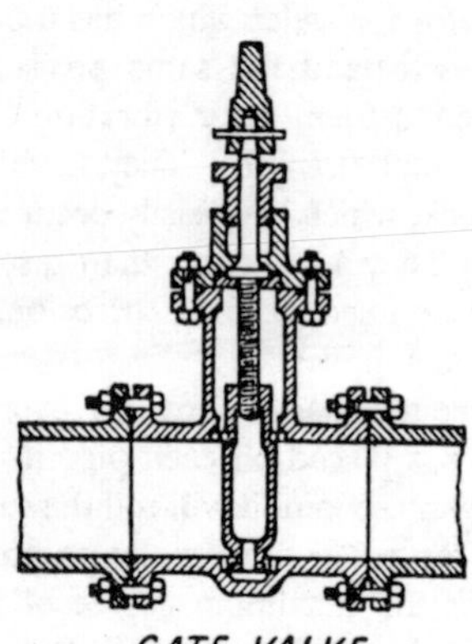

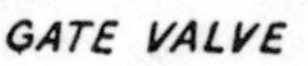
GATE VALVE

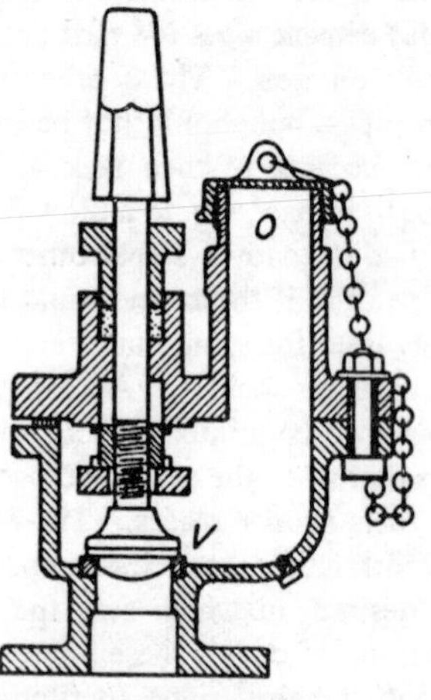
O
V
WATER HYDRANT

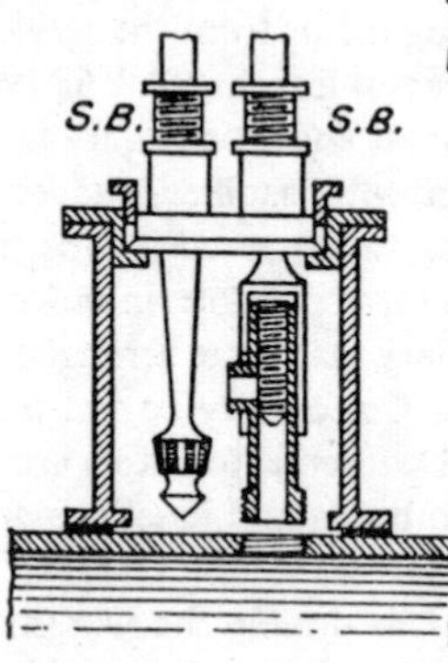
S.B.
S.B.
APPARATUS FOR DRILLING, TAPPING AND ADDING A BRANCH SERVICE TO MAIN UNDER PRESSURE

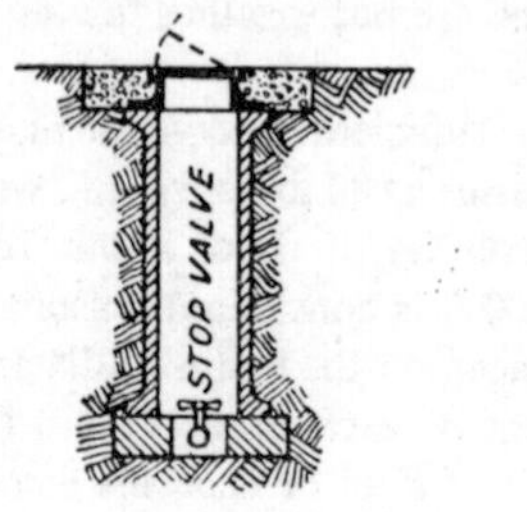
STOP VALVE

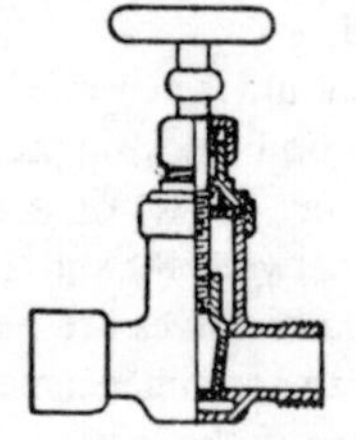

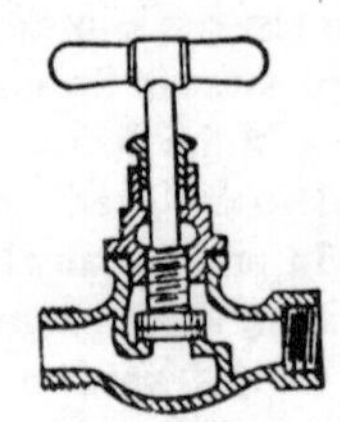

37

yards, for the purpose of fire extinguishing, filling water-carts and for emergency supplies during severe frost, enemy action and the like. A typical example is shown in Fig. 37.

Hydrants are placed in chambers below street level, access being obtained through iron covers.

Formerly "ball" hydrants were much used, in which a gutta-percha or

---

37 *Water Mains Fittings*

(*Top, left*) A SLUICE OR GATE VALVE. The body is of cast iron and valves are also made with spigot and socket joints. The contact parts of the valve are usually of gun-metal and the spindle is usually of bronze. The latter is turned by means of a key fitted on to its square top to raise or lower the "sluice".

(*Top, right*) A HYDRANT. In the example shown, the flange at the base is bolted to a short vertical branch from the main, water flow being controlled by the screw-down valve *V*. The outlet *O* has a screw to receive a hose coupling fitted with a cap as shown to keep out dirt when not in use.

(*Centre*) MAINS TAPPING APPARATUS. This consists of a watertight box which is attached to the main by means of a chain or straps, a watertight joint being made with a rubber washer . It has a revolving horizontal cover carrying two "stuffing boxes", S.B., equidistant from the centre about which it revolves. Through one of these a combined drill and "tap" (or threader) is put, and through the other a connecting ferrule with a branch.

A hole is drilled and tapped, and the cover then revolved to bring the ferrule over the hole, into which it is screwed. The diagram shows the ferrule in this position. A screw-plug is fitted to the ferrule and this is kept screwed down so as to close the branch, as shown, until the house service is laid on. When this is done the plug can be unscrewed and left in the threaded extension at the top of the ferrule permanently.

In recent apparatus there is only one spindle instead of two. After this has been used to drill and tap the hole, it is withdrawn far enough for a valve to be closed underneath it. The cover can then be removed and the ferrule put on the spindle in place of the drill and tap. The cover is then fastened down, the valve opened and the ferrule screwed in.

(*Below*) STOP VALVES. A branch from the public mains to a building must be fitted with a stop valve to enable supply to the building to be discontinued. These are usually placed just outside the boundary of the building's site and they are made accessible by placing them in a small chamber with a frame and hinged cover, of cast iron, at ground level. The diagram at the left shows the arrangement of a chamber of this kind in which the chamber itself is a length of stoneware drain pipe.

The diagrams, *centre* and *right*, show a sluice valve and a screw-down valve respectively, the difference in their operation being clear.

Sluice valves have the advantage of full-bore flow when the valve is open. Screw-down valves are less costly and on small pipes more positive in action. They are more usually fitted on pipes less than 2 in. diam. Valves fitted outside buildings are always key operated, to limit unauthorised interference.

vulcanite ball was held up by the mains water pressure against a metal seating; by screwing on a stand pipe to the fitting, the ball was forced down and the water allowed to rise in the stand pipe. The chief drawbacks to this type are that leakage is easily caused by grit getting between the ball and the seating and that a drop in mains pressure may allow dirt to get into the main. They are no longer allowed by the Minister of Health, although many still exist.

Intermittent water supply. In some places it is the practice to turn on the water for only a limited time each day. This necessitates the installing of large storage tanks (perhaps 300 gallons or so for a household of 6 persons) to act as a reserve when the supply is off. This is called the intermittent system and is unsatisfactory from many points of view. It is now seldom adopted except for small supplies to isolated houses or small groups of houses where it is economic to pump only for a few hours daily.

The constant system. Apart from the cases referred to the constant system, in which the water is always turned on, is almost universal in this country. A cistern is necessary in each house to maintain a supply to sanitary fittings and the hot-water service, when the supply is cut off temporarily for repairs to mains, but this can be much smaller than where the supply is intermittent.

Tapping water mains. Connection of a building's pipework to the water mains is effected by tapping the main and screwing in a connecting fitting. There are appliances which enable this to be done without interruption of the general supply (37).

Water pressure or head. A few notes concerning the pressure exerted by water on the sides and floors of tanks and in pipes will not be out of place here. Water pressures are generally given in lb per sq. in. or in "head" (the height of water in a system of pipework above the point at which the pressure is exerted).

One cubic foot of water weighs, approximately, 62·5 lb., so that the weight or pressure on a level surface 12 in. below the water surface would be 62·5 lb for a sq. ft or $62{\cdot}5/144 = 0{\cdot}434$ lb/sq. in. This pressure, owing to the laws of hydraulics, is exerted upwards and sideways as well as downwards, and is quite independent of the inclination of the surface on which the pressure bears or of the total quantity of water concerned. Thus the pressure on the eardrums of a bather 12 in. below the surface of the water in a small bath would be the same as if he were 12 in. below the surface in mid-Atlantic.

Water brought from a tank in a loft or cistern room, via a ½-in. pipe to a ball-valve of a W.C. tank on the ground floor at (say) 20 ft lower level, will exert a pressure of "20 ft head" on the ball-valve washer, which is equivalent to 20 × 0·434 lb/sq. in., i.e. 8·68 lb., quite irrespective of the size of the service tank or the quantity of water it contains.

The following simple worked examples will clarify further this transfer of pressures by water:

1 Determine the pressure per sq. in. on (*a*) the floor of a reservoir when the depth of water is 20 ft, and (*b*) the wall of the reservoir at a point 8 ft below the surface of the water.

The fact that the walls may be vertical or sloping makes no difference to the answer.

(*a*) Pressure per sq. in. on floor of reservoir

$$= 20 \times 0{\cdot}434 = 8{\cdot}68 \text{ lb/sq. in.}$$

(*b*) Pressure on wall 8 ft below the surface

$$= 8 \times 0{\cdot}434 = 3{\cdot}472 \text{ lb/sq. in.}$$

2 A 24-in. water main communicates directly with a reservoir which discharges into it. The valve at the outlet of the main is shut, and the difference in level between the centre of the valve and the water surface in the reservoir is 190 ft. Find the pressure per square inch on the centre of the valve.

Pressure per sq. in.

$$= 190 \times 0{\cdot}434 = 82{\cdot}46 \text{ lb/sq. in.}$$

(If the valve were *open*, the pressure would not, of course, be the same, but if the pipe will stand the pressure when the valve is shut, it will certainly stand the lower pressure when it is open. The case of pressure in liquids in motion is beyond the scope of this book.)

6

The Building—its Internal Water Services

Service pipes. Pipes conveying water from the mains to a building and those parts of the internal pipework which may be subjected to mains pressure are termed SERVICE PIPES. Pipes of a variety of materials are used but control is exercised over choice by the supplying authority. In some areas, for example, galvanised steel is not permitted where pipes are in contact with the ground. In some areas lead pipes are not permitted because of the danger of lead poisoning which may be likely because of the acid character of that particular supply.

Lead pipes. Pipes of lead or of silver/copper/lead alloy[1] are ideal for service pipes in most areas and particularly in those where the water supplied is "hard". Pipes are readily formed by hand to requirements of pipe positioning and are available in long lengths so that jointing can be minimised.

Pipes are specified by internal diameter and weight per yard. Water authorities usually specify weights of pipes required for different situations on the basis set by B.S. 602 and 1085 which cover lead pipes and silver/copper/lead alloy pipes respectively (Table 12). (See Appendix 1 for physical properties of lead.)

JOINTING of lead pipes is effected by soldering. The traditional form of joint being the wiped solder joint (38) suitable for both joints in straight pipe and junctions between pipes and for connection of lead to other metals. Soldered spigot joints, which require more preparation and make use of fine solder, are suitable for joints in straight pipe and for connection of lead to other non-ferrous metals. They have the advantages of reduced bulk and neater appearance relative to wiped joints (38).

Other methods of jointing lead pipe have been introduced but none have achieved any degree of popularity. These methods include amalgamine

[1] Silver/copper/lead alloy has greater strength and greater resistance to creep and fatigue than lead. Pipes of this material can therefore be of somewhat lighter weight than lead pipes for similar purposes.

TABLE 12

Pipe diameter		Service pipes below ground	Service pipes above ground	Distributing pipes—cold	Distributing pipes—hot
Lead pipes	$\frac{3}{8}$ in.	4	3	3	3
	$\frac{1}{2}$ in.	6	4	4	4
	$\frac{3}{4}$ in.	9	5	5	5
	1 in.	13	8	7	8
Silver/ Copper/ Lead alloy	$\frac{3}{8}$ in.	4	3	3	3
	$\frac{1}{2}$ in.	6	4	4	4
	$\frac{3}{4}$ in.	9	5	5	5
	1 in.	13	7	7	8

Weights, in pounds per yard, of lead and lead alloy pipes for different purposes (*from* B.S.S. Nos. 602 and 1085).

N.B.—Weights for service pipes are for maximum working head of 150 ft and for cold and hot distributing pipes 75 ft and 60 ft head respectively. Savings in weight shown by alloy pipes is more apparent on larger pipes and at greater working heads.

jointing and compression type fittings. In the former pipe ends are shaped by means of special tools to fit together or into the sockets of fittings of lead. A layer of tin-foil is sandwiched between contact surfaces and this fuses to weld the joint surfaces together when heat is applied by a blow-lamp. In the latter pipe ends are shaped by means of special tools so that they can be secured in a way similar to that described below for copper tubes (38). (Joints of this kind are in any case only suitable for temporary works.)

Copper tubes. Copper tubes are highly resistant to internal and external corrosion and since the development of suitable jointing techniques the use of light gauge tubes in water supply installations and plumbing works generally has become widespread. Tubes, particularly smaller diameters, are readily bent to shape and the soft temper tubes[1] now available are supplied in coils and, like lead, can be readily positioned by hand which makes them particularly suitable for use as service pipes.

Tubes are specified by nominal internal diameter, wall thickness and weight per foot. Standards of material and performance are set by B.S. 659 for two grades of tubes—for use in water supply and sanitary installations—and by B.S. 1386 for tubes to be buried below ground (Table 13) (see p. 412 for physical properties of copper).

[1] Copper tubes are normally supplied in straight lengths of "half-hard" temper which permits a reasonable amount of manipulation before tubes become brittle or require to be softened by heating.

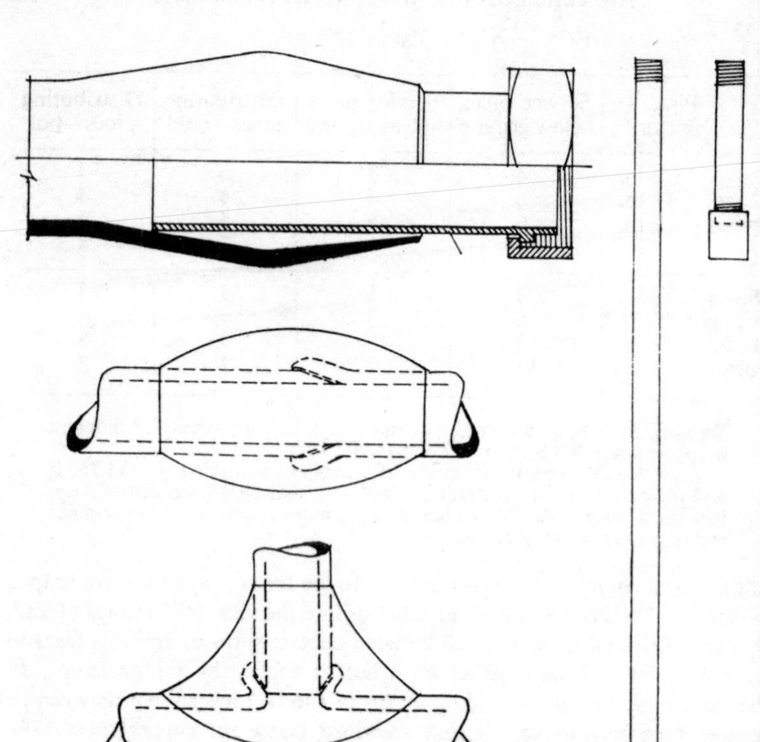

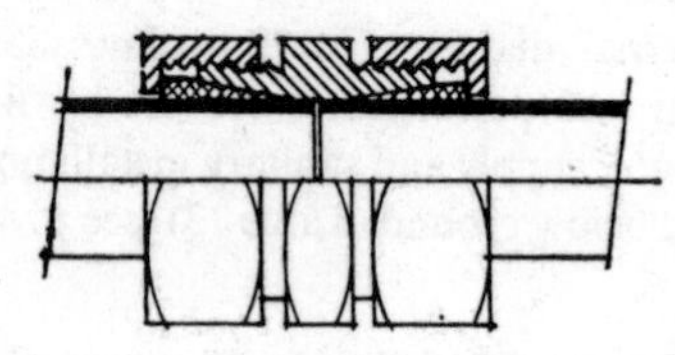

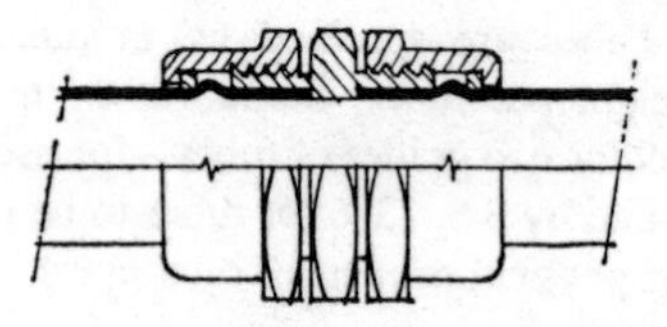

38

TABLE 13

Nominal bore	Standard tubes		Tubes for use below ground	
	Maximum outside diameter	Weight per foot	Maximum outside diameter	Weight per foot
⅜ in.	0·471	0·19	0·471	0·246
½ in.	0·596	0·27	0·596	0·319
¾ in.	0·846	0·39	0·846	0·536
1 in.	0·112	0·62	0·112	0·812

Sizes and weights in pounds per foot of part of the range of light gauge copper tubes covered by B.S. 659 (standard tubes and tubes for sanitation), and 1386 (tubes for use below ground).

Note that external diameters are the same for both grades in spite of the thicker walls of the underground grade. This is true for all sizes of tube and holds good in the sanitary weights. (It enables standard compression and capillary fittings to be used on all grades of tube.)

---

38 *Pipe jointing*

(*Top, left*) Lead pipe joined to a brass coupling nut and liner by means of a soldered spigot joint. The end of the lead pipe is simply formed by the use of special purpose tools. Fine solder is melted by blow lamp at the entry to the joint and is drawn by capillary attraction into the narrow space between pipe and liner. (The coupling nut enables the pipe to be attached to the threaded end of a tap or the outlets from tanks or the traps of sanitary fittings.)
(*Centre, left*) A running joint and a "tee" junction in lead pipe made with wiped solder joints. Pipe ends are formed to fit as shown and joints strengthened by building up with coarse solder "wiped" into shape and position whilst still plastic with a "cloth"—traditionally of moleskin.
(*Top, right*) Galvanised steel tubes and jointing socket. Tubes can be ordered exact lengths or, more usually, cut and threaded for jointing as required.
(*Below*) Typical compression joints for copper tubes. The fitting on the left is a "non-manipulative" fitting, the joint being made watertight by the pressure on the tube wall transferred through the wedge-shaped rings when the joint is tightened.

The fitting on the right is a "manipulative" fitting. The tube ends are shaped by means of a special tool before the joint is made so that tubes are held positively by the shouldered nuts of the fitting. (Most authorities require manipulative fittings to be used for jointing tubes buried below ground.)

Capillary fittings for jointing copper tubes (*not illustrated*) comprise sockets into which tube ends are inserted, the narrowness of the annular space between tube and socket enabling it to be filled with fine solder by capillary attraction to make the joint.

JOINTING of light gauge tubes is effected by means of compression joints, capillary solder joints and by bronze soldering or welding. Compression and capillary joints have the advantages of simplifying preparation for and making the joints, need for skill and manipulation being usually reduced by the use of fittings for bends, junctions, etc., and are most widely used for smaller pipe sizes and smaller scale installation (38). Bronze welding (bronze soldering) is more widely used for the larger sizes of pipe needed in sanitary installations and where repetition of pipe assemblies makes off-site prefabrication suitable.

Galvanised steel tubes. Steel or iron tubes used in water supply installations are required to be protected from corrosion by zinc coating. This is effective in hard and non-acid waters. For cold water supply installations galvanised tubes are now more widely used than tubes or pipes of any other material because of their low cost.

Tubes are difficult to manipulate and fittings for jointing, junctions, etc., are necessary, the zinc coating precluding any but mechanical jointing. Tubes are difficult to manipulate and bend fittings are also widely used. Tubes are specified by bore (nominal), wall thickness and weight. Standards of material and performance for three grades of steel tube are set by B.S. 1387 (Table 14). (See also p. 413 for physical properties of zinc.)

TABLE 14

Nominal bore	Light		Medium	Heavy
	Outside diameter	Weight per foot	Weight per foot	Weight per foot
$\frac{3}{8}$ in.	$\frac{11}{16}$ in.	0·457	0·577	0·690
$\frac{1}{2}$ in.	$\frac{27}{32}$ in.	0·646	0·828	0·983
$\frac{3}{4}$ in.	$1\frac{1}{16}$ in.	0·954	1·07	1·28
1 in.	$1\frac{11}{32}$ in.	1·36	1·65	2·01

Weights in pounds per foot and sizes of part of the range of the three grades of steel tube covered by B.S. 1387 (1957).

Note that external diameters are the same for all grades of tubes so that the same ranges of fittings can be used. Sizes and weights are the same for galvanised and ungalvanised tubes. Tubes of different weights are distinguished by coloured bands: "light"—brown, "medium"—blue and "heavy"—red. For water supply installations most authorities call for "heavy" galvanised tubes for service pipes and medium for distributing pipes.

JOINTING of galvanised tubes is effected by means of threaded sockets into which threaded ends of a tube are screwed (38). A jointing compound is used on the thread to ensure a watertight joint.

Polythene tubes. Polythene is light and strong, does not corrode and resists attack by most acids and alkalis. Tubes are now produced which are suitable for use in water supply and sanitary installations as well as many industrial purposes and their use in cold water installations is increasing rapidly. The low melting point of polythene (about 110–112°C), makes tubes unsuitable for hot water installations but most authorities approve their use in cold water installations. Standards for material and performance for two grades of "Polythene Tubes for Cold Water Services" are set by B.S. 1972.

TABLE 15

Nominal	Normal gauge		Heavy gauge	
	Outside diameter	Weight per 100 ft	Outside diameter	Weight per 100 ft
¼ in.	–	–	0·531	7
⅜ in.	–	–	0·677	10
½ in.	0·686	7	0·840	15
¾ in.	1·000	14	1·096	20
1 in.	1·250	17·5	1·346	25·5

Sizes and weights of polythene tubes covered by B.S. 1972. (Normal gauge tubes are also made in diameters up to 2 in.)

JOINTING. The problem of jointing tubes is resolved in a number of ways. The two grades referred to above are "heavy" and "normal", the former having a great enough wall thickness to allow connection by screwed fittings or standard metal compression fittings. The "normal" grade tubes are too thin to permit threading but can be jointed by standard compression fittings if tube ends are strengthened by the insertion of short metal liner sleeves. A number of manufacturers market special fittings for the compression type which include a supporting core for tube ends and also give them positive grip. Alternatively tubes can be jointed by welding, but fusing temperatures are critical and special hot gas torches are required. Patent methods of welding are sponsored by some manufacturers and these are increasing in popularity. One system makes use of metal formers which are first heated and then bring tubes to be jointed to the right temperature by contact. Another uses fittings which, after assembly of the joint, fuses the contact surfaces together by a small voltage current passed through electrodes incorporated as an integral part of the fittings.

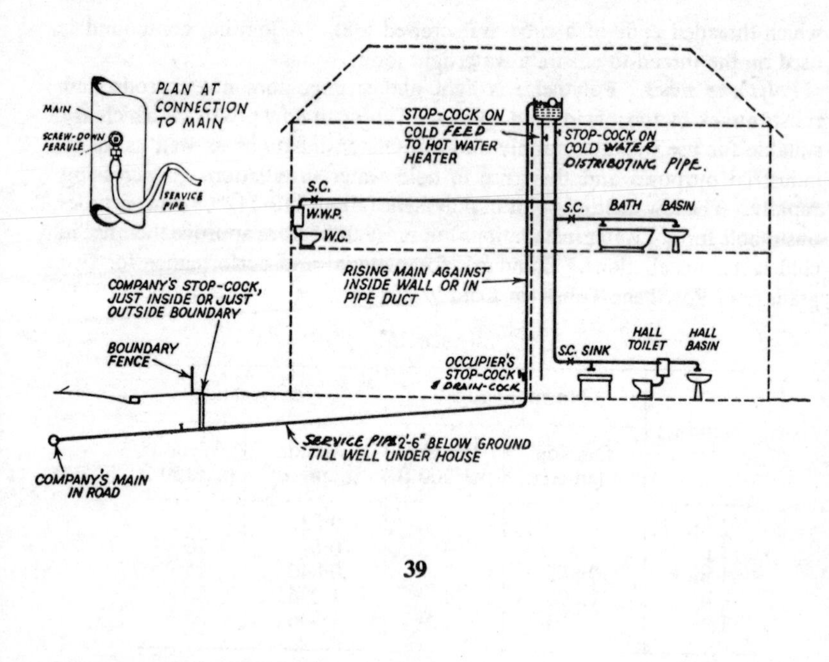

39

39 *Arrangement of Cold Water Installations*

The diagram shows a typical domestic installation. The connection to the main (see p. 160) is usually made on its upper surface and the service pipe, from it (the rising main) looped in the form of a "goose neck", as shown, to prevent any settlement from pulling the connection away. The length of the service pipe below the building is often laid within a protective sleeve of larger pipes, usually second quality stoneware, this also enables it to be threaded into position at any time during the erection if required and/or to be replaced should it ever become necessary.

The internal position for the rising main avoids the risk of freezing which arises when it is placed on an outer wall, particularly at its entry to the roof space where the bend in the vicinity of the eaves is especially vulnerable.

Not shown in the diagram is the mains branch to the kitchen. This would be required by supply authorities as a source of "safe" drinking water but in general domestic buildings would be limited to one such connection.

Stop-cocks shown on all the outlets from the cistern are required by most water authorities but the stop-cocks on the branches to each group of fittings, although desirable, are not insisted upon.

A drain tap is often fitted on the rising main, immediately above the occupier's stop-cock, to enable the length of rising main to the tank to be drained.

Polythene tubes are sufficiently elastic to accommodate expansion of water in the event of freezing without bursting but their high coefficient of expansion and lack of rigidity call for frequent support of tubes (at intervals of 24 times the outside diameter horizontally). They are very light and easy to manipulate and available in long continuous lengths.

P.V.C.—This material is gradually superseding polythene as a material for domestic plumbing services. It is obtainable in normal, high impact and plasticised grades. The latter can be very flexible and is not used in domestic plumbing. The normal grade has sufficient rigidity to support itself over much longer lengths than polythene. Jointing the material is simpler and more satisfactory than for polythene as it can be solvent welded. Use of P.V.C. for water services must be restricted to that complying with B.S.S. 3505. P.V.C. for potable waters. Pipes shall be marked at intervals of not more than 10 ft showing: B.S. 3505 Class & Size. MARKINGS shall be in the following colours. Class AA—yellow; Class B—red; Class C—blue; Class D—green. Class AA is not specified under 3 in. dia., Class B under 1¼ in. dia., Class C under 8 in. dia. (See Table 15A.)

TABLE 15A

Comparison of Minimum Wall Thickness of Polythene and P.V.C.

Nominal Dia.	Polythene (low density) Approx. spec. gravity 0·94 Wall thickness in inches		P.V.C. normal impact Approx. spec. gravity 1·4 Wall thickness in inches	
	Normal gauge	Heavy gauge	Class C	Class D
⅜ in.		0·151		0·05
½ in.	0·093	0·173		0·06
¾ in.	0·125	0·173	0·06	0·075
1 in.	0·125	0·173	0·072	0·094

Arrangement of installations. Many supplying authorities restrict the fitting of supply draw-offs directly to service pipes[1] generally to those points supplying water for drinking or cooking purposes. In the average domestic building one branch only from the servic epipe—to the kitchen—is fitted. In larger buildings agreement of positioning and number of draw-offs with the supply authorities is necessary.

Thus service pipes are arranged to discharge directly into a cold water

[1] This is not the case in all parts of the country but the practice is spreading. Local Water Board Regulations should be consulted.

storage cistern and all supplies to taps, sanitary fittings, etc., other than those referred to above, are taken from the tank by means of distributing pipes. The reasons for this arrangement are to provide a reserve of water from which fittings can continue to be supplied in the event of mains failure; to relieve the mains of excessive and fluctuating demand (delivery at taps has no direct relationship to mains sizes or pressure at storage tanks determine supply and pressure at taps); taps and other fittings within buildings are not subjected to direct mains pressure, which would increase the likelihood of leaks and waste of water and greatly increase the noise created and transmitted by the installation.

A diagrammatic arrangement of a domestic installation is shown and described in Fig. 39. The diagram illustrates the best practice in the positioning of stop taps, most water supply authorities require the fitting of the two stop taps on the service pipe and of stop taps on each outlet from the storage cistern. These enable washers to be changed or repairs to pipework to be carried out without draining the system, i.e. emptying the storage cistern, which would involve considerable waste of water. (Stop taps are illustrated in Fig. 37, p. 160.)

Storage cisterns are made of many different materials but by far the most widely used are cisterns fabricated from steel plate, galvanised after fabrication. B.S. 417 sets standards for standard sized cisterns of two grades, A and B, the former being of heavier material. Most authorities require grade A cisterns to be used in water supply installations.

In general use galvanised cisterns have almost entirely superseded cisterns constructed of slate slabs and cisterns of timber lined with sheet lead or copper. There are however satisfactory alternatives. Self-supporting cisterns of copper are to be preferred where cost allows and these are now available in capacities up to about 60 gallons. They are made to order and are usually circular on plan with walls corrugated for strength. Standard cisterns of asbestos cement or plastic, moulded in one piece, available in sizes up to 100 gallons, are becoming popular in domestic installations.

Problems of galvanic action may arise when galvanised cisterns are used in conjunction with copper tubes. To avoid this, pipework should be arranged so that water does not flow from copper items into galvanised items. If this is not possible cisterns can be protected, e.g. by bituminous coatings applied to their inside surfaces.

Sizes of cisterns are usually controlled by the supply authority. The 1963 edition of the Model Water Byelaws requires minimum capacities where storage cisterns are used in houses to be:

(*a*) 25 gallons if not used as a feed cistern

(*b*) 50 gallons if used both as a feed cistern and for other purposes.

If more than one cistern be used the sum of their capacities shall not be less than that stated above. For larger buildings storage capacities are agreed relative to the building's use, the number of draw-off points required, etc.

Arrangement of cisterns is also carefully regulated. The inlet to a cistern must be automatically controlled by means of a ball valve of approved design, and must be fitted with an overflow pipe which must be arranged so that any discharge from it will be immediately noticed and give warning of water waste. Its outlet from the tank must be set below the ball valve inlet so that the water level in the tank can never rise sufficiently to submerge it. (This might lead to contamination of water in the mains by entry of water from the cistern into them.) The ball float arm must be so adjusted that the highest level the water can reach is lower than the invert of the overflow pipe, by 1 inch for cisterns less than 1000 gallons capacity and by 2 inches for cisterns greater than 1000 gallons capacity. Ball valves are described and illustrated in Fig. 40.

Cisterns are also required to be covered to exclude dirt and vermin but covers should be loose so as not to exclude air. Cisterns are almost invariably placed as high within buildings as possible so that water drawn from them is delivered with as much speed and pressure as possible. In domestic buildings cisterns are usually placed within the roof space and to prevent their freezing in severe weather insulation of the tank, and any pipes exposed within the roof space, is now general practice. Insulation may take the form of timber casing constructed around the tank, the space between tank and casing being packed with sawdust, cork chippings, vermiculite, etc. Alternatively slabs of wood wool or "stramit" may be placed around the tank and wired into position, the tank cover also being formed of a slab of similar material.

In bigger buildings and domestic buildings where costs permit, cisterns are placed within "safes". These consist of trays from which water can overflow, e.g. on to a surrounding flat roof from a tank room, or which are drained to a point outside the building by means of an outlet pipe. Their purpose is to prevent damage to internal decorations and construction should the cistern itself become defective.

Connection to cistern for ball valve inlet and outlets are made by tank connector fittings, usually of brass, which sandwich the cistern wall between wide flanged nuts, resilient washers being used to make the joint watertight. Connector ends vary from direct attachment of pipes of different materials (41).

Distributing pipework. All the materials discussed for use as service pipes are of course equally suitable for distributing pipes and the objections which may be raised to the use of lead or galvanised steel for service pipes would, if valid, also apply to distributing pipes. Distributing pipes are, however,

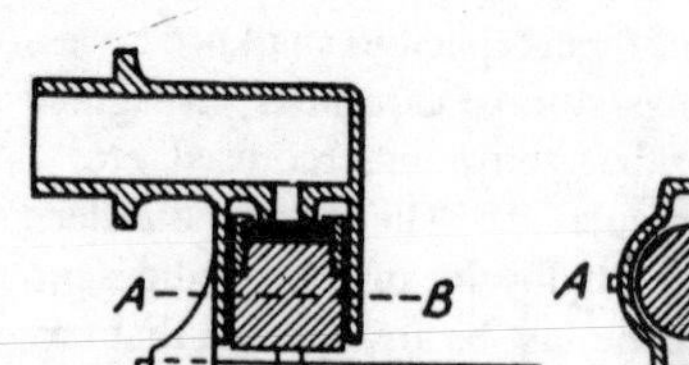
A
B

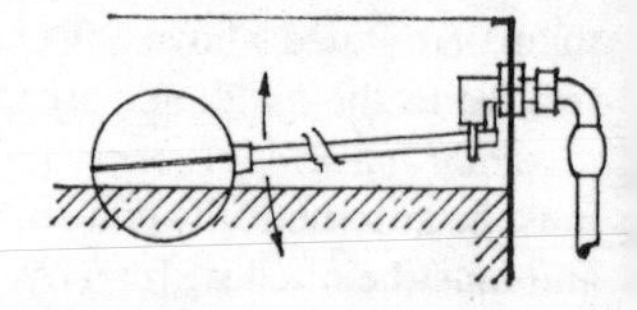

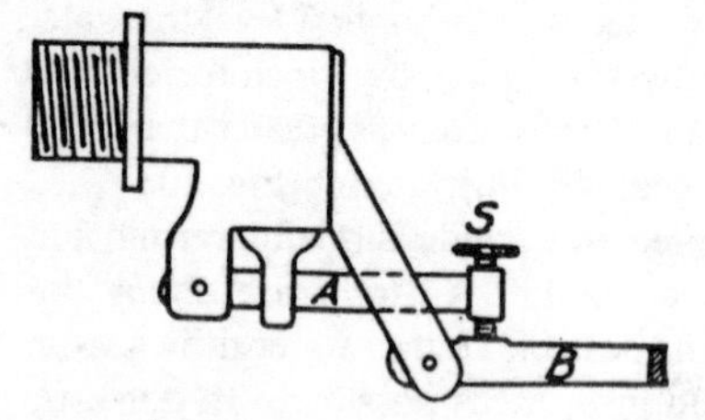
S
A
B

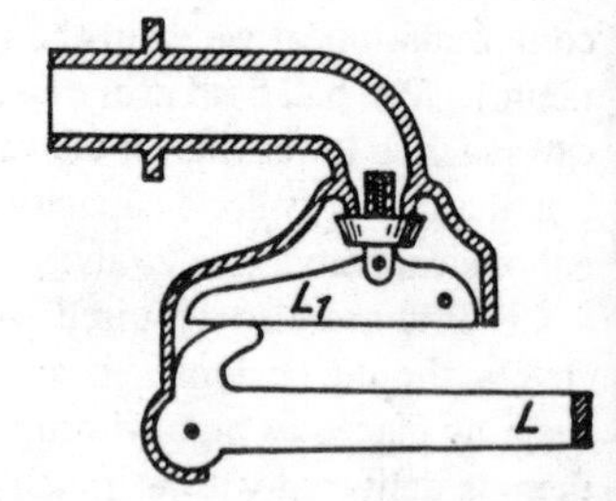
L_1
L

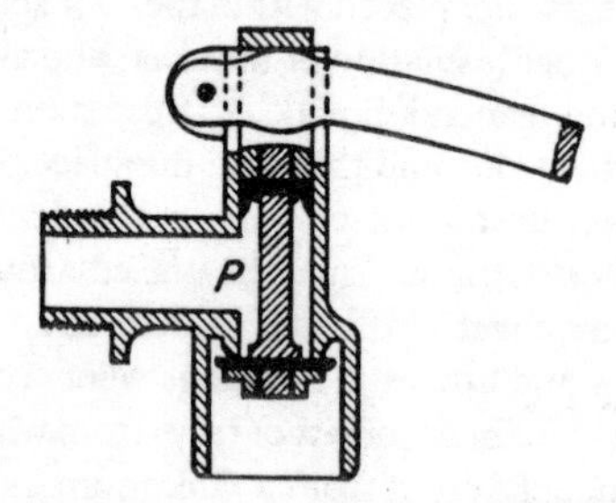
P

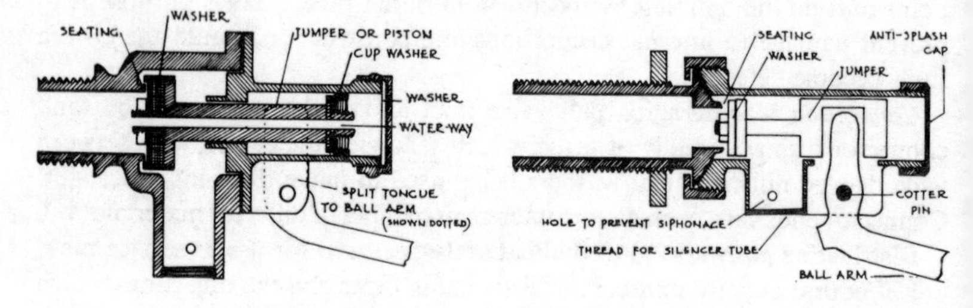
SEATING
WASHER
JUMPER OR PISTON
CUP WASHER
WASHER
WATER-WAY
SPLIT TONGUE
TO BALL ARM
(SHOWN DOTTED)
SEATING
WASHER
ANTI-SPLASH CAP
JUMPER
COTTER PIN
HOLE TO PREVENT SIPHONAGE
THREAD FOR SILENCER TUBE
BALL ARM

40

more accessible for repairs than service pipes and are not called upon to withstand the more severe conditions of contact with soils, some of which may be corrosive. In general work somewhat lower standards may be acceptable in the interests of economy and galvanised steel tubes are used extensively. As the corrosive action of water is greater when hot a very common compromise is to use galvanised steel or perhaps polythene for cold water distributing pipes and copper for hot water distributing pipes. Both copper and steel pipes have the advantage of easier and simpler fixing than lead or polythene.

Pipe fixing is a matter often inadequately considered in installations. The best method is undoubtedly to fix pipes on to a backboard of timber but

---

40 *Ball Valves* (*Top, left*) A Croydon valve is shown in section. The plan AB shows the shaping of the valve to allow water to flow past the jumper (or plunger) when it moves away from its seating by the dropping of the ball arm. A check or stop is provided at C to prevent the ball arm dropping too low and displacing the jumper from the body of the valve. Croydon valves are the simplest and cheapest available but they cannot be fitted with a silencing tube. (*Top, right*) A diagram which shows the action of Croydon valve to a smaller scale. (*Above, centre, left*) An arrangement which permits adjustment of the closing level of the ball arm without recourse to bending the arm (seldom used by reason of cost). (*Above, centre, right*) An arrangement designed to assist closing against high pressure. The force transmitted by movement of the ball arm is magnified by the second lever L^1 (This valve has been superseded by the equilibrium valves). (*Below, centre*) Equilibrium valves. In both examples the jumper (or piston) is subjected to water pressure in both directions, i.e. opening and closing. The piston is therefore in a state of equilibrium and the ball arm simply moves it and is not required to exert a force to close the valve.

N.B.—Ball valves are tested and marked as suitable for closing against low, medium or high pressure, the pressure being 40, 100 and 200 lb/in.^{2} respectively. Equilibrium ball valves are considered suitable for all pressures. Also they are often installed as replacement when trouble has been experienced with water hammer in a system due to vibration or "dancing" of a common ball valve. The horizontal moving piston type (Underhayes Equilibrium valve) seems to be used to a greater extent than other types of equilibrium valve. (*Below, left*) A Portsmouth valve to B.S. 1212. The valve has a split body to enable the working parts to be removed for maintenance without necessity of disconnecting service from tank. Also the seating which may be of nylon, gunmetal or any other equally suitable material can be exposed for refacing should this be necessary. (*Below, right*) The Garston valve is the latest form of ball valve available. Designed by B.R.S. it controls water entry to the cistern by a rubber diaphragm placed over an inlet nozzle of nylon. The diaphragm is positioned to prevent incoming water from coming into contact with the plunger which activates it. So that in addition to being much quieter than normal valves the *Garston* is free from familiar problems of incrustation, plunger sticking, etc., which arises from hardness deposits.

these, in smaller works at least, are almost invariably omitted in the interests of economy. Pipes should, however, be fixed at sufficiently close intervals to prevent sagging or bending, intervals depending on material, pipe size and whether pipes are fixed horizontally or vertically (Table 16). Clips which

TABLE 16

Nominal bore	Copper tubes		G.S. tubes		Lead		Poly-thene	
	H	V	H	V	H	V	H	V
½ in.	4	6	6	8	2	3	⅝	1
¾ in.	6	8	8	10	2	3	⅞	1½
1 in.	6	8	8	10	2	3	1¼	2
1¼ in.	8	10	9	10	2	3	1½	2½
1½ in.	8	10	10	12	2	3	1¾	3

Vertical and horizontal spacing of supports recommended for pipes of different materials. (The spacings are for light gauge copper tubes.)

keep pipes clear of the surface behind are preferable for steel and copper tubes and it is important that steel tubes are not fixed with copper or brass clips and that copper tubes are not fixed with galvanised clips. (Condensation collecting at the clips creates conditions in which galvanic action accelerates corrosion of the galvanised tube in the former case and of the clip in the latter case.)

Lead pipes are so likely to sag on horizontal runs that traditional practice, e.g. where pipes within floor thickness, is to provide continuous support by means of battens spiked to the sides of floor joists.

Taps, or valves (the means used to control the supply of water at draw-off points), of screw-down pattern are by far the most widely used. In general, water authorities require the use of these. They must conform in construction to the standards set by B.S. 1010, or they can be taps which have been tested to withstand specific water pressures. Common alternatives to screw-down valves are knee or elbow operated valves used in hospitals, in which a quarter turn of the spindle is sufficient to fully open the valve, and spring taps in which the valve is held closed by a powerful spring which must be depressed for the valve to deliver water. (These have the advantage from the water authorities' view point of not being capable of being left open by accident and so help to reduce waste of water.)

Screw-down taps vary in outward form to suit different positions they are to occupy. The bib-valve shown in Fig. 41 is designed for mounting on a wall face, for example above a sink, or at the end of a stand pipe such as is found in a garage or workshop. For lavatory basins and baths so called "pillar" taps are more usual. In these water enters vertically, through a threaded shaft which is used to mount the tap on the fitting.

For sinks pillar taps, often with long mounting "pillars" to give greater clearance, or double valves which feed both hot and cold water to a common outlet are used. The latter type of fitting is also popular for baths. (These are not mixing valves which are designed to blend hot and cold water and deliver them at a constant temperature according to their setting. These incorporate controlling thermostatic devices but depend for efficiency a great deal on similar delivery pressures for both hot and cold water. Most water authorities will not in any case permit the connection of mixing valves to service pipes. Their principal use outside industry is in supply shower baths.)

Noise in pipework. Metals are good conductors of sound so that any noise created in a system is transmitted in some degree over its full extent and the noise of filling tanks and flush cisterns is a nuisance most people are familiar with. Some fittings marketed are noisier in action than others and the solution to the problem of avoiding noise in plumbing lies at least partly in intelligent choice of fittings. Thus some types of ball valves can be fitted with "silencer" pipes and are obviously to be preferred to those which cannot (see Chapter 7).

Movement of water through pipes and valves can produce considerable noise particularly when the water pressure is high. The noise of water passing through service pipes is commonly complained of and a disadvantage of installations taken entirely from the mains (still permitted in some areas), is that noise of this kind cannot be avoided. In a more normal installation the solution lies in careful positioning of the service pipes to avoid nuisance.

Water hammer. There are occasional instances in which there are sharp rapping or knocking sounds in the water supply pipes, to which the name of water hammer is given. These are usually caused by quick-closing taps such as plug-cocks, or self-closing or automatic taps. If the taps are near the main, the nuisance is likely to occur and most likely on long lengths of house services. Hammer is also caused by defective ball-valves, their inefficient fixing or improper seating of the valve washers. The remedy is to substitute proper screw-down bib-cocks, or efficient ball-valves, as the case may be.

Buzzing noises in water pipes. A somewhat similar defect sometimes occurs in water pipes when the washer of a bib-valve is worn or the nut securing it is loose, or the "jumper" holding it in place is loose in its socket. Any of these faults may lead to uneven pressure on the washer when the tap is half turned on, so that the washer or jumper rotates or rocks so as to turn the

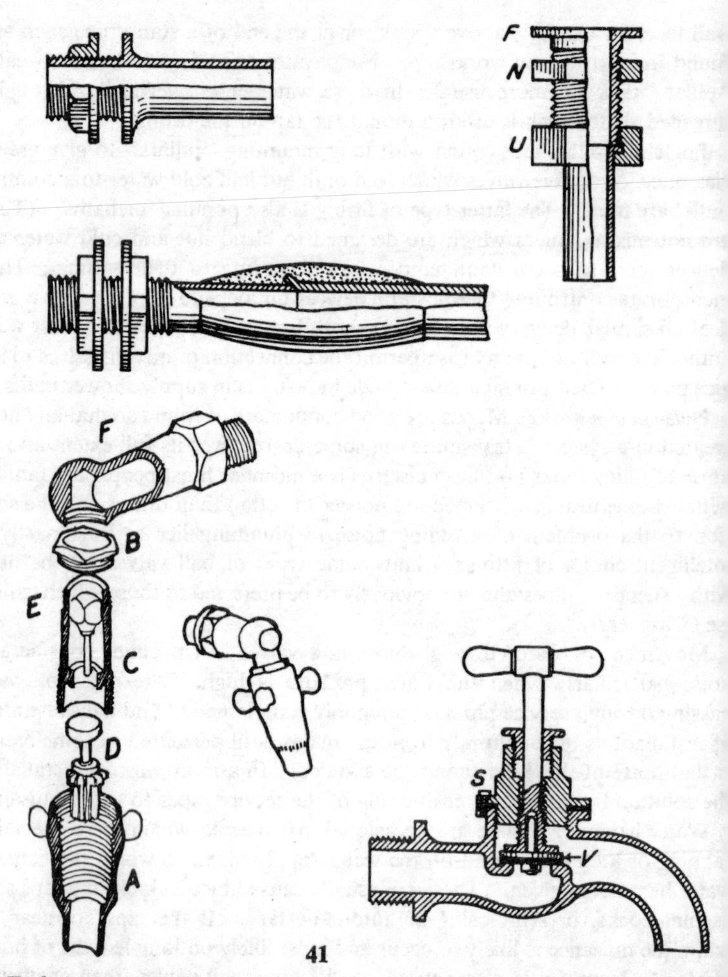

41 *Tank connections and taps*

TANK CONNECTIONS. (*Above*) A one piece connector (*left*), comprising a flanged sleeve for connection of lead pipe and (*right*) a two piece connector in which the connector is threaded for connection of a union nut and lined for connection to lead pipe.

(*Centre*) An alternative one piece connector with lead pipe wiped into position.

N.B.—Standard tank connectors are available for direct connection of copper tube by compression or capillary joints, and for direct connection of galvanised steel tubes. Connectors may be straight as illustrated or in the form of bends.

water on and off rapidly, the succession of short sharp raps merging into a hum or buzz. A little attention soon remedies the fault.

Hot water supply. The most usual way of providing for a supply of hot water is to build up a common hot water storage so that fittings can draw from it as required, the most usual means of heating the water for storage being by means of a boiler. For maximum economy in smaller domestic buildings boilers are often incorporated in open fires, stoves or solid fuel cookers, the traditional "back-boiler". This has the advantage of making one fire serve a dual purpose but has the disadvantage of somewhat reducing the space heating capacity of an open fire or a stove and of restricting the periods when hot water can be made available in comfort to those when a fire is needed for space heating or cooking. For these reasons a self-contained boiler for the supply of hot water is preferable and these are made in small enough capacities to be economic when supplying hot water only for a small household. The traditional form of domestic boiler has an openable front, so that space heating effect can be enjoyed if necessary but the more efficient are more readily controlled are fully enclosed boilers. These are described in Chapter 4 and are increasing in popularity.

Hot water supply produced as an auxiliary to central heating, when this is required, has the advantage of levelling out variations in demand made on the boiler for heating purposes and so making for maximum efficiency.

DRAW-OFF TAPS. (*Below, right*) A BIB-TAP with flange plate for wall mounting. The action is as follows. When the tap is closed the passage of the water is prevented by a small valve, which consists of a circular disc with a guiding pin above it and a washer of leather, fibre or rubber-asbestos composition, shown in black, below it. This valve is kept down by pressure exerted through the screwing down of the spindle, the stem of which has a cavity to receive the guide pin of the valve. The two main parts of the body of the tap are screwed together, with a leather washer between, and if the tap handle gets stiff it is possible that the sudden turning of it might unscrew the upper part of the body of the tap, to prevent which a small screw is sometimes put through the two as shown. When the washer of the valve requires renewing, it is necessary to shut off the water at the nearest stop valve and unscrew the two main parts of the tap. For improved appearance bit-taps, and other forms of screw-down tap, have additional covers which screw on over the upper part.
(*Below, left*) A SUPATAP designed to enable the washer to be renewed without turning off the water supply to it. The body, A, travels up and down the stem, C, the end of which is screwed into the shank, F, the internal flange A bearing on the washer assembly, D, to close the outlet. In normal use the nut, B, is screwed into the upper end of the body so that in opening the tap the body cannot be unscrewed too far down the tapered stem. When changing the washer assembly nut B is loosened and the body A is screwed right off the stem so that the plug, E, falls down to seal the outlet.

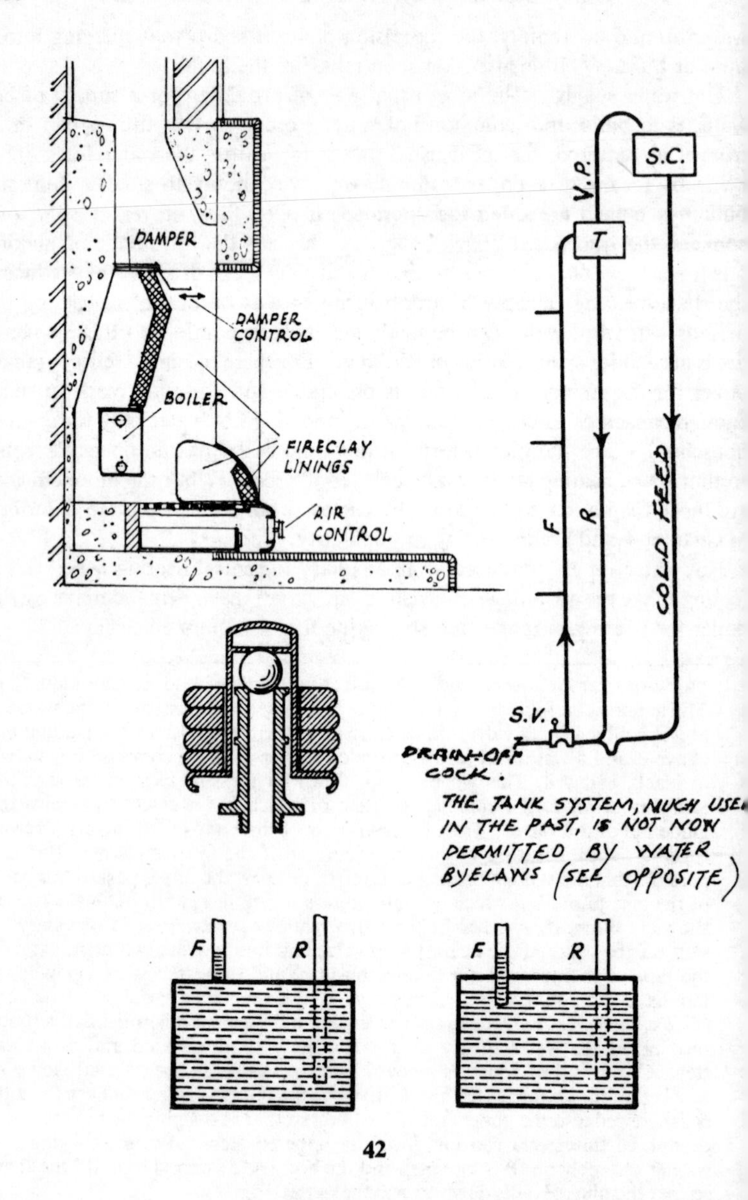
DAMPER
DAMPER CONTROL
BOILER
FIRECLAY LININGS
AIR CONTROL
V.P.
S.C.
T
F
R
COLD FEED
S.V.
DRAIN-OFF COCK.
THE TANK SYSTEM, MUCH USE[D] IN THE PAST, IS NOT NOW PERMITTED BY WATER BYELAWS (SEE OPPOSITE)
F
R
F
R

42

A diagram showing a typical back-boiler arrangement is included in Fig. 42 and an enclosed domestic boiler is illustrated in Fig. 25, p. 94.

Boiler construction. Boilers, i.e. the water "jackets" in contact with the fire, are made of cast iron or welded from steel plate and occasionally of copper. Copper is expensive but has the advantage of great resistance to corrosion, and cast iron has the disadvantage of a tendency to crack under the stresses resulting from rapid changes in temperature. Thus welded steel boilers are most common. These can be made sufficiently highly resistant to

---

42 *Hot water installations*

(*Top, left*) Arrangement of a "back-boiler" as part of a modern overnight burning open fire (see Chapter 4). Movement of the damper opens the passage behind the boiler so giving control over the proportion of the fire's heat devoted to water heating.

(*Top, right*) A direct, "tank", hot water installation. Water heated in the boiler rises to the top of the tank in the flow pipe, F, its place in the boiler being taken by cool water drawn from the top of the tank through the return, R. Cold water to replace that drawn from the system enters the return pipe through the cold water supply pipe, C.W.S., from the storage cistern, S.C.

The arrangement shown has the disadvantage that when water is drawn off through the branch pipe from the flow, F, the head of water in the storage cistern is likely to result in cold water reaching the taps via the boiler instead of hot water from the storage tank. From the safety viewpoint Water Authorities will not permit a hot water storage vessel to be lowered to more than ¾ of its depth by draw-off at a tap, assuming cessation of water supply to system (see Fig. 43). The whole of the water can be drawn in the system shown, by drawing water through the return and boiler.

N.B. Should the system become sealed, e.g. by the freezing of the vent and cold feed, pressure developed by expansion could become dangerous. To avoid this safety valves (SV) are fitted (described in detail in Chapter 4, illustrated opposite).

Should the expansion pipe become blocked, e.g. by freezing, the expansion of water in the boiler and pipework would become dangerous. To avoid this boilers are fitted with safety valves, S.V. (described in detail in Chapter 4).

In the valve shown (*Centre, left*) the outlet is closed by a metal ball held in place by a series of weights carried by the ball retaining cover. Excessive pressures lift the ball to prevent dangerous conditions arising in the installation.

(*Below*) Right and wrong methods of connecting the flow pipe to a boiler.

The flow pipe, F, should be finished flush with the underside of the top of the boiler to prevent any accumulation of air or steam. Thus, in the right hand diagram the flow pipe is wrongly connected. When the system is filled air will be trapped in the space between the surface of the water and the underside of top of boiler. When heated the air expands, depresses water, and escapes through flow pipe. The recoil of the water and the escape of the air give rise to considerable noise, also the presence of air in the system increases corrosion. Fresh water coming into the system gives up some of its air in solution which rises to top of boiler to cause repetition.

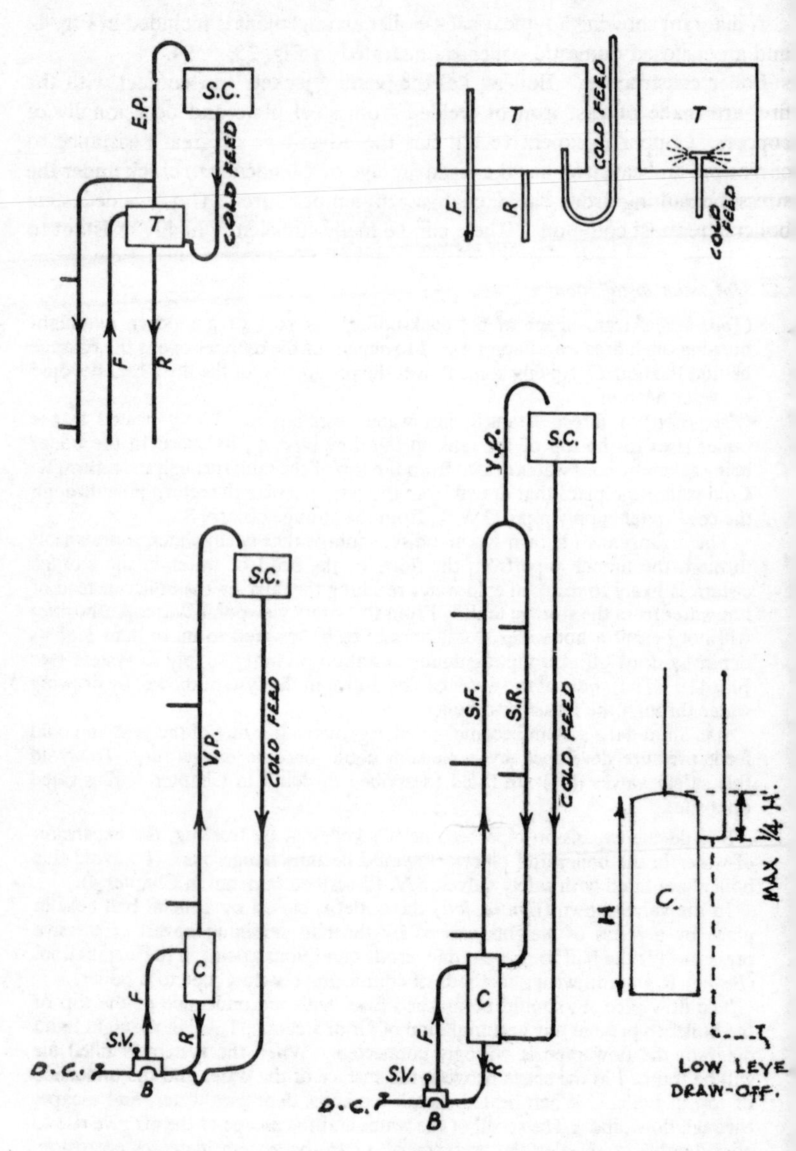
S.C.
E.P.
COLD FEED
T
F
R
T
COLD FEED
F
R
T
COLD FEED
S.C.
V.P.
COLD FEED
C
F
R
S.V.
D.C.
B
S.C.
V.P.
S.F.
S.R.
COLD FEED
C
F
R
S.V.
D.C.
B
MAX 1/4 H.
H
C.
LOW LEVE
DRAW-OFF.

43

corrosion for all general use by the "Bower-Barff" process. In this a surface coating of corrosion-resistant magnetic oxide of iron is formed by means of steam jets directed on to the steel whilst at red heat. Most domestic boilers are provided with access hand-holes with removable covers to enable sludge and scale to be removed.

Arrangement of hot water installations. Hot water is stored by transferring water heated in the boiler to a storage vessel, situated at a higher level, by convection through pipes connecting them together. (The principle of convection is described in Chapter 4.) Detailed arrangement of pipework

---

43 "*Direct*" *Hot Water Circulations*

(*Top, left*) A tank "Expansion Pipe[1] System" in which all the draw-off taps are taken from the base of the expansion pipe. It has the advantage, in small compact buildings where all the fittings to be supplied are near to this point, that all the hot water ready can be drawn off before any cold water emerges and that it complies with requirement to prevent storage being depleted in the event of cold feed being turned off; but it has obvious disadvantages in a larger house, where fittings are scattered over a wide area and branch pipes have to be emptied of cold or tepid water before hot water from the tank can flow.

N.B.—Model Water Byelaws restrict dead legs (pipes without circulation) to 40 ft for ½ in. pipe, 25 ft for ¾ in. pipe and 10 ft for 1 in. pipe owing to consequent waste of water.

(*Top, right*) Connection of the cold water supply to the hot water tank, instead of to the boiler as in Fig. 42, clearly saves plumbing. The method on the left is undesirable because cold incoming water will mix too freely with the water in the tank. The arrangement on the right avoids this defect. The practice of dipping the cold feed to form a trap before connection is made to the tank is to reduce the transfer of heat from the tank to cold water storage cistern.

(*Below, left*) An expansion pipe system using a cylinder near the boiler, suitable for a house of moderate height provided the fittings are close together, branches being taken from the expansion pipe to them. It will be seen that the hot water will rise in the expansion pipe to approximately the level of the water in the supply cistern—a little higher actually, for hot water weighs less than cold and the expansion or vent pipe, as it should be called, must be carried above the top of the water level in cistern ½ inch for every 1 foot of the height between boiler and cistern. This measurement is based on the fact that water expands $\frac{1}{23}$ of its volume in being raised from maximum density 39°F to boiling point.

(*Below, centre*) A more extensive form of the cylinder system, provided with a secondary flow and return taken round past the various fittings so as to supply them by means of short branches taken from both flow and return pipes of the secondary system of circulation. (Secondary flow marked S.F. and secondary return S.R.) The position of the connection of the secondary return to the cylinder is of importance as it frequently leads to the cylinder being drained to below the permissible level when draw-off connections are at a lower level.

[1] The term expansion pipe although frequently used is technically wrong—it is a vent pipe.

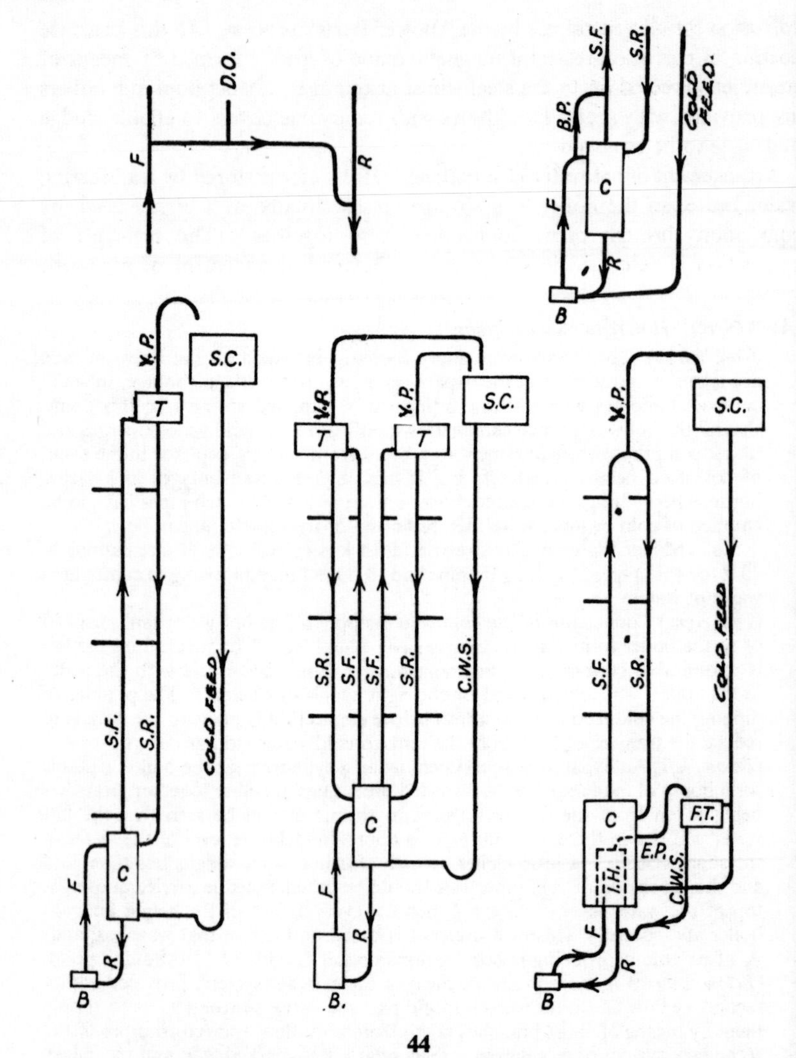

44 *Hot Water Circulations*

(*Above, left*) Secondary flow and return pipes are sometimes necessarily placed at opposite sides of the building, and it is necessary to run a pipe from the one to the other, as shown. In such a case, the slight fall generally available for the pipe is insufficient to ensure a good circulation without a "drop" as shown.

and storage vessel and their relationship to draw-off points vary a great deal. Fig. 42 shows the arrangement of the simplest "direct" form of "tank" system and Figs 43 and 44 illustrate and describe a number of alternative arrangements used for hot water installations.

Direct and indirect systems. In direct systems of water heating the water drawn at fittings is water which has been heated by passing through the boiler so that the water in the boiler and in the pipework of the boiler is constantly changing. This inevitably leads to the formation of scale, hardness deposits, and/or corrosion of boiler and pipework.

In indirect systems water heated in the boiler is contained within a "closed" pipe circuit in which the same relatively small quantity of water is circulated and recirculated between boiler and storage vessel. Heat is transferred to the water in the storage vessel by its contact with the outer surfaces of a pipe coil or water jacket through which the boiler water passes. In current practice the trend is towards indirect systems of water heating (44 and 45). In indirect systems, not only is scale formation and corrosion reduced but one boiler can be used for heating and hot water supply. (The coil in the hot water storage vessel forms part of the heating circuit or is arranged as a loop from it.)

The greater density of the water at lower part of drop increases the velocity of flow through the pipe and through the draw-off branch, D.O.

(*Above, right*) An arrangement sometimes adopted to give a quicker hot supply than would otherwise be obtainable, is to provide a by-pass letting a certain amount of water escape going through the cylinder. Such a by-pass must be of considerably smaller section than the other pipes, or the whole of the water will be short circuited and not pass through the cylinder.

(*Below, left*) A combined tank and cylinder system. The system possesses the advantages of both the tank and cylinder systems and also overcomes the disadvantages of both. The cold feed pipe can be connected to the cylinder, or the boiler, the usual practice being to connect it to the cylinder, as shown. This method of arranging the service gives a good supply of hot water to fittings at all levels. It is, of course, better to take branches from the flow pipe only, if this can be conveniently arranged.

The combined capacity of the two storage vessels would be made about equal to the capacity of the cylinder required if the cylinder only system were adopted.

(*Below, centre*) An extension of the combined system employing two tanks and two sets of secondary pipes. These would be separated as necessary to feed fittings grouped in different parts of a building.

(*Below, right*). An indirect system (see text). The circulation from the boiler through the indirect heater, I.H., is completely self-contained and has its own vent pipe and feed tank.

When the boiler also supplies hot water to radiators these form part of this boiler circulation. With radiators on upper floors the feed tank, F.T., and its expansion pipe would of course be at high level.

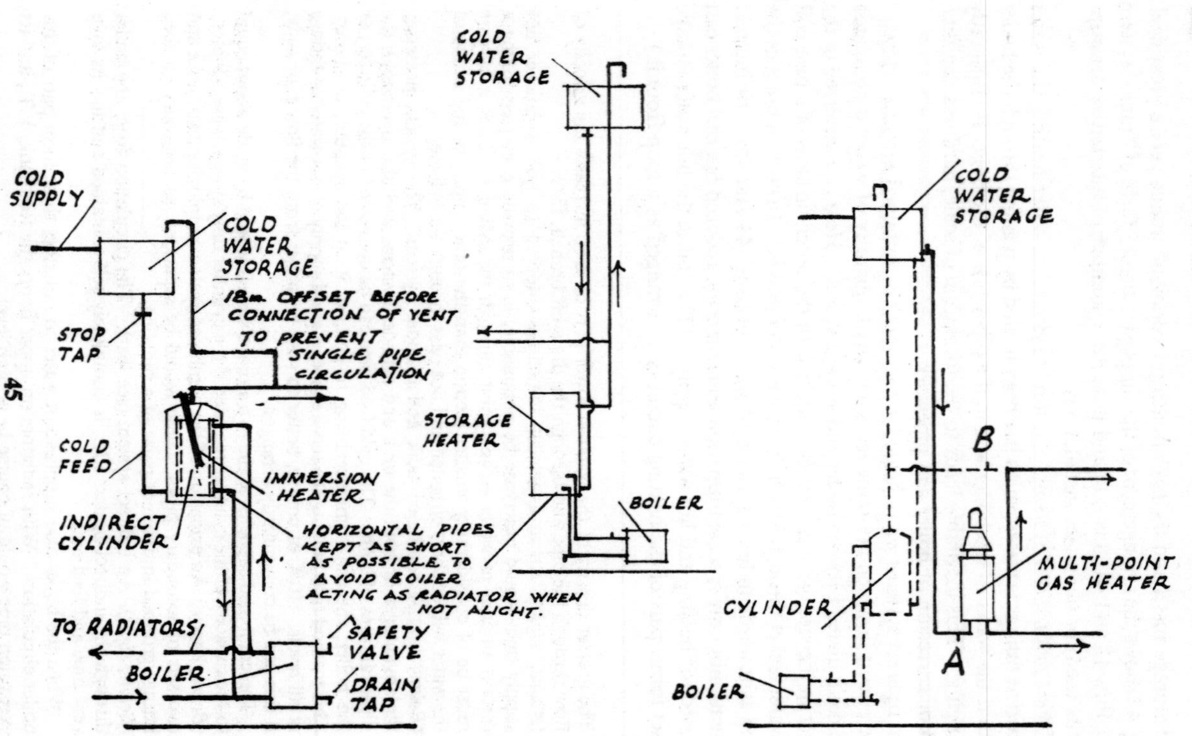
COLD SUPPLY
COLD WATER STORAGE
STOP TAP
18m. OFFSET BEFORE CONNECTION OF VENT TO PREVENT SINGLE PIPE CIRCULATION
COLD FEED
IMMERSION HEATER
INDIRECT CYLINDER
HORIZONTAL PIPES KEPT AS SHORT AS POSSIBLE TO AVOID BOILER ACTING AS RADIATOR WHEN NOT ALIGHT.
TO RADIATORS
SAFETY VALVE
BOILER
DRAIN TAP
COLD WATER STORAGE
STORAGE HEATER
BOILER
COLD WATER STORAGE
B
MULTI-POINT GAS HEATER
CYLINDER
A
BOILER

45

"Direct" installations may be divided into two groups: tank systems in which the hot water vessel because of its lack of resistance to internal pressure must be placed near to the cold water storage tank, i.e. usually remote from the boiler, and cylinder systems in which the hot storage vessel is shaped to withstand greater pressure so that it can be positioned near to the boiler. In direct systems cylinder and tank are often used together (44).

The disadvantages of the tank system are that water often has to travel some distance before reaching the storage tank, so that a good supply is not very quickly obtained, and that heat is lost by radiation from the flow and return pipes and from the surfaces of the tank, if, as is often the case, it is put in a roof or cold cistern room. On the other hand, the system has the advantage of relative cheapness compared with other systems, and of giving a good supply of hot water to fittings which are high up in the building.

The cylinder system, in which the cylinder is placed relatively low down in the system, ensures a good supply to the lower fittings, but often a poor one to those high up. Hot water is obtained in less time than with the tank system. (There is also greater safety when water in the cold-supply cistern runs short, it being impossible to empty the cylinder through the draw-off taps, as ordinarily arranged, since they are all above the cylinder.) The flow and return pipes are shorter and there is therefore less loss by radiation on the way to the storage cylinder: further, the cylinder is generally put in a warmer position than a tank, usually in the kitchen.

On the other hand, the system is rather more costly than the tank system.

Fig. 42 shows the arrangement of the simplest form of direct tank system and Figs 43 and 44 illustrate and describe a number of alternative arrangements of direct installations which may be encountered in existing buildings.

---

45 *Typical domestic arrangements*

(*Left*) An indirect cylinder heated by a loop from the circulation to radiators, radiators and hot water being supplied by a single boiler. In summer when heating is not required and the boiler is shut down, water in the cylinder is heated by the electric immersion heater. (Care must be taken to prevent loss of heat by parasitic circulation. The methods are indicated.)

(*Centre*) An electric storage heater with thermostatic control arranged so that any hot water from a small back-boiler can contribute to the total stored when the fire is lit.

(*Right*) A multi-point gas heater arranged to supply hot water to fittings in warm weather but also so that it can be by-passed by hot water from a storage cylinder when fires are lit and this is in use. When valve A is open and valve B closed, opening of taps draws hot water via the gas heater. When valve A is closed and valve B is open, opening of tap draws water from the storage cylinder and water does not flow through the heater.

Gas and electric water heating. Both gas and electricity are used extensively for water heating particularly to meet domestic and other smaller scale demands.

Electric immersion heaters, thermostatically controlled to cut in and cut out when the stored water falls below or rises above a predetermined temperature, are now almost universal additions to domestic tanks or cylinders supplied by boiler (45).

Self-contained electric storage units in a wide range of sizes are also available. Some of these are designed to occupy a similar position in the installation to that of the normal cylinder but eliminate the boiler and the boiler to cylinder pipework unless this is installed to provide an auxiliary source, e.g. from a back-boiler to a living space open fire or stove (45). Some models are complete with their own ball-valve controlled storage tank so that they can be connected directly to a mains water supply and fixed if required at any level in the building. This has the advantage of reducing distributing pipework to a minimum and is particularly useful when hot supplies are to be added to existing installations.

Heaters, described as instantaneous, are now available and are fitted in the run of a supply pipe, to, for example, a sink. They heat water as it passes through the unit.

Gas storage heaters similar in operation to the electric ones described are also widely used and may be aranged to "replace" the cylinder and boiler of a "normal" installation or as self-contained units incorporating their own feed tank and connected if required direct to a mains supply.

The gas-fired equivalent to the electric immersion heater is the gas circulator. Circulators comprise a small water jacket set around a gas burner, the jacket being connected to the storage tank or cylinder in a similar way to a boiler. The circulator incorporates a thermostat, activated by changes in temperature of the return water from the storage vessel, which reduces or cuts off the gas to the burner when the return water reaches a predetermined temperature.

Instantaneous gas water heaters have been used for many years. The gas supply to the burners of these is regulated by the volume of water flowing through them and heaters are so arranged that gas cannot be supplied unless water is actually flowing through them. Heaters are available to supply single fittings, e.g. for fitting locally in the supply to a sink or lavatory basin, or as multi-point fittings which can be brought into operation by the opening of one or more of a number of taps.

Instantaneous heaters have the advantage of providing hot water without the provision of boiler, storage vessel and circulating pipework. The actual cost of hot water heating is usually higher but this is considered by many to be offset by the greater convenience and lack of need to attend a boiler.

Alternatively a multi-point heater can be arranged on a by-pass loop of a normal boiler-cylinder circulation so that it can be put into use during periods when the boiler is not lit (45).

Recently "local type" instantaneous gas heaters have become generally available which will deliver water at any required temperature up to and including boiling water.

Where the choice of position of the hot water storage is not determined by use of solid fuel boiler in winter and either gas or electricity is used for heating the water there is considerable economy if the hot water storage or heater is placed close to the kitchen sink. This is the position most frequently used for drawing water and if the amount of dead or cold water is kept to a minimum there will be a resultant saving in the consumption of fuel.

7

The Building—its Waste Disposal Pipework and Fittings

Sanitary waste from buildings varies in its physical character and in the extent to which it would become noxious and unhealthy if neglected or improperly collected. Distinctions which reflect these facts are made in the methods used for its collection and treatment, waste from buildings being classified as "soil" (the discharge from waterclosets, shop closets and urinals), "waste water" (the discharge from lavatory basins, baths, bidets and sinks), and "surface water" (the rainwater run-off from roofs, paved areas, paths and roadways).

With the general rapid rise in living standards during the last half-century and particularly with the widespread availability of public water supplies, the water-carriage system of collection and disposal has spread to an extent which encourages many to forget that such standards are not yet universal.

In rural areas where public water supplies are not available the "Conservancy system" of collection and disposal is still used. Earth closets and privies are still permitted to be constructed in some areas although chemical closets offer higher standards of hygiene and convenience and are to be preferred.

When soil waste is disposed of by "conservancy" or "dry" methods it is still necessary to dispose of surface water and waste water. This is done by discharging them to soakaways[1] or to an existing stream or other watercourse. Soakaways usually consist of pits filled with hard rubble and topped by soil. This gives them capacity to receive large volumes of water over short periods which percolates into the surrounding ground over longer periods. Sizes of pits will of course depend on the soil character, heavy clay soils being completely unsuitable.

Conservancy methods for soil waste are described below.

[1] In some areas soakaways may not be acceptable as a means of waste disposal and a cesspool may be required. In this case soil waste would also almost certainly be discharged to the cesspool. See Chapter 8, Drainage.

Privies with middens. The earliest form of closet, or privy, consisted merely of a seat placed over a shallow pit termed a midden. The midden was sometimes lined with brick, slate or stone slabs, but was more often unlined, and was furnished with no means of deodorising the waste matters. More modern forms have either a fixed or movable receptacle, the latter system forming what is termed a pail-closet.

Pail-closets. Special pails are sometimes provided by the local authority, and periodically removed in special vans, being replaced by clean ones. The pails are emptied and disinfected before being used again. The space under the seat, whether furnished with a pail or not, should be of watertight construction, and the seat and riser should be readily removable.

Privy ashpits. In some places the privy is combined with an ashpit, the two being constructed back to back and communicating below the seat. A special shoot conducts the ashes to fall on to the foul matter and act as a mild deodorant.

Bylaws as to privies. Bylaws vary from district to district, but the following list is an average set of requirements in districts where privies are permitted.

1 Entry to the privy must be made only from the open air.
2 A privy must be sited not less than 40 ft from any well, spring, etc., used as a source of drinking or domestic water.
3 Ready means of access for cleansing must be provided.
4 The apartment must be properly lighted and ventilated into the open air, near the top.
5 Floors must be not less than 3 in. above ground, be of non-absorbent material, and fall at the rate of ½ in. to 1 ft towards the door.
6 The space beneath the seat must be lined with non-absorbent material, and the floor be not less than 3 in. above ground.
7 If a movable receptacle is provided, its capacity must not exceed 2 cu. ft or if a fixed receptacle, 12 cu. ft.
8 The space below the seat must have no communication with any drain and must not be exposed to rainfall.
9 The privy is not to be less than 10 ft from any building used as a dwelling or place of business.

It is usual to require some provision for the application of dry earth or ashes from time to time in the case of a privy having a fixed receptacle.

Earth closets. A much better apparatus is the earth closet, which, like the privy, can have either a fixed or movable receptacle, the latter very much to be preferred. Fig. 46 shows the latter arrangement in diagram form. In either case provision is made for the systematic application of dry earth to deodorise the discharges which is best done automatically. There are many kinds of earth closet, the best being those in which the earth is applied merely by the weight of the user on the seat actuating a series of levers.

The earth should be of a loamy, vegetable nature, sand or gravel being of little value as a deodorant. The application of suitable earth turns the excremental matter into a sort of mould, suitable for use as a fertiliser.

Local bylaws as to earth closets. The usual official requirements for earth-closets are the same as for privies, with the addition of the requirement that there shall be a receptacle for dry earth or other suitable deodorising material with suitable means of application. The 10 ft distance, (9) above, is usually dropped however and the earth-closet may be built attached to the building so long as there is no possibility of direct access of air from it to the rest of the house.

Chemical closets. Chemical closets, illustrated in Fig. 46, possess distinct advantages over earth closets. Earth is no more than a mild deodorant, whereas in chemical closets powerful disinfectants are used and these, in a well-designed apparatus, render faeces and urine nearly, if not quite, sterile and absolutely inoffensive. They require less frequent attention and emptying than earth closets and do not form a breeding place for flies and vermin. It is important, however, that the apparatus is designed to bring the disinfectant into intimate contact with every part of the sewage and with any surface liable to be fouled.

Perhaps the earliest type of chemical closet to be placed on the market was the "Elsan", which is available in portable and tank models. The portable model has either a vitreous-enamelled seamless steel or galvanised sewage container of 5 to 7 gallons capacity, which, under normal household use, will need to be emptied daily or every few days according to the number of persons using it. Around the container is a steel ventilation chamber, which is preferably ventilated by a 3 in. diameter pipe passing through the roof, or through a wall or window, with a cowl at its top; there are also small air inlets in the sides of the chamber. Smaller models having no ventilation pipes are available, which are thus more portable. The top of the container is provided with an enamelled guard to prevent urine from passing into the ventilating chamber and the container has a handle to facilitate emptying. The seat and lid are usually of bakelite with chromium-plated hinges.

Before use, a quart or two of water, mixed with a measure of specially prepared chemical liquid, is placed in the bottom of the container. No further attention is needed until the container is full, when the contents can be buried, or mixed with lime and leaf mould and used as manure.

The chemical used in the portable model is a liquid, the most part of which is miscible with water, but which contains a small amount of an ingredient which floats on the surface and, it is claimed, forms a smell-preventing seal.

The tank model is a permanent fixture, intended for schools, sports pavilions and the like (46). Either one, two or three white-glazed earthenware pans, each ventilated by a 4 in. diameter pipe, are connected to a cylindrical tank, placed underground beneath the apartment or apartments, of capacity ranging from 40 to 210 gallons, according to requirements.

As the lid is raised from the seat an anti-splash plate is automatically raised to a position which will prevent faeces falling straight into the liquid, causing unpleasant splashing; when the lid is replaced the anti-splash plate is submerged into the disinfectant. The raising and lowering of the lid also moves an agitator or paddle which helps the chemical to disintegrate the faeces and toilet paper.

The capacity of the tank installed will normally be of such a size as to last an average household for several weeks without emptying and when this is necessary an outlet valve at the bottom is opened and the liquid and disintegrated faeces and toilet paper are allowed to pass through a 4 in. drainpipe to a soakaway well away from the dwelling and at least 100 ft from a well or spring used for drinking purposes. The chemical used for the tank model is usually a solid in the form of easily dissolved flakes instead of the liquid form.

The latest development in chemical disposal comprises a "normal" water-closet and flush cistern (see later in this chapter), which is used and flushed in the usual way. Discharge from the closet enters a settling tank containing a mixture of water and sterilising chemical. This same mixture is pumped up to refill the flushing cistern either by hand or automatically by means of a small electric pump. After a period of use the liquid in the "closed circuit" of flush cistern and settling tank is run off to a soakaway and the tank refilled with a fresh mixture of water and chemical. (The "Destrol" system by Proved and Producing Products Ltd.)

The water carriage system is the name given to the more familiar system in which all wastes including soil are collected by means of underground drains for treatment and disposal, the soil matter being carried through the collecting drains by means of water flushing. Collection and treatment may be undertaken by public authorities or privately. Drain arrangement and construction and sewage collection and treatment are described in subsequent chapters.

For the efficient and hygienic performance of different functions and

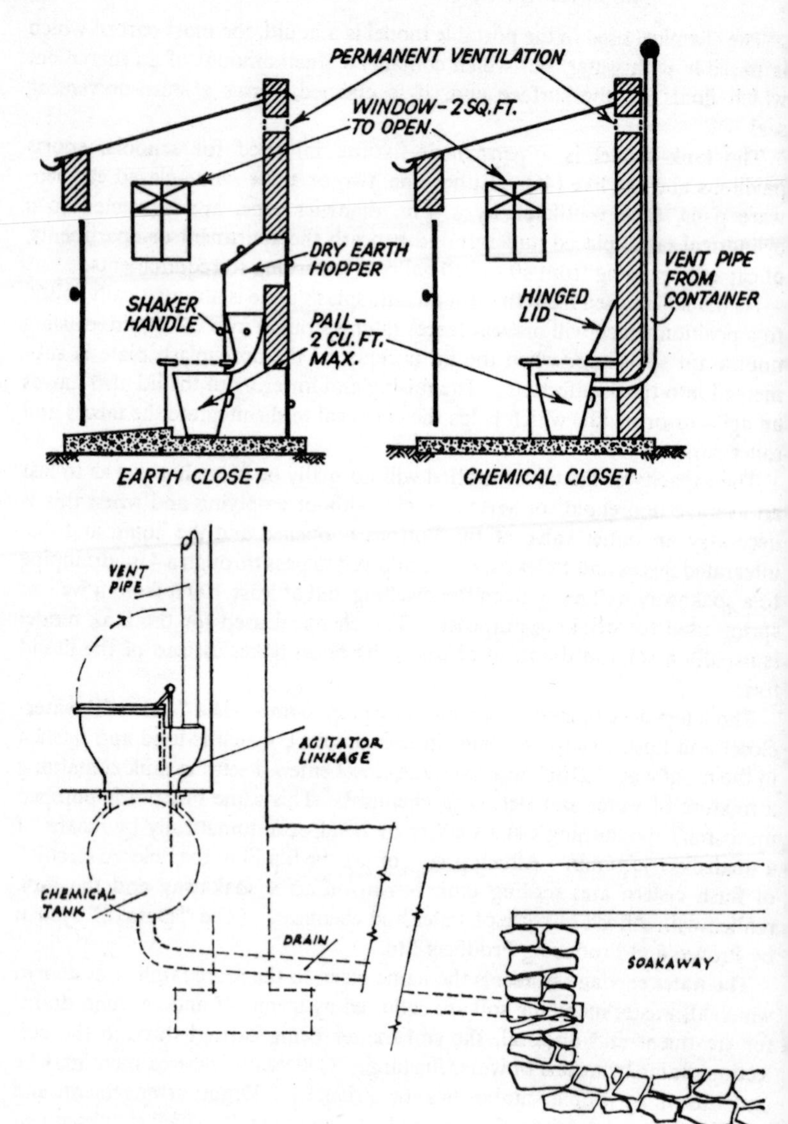
PERMANENT VENTILATION
WINDOW-2 SQ.FT. TO OPEN
DRY EARTH HOPPER
SHAKER HANDLE
PAIL-2 CU.FT. MAX.
EARTH CLOSET
HINGED LID
VENT PIPE FROM CONTAINER
CHEMICAL CLOSET
VENT PIPE
AGITATOR LINKAGE
CHEMICAL TANK
DRAIN
SOAKAWAY

46

discharge of the waste they produce, a variety of specialised "sanitary fittings" have been developed.

Sanitary fittings[1] of all kinds need to fulfil a number of obvious requirements. The materials of which they are made must be impervious and have surfaces which present no lodgement for dirt and germs. Fittings themselves should be shaped not only to suit their particular uses but also so that their surfaces are easily cleaned and arranged so far as possible so that all parts are accessible. Fittings which are liable to be fouled should be designed to reduce this to a minimum. In addition it is obviously desirable that fittings should appear to be clean as well as be clean and that so far as is consistent with other needs should be shaped as attractively as possible.

Materials for fittings. Glazed claywares of various kinds are the traditional materials for fittings and are still by far the most widely used.

Vitreous china is produced from naturally white clays which fuse when fired to form a completely impervious body. Items are moulded to shape from plastic clay and dried and then glazed and fired. China is the most expensive clayware. It has the advantages of being impervious through its whole thickness so that surface damage does not render it unhygienic, of allowing delicate shaping, minimum thicknesses and weight, and has a very high standard of appearance. China is not suitable for larger fittings.

Stoneware shares with china the property of fusing to produce a completely impervious body when fired but because of its darker colour fittings made from it depend on the capacity of the covering glaze for their colour. Its greater strength makes it suitable for larger fittings although shrinkage and movement during firing are difficult to control and fittings are heavy.

Fireclay has the properties of great strength and resistance to movement during firing and is widely used for larger fittings. Bodies of fittings are, however, yellow in colour and porous and depend on the finishing glaze for impermeability and colour.

Earthenware like fireclay produces fittings with porous bodies but of white colour. This and the finer texture of the material enables fittings to be of more delicate form and better appearance. Earthenware is much used as a slightly less costly alternative to china for small fittings.

[1] The term fittings is not now used for basins, W.C. etc.: they are referred to as "Sanitary appliances" or sometimes Sanitary fitments. The term fitting now implies taps, waste outlet connections, etc.

46 *Closets* (*Above, left*) An earth closet of removable pail type. (*Above, right*) A typical chemical closet. Both diagrams illustrate the byelaw requirements listed in the text. (*Below*) A diagram illustrating the tank form of chemical closet described in the text. (Elsan Manufacturing Co. Ltd.)

Cast iron coated on inner surfaces with porcelain enamel, fused to the metal by firing, is widely used for waste fittings. It is mainly associated with baths, where its great strength enables substantial reduction in weight relative to clayware, but its use for other fittings has increased in recent years. Fittings are robust and even more resistant to abrasion and damage than clayware.

Steel sheet, pressed to shape, has been increasingly used for fittings whose shape permits formation in this way. For baths and lower cost sinks inner surfaces are coated with vitreous enamel and fittings have the advantages of good appearance and minimum weight but fittings are not so invulnerable to denting and chipping or so resistant to abrasion as fittings of cast iron.

Fittings pressed from stainless steel, or similar steel alloys, avoid these disadvantages but costs are high. All sheet steel items need the application of sound deadening material to reduce noise during use.

Plastics. Waste fittings of perspex and resin-bonded fibre glass are now being marketed. These are light and of good appearance but it is suggested by many that resistance to wear and abrasion are as yet not great enough for general use.

Lead and copper as sheet linings over timber were once widely used for sinks where their use was confined in general to washing of crockery and glassware, i.e. where their resilient surfaces reduced breakages to a minimum. These are nowadays almost completely superseded by pressed metal fittings which have similar qualities of resilience but much more hygienic surfaces.

Timber, teak or similar water resistant species, was in the past much used as an alternative to metal linings over timber. Its use is now generally confined to the construction of surrounding working surfaces.

Standards of material and performance are set, along with dimensional standards, by British Standards Specifications referred to below relative to different fittings. All waste fittings are required to be provided with provision for overflow, to prevent overfilling and overspill during use, and all need provision to enable them to retain their content during use and the user to readily empty them after use. Methods of connecting fittings to the collecting drain system are discussed later in this chapter. Different types of fittings are considered below.

Lavatory basins, or wash basins, are designed to empty rapidly, to ensure as far as possible that they are self-cleansing as well as to offer an adequate volume of readily accessible water for the user. Some designs represent a compromise between convenience and economy, i.e. the quantity of water, usually hot, required during use but the basic problems of design are the arrangements for water retention and overflow.

Many variations in the detailed design and arrangement of the common essentials have been employed. Study of the forms described in Fig. 47 (some of which are obsolete although they may still be encountered in existing buildings), and of the very extensive range of current fittings offered by manufacturers show a desire to eliminate the chain and plug. The majority of highly priced basins marketed do this in spite of the fact that however well designed they are some parts of the plug-operating linkages are either inaccessible or involve considerable effort in cleaning. This minor defect is outweighed by the greatly improved appearance and the elimination of the chain nuisance during use. Basins are almost invariably of ceramic ware. Earthenware and vitreous china meet the demand of strength and dimensional stability and are used almost to the complete exclusion of fireclay (see above). Basins conforming to dimensional standards have for some time been manufactured of porcelain enamelled cast-iron, enamelled pressed steel, stainless steel and monel metal and more recently basins moulded of "fibre glass" have been introduced. Dimensional and performance standards are set for lavatory basins by B.S.S. 1188 and 1329.

The Standards cover two sizes of basin—25 in. × 18 in. and 22 in. × 16 in. —and these when provided with pedestals or standard supporting legs (see below) are fixed with their rims 31 in. above floor level.

Support of basins. Lavatory basins are commonly fixed on brackets of cantilever form so that the space below them is uninterrupted and accessible. The wall behind them should be faced with non-absorbent material, such as tiling.

An alternative fixing—a little more expensive—is to support the basin on a pedestal of the same material as the basin. This gives a neater appearance by concealing supply and waste pipes but objections are raised that the open back of the pedestal provides a catchment for dust which is quite inaccessible for cleaning. Pedestals also add to the difficulties of fitting the floor covering.

Still another method is to support the basin on a metal frame with adjustable legs resting on the floor. Only two legs are necessary and this method leaves better access to the pipes for the plumber and to the floor for the housewife, while the floor covering can be slipped under the base of the legs when the adjusting screws are removed and the set screws can then be screwed up to give proper support afterwards.

Basins in bedrooms. The popularity of basins in bedrooms has increased in recent years. From a purely sanitary point of view objections may be raised to any opening to the drains in a bedroom, but there is no question as to the convenience and saving of labour which result. The reliability of fittings and traps now available make the objections perhaps more fanciful than real. Care should be taken to choose a basin with a sanitary type of

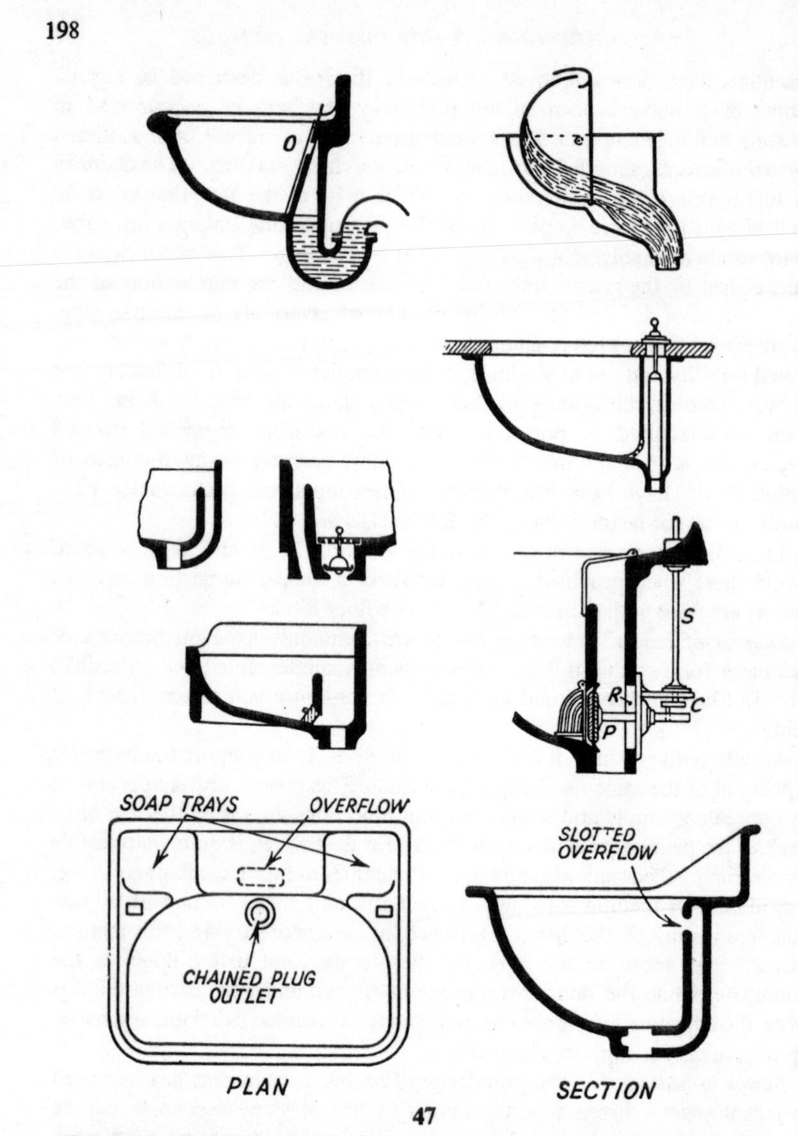

47

47 *Lavatory Basins*

(*Top, left*) A basin fitted with a so called "gate" waste, now obsolete. Across a recess in the back of the basin is a plate of metal, or vulcanite, sliding in grooves and shown by a thick line in the sketch. An overflow opening is cut

overflow and a precaution sometimes taken is to choose a trap of anti-siphonic or "resealing" type, unless the trap is provided with an anti-siphonage pipe. These are difficult to mask and make the plumbing more obtrusive. (They are described later in this chapter.)

Lavatory ranges. For schools, offices and other buildings where a number of basins is required, it is often an advantage to arrange the basins in a double row in the centre of the floor in the form of an island. A dwarf wall is built up to the level of the range of basins to provide support and is often made wide enough to enclose a plumbing cavity in its centre with a neat enamelled steel or tile covered cover along the top to provide access to pipework. This arrangement leaves the walls of the apartment free for the accommodation of urinal stalls, W.C.s, etc.

Sinks are made from all the materials referred to above.

Clayware sinks, i.e. of stoneware or fireclay, are the most widely used (48). They are relatively cheap and their impervious surfaces are highly resistant to

---

in it as at O, and the lifting of the plate allows the water to run away. On removing the plate the whole of the overflow passage is accessible. In the particular example shown, the trap is partly formed in the basin itself to obviate the existence of even the short length of pipe that would otherwise occur above the trap and be liable to become fouled. (Traps and their connection to fittings are described later in this chapter.)

(*Top, right*) A "tip-up" basin in which the bowl pivots as shown for emptying. This form is now obsolete. The chamber below the basin, and the underside of the latter, are apt to become coated with dirty soap suds and, while this can be readily removed by lifting the basin out, a fitting which requires no such attention is obviously preferable.

Weir type overflows

(*Centre, left*) Those in which the overflow passage is required to bend are less accessible than the wider straight type shown immediately below.

(*Centre, right*) The combined waste and overflow shown above is unsatisfactory because of the inaccessibility of the chamber housing the outlet sealing plug. This is in the form of a hollow tube with an open top to permit overflow.

The arrangement below is satisfactory but expensive. Both overflow and outlet are guarded by gratings. Behind the outlet opening is a plug, capable of being moved backwards and forwards by a lever handle at the top of the spindle, S. When the waste outlet is opened by a turn of the handle, the plug, through the agency of a crank at C, passes back into a recess, R, leaving both outlet and overflow fully open. It will be seen, too, that the overflow passes vertically down to the trap and is quite accessible.

(*Below*) A typical modern basin shown in plan and section. In spite of the apparent advantage of weir overflows these are rare in modern basins, slot overflows of the type shown being recommended and to be preferred on grounds of appearance and their being less likely to accidental fouling—e.g. by soap remnants or other foreign matter.

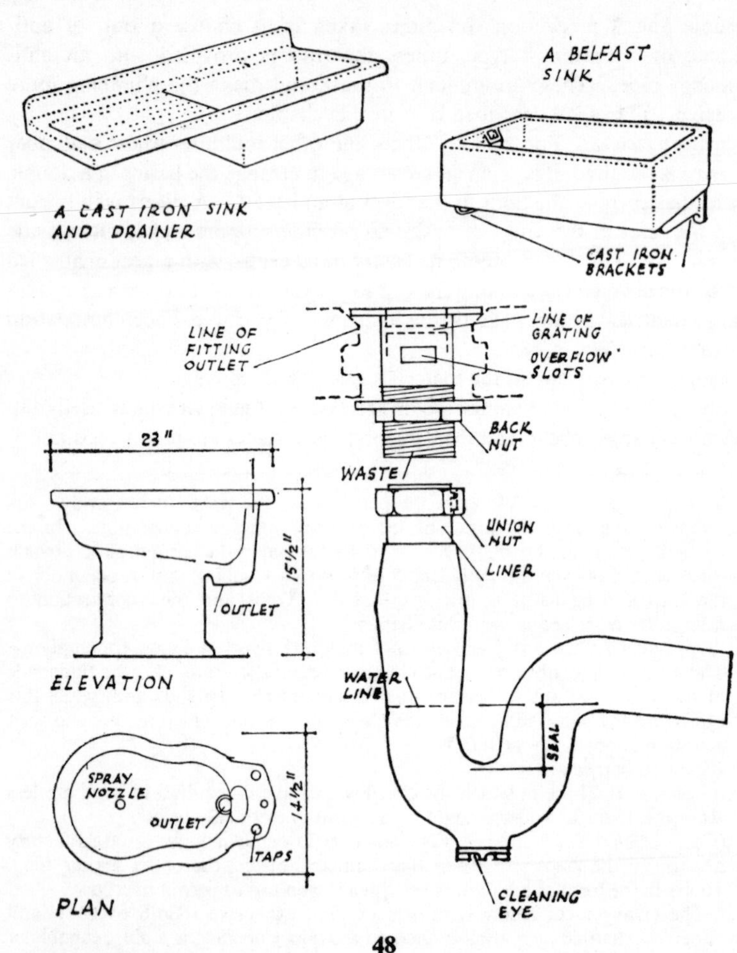

48 *Sanitary Fittings*[1]

(*Above*) A cast-iron sink and drainer unit (*left*) and a fireclay Belfast sink with end outlet and overflow (*right*).

British Standard size for sink and drainer unit of cast-iron and other metals, as shown is 42″ × 21″ and for units comprising sink, drainer and work slab is 63″ × 21″.

British Standard sizes of Belfast sinks are shown as 30″ and 24″ × 18″ × 10″ and 36″ × 24″ × 12″. For similar sinks with a back shelf holed for tap fixing 30″ and 24″ × 21″ × 10″.

[1] See footnote, page 195.

abrasion and any but the hardest knocks. They have disadvantages of heavy weight particularly if sink and drainer are formed in one piece and although sinks are available with integral drainers these are in general considered too hard on crockery. Separate draining and working surfaces are usually provided adjacent to the sink, arranged to oversail and drain into it. Sink tops built up from teak and which oversail the sink on all sides, with a wider margin behind the sink through which taps are fixed, are usually found more generally satisfactory than the standardised "clip-on" drainer units available in metal, asbestos, etc. A large range of standard sinks of two patterns are marketed, a shallow or "London" pattern and a deep or "Belfast" pattern, the latter being the normal domestic fitting.

Specialised sinks are offered as standard by most manufacturers and tubs, for clothes washing, designed to fit alongside a standard sink, or available as combined sink and tub units, have been standardised for use in smaller houses.

Standards of material and dimension for sinks and tub and sink units of ceramic materials are set by B.S. 1206 and 1229 respectively. Manufacturers offer much wider choice of sink sizes than those listed as standard by B.S. 1206.

Metal sinks have the very real advantage of having the sink and its adjacent draining surface formed in one piece. B.S. 1244 sets dimensional standards and material standards for sinks of pressed mild steel (porcelain enamelled), stainless steel, monel metal and cast-iron (porcelain enamelled). Alternatives covered by the standard include sinks with or without a back ledge, holed for the fixing of pillar taps, and sinks with a draining or working surface on one or both sides.

The ranges of pressed metal fittings offered by manufacturers include, as well as alternative sizes, units with double links, units complete with taps and/or traps and units combined with supporting cabinets designed as self-contained units of kitchen furniture.

Disadvantages associated with sheet metal sinks are their tendency to

---

(*Below, left*) A typical bidet (see text, p. 206).
(*Below, right*) A typical waste and trap assembly. The flanged and threaded waste complete with back-nut is a standard brass item in sizes for use with B.S. sinks, lavatory basins and baths. As shown the sleeve of the waste is holed to receive overflow from slot type overflows, see Fig. 47.

The threaded end of the waste sleeve is suitable for connection of standard traps of any material. Shown is a lead 'P' trap jointed by soldered spigot joint to brass liner and union nut for connection to the waste. (The internally shouldered union nut engages on the flanged end of the liner to pull the liner tight against the end of the waste.)

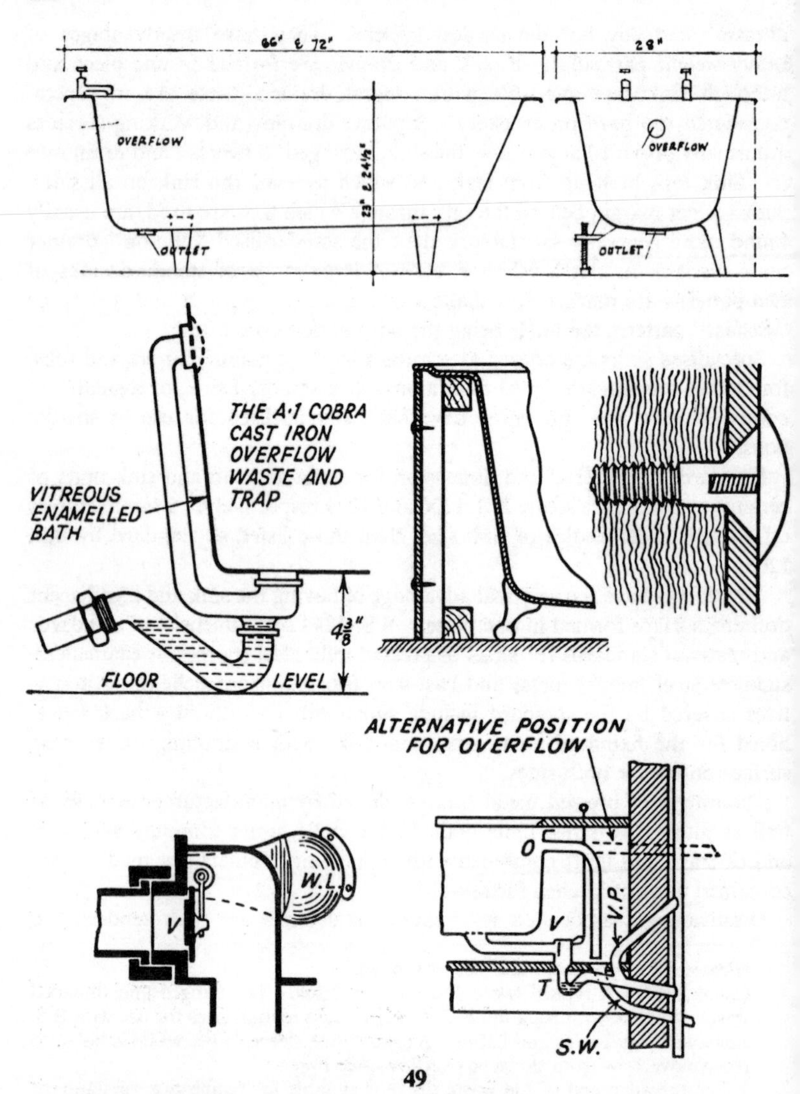

49 *Sanitary Fittings*

(*Above*) Longitudinal and cross sections through B.S. cast-iron baths. The cross section shows alternative forms of leg available—the threaded form allowing adjustment to level the bath on uneven surfaces.

"drum" which is not completely eliminated by sound deadening materials applied (usually a layer of cork chippings set in bitumen), and their liability to dent or have their protective enamel damaged by hard knocks.

Cast-iron sinks (48), although more robust, are heavy and hot water placed in them is said to cool too rapidly by many users. They lack the resilience of sheet metal sinks and crockery breakage is more likely.

Baths. Although baths can and sometimes are built up with tiled or marble surfaces manufactured items are nowadays almost invariably of enamelled cast-iron or enamelled pressed steel. The latter, because of their lack of robustness and in spite of their lower cost, have not been widely used. One-piece baths of fireclay are still produced but their great weight and cost have made them a rarity. B.S. 1189 and 1390 set material and dimensional standards for cast-iron and pressed steel baths respectively.

Manufacturers offer baths in many alternative sizes to standard and in almost unlimited variety of design. (E.g. baths with integral enclosing aprons, baths incorporating grip handles, baths arranged for alternative tap positions, etc.)

At one time, baths were often enclosed in a mahogany or other wood casing. There was seldom an effective seal at the top and the interior often got damp and musty. There was generally a hinged access door to the plumbing and the housemaid often used the interior as a store cupboard for wet housecloths and other cleaning kit, making matters worse. Then came a reversion to the free-standing bath with a roll top on dwarf feet, to avoid

---

The alternative heights effected by different leg lengths are to accommodate traps of either 1½ in. or 3 in. seal (see later in this chapter).

(*Centre, left*) The COBRA overflow and trap unit (Allied Iron Founders Ltd). A cast-iron unit, vitreous enamelled internally which greatly simplifies the trap and overflow pipework (see below).

(*Centre, right*) Arrangement of timber framing for enclosing panels and a detail of the dome covered fixing screws used.

(*Below, right*) Some water authorities will not allow a bath overflow to be joined to the waste pipe, but require it to be treated as a warning pipe. The diagram shows the arrangement of the pipes which results in such a case and shows the use of a valve outlet. It will be seen that the overflow pipe discharges over the mouth of the waste pipe of the lead safe under the bath. The valve leads into a trap, T, which is provided with a ventilating pipe, V.P. Alternatively the lead safe is omitted and the overflow taken straight through the external wall to discharge over a garden bed or yard, as shown by the dotted lines.

A detail of the valve working is shown left. The valve, V, is controlled by a weighted lever, W.L., and a chain or lever connects the lever with the top of the bath.

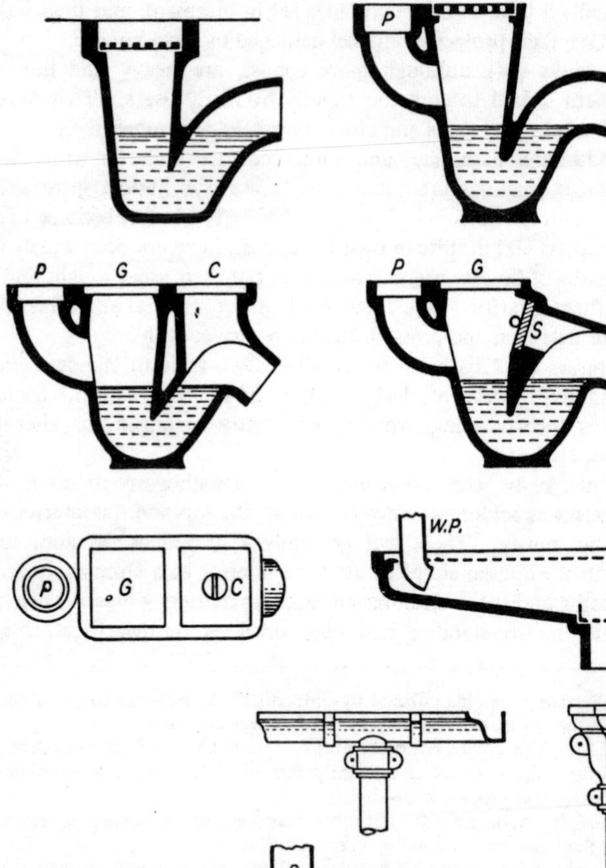

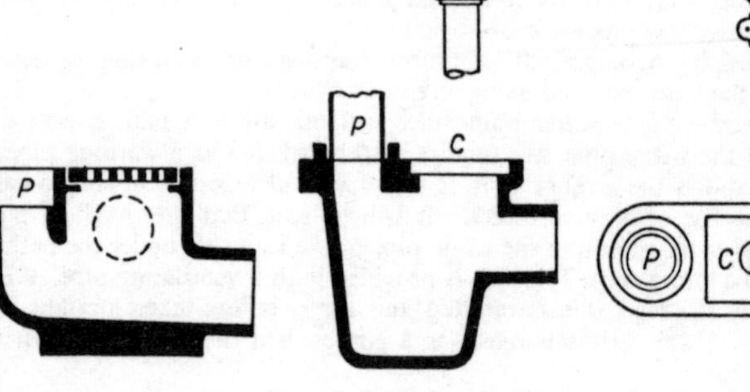

50

the wood casing. This type would be perfectly hygienic in a large bathroom, but in the modern small house where the bathroom may not be much bigger than 6 ft × 5 ft, the space under and around the bath is very inaccessible and difficult to keep clean, especially if the floor is of wood and the linoleum or other floor covering is laid by the occupier with a rather bad fit against the walls and around the short feet of the bath. Splashes and dust pass in between the walls and the roll top of the bath to accumulate in the angles and behind the (possibly) curled up edges of the floor covering to defy the housewife, trying to keep the apartment clean. As a result, most baths today are parallel-sided, fitting closely with watertight seal up against two or even three bathroom walls, with the remaining side or sides panelled.

Fig. 49 illustrates a standard rectangular bath which in even lower cost domestic work is almost universal. The rectangular shape and the shaping of the edges enables hygienic abutment to surrounding surfaces and permits easy fitting of enclosing panels to the space below the bath.

Bath panels may be of many materials ranging from slabs of marble and vitrolite to painted hardboard. Most manufacturers of sanitary fittings offer

---

50 *Gulley Traps*

(*Top*) One-piece gulleys of stoneware. Both have seals of at least 2 in. and 4 in. diameter outlets to the drain. When installed gulleys are set on a foundation of concrete, usually 4 in. thick and often completely encased in concrete.

The example on the *left* is arranged with its grating within an upstanding rim and is designed to receive discharges from pipes above its grating.

The example on the *right* has a back inlet socket into which the end of a discharging pipe can be set. Note that the actual discharge is made above the water level in the gulley and technically in the open air by virtue of the open grating.

(*Centre, above*) Two examples of accessible gulleys. In the example on the *left* access to the drain for rodding is provided by a sealed cover, C, set at ground level (see plan below).

In the example on the right the access is provided by an airtight stopper, S, set below the grating. The diagram below shows in section a channel top for a gulley. This fitting originally found use when sinks with waste pipes less than 6 feet in length were not provided with traps but, instead required to discharge into a channel at least 3 feet from a gulley. The method is considered obsolete although still permitted by many byelaws.

(*Centre, below*) Typical entries to rainwater pipes. *Left*, directly from a gutter by means of an outlet piece set in the length of the gutter and, *right*, via a rainwater head.

(*Below, left*) A rainwater shoe for connection of rainwater pipe direct to surface water only drain and, *right*, a trapless gulley shown in section and plan. The sump in this example collects detritus and rust which is otherwise carried into the drain.

side and end panels as standard accessories and B.S. 1189 sets standards for standard panels of hardboard, asbestos cement, glass, tiled slabs and cast iron.

Panels are supported by screwing to timber framework and should be removable to provide access to trap and pipework (49).

Bidets. The bidet is a waste fitting designed for personal toilet and used chiefly by women. It is found in the bathrooms of well-appointed private houses, in some hotels and in public or semi-public institutions of various kinds. It is fitted with hot and cold taps, plug, waste and overflow and has a flushing rim and pedestal support about 16 in. in height. As the user has to sit on the fireclay or vitreous china of the flushing rim, the hot and cold water controls deliver into a mixing chamber leading into the flushing rim, warming it as the basin fills. An extra lever on the control pillar is generally provided to operate a warm vertical jet from the base of the basin. In the past, Local Authorities have been in some doubt as to whether the bidet should be connected to the soil pipe with the W.C.s and urinals or to the waste pipe with the baths and basins but it is now universally accepted that the bidet is a waste fitting. Fig. 48 illustrates a typical example.

Connection of waste fittings to drains. All points at which waste of any kind enters a drain are "trapped", i.e. a water seal is created which, whilst permitting the passage through it of liquid into the drain, prevents the escape of odours and fouled air from the drain. The size of the trap and the depth of its seal are related to create a bulk of water sufficient to preserve the seal against variations of air pressure which may occur within the drain.

The discharges from waste fittings reach the drain in two ways: by discharge over a trap fitting, a gulley trap, or into a collecting pipe which in turn discharges over a gulley; by discharge into a collecting pipe which is connected directly to the drain. (Several forms of gulley trap are illustrated in Fig. 50.)

In the latter case the need for a trap between the fitting and the collecting pipe is obvious as also is the need that this trap in itself constitutes an effective cut off from the drain. Bylaws require that for such direct connections the seals of traps less than 3 in. in diameter should be at least 3 in. in depth.

Even when the actual cut off from the drain is provided by a gulley trap a second trap below a waste fitting is necessary. The interior surfaces of waste pipes inevitably become fouled. Because of the higher temperatures which obtain within buildings than outside them movement of fouled air through waste pipes and into buildings would be unavoidable if traps were not fitted. Bylaws require such traps but permit seal depth to be reduced to 1½ in.

Traps to waste fittings, whatever their depth of seal, should be fitted as close to the fitting outlet as possible. Fig. 48 illustrates a typical trap and the method of connection to a waste fitting outlet. (Methods of waste collection and connections to drains are discussed more fully later in this chapter.)

Waste traps should be formed so as to be self-cleansing, i.e. simple in form and free from angles and inaccessible corners or cavities. They are made principally of non-ferrous metals, formed from lead or copper tube or cast in copper alloy. Waste traps of cast-iron are available but the roughness of internal surfaces makes it necessary for these to be vitreous enamelled.[1] More recently traps of moulded polythene have been marketed and used in increasing numbers.

Optimum trap shape and dimensions have now long been established and British Standards set material and dimensional standards for traps of lead (B.S. 504), copper (B.S. 1184), copper alloys (B.S. 1184) and cast iron (B.S. 1291). Many early forms of trap may still be encountered however in existing buildings and some of these as well as current forms of trap are described in Fig. 51.

RAINWATER COLLECTION

Rainwater reaches a soil drain in a similar way to waste water, that is it is discharged into or over a gulley trap fitting (Fig. 50). In some areas it is permissible to use the same system of above ground pipework for both rainwater and waste water and it is quite common to see waste branches from fittings on an upper floor discharging into a rainwater head on a rainwater pipe. This, however, is an unsatisfactory arrangement, because of the fouling of the rainwater head and the resulting smell, and is not allowed in the London area and many others.

Rainwater reaches the rainwater pipes from gutters set behind parapet walls after discharge into rainwater heads or from eaves gutters set along the edges of pitched or flat roofs.

Gutters are metal or asphalt lined to render them watertight when set behind parapet walls (see Chapter 2), or are fabricated from a wide variety of materials as standard sections and fittings for assembly as eaves gutters. These are supported by suitably shaped brackets screwed to eaves fascia boards or the feet of roof rafters. Gutters are set to fall, usually ½ in. in 10 ft is sufficient, and built up from straight lengths (usual standard is 6 ft), corner pieces, stop end fittings and outlet pieces all available as standard items.

[1] In larger sizes and particularly in soil collections and drainage work treatment of inner surfaces of cast-iron traps and pipes is unnecessary on the score of roughness.

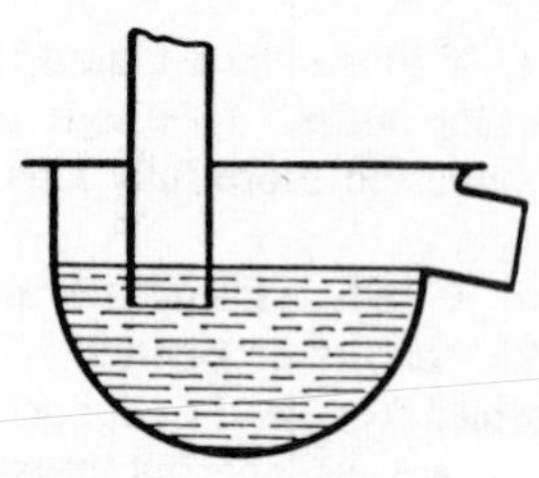

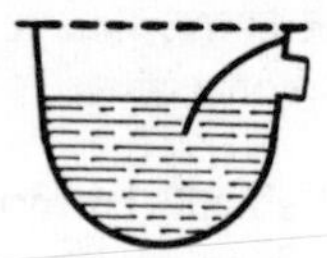

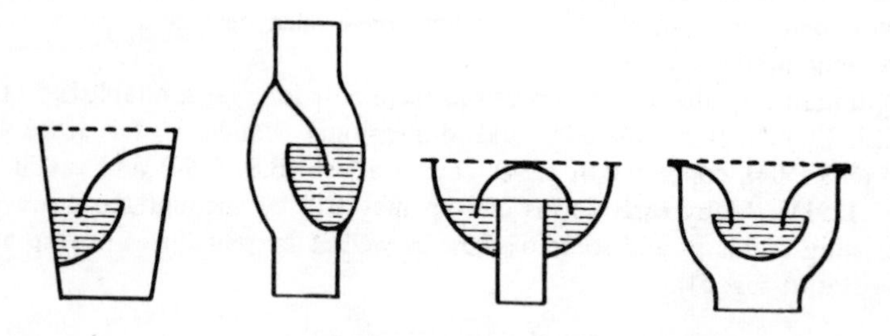

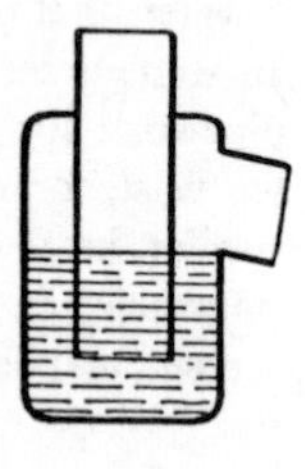

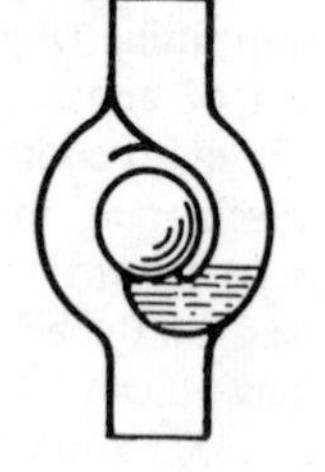

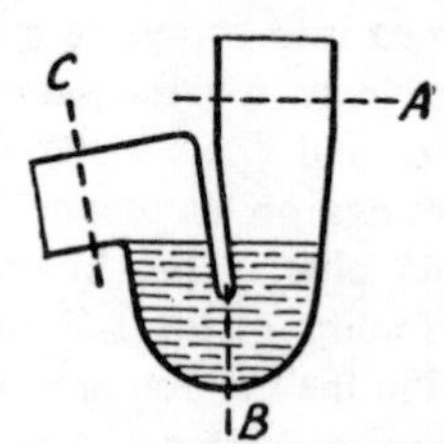

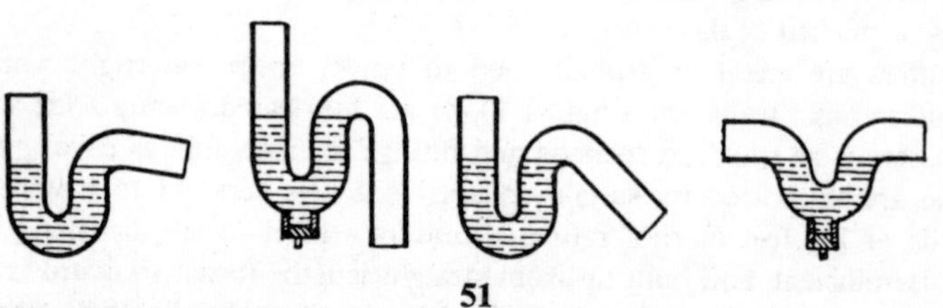

51

51 *Waste Traps*

(*Top*) A "D" trap, *left*, and a "lip" trap. Neither form is self-cleansing (both have inaccessible surfaces and both hold too much water).
(*Centre*, *above*) Two alternative forms of "lip" trap which have similar shortcomings, *left*, and two forms of "bell" trap.

Cast-iron gutters. Cast iron is the traditional material for gutters and these are available in a variety of different sections. Most usual are those of "half-round" and "Ogee" section, material and dimensional standards for which are set by B.S. 1205. (Pipes for rainwater are usually of lighter weight than those used for waste and soil collections but similar in dimension.)

Gutters and gutter fittings are of spigot and socket form, sections being

---

The bell trap was at one time largely used for sinks. The dotted line shows the grating outlet of the sink, to which is attached a bell or dome, the latter dipping into a channel of water, circular on plan. It was very liable to get choked, when it could be at once unsealed by lifting up the grating. To overcome this objection, the "inverted bell" trap was introduced. It will be seen that in form it is open to as much condemnation as the ordinary bell trap, though it could not be so readily unsealed. (The inverted bell is kept in position by light metal stays, connecting it to the casing of the trap.)

(*Centre, below*) A trap of entirely different form, the bottle trap, *left*. It has a good seal, but is open to serious objections unless its interior is accessible which was not the case in early models. Accessible bottle traps are now made, either in polished aluminium,[1] chromium-plated brass or gun-metal, or stainless steel. These are less ugly than ordinary types of trap and consequently are often preferred when pipework and fittings are exposed to view.

Mechanical traps were at one time very popular, but they are unnecessarily complicated and possess no advantages. An example of such a trap, a ball trap, is shown. The ball can be of vulcanite rubber, and is intended to supplement the small water seal.

N.B.—All the traps described, except the accessible bottle trap, must be regarded as unsatisfactory and are obsolete.

The "Anti-D" trap, *right*, fulfils most of the essentials of a satisfactory trap. (The funnel-shaped inlet is not bound to be present in a trap of this type, but it is a desirable feature.) A cross-section at A is circular, at B oval and at C a square with the corners rounded. The object of the last-mentioned feature was the prevention of siphonage of the water seal and, whilst this was often effective byelaws demand other means of guarding against siphonage. The peculiar section of the outlet also made the "Anti-D" trap a little more difficult to connect to pipes.

Interest in "Anti-D" traps has been revived in recent years for use in "one pipe" plumbing systems (described at the end of this chapter). For this purpose, the "Anti-D" trap has been made in brass with a deep (3-inch) seal and a brass screw-union to connect it to the fitting and waste pipe. Normal deep seal traps are fully satisfactory however and are almost invariably used.

(*Bottom*) Modern traps—*left* to *right* the "*P*" trap, "*S*" trap, "*Q*" trap (so called because of their resemblance to these letters) and a "running" trap.

All are of circular section throughout and all have screw-in cleaning eyes as shown on the "S" and "running" forms. (Drawn copper traps are often made in two pieces linked by a demountable joint—the cleaning eye then being unnecessary.)

[1] Aluminium has not proved satisfactory as corrosion products are easily produced which seize the threads of the trap and waste outlet fittings.

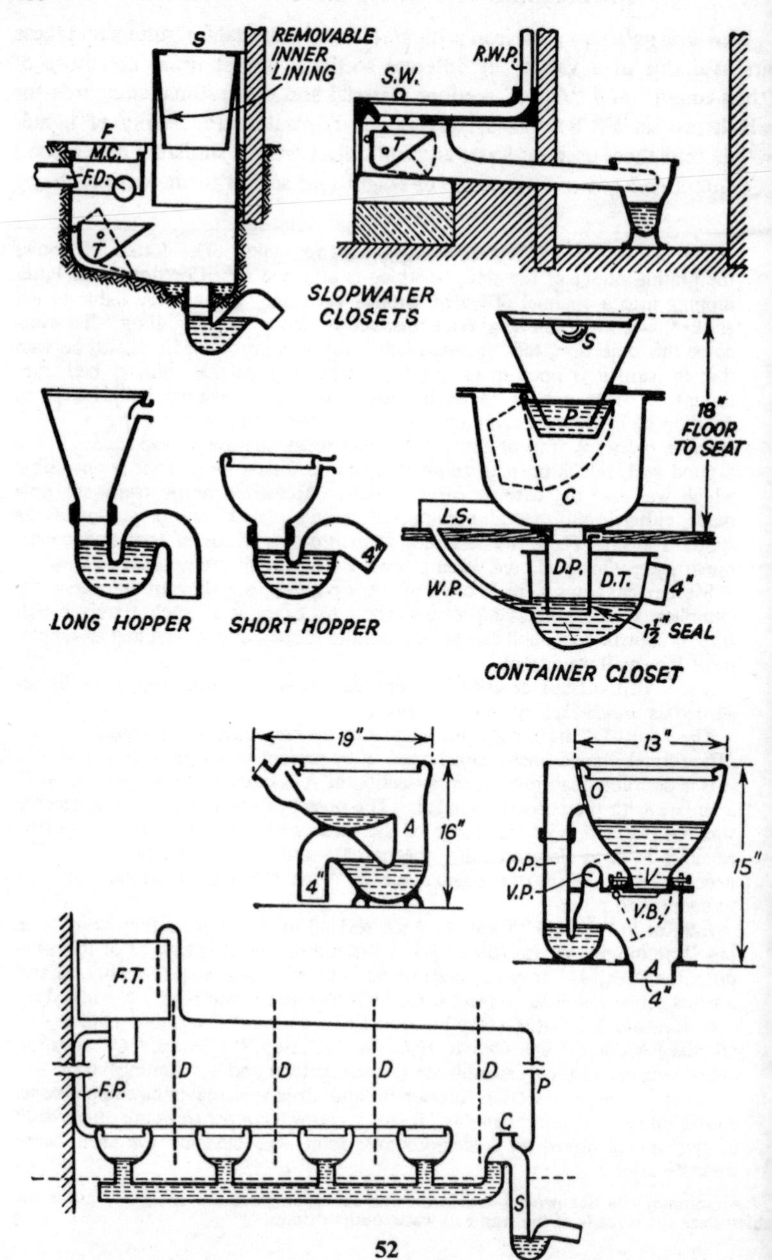
S
REMOVABLE INNER LINING
F
M.C.
F.D.
T
R.W.P.
S.W.
T
SLOPWATER CLOSETS
S
P
C
18" FLOOR TO SEAT
L.S.
D.P.
D.T.
4"
W.P.
1½" SEAL
CONTAINER CLOSET
4"
LONG HOPPER
SHORT HOPPER
19"
A
16"
4"
13"
O
O.P.
V.P.
V
V.B.
15"
A
4"
F.T.
D
D
D
D
F.P.
P
C
S

52

52 *Obsolete Water-closets*

(*Above*) Slopwater closets in which the flushing action is provided at intermittent and unpredictable intervals by the flow from waste or rainwater drains. In each case flow from the flushing drain is collected in a pivoted tipper which provides the flush by overbalancing when full. In the diagram on the *right* the flush is directed into a pan with a normal water seal.

(*Centre, above*) Old forms of water-closet. Both the "long hopper" and "short hopper" may have a flushing rim, as shown in the short hopper, or merely a spreader. Both types are to be condemned where found, because there is no water in the pan itself into which discharges may fall and the pan is very liable to be fouled.

The "pan" or "container" closet shown is also a very insanitary apparatus. It has a conical basin of glazed earthenware, fixed over a cast-iron container, C, the outlet of the basin being closed by a hinged copper pan, P, holding water. When a handle in the seat is pulled the pan falls to the position shown by dotted lines, throwing the contents into the container, which becomes very foul. The water is admitted to the basin behind a spreader, S. The sketch shows the outlet of the container joined to a D trap, D.T., by the dip pipe, D.P., there being a lead safe or tray, L.S., on the floor, the waste pipe, W.P., of which communicates with the trap.

(*Centre, below*) The "washout" closet, *left*, is less objectionable than the "container" type, but is far from satisfactory. The pan is so constructed that there is a shallow basin of water directly below the seat. (This water being of insufficient depth to cover deposits, smells inevitably result and the water cannot be made deeper as the force of the flush from the cistern would be insufficient to wash out the solids and change the contents of the basin.) Washing out of the basin throws solid matter against the side at A, leaving it to decompose until possibly washed out by the next flush, while the water merely falls into the trap without force. This type of pan should be condemned wherever found.

The valve closet, *right*, has been much discredited. It is rather complicated, and in the old forms had many objectionable features. In the most modern forms, however, it can be classed as a sanitary fitting. The chief advantages claimed for it are (1) that it is almost noiseless in action; (2) the discharges fall into a fairly deep body of water; and (3) if the house is unoccupied for a long time there is great protection given by the depth of water against evaporation.

Even if the water above the valve evaporates some protection is provided by the valve fitting tightly against the outlet and there is still the trap with its water seal below the point A.

In London the regulations of the Metropolitan Water Board, which provide that all valve closets shall be flushed by water waste-preventing cisterns, negative the valve closet's principal advantage—the noiseless action.

The valve, V, is held up by leverage, and opens downwards on pulling up the handle in the seat, the contents passing through the valve box, V.B., into trap below. It is possible that the valve may by accident become set fast, and an overflow is therefore provided. The overflow openings, O, communicate with the overflow pipe, which is open at the top for access. The overflow pipe is isolated from the valve box by a trap, and the valve box is provided with a

bolted together over a packing of red lead putty. Pipes are jointed by caulkings of red lead putty over yarn gaskets or joints are left dry.

Asbestos cement gutters and pipes are widely used for rainwater collection and have the advantage of not corroding and requiring no painting unless appearance demands it. Similar in dimension and form to cast-iron gutters asbestos fittings differ in jointing techniques. Gutters are bolted over jointing compounds best supplied by their manufacturers and pipes, if jointed, with cement mortar caulked over yarn. Asbestos cement has the disadvantage of becoming brittle with age.

OTHER MATERIALS are used for gutters similar in form to those described. Gutters are also manufactured from sheet steel, galvanised, from sheet copper and zinc and from cast and extruded aluminium.

Pipes and gutters are also available in vitreous enamelled steel, in colours to choice, which need no painting. More recently gutters and pipes moulded from P.V.C. have been marketed and although expensive these are claimed to offer permanence, lightness and complete freedom from maintenance.

SOIL FITTINGS[1]

W.C. Apartments are nowadays required to conform to hygienic standards in both their form and construction and in their general arrangement relative to their approach from other parts of buildings, their ventilation, etc.

[1] See footnote, page 195.

ventilating pipe, V.P., carried to the outside of the building. The pan is of glazed earthenware, and the valve box and overflow pipe should be of cast iron glass enamelled inside. Valve closets are usually cased in with a wooden seat and "riser" right across the apartment. In some of the later forms of valve closet, there is a vitreous-enamelled valve box, an accessible overflow pipe and the working parts are made so compact that the whole can be enclosed in a glazed earthenware casing or "pedestal", but the fitting has too many working parts and is too complicated to be a good form of water-closet.

(*Below*) An old arrangement of water-closets as a range with a common siphonic flushing arrangement.

The separate pans are divided by divisions or partitions, D, and communicate with a longitudinal pipe, the end of which is raised to provide a body of water in each pan. A siphon, S, is fitted at the end of the range of pans, with an access cover, C, at the top of the bend. Each pan has a flushing rim, and the flushing pipe has a branch to each. An automatic flushing tank, F.T., provides the flush at frequent intervals and, after flushing, the siphonage is checked by a small pipe, P, which lets air into the siphon as soon as the water level in the flushing tank drops below the end of the pipe, shown by dotted lines inside the tank. The flushing tank would, of course, be higher than shown in the sketch, which is broken to save space.

Unless adequate mechanical ventilation,[1] with safeguards in the event of failure in the form of duplicate fan motors with automatic switch over arrangements, is provided, the arrangement of compartments containing water-closets is rigidly controlled.

Ventilation and lighting must be provided by means of openings directly to the open air, e.g. through the ceiling or an external wall. These must have opening portions equal in area to at least one twentieth of the floor area of the room. Additional permanent ventilation in the form of an air brick or grating is required in some areas.

Water-closets must not be entered directly from any room used principally for human habitation or for the preparation or storage of food for human consumption. One exception to these requirements is that a water-closet may be entered directly from a bedroom or a dressing room.

Early forms of water-closet fittings were often insanitary and although these are of interest and still encountered occasionally in older buildings (52), contemporary fittings are required to be efficient in operation and hygienic in construction. Model bylaws require the pan to have a smooth and readily cleansed, non-absorbent surface and be constructed to pass the discharge directly to a soil pipe or drain through an effective trap of suitable dimensions (in the case of "wash-down" fittings, Fig. 53, not less than 3½ in. diameter with a water seal not less than 2 in. in depth); flushing apparatus which secures prompt and effective emptying and cleansing of the pan, (this must be done in many areas, e.g. that covered by the Metropolitan Water Board with a flush not exceeding 2 gallons).

Flush cisterns. In early forms of cistern water was released simply by the opening of a valve which had to be held open for the duration of the flush. To deliver the flush water more quickly and forcefully, as well as to ensure complete flushing, cisterns which empty siphonically (and automatically once their action is started) were introduced. Current standards set for cisterns and the need to prevent water waste make siphonic action essential.

B.S. 1125 sets standards for cisterns which may be constructed of a wide variety of different materials. The Standard covers dimensions and capacity and minimum rates of flushing—2 gallons in 5 seconds for high-level cisterns; 2 gallons in 6 seconds for low-level cisterns. Cisterns are required to be fitted with ball valves to control water inlet and warning overflow pipes to prevent water waste. Overflow outlets are required to be fitted at lower level than the inlet to prevent possible entry of water from the cistern into the supply pipework in the event of failure of the ball valve—and to be of larger size than the inlet (usual sizes are ½ in. diameter for inlets and ¾ in.

[1] Three complete changes of air per hour is the minimum standard.

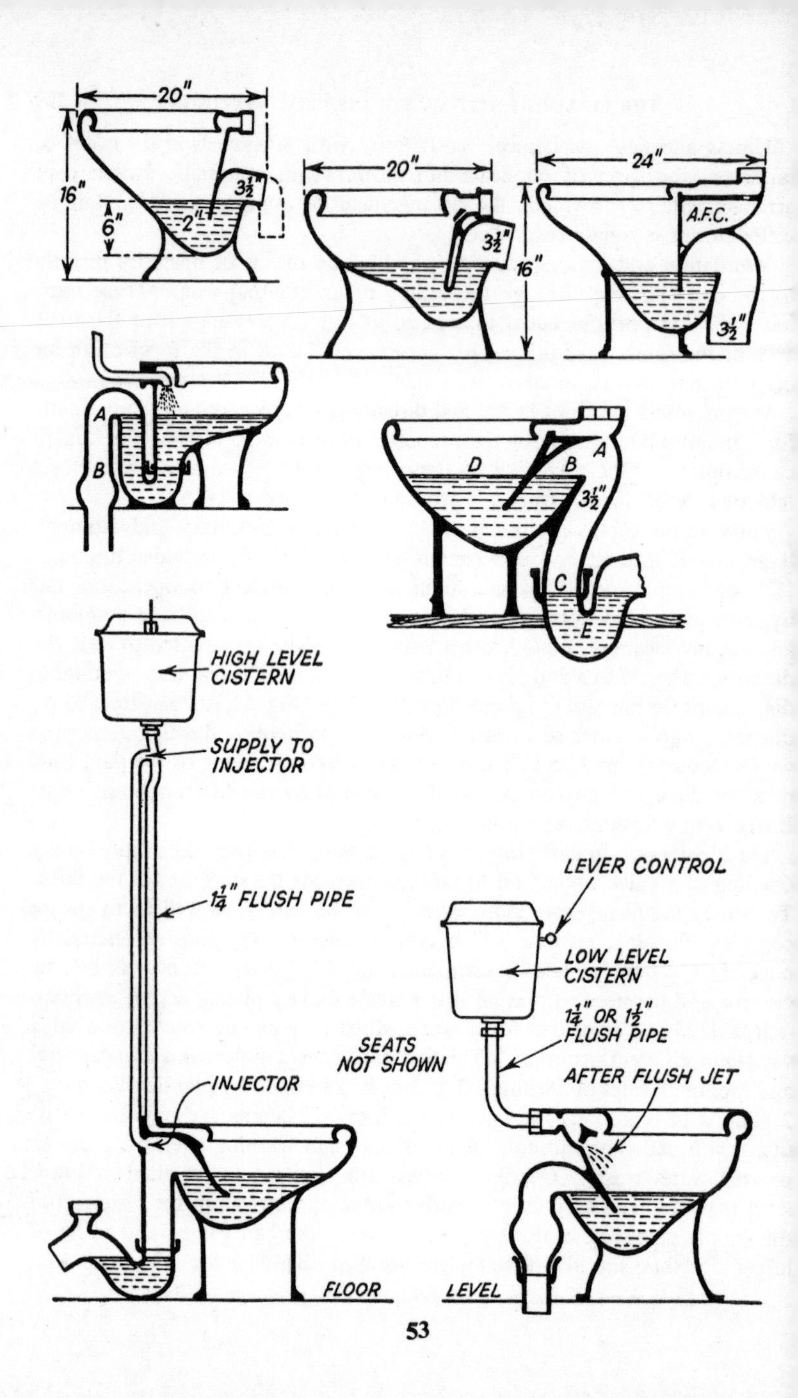
20"
16"
6"
2"L
3½"
20"
3½"
24"
A.F.C.
16"
3½"
A
B
D
B
A
3½"
C
E
HIGH LEVEL
CISTERN
SUPPLY TO
INJECTOR
1¼" FLUSH PIPE
INJECTOR
LEVER CONTROL
LOW LEVEL
CISTERN
1¼" OR 1½"
FLUSH PIPE
SEATS
NOT SHOWN
AFTER FLUSH JET
FLOOR
LEVEL

53 *Modern Water-closets*

(*Above*) The simplest and most widely used form of closet is that known as the "wash-down". In the example on the *left*. It will be seen that it is a development of the hopper type, but that the outlet of the pan is sealed by water having a reasonable surface area. The back is made nearly vertical, and in some varieties of this type, quite vertical, to guard against fouling. There is a good seal to the trap, and a proper flushing rim is provided around the top of the pan. This is the form recommended in B.S. 1213.

In some types of wash-down pan the trap is separate, and in such case the joint between it and the pan should be below water level, so as readily to indicate any defect in the joint. This type carries with it the disadvantages of a slight roughness at the joint in the entrance to the trap, while the trap itself is often of a different material, spoiling its appearance. The only advantage of a separate trap is that outlets can swivel in any direction.

One wash-down pan, known as the "pivot" closet, is designed with three-quarters of the trap made in one piece with the pan, but with the spigot of the outlet vertically upwards and just below the water level on the outlet side. The remainder of the outlet arm completing the trap can be supplied to form either a "P" or "S" type of trap and to swivel in any direction through approximately 180° as in the older forms of loose trap closet without any of their disadvantages.

The examples, *centre* and *right*, show a "wash-down" with large water area (with this type fouling of the pan is much less likely) and a "wash-down" differing from the two previous examples in the addition of an after-flush chamber, A.F.C., between the top of the trap and the underside of the flushing arm of the pan. (When the pan is flushed, water enters this chamber and fills it, while the bulk of the water from the cistern passes on to flush the pan. The outlet of the after-flush chamber is small, and the water comes from it slowly to ensure there being sufficient water left in the trap at the end of the flush.)

(*Below*) *Siphonic closets.* Two examples of double-trap closets and two examples of single-trap closets are shown. In the former type flush water flows around the flushing rim and so into the pan, but a small amount passes through the small aperture at A. As the pipe between A and C is enclosed, the air in it is compressed, forcing down the level of B and C and raising the level of water in the pan at D, which is further raised by the water from the flushing rim. As soon as the water level in the trap at C is depressed to the level of the bend at E, the air escapes and the water in the pan rapidly overflows into the outlet pipe and fills it completely, with the result that solids are removed from the pan by siphonage.

In the lower example of double-trap closet the action is started by means of an injector pipe to the space between the traps.

In the single-trap forms, the enlargement and then reduction of the outlet results in the first flow from the pan reducing the air pressure behind the trap sufficiently for the pan to empty siphonically.

The lower example shows a contemporary one-piece closet with a low-level flushing cistern.

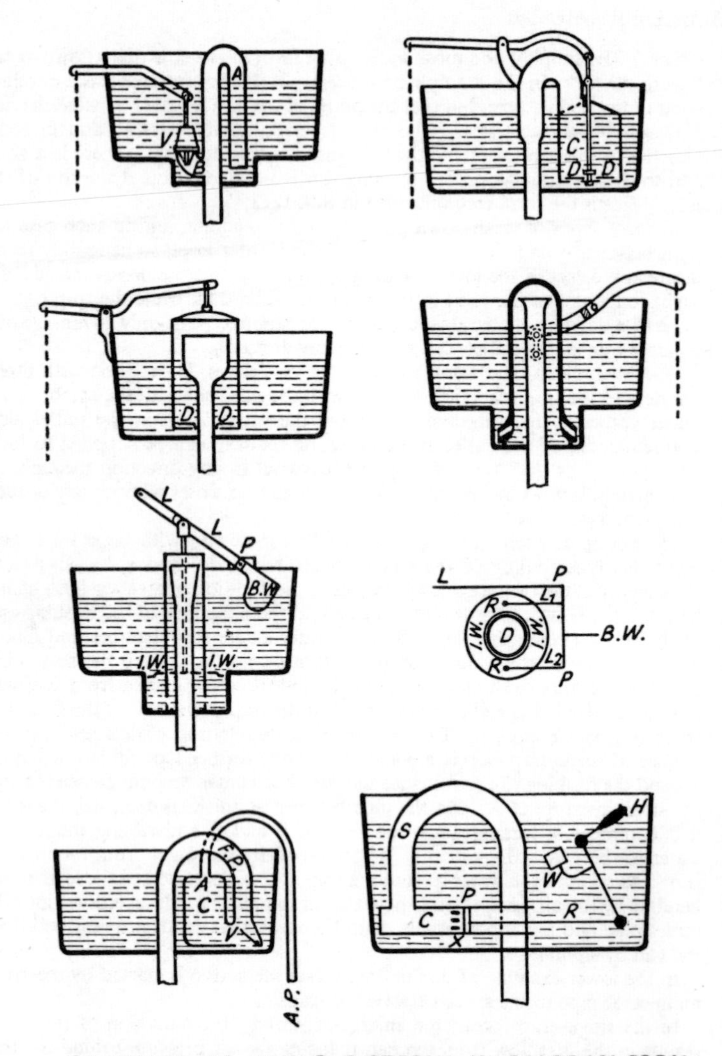

EXAMPLES OF W.W.P. CISTERNS IN DIAGRAM FORM.
(COVERS ARE OMITTED FOR SIMPLICITY)

54

diameter for overflows). (See "Storage cisterns", p. 172.) Fig. 54 illustrates diagrammatically a number of arrangements of the flushing mechanism used in cisterns.

Most water authorities limit the capacity of flush cisterns to 2 gallons, low-level cisterns usually having slightly larger flush pipes than high-level cisterns.

---

54 *Flushing Cisterns.* (Ball valves, overflows and cistern covers not shown.)

(*Top, left*) An old form of valve cistern. On pulling the handle the valve, V, is raised and allows water to rush through the branch, B. The effect of this is to lessen the pressure of the atmosphere on the small surface of water, A, with the result that the water rises over the bend and sets the siphon in action, the water continuing to flow until it falls below the level of the open inlet of the pipe. Most water supply authorities object to this form of cistern because of the likelihood of waste via a leaking valve.

(*Top, right*) In this example the pulling of the handle lifts a body of water into the bend and so starts the siphon. The end of the flush pipe terminates in a cylinder, C, closed at the top and open at the bottom so that water can rise into it when the cistern fills. Through this cylinder passes a vertical spindle which lifts a circular disc, DD. This disc fits loosely in the cylinder so that water can flow past it and so that it can return to its original position after use.

(*Centre, above*)

Left: A similar principle applied to a cistern in which the cylinder is movable.

Right: A common form of high-level cistern in which the lifting and release of a heavy cast iron "dome" or "bell" causes a surge into the flush pipe to start the siphon action.

(*Centre, below*) A cistern in which the action is started by a downward thrust shown in section and plan. Around the dome, which in this case is fixed, is an iron disc or washer, I.W., which on being forced down forces the water up under the dome and into the mouth of the flushing pipe. There are three levers all joined together in one casting and pivoted on the line PP. At the end of lever L is the handle, and at the ends of the levers L_1 and L_2 are vertical rods, RR, connected to the iron washer. As the handle is pulled down, the rods go down too, forcing down the washer; the equilibrium of the apparatus is restored by a balance weight, B.W.

(*Bottom, left*) A cistern operated pneumatically. The loosely hinged valve, V, enables the water to rise into the open end of the flush pipe, F.P., and into the chamber, C. The small pipe A.P. is an air pipe passing down to a point about 2 ft above the seat, where it terminates in a small circular leather bellows actuated by a push button like that of an electric bell. On pushing the button, sufficient force of air is exerted at A to drive the water out of the chamber and over the bend of the flushing pipe.

(*Bottom, right*) In this example the pulling of the handle pushes a loosely fitting piston, P, along the open end of the pipe and forces a body of water over the bend.

N.B.—Simplicity in action and a minimum of moving parts make for maximum efficiency and most cisterns now are of the fixed cylinder type (*top, right*) or the heavy bell type.

Cistern and water-closet, complete with fittings, are nowadays usually marketed as a "suite" and it should not be overlooked that siphonic suites sometimes require larger flush capacity than the standard 2 gallons.

Common materials nowadays for cisterns are steel or cast iron enamelled to match water-closets, clayware glazed to match water-closets, asbestos-bitumen composition, usually black. Cisterns of painted cast iron or of timber lined with lead or copper have been almost completely superseded.

Flushing troughs. Closets in ranges, as in schools and factories, are often provided with a common flushing trough. This has a common inlet but each water-closet has a separate flushing pipe, discharge through which is controlled by an individual siphon mechanism which measures off an appropriate flush from the common source. The arrangement has the advantage of providing for successive flushes at short intervals, i.e. without the time lag associated with normal cistern filling.

Flushing valves. Efficient flushing valves which deliver accurately a predetermined volume of water each time a button is pressed have been available for some years. Although they dispense with flushing cisterns water authorities regard them as a possible source of contamination of other water supply pipework in the building and usually require such valves to be supplied from independent storage tanks and independent pipework. Flushing valves are also regarded with disfavour because of their invitation to repeated flushing with consequent waste of water and because of wear or bad adjustment may permit valve to flush more than its design quantity.

Slop hoppers closely resemble water-closets in action and in form. In addition to a flushing cistern hot and cold supply taps are usually positioned above the fitting, the clayware of the pan rim being protected from damage by timber or similar insets and the seat replaced by a hinged open grating on which buckets or other receptacles can be placed for washing or filling.

Urinals are required to fulfil the simple-sounding requirements of providing a durable easily cleaned surface from which washings can be readily run off.

Examples in use range from rendered and/or tarred wall surfaces at the base of which is set a half-round glazed stoneware channel to elaborate one-piece mouldings of glazed fireclay. In general only glazed clayware surfaces are adequately hygienic and sufficiently readily cleansed. On appearance and cost grounds they have completely superseded the once popular slate slab form.

Fireclay, because of its strength and suitability for larger items, is nowadays used almost exclusively for the production of "stall" units, designed for individual use or as end and intermediate sections for assembly in continuous ranges. Stall units are generally shaped to localise fouling and to ensure more efficient flushing as well as to provide a degree of privacy during use.

A less costly and much used alternative to stall urinals is the building up of urinals from glazed fireclay slabs, channel sections, etc., standardised for assembly as single urinals or ranges, slab sections which project as screening partitions being a standard part of such assemblies if required.

Arrangement of urinals. Although there are no official dimensional standards, space requirements for single urinals or urinals in ranges have become established as 2 ft per stall or space. Traps are fixed immediately below the channel outlet and are made accessible from above by means of removable gratings set at channel level. Projection of traps into floors or rooms below are often avoided by raising urinal channels above the floor of the compartment and forming a step in front of the range. This step or the floor surface in front of a urinal should be set to fall into the channel to limit fouling of floors. Some urinals include a channel and a grooved front standing platform as part of the single unit.

Traps vary in diameter from 2 in. upwards and may be of stoneware, cast iron, lead or copper alloy to suit circumstances. Connections must be made directly to drains, as for other soil fittings, and seal depth of 2 or 3 in. provided for diameters of over 2½ in. and smaller respectively.

FLUSHING. Arrangements for regular flushing must be made. These may take the form of manually operated flush cisterns as for W.C.s for single urinals but flushing of urinal ranges is required to be automatic. Automatic flush cisterns are designed to fill at a predetermined rate by means of a controlled inlet (usually fitted by the water supply authority), and then discharge their contents siphonically when full. In the London area a flush of 1 gallon per urinal stall every 25 minutes is set as a minimum standard.

Flushing is effected by small diameter pipes connecting the cistern to an outlet rose mounted on each stall or in the case of slab urinals through a continuous perforated pipe, a "sparge pipe" extending the full length of the range.

Approach to rooms containing a urinal and their ventilation are controlled by bylaws as for water-closets.

URINAL BOWLS have the advantage of economy but the greater likelihood of fouling surrounding floor surfaces limits their use.

Connections of soil fittings to drains. Because of the need to ensure efficient evacuation of water-closets and slop-closets, as well as the need to retain water in these fittings, the traps cutting them off from the drain are, as seen above, almost invariably part of the fitting itself. Discharge from soil fittings is required to reach the drain itself with no further obstruction to its flow.

Closets are connected directly to a socket at the end of a branch drain or

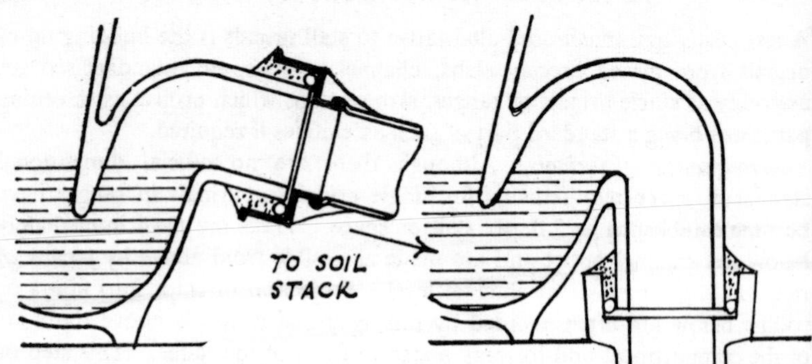
TO SOIL
STACK
TO
DRAIN

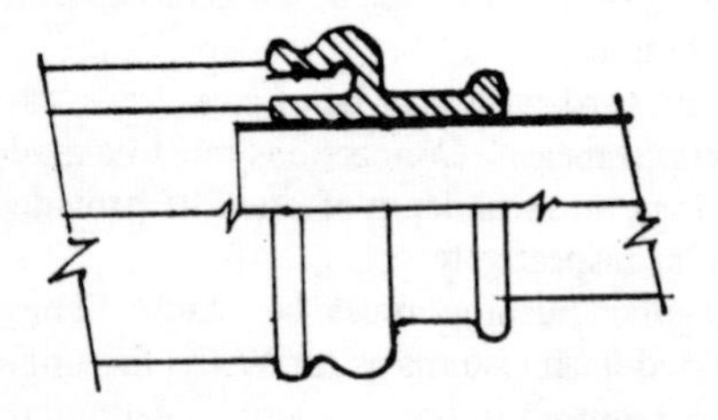

PAN
INLET

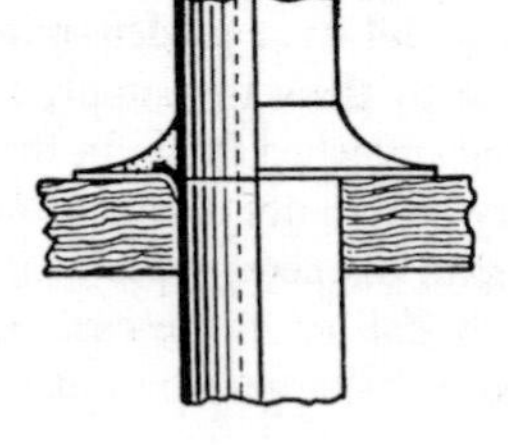

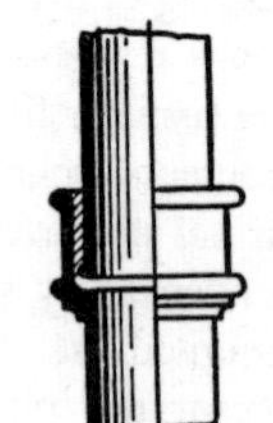

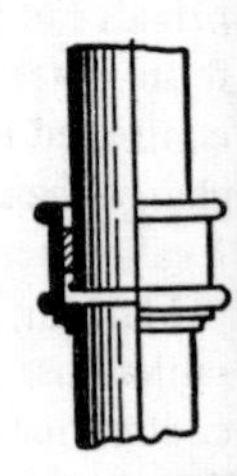

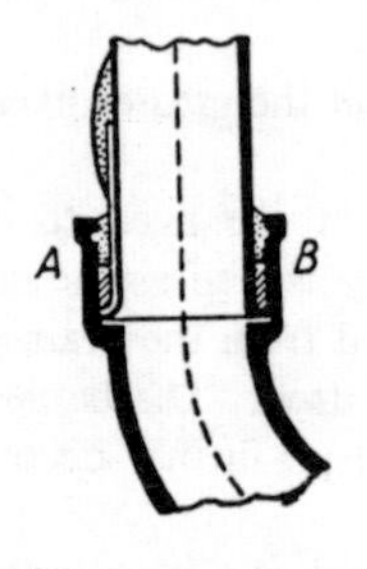
A
B

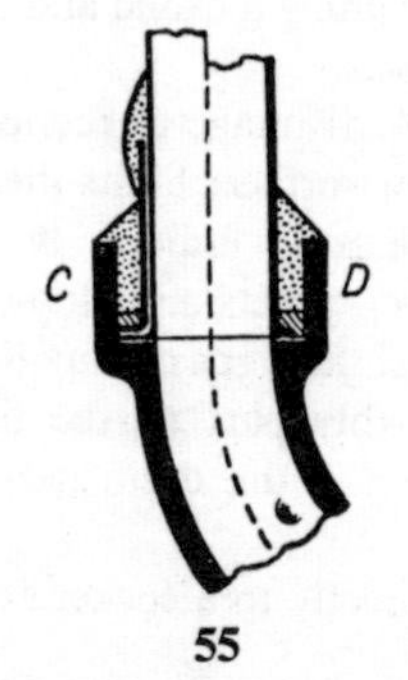
C
D

directly to a collecting or soil pipe above ground which in turn runs directly to an inspection chamber and the drain. The former method is used for fittings at ground level. Fittings with S trap outlets are chosen and these are set directly into the upturned sockets of branch drains brought through the outside wall and the floor of the building. Material commonly used for drains are glazed clayware and cast-iron, and for soil pipes above ground cast iron, asbestos cement and copper or lead. Joints between the clayware outlets of closets and sockets of clayware, and asbestos cement or sockets of copper or copper alloy are all made in a similar way.

The outlet spigot of the fitting is first positioned and aligned in the pipe or drain socket by caulking with yarn or gaskin (loosely twisted hemp yarn). This also serves to prevent the 1 : 1 Portland cement and sand mortar used to fill the joint from being pushed through to the pipe interior (55).

---

55 *Connections*

(*Top*) CONNECTION OF W.C. OUTLETS TO DRAINS. *Left*, to a branch from a soil stack and, *right*, to a socket of a branch drain. The joint in both cases is made with 1:1 cement mortar placed over yarn gaskin.

In the connection to stack detail the branch is assumed to be of lead and to enable it to be connected to the pan spigot a brass socket or "thimble" is soldered to the end of the lead pipe. (The connection of the lead branch to the stack is a caulked lead joint, a brass spigot being soldered to its end to make it strong enough for caulking into the socket on the stack—see "lead to iron" joint below.)

(*Centre, left*) CONNECTION OF FLUSH PIPE to flushing inlet of a W.C. pan by means of one of the many types of rubber cone now available. This grips tightly the flush pipe and the spigot of the pan inlet.

(*Centre, right*) PIPE JOINTING. *Left*, a joint in heavy lead pipe. The solder used in the joint is formed into a supporting shoulder and also attaches the sheet lead flange to the pipe. The supporting slab is usually of stone and for best results the pipe should be set within a chase in the wall. (Lead soil pipes are very rarely used nowadays. Alternative methods of jointing follow the lines of those described earlier for lead water and waste pipes, support being provided by means of "ears" soldered to the pipes.)

Centre, a caulked lead joint for cast-iron pipes—molten lead or lead wool (finely shredded lead) caulked over a yarn gasket.

Right, an expansion joint for cast iron stacks—the joint is made over a tightly packed band of greased hemp. (These joints are rarely considered necessary.)

(*Below*) JOINTING OF STACK TO DRAIN.

Left, cast-iron and lead pipes jointed to a cast-iron drain socket and, *right*, jointed to a stoneware drain socket. In both cases the lead is strengthened by brass spigot thimbles soldered on to enable caulking with lead in the case of jointing to cast iron, or cement mortar in the case of jointing to stoneware to be carried out.

Alternatives to cement mortar for making the joint are a mixture of white lead and linseed oil or, more rarely, bituminous compounds. These materials have the advantage of being able to accommodate slight movements of the fitting relative to the pipework.

Connection of the flush pipe to the fitting is nowadays almost invariably effected with a specially moulded rubber or plastic "cone" (55), although many other methods are encountered in existing buildings.

Some joints are made with rubber rings compressed by screw collars, so as tightly to pack the space between the flush pipe and earthenware. Another method is to use special collars of lead, hinged together in two pieces and secured by a small bolt. The collar connects the pipe to the flushing arm and is packed inside with red and white lead. In low-cost housing schemes, the flush pipe is often of telescopic pattern, in two or three sections, so as to be adjustable for different cistern positions. The material is then thin galvanised or vitreous enamelled steel and the sections are slightly varied so that the upper length can make a close fit inside the middle length and the middle length inside the bottom section. The sections are coated with a thick paste of red and white lead putty before being fitted into one another and adjusted, any surplus paste being cleaned off after the fixing is complete.

Connection of the flush pipe to the cistern is made by means of a flanged threaded sleeve in a similar manner to the connection of traps to waste fittings (see 48, p. 200). In some cases the threaded sleeve to receive the union nut is part of the cistern and to simplify the connection still further the end of the flush pipe, nowadays usually galvanised or enamelled steel or copper, is prepared to provide a purchase for the shouldered union nut.

Collection of Waste Above Ground

It is obviously essential, for reasons of both appearance and economy, that where a number of fittings discharge in the same area common collecting pipes be used. Whenever this is done conditions are created in which the seals of traps to fittings may be destroyed or reduced.

Whenever pipes discharge at or near full bore an area of reduced air pressure is created immediately behind the moving water. This is of course restored to normal by the movement of air in the pipe above or behind the discharge. When a number of branches join a common discharge pipe, however, the area of reduced pressure following a discharge results in movement of air from the branch pipes it passes. This, because of the resulting difference between the air pressure within the branch and the air pressure on the outer surface of the trap sealing off the branch, causes partial or complete movement of water from the trap.

This phenomenon is described as "induced" siphonage and occurs in both horizontal and vertical arrangements of collecting pipework. Drainage bylaws require that vent pipes be provided and arranged to make good the air loss from branch pipes and so protect traps from loss of seal in this way. Fig. 56 illustrates typical arrangements of pipework.

Self-siphonage. Similar conditions of varying air pressure leading to loss of trap seal may also occur when pipes carrying discharge from a single fitting are arranged so that they run at full bore during a discharge—e.g. when pipes are long and/or steep (see later under "Single stack collections").

Arrangement of a collecting system of pipework will vary to suit particular circumstances, e.g. the planning and distribution of sanitary fittings, and may be a "two-pipe" system in which discharges from waste pipes are connected to a collecting stack carrying waste only. In this arrangement the waste stack is required to discharge over a gulley as described earlier (waste connection to a drain), and its upper end is required to be open to the air, the open end being positioned where it will not cause nuisance or danger to health. Precautions in the form of vent pipes to prevent loss of trap seals are required for both waste and soil pipes (56). Alternatively the collecting system may be a "one-pipe" system in which both soil and waste discharges are connected to a common stack. Venting of the system is required as for a two-pipe system (Fig. 56), but because the waste fitting traps have now become their only cut-off from the drain (i.e. the soil pipe), these traps are required to have a 3 in. deep seal.

Specialised fittings have been developed designed to simplify the complete system of pipework often needed for collections of the kinds described.

Anti-siphon or resealing traps for waste fittings are marketed in a variety of different forms. They make venting of waste traps unnecessary and although they differ greatly in the arrangement of their "working parts" all operate on a similar principle. Internal "shoulders" or projections or by-passing water-ways are arranged so that during periods of siphonage part of the water content of the trap is retained (57).

When siphonage conditions end this retained water returns to the base of the trap to reseal it. Seals of traps are reduced and some authorities are reluctant to permit the use of these traps, partly for this reason and partly because the complexity of the inner-surfaces of some types leads to fouling by waste scum and grease.

The Spruce Thrower unit is a patent cast iron fitting designed to simplify the pipework required for vented systems of collection as well as reducing the labour involved in its installation. A typical example of this fitting, which is available in a wide range of sizes to meet variations of dimensional

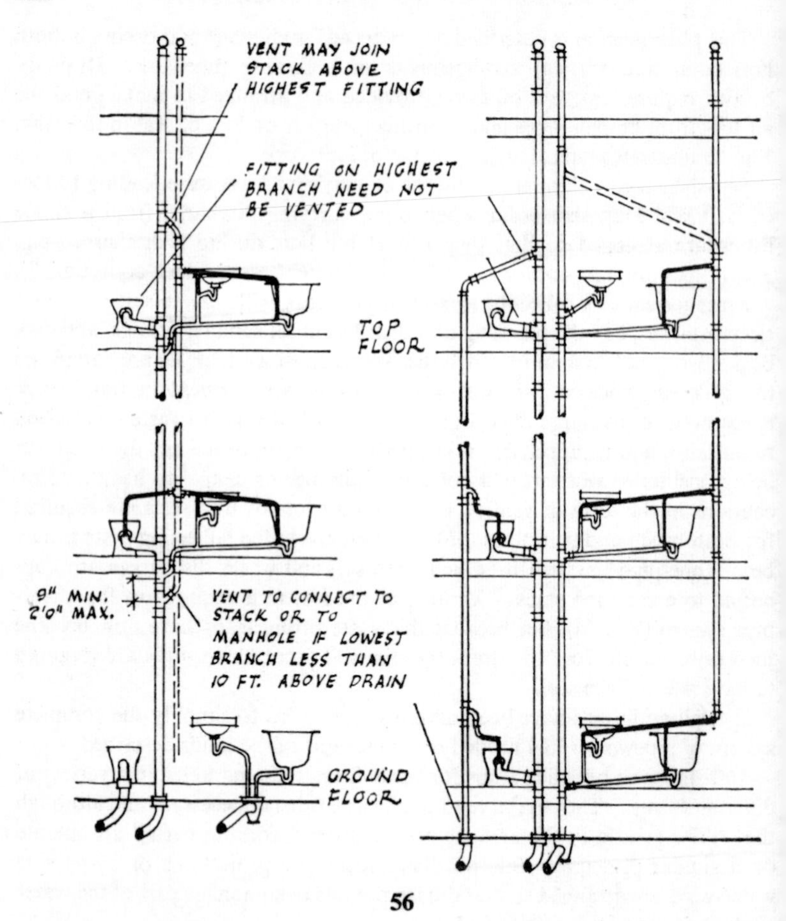

56 *Vented collections for Soil and Waste*

(*Right*) A two-pipe system of pipework in which soil and waste water are collected separately. The main waste stack discharges into a gulley trap (above its water level), which provides the necessary separation from the drain. Traps beneath fittings are required to have a seal of only 1½ in. Each fitting subjected to siphonage must be vented as shown—connection of the vent to the waste branch must be made not further than 18 in.[1] or nearer than 3 in. from the crown of the trap and its connection made in the direction of the flow through the branch. (Connection of the trap outgo to a vertical waste/vent

[1] The maximum in the London area is 12 in.

requirements on site (e.g. differences in wall thicknesses and positioning of fittings relative to stacks), is shown in Fig. 57.

Fittings are also obtainable with cast-on threaded bosses for direct connection of trench wastes.

SINGLE STACK COLLECTIONS

More recently the possibilities of effecting economies in plumbing pipework by the omission of trap vents and their accompanying vent pipework have been made the subject of a great deal of both laboratory and field research. This has shown that if pipe sizes, pipe junctions and pipe gradients are scientifically arranged and related to each other, both the self-siphonage and induced siphonage resulting from discharges from fittings and through collecting pipework can in many instances be effectively resisted by normal trap seals. Collecting systems arranged in this way are described as "one-pipe-single stack collections" to distinguish them from the earlier, so called, one-pipe systems which required trap venting pipework (56). Design principles have been formulated and most authorities will now approve single stack collections if these principles are adhered to. They are summarised below.

Self-siphonage is more likely to occur at traps of waste fittings but self-siphonage conditions are less severe if the branch waste from the trap to the

---

length of pipe as shown ensures that the end of the vent is never fouled by waste deposits.)

(*Left*) A one-pipe system of pipework in which soil and waste water are carried in the same pipe. Because they are the only separation between the drain and the interior of the building, drops below waste fittings are required to have seals 3 in. in depth.

N.B.—The connection of the lower end of the vent pipe to the stack (or to a manhole at high level), when lowest fittings are relatively near the drain is required to prevent any resistance to the escape of air pushed ahead of a high-level discharge from building up any pressure within the pipework and the "blowing through" of traps to low-level fittings which might result.

The horizontal sections of branch vents should preferably be set above the level of the overflows from waste fittings to prevent their fouling in the event of stoppages in the waste pipework.

Size of vents required varies. From W.C.s branch vents not less than 2 in. diameter are required in the London area, not less than 1¼ in. diameter by provincial bylaws.

Branch vents to waste fittings are required to be ⅔ the waste-pipe diameter but not less than 1¼ in. in London or 1 in. in provincial areas.

Sizes of main vent pipes vary with condition but must be never less than 2 in. in London or 1¼ in. in the provinces.

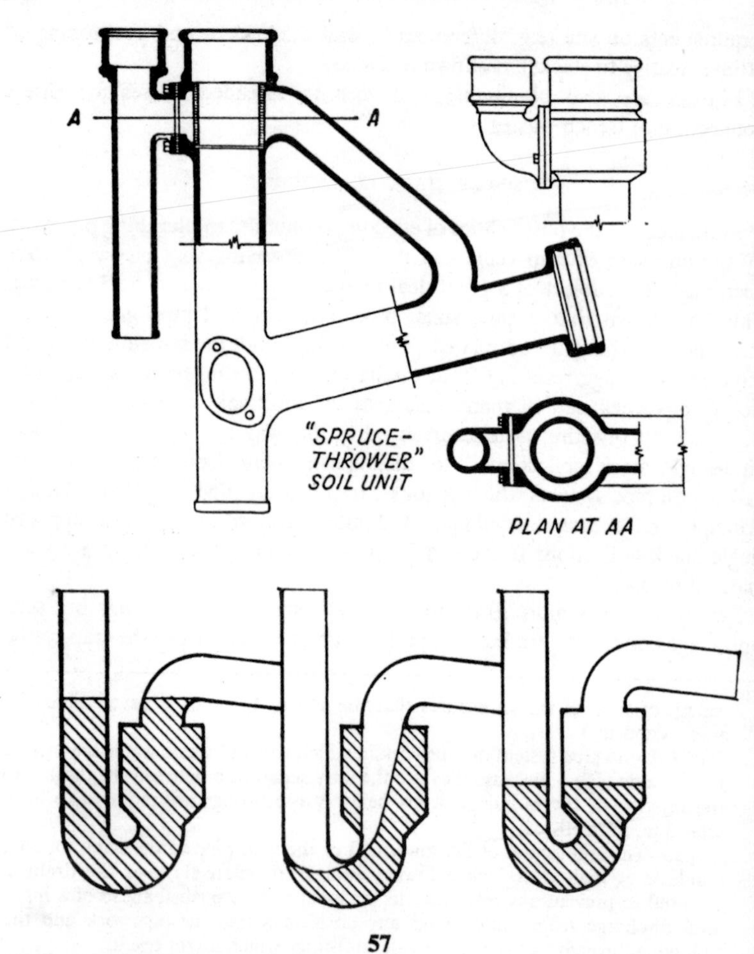

57 *Vents and traps*

(*Above*) A typical "Spruce Thrower" unit. As the diagram shows the fitting combines W.C. socket, vent arm and vent and soil stack sections in a single unit. This results in great simplification of pipework and its installation.

The vent can be positioned immediately behind the soil stack as shown, or set on either side of it. In all cases the "passing" of the soil pipe by the vent arm eliminates crossings of pipes and in addition to simplification saves a great deal of space when pipes are positioned within buildings. (The diagram, *top right*, shows a modified vent connection when this does not need to be carried below the lowest fitting on the system (see Fig. 56).)

stack is kept short and its gradient kept shallow. Thus rules for relating the length and gradient of branch wastes from fittings have been established. These set length maxima for wastes from different types of fittings and the maximum gradient which can be tolerated for each length (58).

The greater the length of a waste branch the shallower is its permitted gradient and advantage has been taken of this fact in designing specialised fittings to simplify single stack pipework installations. These fittings are designed with prepared inlets for branch wastes (in combination with a soil branch and socket, or independently of these according to circumstances), the fittings being dimensioned so as to place these inlets at the required levels above the floor. Fittings' design and satisfactory use depends, of course, on precise knowledge of the height of outlets from traps of fittings. When sanitary fittings and traps conforming to B.S.S. are used this information is known in advance so that not only can pipe fittings be standardised but their early positioning on the works can be specified with confidence.

N.B.—In the case of sinks and lavatory basins the fittings, their traps and their heights above floor must all conform to standard. Specification of British Standard traps (of any of the different materials covered), together with the specification of standard heights to rim of lavatory basins and sinks (31 in. and 36 in. respectively), meets this requirement.

Fig. 59 illustrates standard cast-iron single stack fittings and their application. Similar standard fittings of other materials are available also and purpose-made fittings to meet special needs are readily available in cast iron, copper and galvanised steel.

Connections to stack. Branch inlets to vertical collecting stacks must be positioned to avoid the effects of induced siphonage so far as possible and the risk of back flow, or arrested flow, in waste branches (e.g. such as might occur if say a bath waste branch inlet were placed exactly opposite a W.C. inlet). Fig. 58 illustrates requirements in this respect.

Back pressure. Provision must be made to avoid "blowing" of low level traps such as may occur if air movement from the base of a vertical stack is restricted—e.g. by a restricting bend at its foot or its connection to a drain which is overcharged—or may on occasions be overcharged.

Application of single stack collections[1] is limited—i.e. there is a limit to

[1] Information from *BRS Digest No. 32* Second Series.

(*Below*) The McAlpine resealing trap. This is probably the simplest form of resealing trap and illustrates the basic principles on which these fittings operate. The diagrams show the position of the water content of the trap before, during and after siphonage.

Recurrence of siphonage does not further reduce the residual seal.

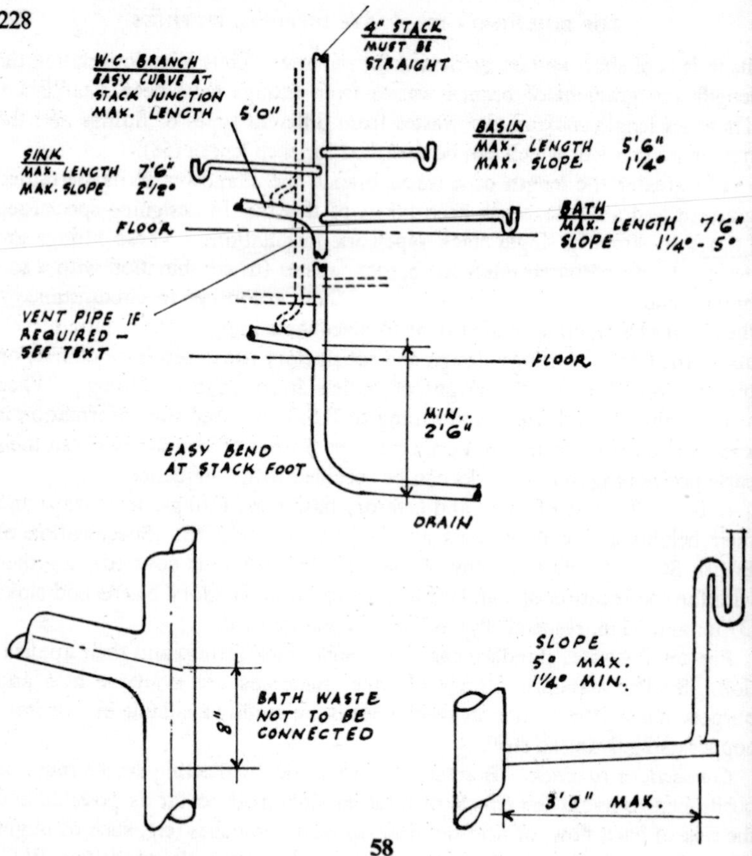

58 *Single Stack Collections*

(*Above*) Diagram showing the basic requirements to be met when soil and waste collections are made without vents to fittings traps.

(The vent pipe shown dotted enables the principles to be applied to collections of greater extent without full venting of traps as in traditional methods—see text.)

The "easy bend" at the stack foot may be formed with a large radius 90° bend (stoneware), but preferably with two 135° bends to give a larger radius.

The requirements of the easy curve at soil branch connections to stack are satisfied if standard cast iron fittings are used.

(*Below, left*) Detail at W.C. branch connection showing the restriction placed on the positioning of the bath waste connection.

(*Below, right*) An alternative arrangement for the lavatory basin waste and the dimensional requirements to be satisfied if it is used.

the number of fittings which can be safely connected to one vertical collecting stack.

Using 4 in. diameter stacks, current experience shows that completely unvented systems are satisfactory (so long as the detail arrangements illustrated in Fig. 58 are adhered to), up to the following limits:

up to 5 storeys in height for flats when either one or two flats are served on each floor.

up to 4 storeys in height for maisonettes when either one or two maisonettes are served at each "collecting level" or 8 storeys when only one maisonette is served at each "collecting level".

By partial ventilation of the pipework the application of single stack principles can be extended as follows:

by adding a 2 in. diameter vent pipe to the system with a branch to one W.C. on each alternate floor satisfactory results are obtained for flats up to 11 storeys in height when either one or two flats are served on each floor;

a similar arrangement extends the application to maisonette collection up to 8 storeys high when two maisonettes are served at each collecting level;

with the addition of a 2 in. main vent with a branch to one W.C. on every floor the system is satisfactory for maisonettes or flats, arranged singly or in pairs, up to 15 storeys in height;

Increasing the diameter of the main vent to $2\frac{1}{2}$ in. the system is suitable for flats up to 20 storeys in height serving one W.C. group per floor with one vent branch per floor or for maisonettes up to 20 storeys in height serving one or two W.C. groups per floor with branch connections on alternative (bathroom) floors.

Increasing the diameter of the main vent to 3 in. the system is suitable for flats up to 20 storeys in height with two W.C. groups per floor, one W.C. vent per floor being connected.

A group is considered to consist of a W.C., bath, basin and sink.

PIPEWORK FOR SOIL AND WASTE COLLECTIONS

Many materials are satisfactory used for pipes and fittings for soil and waste collections. Choice is dependent on considerations of initial cost and standards of performance, appearance, resistance to damage and amount of maintenance likely to be required. By far the most widely used material is cast iron, particular requirements of some kind usually being necessary to influence choice of alternatives—e.g. the need for minimum initial cost or a particular degree of permanence or lack of need for maintenance.

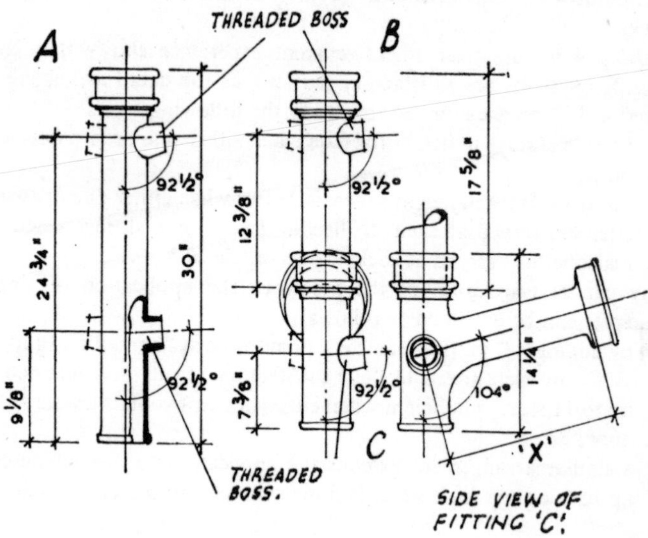
THREADED BOSS
A
B
92½°
92½°
24 ¾"
30"
12 ⅜"
17 ⅝"
9 ⅛"
7 ⅜"
92½°
92½°
104°
14 ¼"
C
'X'
THREADED BOSS.
SIDE VIEW OF FITTING 'C'.

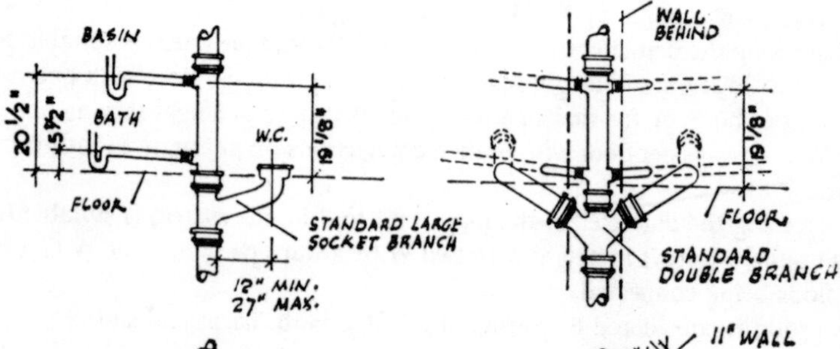
BASIN
BATH
20 ½"
5½"
19 ⅛"
W.C.
FLOOR
STANDARD LARGE SOCKET BRANCH
12" MIN.
27" MAX.
WALL BEHIND
19 ⅛"
FLOOR
STANDARD DOUBLE BRANCH

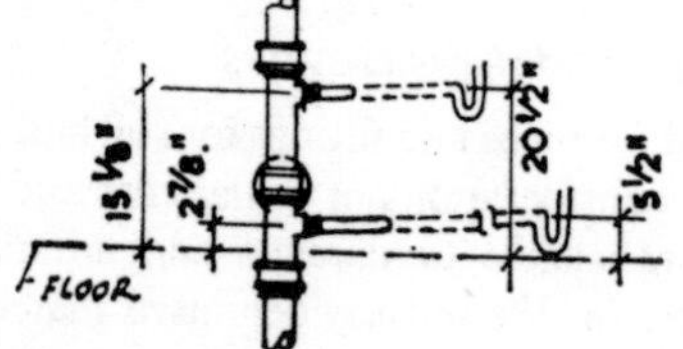
15 ⅛"
2⅞"
20½"
5½"
FLOOR

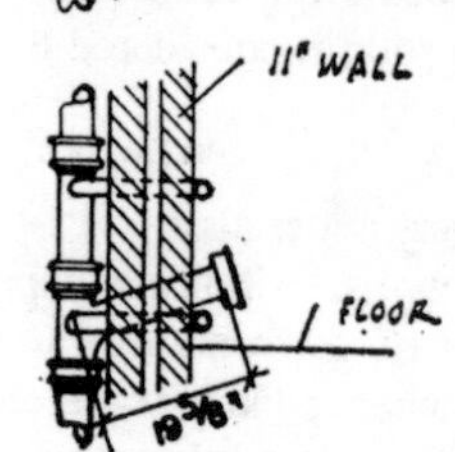
11" WALL
FLOOR
19 ⅝"

Cast-iron pipes and fittings are strong, rigid and easily fixed. Variations a arrangement are provided for by a large range of standard fittings. Protec-ion against corrosion is necessary and painting is the usual way of providing his, for reasons of appearance, when pipes are exposed. Coating with ituminous compounds is considered adequate when pipes are not exposed. Material performance and dimensional standards are set by **B.S. 416.**

Joints are spigot and socket joints made with lead poured molten and aulked to compaction above tarred yarn packing, which enables accurate lignment of pipes and prevents internal projection of the lead.

Galvanised steel pipes of spigot and socket form are sometimes used as an lternative to cast iron where pipes are inside buildings. Joints are usually nade with proprietary compounds placed over a yarn caulking. (Pipes may e painted, after treatment with a mordant solution, if appearance demands t, but they are not so resistant to corrosion as cast iron pipes.)

Asbestos cement pipes and fittings do not corrode but are more liable to racture under impact than cast iron. Standard fittings are similar to those produced in cast iron. Joints are spigot and socket joints made in 1:2

---

59 *Single Stack Collections*

(*Above*) B.S. cast iron fittings designed for single stack installations. Waste inlets are threaded to receive standard unions for lead or copper waste connections or direct connection of G.S. wastes.

Fittings are available for single or double collections, as shown, and designed for use (*A*) in combination with normal cast-iron branch fittings (see below), or (*B*) for use in combination with a specialised soil branch fitting (*C*).

Waste inlets are positioned on the fittings so that when used in conjunction with normal cast-iron soil branches, or with the standard special branch *C* their distance above floor will produce the permissible gradients in waste branches shown in Fig. 58.

N.B.—These pipe fittings and the dimensional results they produce are based on the use of sanitary fittings and traps which conform dimensionally to British Standards (most fittings do this).

(*Centre, left*) Fitting *A* used in conjunction with a standard cast-iron socket branch fitting. (The dimension, 19⅛ in. is a check dimension to ensure that waste entries are correctly positioned.)

(*Centre, right*) Fitting *A* used in a double collection in conjunction with double branch to W.C.s.

(*Below*) Fittings *B* and *C* used together shown in front view, *left*, and side view, *right*.

Dimension *X* in fitting *C* (see diagram above) is available as standard as 14½, 17⅝, 19⅝ and 21¾ in. for 3½ in. diameter branches and 14¾, 17⅞, 19⅞ and 22 in. for 4 in. diameter branches. These alternative lengths are intended to allow for variations in wall thickness and pan position. The diagram shows the fitting in use where the building wall is 11 in. thick.

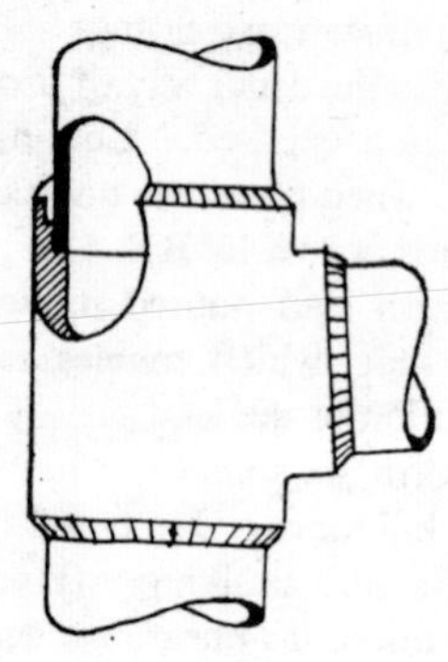

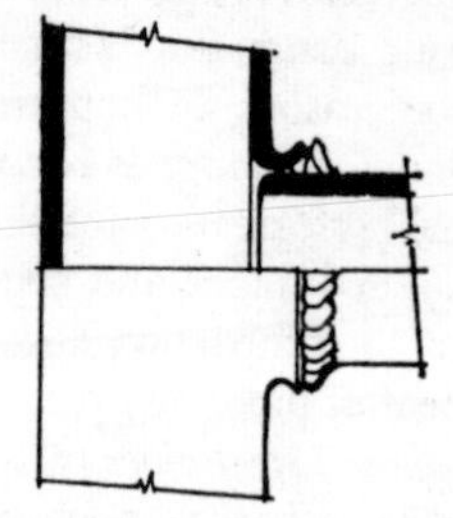

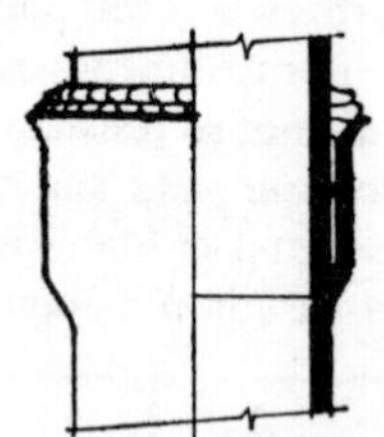

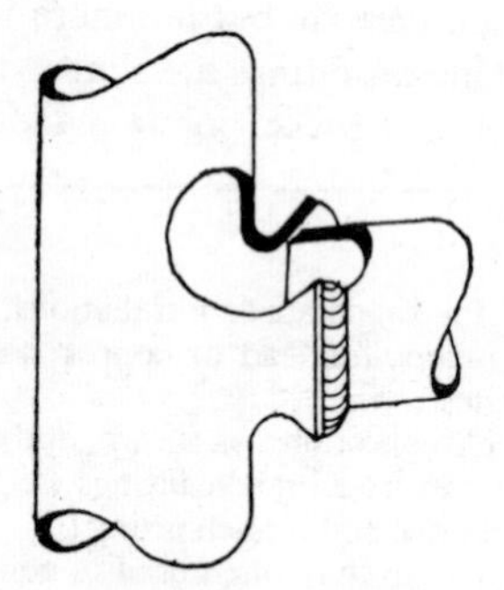

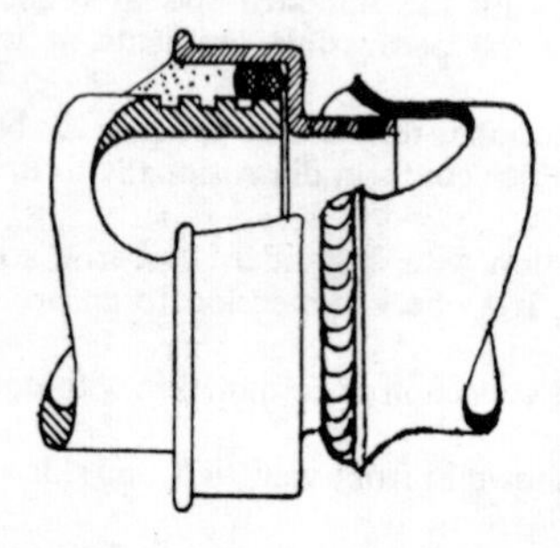

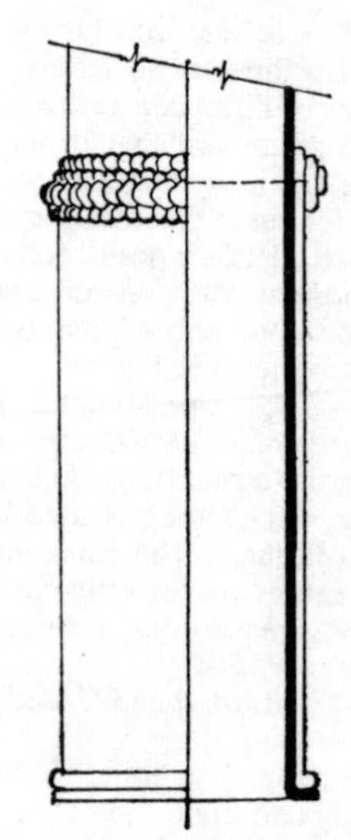

60

cement mortar placed over a caulking of tarred or untarred yarn. Material and dimensional standards for pipes and fittings are set by B.S. 582 and pipes and fittings to this standard are generally acceptable to Local Authorities for external use. The Standard requires pipes to be coated with bituminous composition but they may be supplied without coating when pipes are to be painted. (Pipes need special priming or to be exposed to weather before painting.)

Lead pipes have the advantages of extreme resistance to corrosion and ease of working and manipulation. Joints are soldered joints as described in Chapter 6 or lead burned, i.e. welded, joints (60).

Lead has the disadvantages of very high cost, great weight and a lack of rigidity, which may result in fatigue, and which presents difficulty in extensive installations. For these reasons, though principally because of cost, the use of lead pipes is nowadays generally limited to branch pipes where its advantages of flexibility and easy manipulation and installation override other considerations.

Copper tubes. In addition to extreme resistance to corrosion copper tubes are light and rigid and are also easily formed and manipulated. Cost is, however, high and this often restricts the use of copper tubes to branch pipes rather than complete installations. (N.B.—Copper branches should not be used in combination with galvanised steel stacks without special insulating precautions being taken. This is because of the galvanic action likely between the two materials.)

Jointing is often by means of compression or capillary fittings, as described for water service pipes in Chapter 6, particularly for branch wastes. When used for main soil or waste pipework autogenous or bronze welding are more usual for jointing (60).

---

60 *Joints*

(*Left*) WELDED JOINTS FOR COPPER PIPES

(*Top*) A branch fitting with "shouldered" entries. Pipe ends are square cut and welded after positioning.

(*Centre*) A bronze "cup" weld to a branch junction. The main pipe is penetrated and worked to shape manually before the square cut branch is fitted and welded.

(*Below*) A brass socket thimble for W.C. connection bronze welded to a copper branch.

(*Right*) LEAD BURNED JOINTS

(*Top*) A branch connection. The weld metal is built up in three applications to give strength to the joint.

(*Centre*) A "running" joint and (*below*) lead pipe "burned" to a brass spigot thimble to enable the pipe to be caulked to a cast-iron or stoneware pipe socket.

Pitch fibre pipes have recently been approved by many authorities for soil and waste pipes. Their use, because of the lack of capacity of the material for manipulation, is confined to main pipework. Branch fittings are available for soil connections and pipe walls are readily drilled at any position for the attachment of small branch inlet fittings to which branches of copper or other materials can be connected directly by compression fittings. The material is light, strong and permanent and is particularly low in cost.

Polythene pipes and fittings are now available for soil and waste pipework, fittings following in general form those produced in cast iron. Joints are usually made by fusing the contact surfaces within the spigot and socket joints after or during assembly. The material is strong, light, completely permanent and free from maintenance but at present expensive. Where resistance to chemical attack is necessary it has, however, distinct advantages over other materials.

P.V.C. This material is a plastic which is superseding polythene for many purposes. It is more rigid, has lower coefficient of expansion being less than half that of polythene. It also has the great advantage in that it can be solvent welded. Its resistance to most forms of attack makes it an eminently suitable material for soil and waste stacks.

8

The Building—its Drainage: I

Drains, as in the case of above ground collecting pipework, are often required to collect surface water separately from soil and waste water although it is more usual for soil, waste and rainwater to be collected by the same drains. The two methods are referred to as "separated" and "combined" systems of collection respectively.[1] Whenever drains carry soil or waste discharges they must obviously meet the basic requirements of functioning with a minimum of attention and nuisance; of being constructed in a way which will preclude all possibility of danger to health and of being arranged to permit easy maintenance and immediate rectification of any faults which may develop. Methods, materials and fittings used in their construction and arrangement are well established and principles of design and layout remain the same for all drains and may be summarised:

1 Drain pipes should be of impervious material, with non-absorbent surfaces offering minimum resistance to flow, and be constructed with watertight joints and in a way which will prevent damage by settlement.

2 Drains should be self-cleansing, i.e. laid to gradients which will ensure that flow through them will be fast enough to keep them clear of deposit.

3 Drains must be of suitable size and gradient to produce the requirement (2) above relative to the amount of waste carried.

4 To permit easy access for cleaning, testing and clearance of stoppages by "rodding"; means access to the drains, which usually takes the form of inspection chambers built over the drains, should be provided at all

[1] Economies are often possible in separated systems of drains because standards of construction and material can be relaxed for drains carrying relatively harmless surface water only and because entries to them can be made more simply and cheaply (see Chapter 7). Apart from this, however, their principal advantage lies in the fact that similar economies are much more telling when applied to the construction of the publicly owned sewers into which drains discharge. The more carefully constructed soil sewers can be very much smaller and the major part of the sewage collection (from the surface water only sewers) disposed of with little or perhaps no purifying treatment. (This is dealt with more fully in Chapter 10.)

changes in direction or gradient. Drains between points of access should be laid in straight lengths.

5 Junctions of branch to main drains should be made in the direction of flow of the main drain preferably, in the case of soil drains, within an inspection chamber. (Many local authorities insist on this or the provision of other means of access to the branch drain, e.g. accessible gulleys—see p. 206.) Branch drains should be as short as possible.

6 Drains must be ventilated, i.e. arrangements made for air to enter and escape from drains at positions which will ensure as far as is practicable freedom of movement of air through the whole of the drainage pipework.

7 All entries to the drains must be made through sealing traps as described in the last chapter and the inlets and outlets referred to in (6) above must be positioned or arranged so that foul air from the drains does not cause nuisance or danger to health.

In addition drains must obviously be laid at sufficient depth to prevent their accidental disturbance and in positions in which disturbance by foreseeable agencies such as tree roots will not occur. Drain layouts should be planned to keep their length to a minimum consistent with other requirements and, in general, entries to drains within buildings and drain runs positioned beneath buildings should be avoided.

Disconnection from sewer. In many areas intercepting or disconnecting traps must be inserted in the run of a drain before its junction with the sewer. The water seal in these traps prevents the passage of air or gas in the sewer into the drain, the traps being fitted with a by-pass arm with a removable sealing cover to permit access to the short length of drain between the trap and the sewer should this be necessary. (Disconnecting traps are discussed more fully later in this chapter.)

MATERIALS FOR DRAINS

The traditional material for drains is glazed clayware. This is still most widely used and specified wherever there are no exceptional conditions of pressure, vibration or settlement—such as may be anticipated in positions beneath buildings or roadways or in recently made up ground. As an alternative to clayware for use in comparable positions pipes and fittings of pitch fibre have been successfully used in recent years.

In situations where greater strength is required as well as those in which drains are necessarily suspended, e.g. within buildings which extend to a lower level than the sewers or sometimes where ground levels and drain gradients combine to make it necessary to expose drains above ground, pipes and fittings of cast iron are used.

Stoneware and fireclay pipes. The clay for stoneware pipes comes chiefly from Dorsetshire and Devonshire and that for fireclay pipes chiefly from the Midlands and north of the Scottish border. (See p. 195 for methods of manufacture.) Stoneware pipes are almost completely non-absorbent, even when unglazed, whereas fireclay pipes, on fracture, expose a very absorptive surface.

Salt-glazed stoneware drainpipes are most commonly used in the south, but in Scotland, where their use entails greater expense in transport, fireclay is more commonly used. Pipes are given an interior glass (vitreous) enamelling in addition to the salt glaze, which makes them perfectly suitable for drainage work, and even better able to stand acid effluents than stoneware pipes owing to the double glaze. Such pipes are known as "salt-glazed, glass (vitreous) enamelled drain pipes", and are covered by B.S. 540, while drain fittings of the same class, as well as those of salt-glazed ware, are included in B.S. 539. Salt-glazed stoneware pipes are covered by B.S. 65 and the fittings to be used in conjunction with them by B.S. 539. B.S. 65 covers two grades of pipes, "British Standard Salt-glazed Pipes" or "British Standard Tested Salt-glazed Pipes". In the former case every pipe is expected to comply with the specification and can be rejected if it does not do so, but only a small proportion of the pipes have actually been tested at the manufacturers' works; in the latter case every pipe will have been tested by hydraulic test and stamped as a sign that it does comply. The hydraulic test referred to is an internal pressure of 20 lb per sq. in. for 5 seconds which pipes must withstand without fracture or leakage.

"*Tolerances.*" Standard thickness, permissible deviation from it, permissible deviation from standard diameter, depth of socket, and from straightness in a 3-ft length, are specified by the standard:

TABLE 17

Dimensions of Salt-glazed Pipes

Diameter	Deviation from Diameter	Thickness	Deviation from Thickness	Depth of Socket	Deviation from Straightness
4 in.	$\frac{1}{8}$ in.	$\frac{1}{2}$ in.	$\frac{1}{16}$ in.	2 in.	$\frac{5}{16}$ in.
6 ,,	$\frac{3}{16}$,,	$\frac{5}{8}$,,	,,	$2\frac{1}{4}$,,	,,
9 ,,	$\frac{1}{4}$,,	$\frac{3}{4}$,,	,,	$2\frac{1}{2}$,,	,,
12 ,,	$\frac{5}{16}$,,	1 ,,	,,	$2\frac{3}{4}$,,	,,

The interior of the sockets and the exterior of the spigots of pipes are grooved with grooves of a depth of not less than $\frac{1}{16}$ in., as a key to the cement mortar.

The pipes may be obtained salt-glazed inside and out, or salt-glazed on the outside and glass-enamelled inside if this is expressly specified.

Other diameters, intermediate between those in Table 17, can be obtained. Standard pipe lengths are either 2 ft, 2 ft 6 in. or 3 ft.

Jointing of clayware pipes. Recent research[1] has revealed that traditional methods of jointing and bedding clayware drains are far from satisfactory.

Cement joints (top, Fig. 61) are too rigid to permit even the slightest movement. Cement and clayware are incompatible as materials for spigot and socket jointing. The much greater coefficient of expansion of cement will set up pressure within the socket and fracture it. Atmospheric temperature changes which take place while the drain is lying in open trench are sufficient to cause fine cracks which later develop into serious damage.

It has been known or suspected by many authorities that the jointing of stoneware or fireclay drains with cement and sand was unsatisfactory and a few methods have been used to combat the difficulty. Although none proving sufficiently economical or simple to encourage their use voluntarily.

Flexible joints. The two most frequently used were either the joint which had premade fairings of hard bitumen on both the socket and spigot, the splayed faces of the bitumen meeting when the spigot is fully inserted into the socket; or by jointing with a bituminous mixture, composed of bitumen and sand boiled together in a cauldron alongside the trench and filled into the socket in a molten state by the aid of special moulds or a rough mould made of clay and placed around the joint.

The most recent developments in the joint use compressible rings set in the socket, both socket and spigot having plastic fairing to ensure ease of assembly and true alignment (Fig. 61).

Foundation, bedding and loading on drain. If joints are to be flexible there is little point in making an inflexible foundation which is bonded to the drain, unless the strength required to resist stress entails the formation of a beam structure. Such an occurrence should receive proper consideration. For the pipeline as a whole, however, to place it on a concrete base and then tie the drain to it means that failure of the base results in failure of the drain. A less rigid but carefully selected bedding material would not result in failure if used in conjunction with flexible joints. The selection and grading of the bedding

[1] *B.R.S. Digests 124, 125* and *134*. Papers by Clews, Noble and Williams to the Building Exhibition Nov. 1963 and by Young to the Public Works and Municipal Services Congress Nov. 1964 give the details of work done.

is most important as uniformity of bearing must be achieved. Lumps of hardcore protruding through the bedding and making contact with the drain will create point loading and failure. If a very fine material is used such as sand the compaction of the bed to eliminate settlement under loading becomes difficult and time consuming. A bedding of granular material gives adequate and even bearing and eliminates the necessity for compaction. Tests by B.R.S. suggest that $\frac{3}{16}$ in. – $\frac{3}{8}$ in. crushed limestone is the most suitable material and if limestone is not available in the area the nearest material to provide similar bedding could be used. The more angular the material the better as it gives less settlement than a "pea shingle".

Of equal importance is the provision for superimposed loads. This is not referring specifically to drains under buildings or roads, which in any case are best laid in cast-iron, but to the loading which is placed on a drain by backfill and if the depth is great the load will be considerable. Surrounding in concrete, however, is not justified unless the load to be carried is greater than the crushing strength of the pipe (allowing margin of safety) which it is unlikely to be for housing and normal building. Prevention of point loads can again be avoided by granular filling to above the crown of the pipe. If the trench sides are supported with timber and the width of the trench is such that withdrawal of the timber does not allow movement of the bedding immediately under the drain, little or no harm will result with granular bedding. A sand bedding would not give the same satisfaction as its compaction would be lost.

The results of this research have not yet been incorporated in byelaws but it is anticipated that both they and the Code of Practice on Building Drainage 301, which is at present under revision, will do so in future. Until such takes place use of the recommendations should be discussed with the Local Authorities concerned. The present position is that L.C.C. byelaws require 6 in. of concrete under drain extended on either side by 6 in. and that drains be haunched continuously to half their diameter in concrete. Model Byelaws are less specific, but usually required 4 in. depth of concrete extended each side of the drain by its diameter.

Where stoneware drains are positioned beneath buildings additional protection against leakage and damage in the form of complete encasing in concrete at least 6 in. thick is required by byelaws.

Short branches. The reason that branch drains should be as short as possible is that there are not such good facilities for their inspection as for the inspection of main drains. Also branch drains are seldom ventilated, so the shorter they are kept the smaller the available space for stagnant air. As has been shown, gullies are obtainable with access stoppers so that a cleaning rod can be passed through the gully into an inspection chamber, or vice versa, but

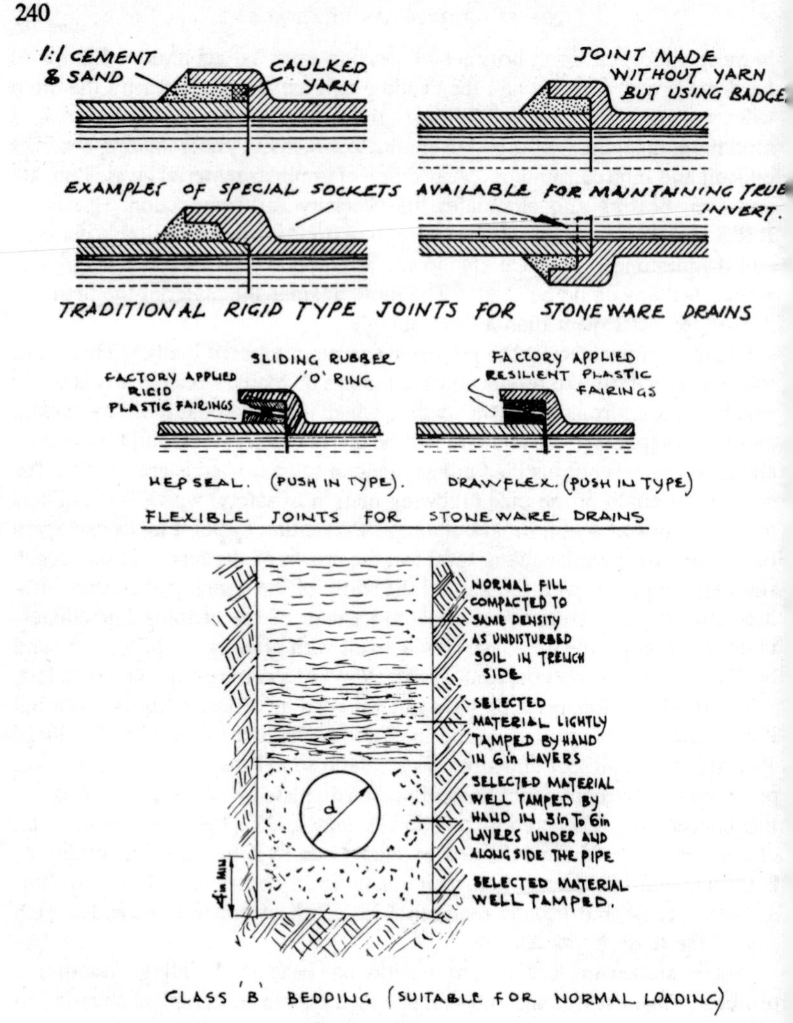

61

61 *Joints and bedding for stoneware pipes*

(*Top line*) Section through a normal cement joint. (*Left*) The yarn is first caulked into the joint to give true alignment of the spigot in the socket and also to prevent the cement mortar finding its way to the inside of the pipe. The cement mortar which should not be stronger than one part cement to one part of sand is finished with an angle of 45° to the edge of the socket and trowelled

these gullies are not so largely used as they should be. When they are used, it is most important that they should not be tampered with by incompetent persons owing to the risk of the stopper being insecurely replaced and thus leaving a ventilating opening to the drain at ground level and adjacent to the building—in fact, of negativing the value of the gully.

Most local byelaws require branch drains over 20 ft long and carrying "soil" to be ventilated, even if no soil-pipe discharges into it.

Damage done by tree roots. Considerable damage is often done to drains owing to the roots of trees exerting sufficient force, in expanding during growth, to crack the pipes. Not only is the pipe cracked, it is often burst in and a stoppage caused by the earth and the roots penetrating.

No right-angled junctions. If a main pipe, with liquid flowing through it, has a branch pipe connected to it at right angles, two things occur: the velocity of flow in the main pipe is slightly checked, and the liquid flowing from the branch pipe runs straight *across* the main pipe and rebounds, instead of its force being spent in aiding the flow along the main pipe. Both these circumstances are avoided by making the connections by a bend pointing in the direction of flow in the main pipe and jointed into a junction fitting with a branch at 45° set in the drain run.

Straight runs for drain pipes. The necessity for laying drains in straight lines from point to point, both in plan and in section, has long been recognised, owing to the fact that in such case there is a minimum of retardation to the flow of sewage and that satisfactory means of inspection can thereby be obtained.

Means of inspection. In every system of drainage there should be ample

---

smooth. (*Top, right*) The whole of the joint in this case is made with cement mortar and the drain is supported throughout its length by the bedding to ensure true invert. The inside of the joint must be cleaned with a Badger (see page 282) when it was made, to remove any mortar which may have squeezed into the pipe. When this method is used the joints must be made as the drain is bedded, i.e. one length at a time to facilitate the cleaning of the mortar from the inside of the pipe. Also shown are cement joints made with pipes with modified sockets to maintain a level invert. The shoulders may be around the whole circumference (*left*) or at invert only (*right*). (*Centre*) Proprietary flexible joints for stoneware. The joints shown are typical of those produced to meet the requirements specified by recent work of B.R.S.

(*Bottom*) Class B bedding suitable under normal conditions of loading (i.e. not under roads, etc.) on concrete drains.

4 in. diameter unlimited cover
6 in. diameter 26 ft. of cover
9 in. diameter 10·5 ft. of cover
12 in. diameter 6·5 ft. of cover.

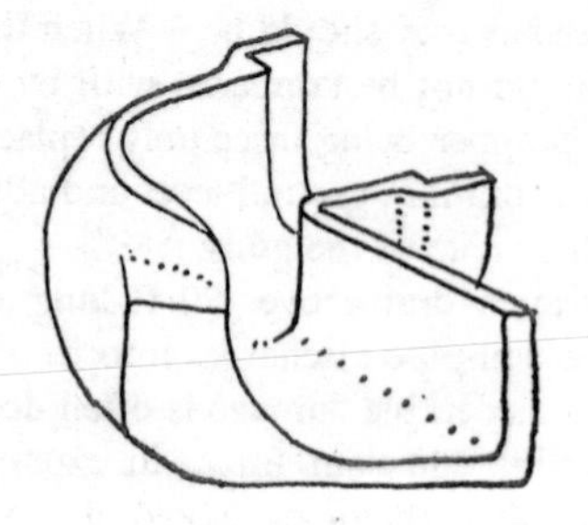

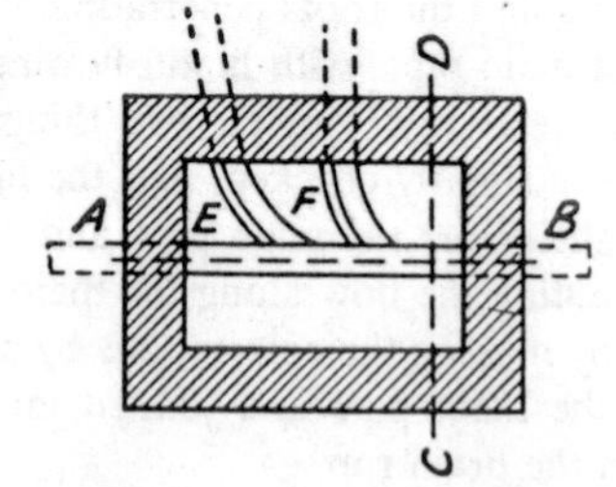

FLOOR OF INSPECTION CHAMBER. PLAN AND SECTIONS

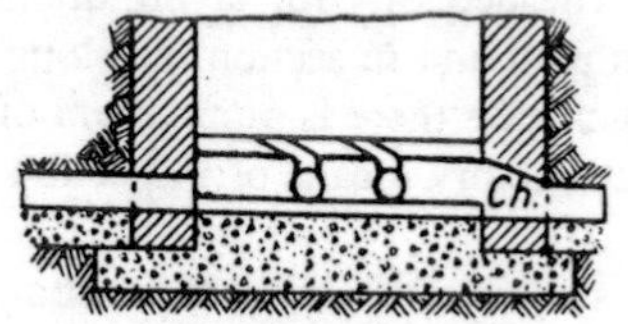

SECTION A-B

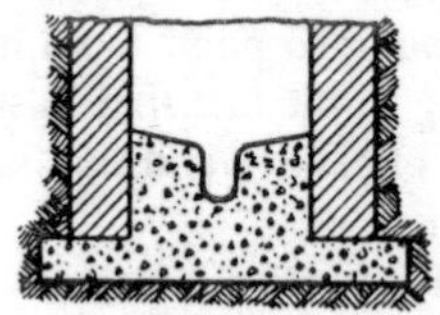

SECTION C-D

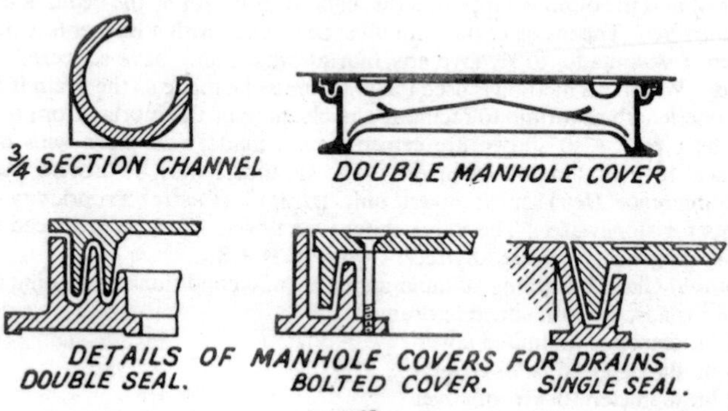

3/4 SECTION CHANNEL

DOUBLE MANHOLE COVER

DETAILS OF MANHOLE COVERS FOR DRAINS

DOUBLE SEAL. BOLTED COVER. SINGLE SEAL.

62

means of inspection. These sometimes take the form of inspection bends or junctions, but more usually and properly of proper inspection chambers or manholes. At the manhole at the lowermost end of the drain, just inside the boundary of the premises, a disconnecting or intercepting trap is generally put to disconnect the drain from the sewer. In some places the use of intercepting traps is optional, and there is much to be said for and against their use (see p. 250).

Inspection bends. If the drain is not more than 2½ ft below the surface, means of inspection may be provided by an inspection bend or inspection junction. Figure 62 shows a plan of the latter, in which two drains meet at a right angle. (Junction for drains meeting at other angles are obtainable.) It will be seen that the point of junction is open, a socket pointing upwards from it and receiving the spigot of either a 15-in. or an 18-in. pipe, which is built in and carried up to ground level. It is covered there with a stone slab or a small block of concrete is set around it, and an airtight cover provided. This is a cheap substitute for a manhole and its use should be limited to a single junction and only if the branch drain carries rainwater.

Inspection chambers. In any other case, or if the depth of the drain is greater than 2½ ft, a proper manhole should be used. The size will of course depend on the depth and the number of junctions. If only about 3 ft deep it will be easy to reach to the bottom of it, but if of greater depth it must be

---

62 *Inspection chambers*

(*Top, left*) A "blocked" channel bend. Left- or right-hand bends to effect changes of direction from 10° to 165° relative to the main channels are available. (*Top, right*) An accessible junction with large access socket sometimes used in place of an inspection chamber (see text).
(*Centre*) A typical inspection chamber in plan and longitudinal and cross sections. The cross-section CD shows the sides of the main channel benched up with concrete, to give a greater depth to it than would be furnished by the semicircular section of the straight channel. The longitudinal section A–B shows the bends discharging over the edge of the main channel, which prevents water backing up the branches when the main drain is running nearly full. A chute or enlarged entrance (Ch.) is sometimes provided at the outlet end of the main channel to facilitate the passing of drain rods through the drain for cleansing purposes. (*Below*) A three-quarter channel shown in section, *left*, a double manhole cover and alternative arrangements of edge seal for single manhole covers. The screw-down form would be used within buildings over covered invert drains illustrated in Fig. 63.

In the double cover shown the lower cover fits into a deep groove and is of a domical shape. The moisture in the air of the drain condenses when it comes in contact with its cold iron surface and the water trickles down its under side to the channel or groove and forms a sound water seal. Over this cover is another, fitting into a groove filled with grease, sand or plastic cement.

made large enough for a man to get inside and bend down. The size may therefore range from about 2 ft × 1½ ft, up to 4½ ft × 2½ ft.

The manhole is usually formed with open channels in the floor of it, though there is much to be said for using closed channels, thus confining any foul air to the pipes, instead of making the manhole a receptacle for its collection.[1] As ordinarily constructed, however, a manhole can be formed with brick or concrete walls, finished with cement rendering. Sometimes chambers are lined with salt-glazed bricks, which is much better for testing purposes, as the walls can then be made practically non-absorbent. The floor of the chamber should be of concrete, and if open channels are used they are best of white glazed fireclay. Figure 62 shows a plan, and longitudinal and cross-sections, of such a manhole floor. The plan shows two branch drains connected by means of channel bends. To prevent the sewage flowing over the sides of the bends three-quarter section bends are used. These prevent the water from a steeply inclined side branch entering with a sharp curve from banking up on the outside of the bend and overflowing the floor of the manhole, thus fouling it. Channel bends are also available in the form of blocks with flat bases, to facilitate laying, and their outlet faces arranged so that a number of bends together, irrespective of the change in direction effected by their channels, combine to form continuous glazed surface above the sides of the main channel (62).

An alternative method of effecting junctions between branch drains and main drain is to use "channel junction" sections and "branch bends". The former are half-round junction pieces with branch sockets set at 45° or 90° to the main channel into which half-round bends of varying curvatures are set to make the necessary change in direction between main and branch drain. In this method inverts of branch and main drains are, of course, at the same level.

N.B.—It is essential that the whole of the change in direction between branch drains and main channels be effected within the inspection chamber so that runs between chambers are completely straight for rodding.

Manhole covers are usually of cast iron, cover and frame being marketed as a unit which fits together to form an airtight closure to the chamber. Covers are kept as small as access requirements permit so that although the frame can often be set in cement directly on top of the walls to small chambers a concrete slab, holed to match the cover size, is needed over larger chambers. To make the closure airtight the groove of the frame in which the edge of the

[1] The open channel manhole does however have the advantage that the bulk of air acts as a cushion preventing excessive positive or negative pressure. The reason for permitting a number of W.C. connections to go straight to a manhole without individual venting stems from this advantage.

covers fits is often filled with thick grease or tallow (62), and some patterns of cover have double groves to make this seal more effective.

When inspection chambers are of necessity positioned within buildings extra precautions against the escape of foul air through their covers are required. When the nuisance this would cause is relatively small, e.g. from a chamber in an outhouse or garage, a double cover of the kind illustrated (62) may be acceptable but more usually drains within buildings are required to be closed off by covers bolted in position at "invert" level wherever access to them is provided.

Covered inverts. Manholes with closed channels can be formed if the drains are of stoneware. Figure 63 shows a plan and sections of an example, together with the method of arranging the disconnection from the sewer. The plan shows the drain pipes with an access cover at the point of junction. The concrete over them is sloped down from all four sides to the rectangular cover in the centre, as shown in the section. The part section C–D shows more clearly how the channel is closed. An iron frame, protected against corrosion, is set in cement, in a socket found in the stoneware. Inside this is a flat iron plate bedded on a prepared felt washer, and kept tight by a bolt passed through a crossbar which passes through openings in the frame at its two ends. A similar stopper circular in form is used for the opening marked 2 on the intercepting trap. No. 1 opening receives the end of the fresh-air inlet pipe. (See later.)

Intercepting traps intended to be used with covered invert manholes should have a branch or socket offset to one side, so that the air-inlet pipe does not obstruct the insertion and manipulation of drain rods if the length between the intercepting chamber and the sewer needs to be rodded, the socket in the position shown in the diagram being fitted with a sealing cover and used for access to the trap itself.

Pitch-fibre pipes are now being used in increasing quantity as an alternative to clayware pipes. Pipes are made from wood fibre impregnated under pressure with pitch, finished pipes being 75 per cent by weight pitch. They are light, possess great tensile strength so that they withstand bending, i.e. subsidence or over-pressure, and resist corrosive effluents. Standards for pitch-fibre pipes are set by B.S. 2760. Pipes up to 6 in. in diameter are available and 4 in. and 6 in. diameter pipes are made in standard lengths of 8 ft.

JOINTING of pipes is effected by driving tapered spigot ends of pipes into loose collars, also tapered and of pitch fibre, no jointing material being required to produce a permanent watertight joint. When pipes need to be cut tapers can be readily formed on pipe ends on site with a simple hand tool. Cutting is done with an ordinary wood saw. (Driving of pipes for

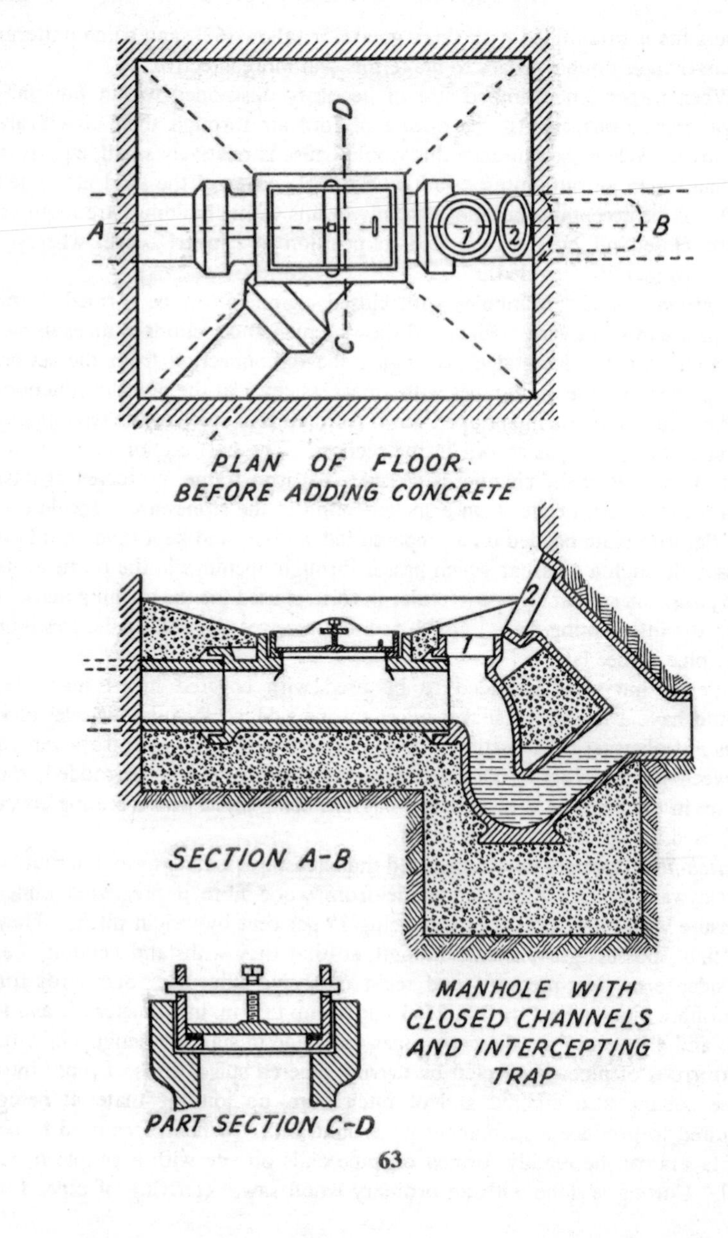

MANHOLE WITH CLOSED CHANNELS AND INTERCEPTING TRAP

63

jointing must be done with couplings in position or pipe ends protected against damage by means of a timber "dolly".)

FITTINGS available comprise bends and angled couplings (5° deviation from straight), to give changes in direction, junction fittings and adaptors for jointing fibre pipes to other materials (64). Jointing of fibre pipes to stoneware is done with sand/cement mortar as for stoneware installations, jointing to cast iron in a similar way or caulked lead joints, with lead poured in two stages, may be used.

Channel fittings, where required, are cut from pipe or fittings.

INSTALLATION. The material does not lend itself to intricate formation and usual installation technique is to link pipework of pitch-fibre to inspection chambers constructed with stoneware channels and fittings and, of course, to standard stoneware gullys, traps, etc.

Pitch-fibre pipes have the great advantage of needing no foundation, pipes can be laid directly on firm earth, and this and the fewer number of joints makes installations particularly economic, especially when drains include straight runs of any length.

Pitch-fibre pipes and installation as described are now approved by most drainage authorities.

Drain ventilation. For many years it has been an established principle that there should be at least two untrapped openings to a system of drainage, an outlet at the highest point, and an inlet for fresh air at the lowest, that is to say, at the position of the intercepting chamber.

The objects of ventilating a system of drainage are: to prevent bad air from accumulating in the drains; to divert any that may accumulate to places where injury to health or annoyance cannot be caused and to enable air to enter the drain when the water level falls in them and to leave the drain when the water level rises. The vitiated air which accumulates inside the drain and is often, owing to discharge of hot water from sinks, warmer than the atmosphere, and consequently more rarefied and lighter, will rise to the higher end of the drain. A more or less constant circulation of fresh air is thus promoted from inlet to outlet.

There should be outlet ventilating pipes at the upper end of the main drain, and of every long branch drain, these pipes being arranged with a minimum of bends. The upper ends of pipes should be finished in as exposed a position as possible, and protected at the top by a domical wire grating. They

---

63 *Covered inverts*

Arrangement of a stoneware drain with covers at invert level as required for drains within buildings.

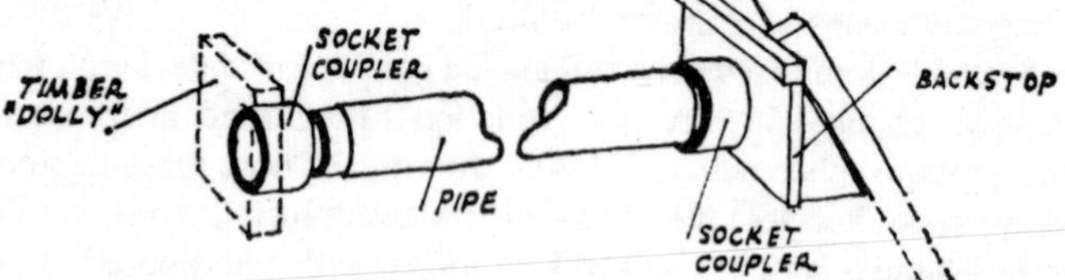

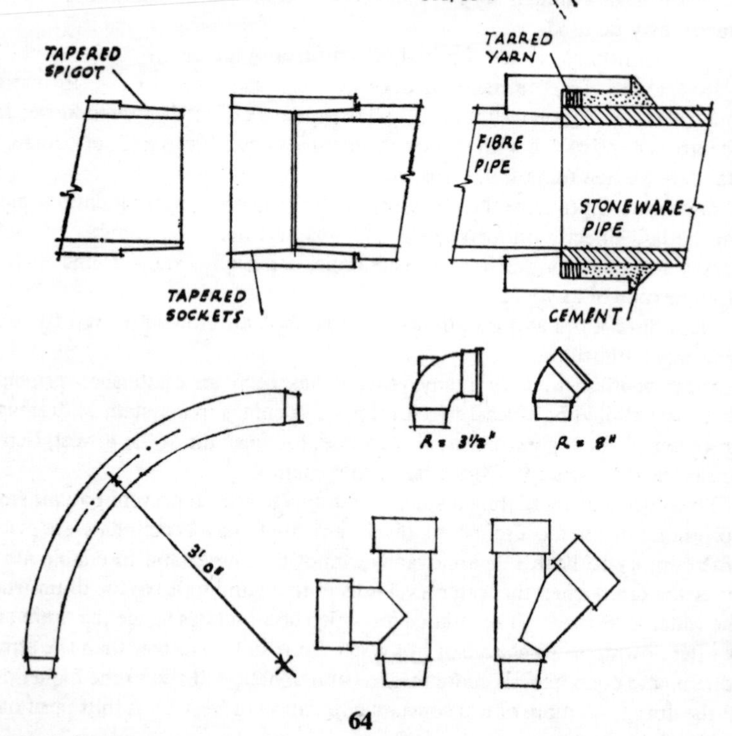

64

64 *Pitch fibre pipes*

(*Top*) Diagram showing method of assembling pipe runs by driving tapered pipe spigots into tapered sockets of loose coupling fittings.
(*Centre*) Details of pipe spigot, *left*, the pipe coupler, *centre*, and adaptor fitting, *right*, for connecting fibre and stoneware spigots. (Fibre spigot to stoneware socket joints are made with yarn and cement mortar as for stoneware.)

Length of spigot taper in all pipe sizes is 2 in. and coupling pieces are 4 in. long.
(*Below*) Fibre pipe fittings. *Left*, a 90° bend fitting. 45° and 22½° bends are also available with radii of 6 ft and 12 ft respectively.

should finish 3 ft above the head of any window within them 10 ft laterally and usually above the eaves. By carrying the pipe up in this way, an exhaust draught is caused by passing of wind across the top. The air at so high a point, being much more in motion than that close to the ground, produces lower air pressure at the top of the pipe than exists at the bottom, to cause up-draught, thus assisting the natural ventilation already referred to.

If the vent pipe is a vent pipe only, i.e. does not serve the purpose of a soil-pipe, it should be of the same diameter as that of the drain to which it is connected, and should be furnished with a rust pocket at its foot.

No matter how many outlet vent pipes there may be on a system of drainage, there should be only one inlet for fresh air, communicating with the intercepting chamber. If the latter is some distance from the building, and not near the road, an iron grating over the manhole may serve the purpose. Generally special fittings are used. The sectional area of these should be approximately equal to the combined sectional areas of the outlets. Thus a 4-in. pipe should be used to balance one 4-in. outlet, a 5-in. two, a 9-in. three, and so on.

The fresh-air inlet. One method of dealing with the fresh-air inlet pipe is to carry it up 3 or 4 ft from the ground and finish it with a mica flap inlet[1] valve, placing the pipe well away from any windows in case the valve gets out of order and acts as an outlet. The mica flap is protected from damage by a louvred cover bolted into position in front of it. (Thin aluminium flaps are also widely used.)

These "valves" are open to serious objection and were one of the points of inquiry by the Intercepting Trap Committee. They are often placed in unsatisfactory positions, and finished with inferior valves which soon get out of order, the flaps becoming set, and either opening or closing the aperture permanently. In the case of cottage property, one often finds the front grating of the valve kicked in, and the flap missing. On good-class property this defect should not occur, but it is still indispensable that the valve should be of first-class quality if it is to remain efficient.

An alternative method is to carry up both inlets and outlets well above the roof. If an inlet is used at all, this is the only method that should be adopted

[1] Many Authorities including L.C.C. will not accept an F.A.I., but require a vent with safe outlet (i.e. where it won't cause nuisance); this could be at low level in some cases.

(*Right*) Short radius bend fittings available for 4 in. diameter pipes, *above*, and typical junction fittings, *below*.

Junctions with branch set at 95° and 112½°, as well as 90° and 45°, as shown, are also available. N.B.—Short radius bends and junctions incorporate coupling sockets as shown.

in dealing with cottage property, and it is really a desirable one in all cases At the same time it should be pointed out that the Intercepting Trap Committee conducted experiments which satisfied them that an inlet is unnecessary; in other words, that a drain requires a means by which air can go in and out, as the water level in the drain rises and falls, rather than a means of creating a through current of air.

Byelaw requirements. The model byelaws require "at least one ventilating pipe not less than 3 in. in diameter, situated as near as possible to the building and as far as practicable from the sewer", and so leave the provision of an air inlet optional. On the other hand, the byelaws of the London County Council require two ventilation pipes if an intercepting trap is used, one as near as possible to the trap, the other as far as possible from it.

Disconnection of drains from sewers. The requirements for drain ventilation described above are for drains separated, i.e. disconnected from the sewers into which they discharge. If no disconnection is made air or gas can move through the drains from the sewer and, so long as air can enter the sewer, the need for a fresh-air inlet at the lower end of the drain disappears. In fact the sewer and drain are both ventilated through the vents provided at the head of the drain. This is thought to entail disadvantages by some people and is more fully discussed later.

Intercepting traps follow in general design the form of the example illustrated in Fig. 63 but in general application in stoneware drains they are fitted to open invert chambers. Figure 65 illustrates and describes several types of interceptor, including the form referred to in the last chapter designed for the separation of surface water drains installed without trapped inlets from a soil drain.

Arguments for and against interception. There has been a good deal of difference of opinion as to the desirability of separating drains from sewers. Arguments offered are summarised:

ARGUMENTS IN FAVOUR

1 The trap keeps tainted sewer air out of the house drain.
2 The use of the trap enables each householder to keep complete control of his drain ventilation scheme.
3 In sewers which are infested with rats the trap forms a deterrent to the rats entering the house drains (providing the access cap to rodding arm is secure).

ARGUMENTS AGAINST

1 If the trap is omitted, the local authority can ventilate the house drains and the sewers collectively as a single unit, utilising all the soil and vent

pipes of a given group of houses for outlet ventilation and providing inlet ventilation at certain points along the sewer to complete the scheme.

2 That the majority of drain stoppages are caused at (and because of) the intercepting trap. This undoubtedly is true, though a well-designed intercepting trap of B.S. design, in a properly laid drain used in a normally reasonable way, will not cause obstructions.

For many years, in this country, local byelaws compelled the installation of the intercepting trap and the fresh-air inlet just inside the boundary and as near to the public sewer as possible.

In recent years municipal engineers and surveyors have, in large measure, come to feel that the disadvantages of the trap outweigh the advantages and to-day an increasing number of local authorities, in their drainage byelaws, either make the use of the trap optional or forbid its use and that of the F.A.I.[1] in the case of all new houses and buildings erected in their areas.

As requirements vary from district to district local practice must be determined before drainage schemes are designed.[2]

Interception from cesspool or septic tank essential. Whatever the opinions may be as regards drains discharging into public sewers, there is no doubt at all in the case of those discharging into cesspools or septic tank installations. Here, an intercepting trap and F.A.I. are essential.

Size of drains. The minimum size of soil drain permitted by byelaws is 4 in. diameter and it is very rare that smaller drains of any kind are advisable. For a small house both branch and main drains should be made of 4-in. pipes. In the case of extensive drainage schemes larger drains are necessary, but it should always be remembered that the smaller the diameter of a drain, provided that it is large enough to carry off the requisite quantity of sewage, the more self-cleansing will it be.

B.R.S. Digest No. 6 Second Series, Drainage for Housing, suggests for soil drain 20 houses on a 4 in. drain at 1–70 and 100 houses on a 6 in. drain at 1–150. The surface water drainage should be based on a rainfall rate of 2 in. per hour.

Self-cleansing gradients. To be self-cleansing drains should have such inclination as will produce a minimum velocity of 3 ft per second. The depth of the sewer, into which the drain is to be connected, is one of the controlling factors in determining the inclination, and, in the erection of new

[1] See footnote, page 249.

[2] When Building Regulations, to be made under the provisions of the Public Health Act 1961, are published they will apply to the whole country. (There is some doubt about London as the L.C.C. was given special powers which may not be passed to all areas of the new G.L.C.)

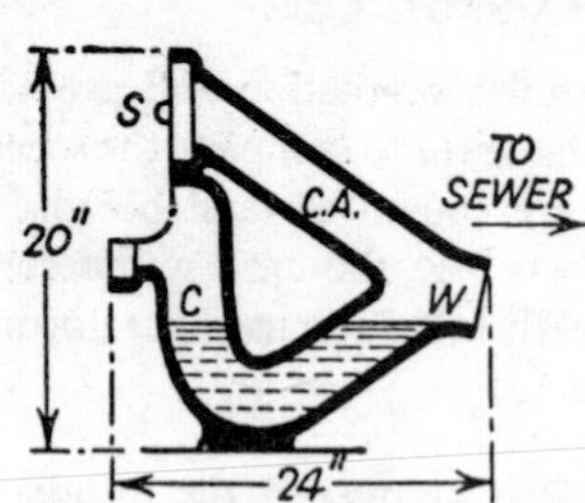

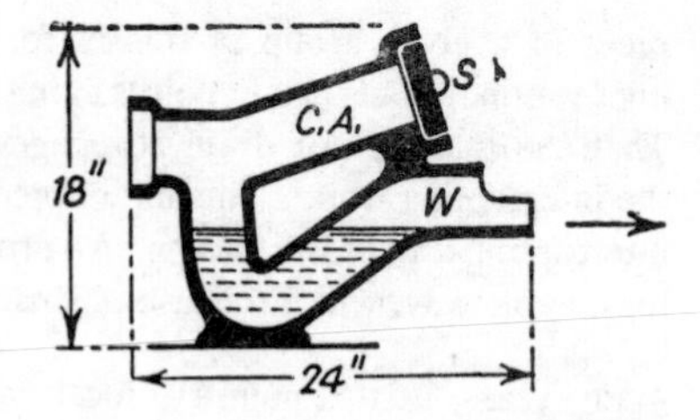

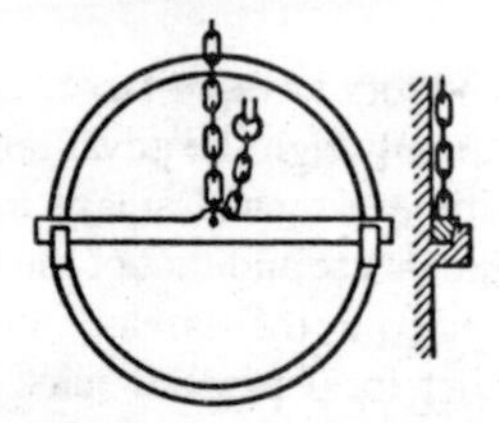

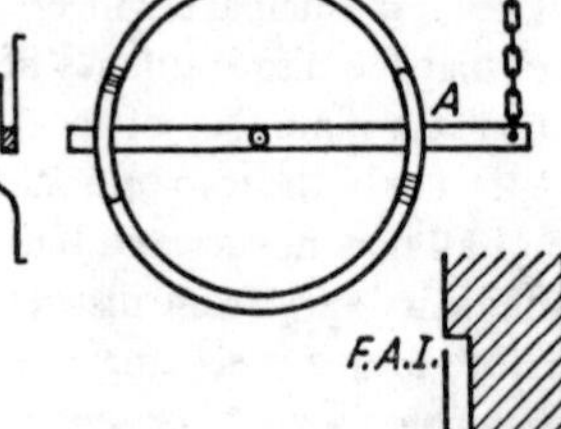

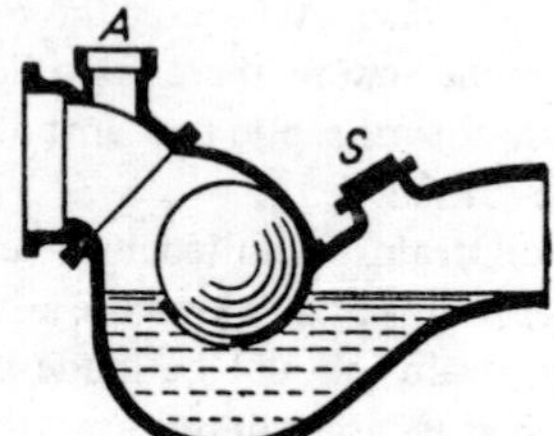

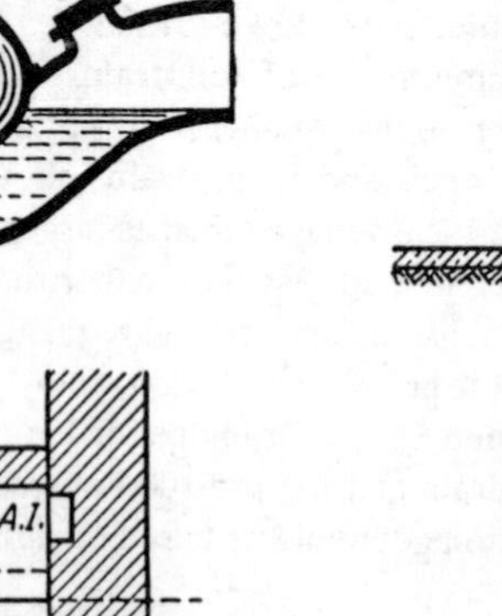

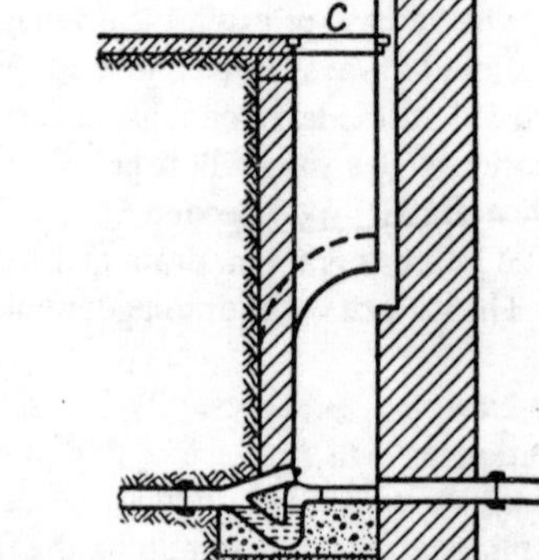

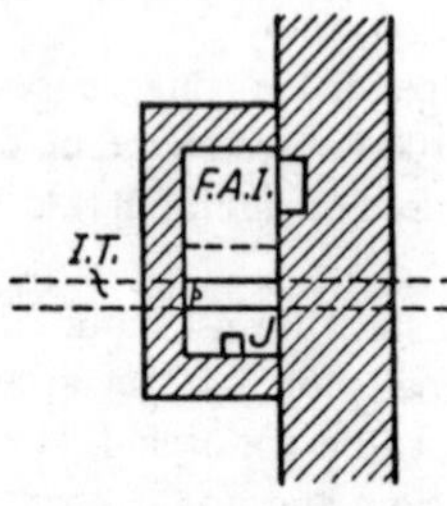

65

65 *Intercepting Traps*

(*Top, left*) A B.S. type for use with open channel manhole, with stoneware drains.

There is a cascade at C and a small weir at W. The cleaning arm, C.A., should have a very secure stopper at S.

Much of the trouble in intercepting traps has been due to the defective fixing of the stopper. They are often jointed by means of the Stanford and similar joints, sometimes proved unsatisfactory where a blockage has occurred, as the stopper could not readily be removed to allow the accumulated sewage to run away and make it possible to get on with the clearing of the obstruction. Sometimes the stopper has been fixed so loosely that a reverse rush of air from the sewer has pushed the stopper out to fall into the mouth of the trap, thus causing the blockage.

As an alternative to a cleaning arm stopper, a circle of glass is sometimes used. This is firmly fixed with cement or putty. In the event of stoppage the glass can be readily broken to allow the dammed-up sewage to escape and a new circle of glass can then be cemented in when the clearance is complete and the manhole has been cleaned. A better arrangement is to provide mechanical stoppers as shown immediately below.

In both these forms a chain is attached to the crossbar and provided with a ring which hangs on a hook at high level on the manhole wall. On a blockage occurring, a pull of the chain releases the stopper and the accumulated sewage. (This is the form recommended by the British Standard Code of Practice on Building Drainage.)

(*Top, right*) A reverse interceptor. This is fitted to the end of an incoming drain to an inspection chamber—e.g. a rainwater drain entering a chamber over a soil drain. Whilst separating the incoming drain from the through drain the former can still be cleared by rods through the clearing arm.

A good intercepting trap should have a seal of not less than 2½ in. and hold only a relatively small quantity of water. (Average figures are: a 4-in. trap holds from 3½ to 5½ pints, and a 6-in. from 6 to 9 pints.) The trap should have a drop down to the water at its entrance of about 2 in. in the case of a 4-in. intercepting trap, a little more in the case of a 6-in. trap, to give a cascade action to submerge light floating matters and force them down the drain.

The inlet should be made very steep or even vertical so as to help in this effect, while the outlet then leads up far more gradually to the weir or outlet, enabling heavy faecal matter to make its way up and over on its way to the sewer. These points are very pronounced in the British Standard traps illustrated.

(*Centre*) A special type of interceptor, designed for use in positions in which the branch leading to the sewer is subject to back flooding. It has a light ball which is held up against the inlet whenever sewage backs up the drain. It will be seen that an air-inlet socket is provided at A, and an access stopper at S. This type has been used by H.M. Office of Works on the drains of public buildings near the Thames at Westminster, where, of course, the river is tidal.

(*Below*) A plan and section through a disconnecting chamber suitable for use under a street pavement, where the building fronts the edge of the street. It is just wide enough from front to back to give room for a man to enter, and about 5 ft wide the other way at the lower part; part of this 5 ft width is arched over, reducing the size of the chamber to merely an access shaft in the upper part. Manholes over 5 ft deep are often provided with built-in step-irons at vertical intervals of 12 or 15 in., the step-irons being shown on the plan. They

property, the level of the lowest point from which water or sewage has to be conveyed should be so adjusted to the level of the sewer as to allow of an inclination that will produce a self-cleansing velocity in the drain throughout its whole length. On the other hand, it should be pointed out that too steep a gradient is almost as bad as one which is too flat, as there may then be insufficient depth of sewage to keep solid matters floating.

Maguire's rule. A very simple rule, known as Maguire's, gives suitable gradients for drains of different diameters. It is that the gradient shall equal 1 in (diameter in in. × 10). Thus a 4-in. drain should have a fall of 1 in 40, 6-in., 1 in 60, and 9-in., 1 in 90, or thereabouts.

It is, however, seldom that these ideal gradients are suitable to the available fall of the land, and any gradient between *twice* and *one-half* the gradient according to Maguire's rule will generally be permissible.

The British Standard Code of Practice on "House Drainage" describes a method of estimating the volume of flow which is likely through drains and provides a table listing volumes of flow which will produce self-cleansing velocities in pipes of different sizes at different gradients. (The Code assesses "self-cleansing velocity" at 2·5 ft/sec minimum.) Any assessment of volume of flow is necessarily inexact. The Code suggests an allowance of $\frac{2}{3}$ cu. ft/min per 100 persons and that surface water be based on an assumed rate of rainfall of $1\frac{1}{2}$ in./hr over the whole horizontal area from which water reaches the drain.

Self-cleansing velocities are produced in 4 in. diameter pipes by 2 cu. ft/min when pipes are laid to a gradient of 1 in 40, by 3 cu. ft/min when gradient is 1 in 50 and by 4 cu. ft/min when gradient is 1 in 60.

The Code recommends that branch drains (4 in.) should not be laid to shallower gradients than 1 in 40.

Velocity of flow calculations. A number of formulae have been developed to determine the gradient necessary for any particular set of conditions, the velocity produced by any particular gradient, and the amount discharged by drains of various sizes laid at varying gradients.

One of the best-known, equally applicable to a stream or river, is that known as Chezy's, expressed as follows:

---

are subject to rusting by the condensation always present in manholes and the B.S. Code of Practice on Building Drainage discourages their use and advises a short ladder when inspection becomes necessary. The fresh-air inlet is shown formed in a chase or recess of the wall, marked F.A.I. on plan and section, finishing with a grating at a reasonable height above ground, the grating being backed by a flap of mica to prevent back draught. An airtight cover is provided at C.

$$V = C\sqrt{RS},$$

in which V = velocity of flow in ft per sec,

C = a coefficient,

R = hydraulic mean depth (H.M.D.),

$= \left(\frac{\text{sectional area of flow}}{\text{wetted perimeter}}\right)$ in ft,

$S = \frac{\text{fall}}{\text{length}}$ (sometimes given as "sine" of slope).

N.B. The letters M and I are frequently used for R, S, respectively.

Various authorities have given different values for C: Beadmore's 94·2, Eytelwein 94 and Downing 100. The coefficient however cannot be given a fixed value in the Chezy formula because C varies not only with the degree of roughness of the pipe surface, but also with the depth of H.M.D. The value of C in the absence of any directive has frequently been taken as 100 but for 4 in. C.1 and stoneware pipe it may be as low as 85 and for 24 in. dia. pipe as high as 120. This variation could lead to considerable inaccuracy in estimating rates of flow unless taken into account. A number of formulae do this by raising the power of the H.M.D. above 0·5 which makes C nearer a true constant. Such a formula, much used by engineers, is Crimp and Bruges in which $V = 124M^{\cdot 67}I^{\cdot 5}$.

Whatever formula is used to calculate velocity volume of discharge is given by

$$Q = AV,$$

in which Q = quantity discharged in cu. ft per sec.

A = sectional area of flow in sq. ft, and

V = velocity of flow in ft per sec.

Drains do not always flow full and confusion sometimes arises over the use of such terms as "a drain flowing one quarter full" being given the interpretation of flowing depth one-quarter of its diameter.

The term flowing $\frac{1}{X}$ full should not be used, but the more precise definition given as either flowing to $\frac{1}{X}$ of its depth, $\frac{1}{X}$ of its full bore flow discharge capacity or flowing to $\frac{1}{X}$ of its sectional area. The latter is seldom used in relation to horizontal drains but is frequently used in connection with flow in vertical soil pipes.

HYDRAULIC MEAN DEPTH. If flowing full or half-full the H.M.D. = diam./4 ft, a statement which can be readily proved, thus:

$$\textit{If full}, \text{ H.M.D.} = \frac{\text{sectional area}}{\text{wetted perimeter}}$$

$$= \frac{\text{area of circle}}{\text{circumference}}$$

$$= \frac{3{\cdot}1416 \times \text{radius}^2}{2 \times 3{\cdot}1416 \times \text{radius}}$$

$$= \frac{\text{radius}}{2} \text{ or } \frac{\text{diameter}}{4}.$$

$$\textit{If half-full}, \text{ H.M.D.} = \frac{\frac{1}{2} \text{ area of circle}}{\frac{1}{2} \text{ circumference}}$$

which it will be seen must give the same result as the above, the $\frac{1}{2}$ cancelling out in numerator and denominator.

If the drain is flowing with a depth equal to any other proportion of its diameter, the H.M.D. must be taken from a table, or worked out as follows:

EXAMPLE.

Find the H.M.D. for a 9-in. drain flowing

(*a*) one-third depth and (*b*) two-thirds depth.

Figure 66 on p. 260 illustrates these conditions diagrammatically. (*a*) The case where the sewer is one-third depth.

The depth EC will be 3 in., and DE will be 1·5 in.

First find the wetted perimeter, i.e. the arc ACB.

The cosine of the angle ADE $= \frac{DE}{AD} = \frac{1{\cdot}5}{4{\cdot}5} = \frac{1}{3}$; so that $\angle$ ADE = 70° 32′, and $\angle$ ADB = 141° 4′ = 141·067°.

$$\text{Arc ACB} = \frac{141{\cdot}067}{360} \times \text{circumference of circle}$$

$$= \frac{141{\cdot}067}{360} \times \pi \times 9 = 11{\cdot}08 \text{ in.}$$

The sectional area of flow equals the area of ACBD, minus the area of ADB

$$= \frac{\text{Arc ACB} \times \text{DC}}{2} - \frac{\text{AB} \times \text{DE}}{2}.$$

Now AE = AD sin 70° 32′ = 4·5 × 0·9428 = 4·24 in.; so that AB = 8·48 in.

$$\text{Area of ACBD} = \frac{11{\cdot}08 \times 4{\cdot}5}{2} = 24{\cdot}93 \text{ sq. in.}$$

$$\text{Area of ADB} = \frac{8{\cdot}48 \times 1{\cdot}5}{2} = 6{\cdot}36 \text{ sq. in.}$$

Area of segment ACBE = 24·93 − 6·36 = 18·57 sq. in.

$$\text{H.M.D.} = \frac{\text{sectional area}}{\text{wetted perimeter}} = \frac{18{\cdot}57}{11{\cdot}08}$$

$$= 1{\cdot}68 \text{ in., or } 0{\cdot}14 \text{ ft.}$$

(*b*) The case where the sewer is flowing two-thirds depth.

$$\cos \angle \text{ADE} = \frac{\text{DE}}{\text{AD}} = \frac{1{\cdot}5}{4{\cdot}5} = \frac{1}{3};$$

so that $\angle$ ADE = 70° 32′, and $\angle$ ADB = 141° 4′ = 141·067°.

The reflex angle ADB (i.e. sum of angles ADC and CDB) = 360° − 141·067° = 218·933°.

$$\text{Arc ACB} = \frac{218{\cdot}933}{360} \times \text{circumference}$$

$$= \frac{218{\cdot}933}{360} \times \pi \times 9 = 17{\cdot}19 \text{ in.}$$

The sectional area of flow is the area of ACBD, plus the area of ADB.

$$= \frac{\text{Arc ACB} \times \text{DC}}{2} + \frac{\text{AB} \times \text{DE}}{2}.$$

Now AE = AD sin 70° 32′ = 4·24 in., as before; so that AB = 8·48 in.

$$\text{Area of ACBD} = \frac{17{\cdot}19 \times 4{\cdot}5}{2} = 38{\cdot}68 \text{ sq. in.}$$

$$\text{Area of ADB} = \frac{8{\cdot}48 \times 1{\cdot}5}{2} = 6{\cdot}36 \text{ sq. in.}$$

Area of segment ACBE = 38·68 + 6·36 = 45·04 sq. in.

$$\text{H.M.D.} = \frac{\text{sectional area}}{\text{wetted perimeter}} = \frac{45{\cdot}04}{17{\cdot}19}$$

$$= 2{\cdot}62 \text{ in.} = 0{\cdot}22 \text{ ft.}$$

HYDRAULIC TABLES. Table 18 gives the values of both the H.M.D. and the sectional area of flow, the latter being required when finding the discharge.

The letter D throughout the table stands for diameter of drain, or sewer, in feet. (Values for sewers of egg-shaped section have been included here.)

TABLE 18

Sectional Form of Drain or Sewer	Pipes Flowing							
	$\frac{1}{3}$ depth		$\frac{1}{2}$ depth		$\frac{2}{3}$ depth		Full	
	H.M.D.	Sec. Area	H.M.D.	Sec. Area	H.M.D.	Sec. Area	H.M.D.	Sec. Area
Circular	$0{\cdot}186D$	$0{\cdot}229D^2$	$0{\cdot}25D$	$0{\cdot}393D^2$	$0{\cdot}291D$	$0{\cdot}556D^2$	$0{\cdot}25D$	$0{\cdot}785D^2$
Egg-shaped	$0{\cdot}206D$	$0{\cdot}285D^2$	$0{\cdot}268D$	$0{\cdot}509D^2$	$0{\cdot}316D$	$0{\cdot}756D^2$	$0{\cdot}29D$	$1{\cdot}149D^2$

Values of Hydraulic Mean Depth for different shaped pipes under different conditions of flow.

An example will show the use of the formula and the table:

EXAMPLE

Determine the gradient at which a 6-in. drain must be laid in order that the velocity of flow through it shall be 4 ft/sec. when only one-third full. Also find the quantity, in cu. ft per min., that it will discharge when flowing two-thirds full at that gradient.

$$V = c\sqrt{rs},$$

$$c = 100,$$

$$s = \frac{\text{fall}}{\text{length}} = \frac{1}{x} = \text{gradient},$$

$$r = \text{H.M.D.} = 0{\cdot}5 \times 0{\cdot}186 = 0{\cdot}093,$$

$$v = 4.$$

Transposing the formula we get:

$$V = 100\sqrt{rs},$$

$$\frac{V}{100} = \sqrt{rs},$$

$$\frac{4}{100} = \sqrt{0{\cdot}093 \times s},$$

$$\frac{16}{10{,}000} = 0{\cdot}093s,$$

$$\frac{16}{10{,}000 \times 0{\cdot}093} = s = \frac{1}{x}.$$

$$\therefore x = \frac{10{,}000 \times 0{\cdot}093}{16} = 58{\cdot}12.$$

$\therefore$ Gradient = 1 in 58.

When $\frac{2}{3}$ depth, the velocity will be more than 4 ft/sec.

$$r = 0{\cdot}5 \times 0{\cdot}291 = 0{\cdot}146.$$

$$s = \frac{1}{58}.$$

$$\therefore v = 100\sqrt{0{\cdot}146 \times \frac{1}{58}} = 100\sqrt{0{\cdot}00252} = 100 \times 0{\cdot}05 = 5 \text{ ft. per sec.}$$

$$Q = 0{\cdot}556D^2 \times 5 \times 60 = 0{\cdot}556 \times 0{\cdot}5 \times 0{\cdot}5 \times 5 \times 60 = 41{\cdot}7 \text{ cu. ft/min}$$

Drains with insufficient fall. Drains or sewers may have to be laid from buildings or other discharge points at fixed level to existing sewers so creating conditions in which the available fall is insufficient to give a self-cleansing velocity. Various means are available for automatic flushing. Figure 66 shows a section through a siphonic flushing gully suitable for a branch drain. It is made of glazed stoneware and is designed to hold up the collected waste water from sinks, lavatories, or rainwater pipes, releasing it with considerable flushing force when sufficient water has accumulated to start the siphonic action.

Figure 66 also shows a tipper arranged for the same purpose at the head of a drain, the mouth of the drain being enlarged to utilise the flushing power to the best advantage. This is done by the use of tapering pipes. The pipe next to the tipper is tapered from 12 to 9 in., the next one from 9 to 6 in. and the third from 6 to 4 in. The tipper is housed in a rendered brick chamber, with a smooth concrete floor, and is fed by waste pipes from baths, lavatories, etc. A capacity of about 20 to 25 gallons is usual.

Flushing tanks. The best method of flushing a main drain is by means of an automatic tank, of which there are various patterns. Figure 66 shows a section of the Field flushing tank. For small sizes it can be made of iron, and for larger sizes of a combination of brickwork and iron. It is usually placed adjacent to a manhole at the head of a main drain, and can be supplied with water from a water main, or rainwater can be utilised. (Such tanks do not work satisfactorily with dirty water, such as sink wastes.)

Size of flushing tanks. The capacity of the flushing tank depends on the diameter of the drain and its length. Table 19 gives an idea of the necessary provision.

TABLE 19.—*Sizes of Drain Flushing Tanks*

Flushing Tanks			
Diameter of Drain	Length	Capacity in Gallons	Diameter of Flush Pipe
4 in.	50 ft	30	3 in.
4 ,,	100 ,,	60	3 ,,
6 ,,	50 ,,	60	4 ,,
6 ,,	100 ,,	100	4 ,,
9 ,,	100 ,,	200	6 ,,
9 ,,	150 ,,	300	6 ,,

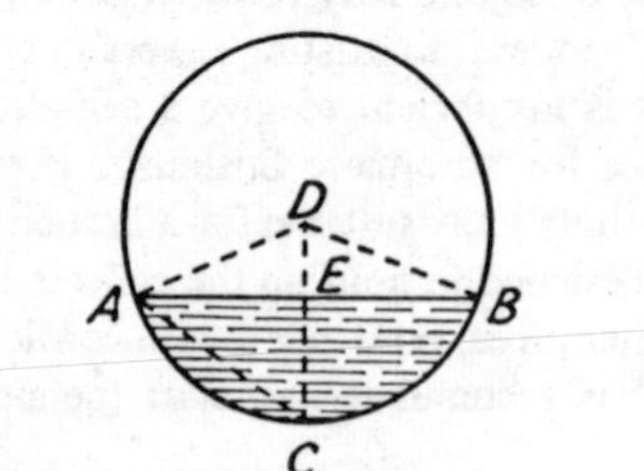

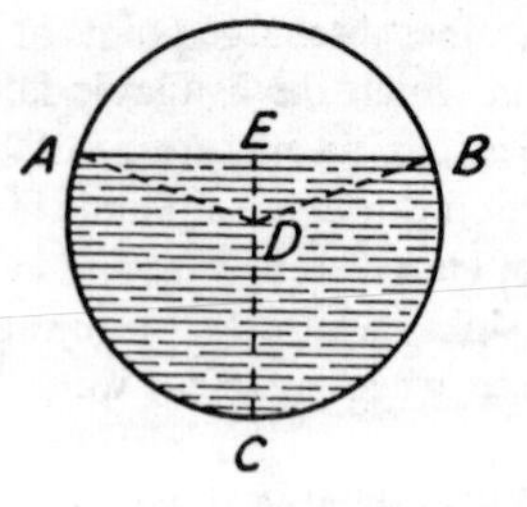

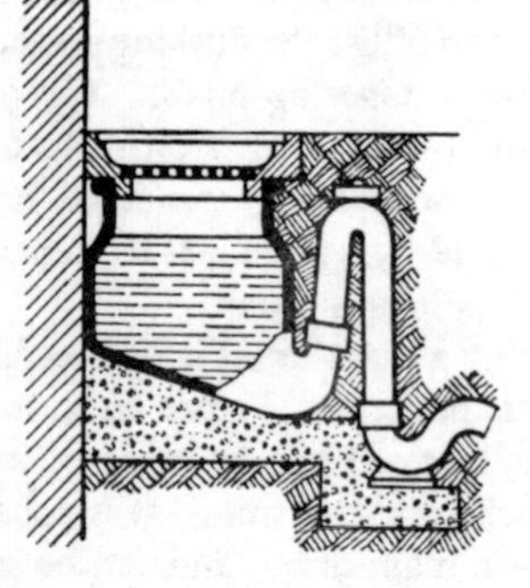

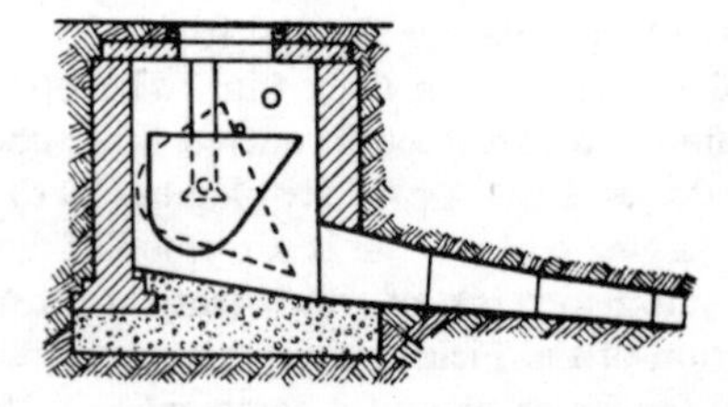

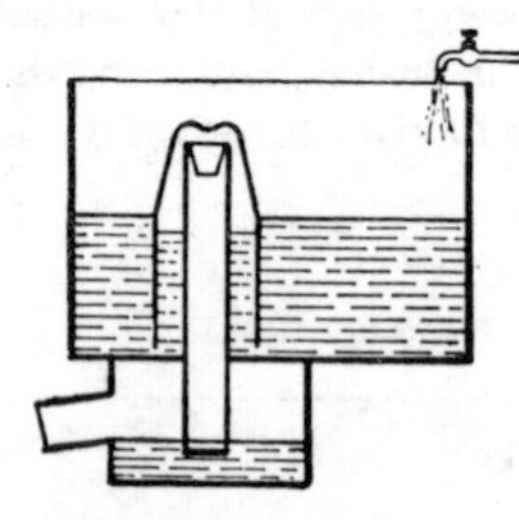

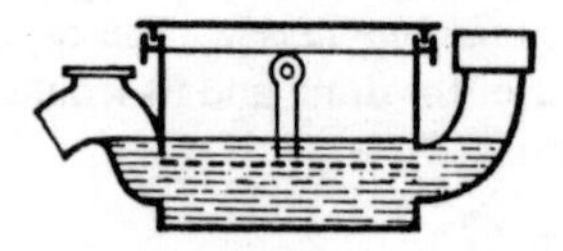

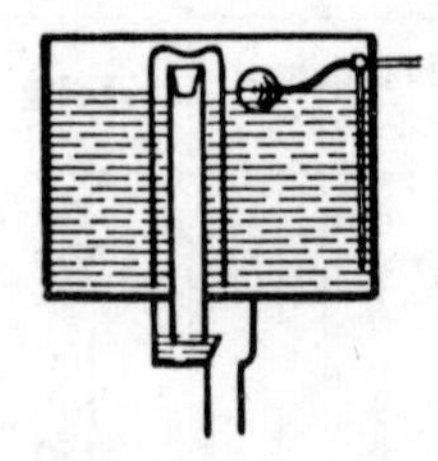

66

Drains with too steep a fall. If the gradient of a drain is too steep the velocity will be too, and there will be a tendency for the liquid to run away from the solid matter, leaving it stranded. The risk is not great unless the volume of flow is small, and in any case the fault is not serious unless steep gradients are necessary over long lengths. In this case they can be avoided by use of a "drop manhole" or "ramp". These are sometimes referred to as "tumbling bays". (Typical "drop" chambers are illustrated in Figs 82 and 85, see pp. 302 and 310.)

---

66 *Drain flow*

(*Top*) Diagrams referred to in velocity of flow calculations on p. 256.
(*Centre, above*) Drain flushing methods. A siphonic flushing gulley, *left*, and a tipper flush, *right*.

The siphonic flushing gulley works in a similar manner to the flushing tank, *below, left*, the trap taking the place of the lower tank in the latter. The flushing tank operates as follows:

There are two compartments, an upper main tank and a smaller one, termed a trapping box, below. The lower one contains a small quantity of water for the purpose of trapping, or sealing, the lower end of a pipe which passes up through the water in the tank above. This pipe is covered by a "dome" which reaches nearly to the floor of the main tank, being supported on feet. As the water rises in the tank, it can also rise under the dome and will at first rise an almost equal amount both inside and outside. Between the surface of the water which is rising under the dome, and the surface of the water at the foot of the pipe, air is being gradually compressed and, when the water under the dome reaches the mouth of the pipe, it falls over through this highly compressed air, displacing, by agitation, the resistance offered by the seal at the foot of the flushing pipe. This sets up the siphonic action and the whole content of the main tank is then driven out by atmospheric pressure. It should be noted that the mouth of the pipe has a funnel-shaped inlet. Were it not for this, the water would form a sort of lining to the pipe, running away to the trapping box without causing the breaking of the seal at the foot. At the end of the flush the trapping box retains sufficient water to restore the seal.

(*Centre, below*) A common form of grease trap, *right*. The large volume of water in the trap cools incoming hot, grease carrying, water sufficiently for grease to rise to the surface and coagulate above the perforated tray indicated by the dotted line. The tray is removed periodically for cleaning.

(*Below, left*) Another form of grease "trap". A flushing gulley in which accumulated grease is broken up and carried away to the drain instead of being removed by hand. (This fitting is now obsolete.)

Waste entries are made to the central section of the gulley and the flushing water entry made to the top section. Flushes are provided by automatic flush tanks of the kind illustrated, *bottom, right*. These operate in a similar way to the drain flushing tanks described above. In both cases flush intervals are determined by adjusting the inlet rate to the tank. (The ball valve is a precaution against overflows, necessary when tanks are inside buildings.)

Specialised fittings

In addition to preventing leakages from and the creation of nuisance by drains it is also sometimes necessary to prevent the entry of undesirable matter to the drains and sewers if these are to remain efficient and safe.

Grease gulleys. Where large quantities of grease are likely to be accumulated it is usual for precautions to be required to prevent its entry to the drains and sewers. Thus at waste water entries from hotel or restaurant kitchens it is usual for grease gulleys to be called for.[1]

One form of grease trap is shown in Fig. 66. It will be seen that it has a solid cover, and an inspection stopper on the outlet. The dotted line shows the base of a perforated iron tray capable of being lifted out by means of a handle at either side, one handle being shown in the sketch. The accumulation of grease can be lifted out by this means, and it is important that such fittings should receive regular attention. Some such grease trap as that shown would be used where the grease must be intercepted from the drains.

Flushing gulleys. An obsolete form of grease trap is the flushing grease gulley, also illustrated in Fig. 66. It is arranged to take two or three waste pipes, and has a flushing rim connected to an automatic flushing tank, which can be above ground and inside the building. The gulley is in three pieces, the centre one being capable of being turned in any direction. The force of the flush breaks up the accumulation of grease and washes it through the drain. (A suitable type of automatic flushing tank for this purpose is shown.)

N.B.—In any form of flushing tank inlet taps should be key operated to prevent unauthorised tampering. In some areas supply authorities insist on setting water rate entry and sealing the setting to prevent excessive use of water.

Stable drainage. The general practice in draining stables and similar buildings is now very different from what it used to be, it being recognised now that openings to a drain, inside them, are as likely to be injurious to animals as they are to human beings in a domestic building. The floors of such buildings should be of hard, non-absorbent material, such as Staffordshire blue bricks, adamantine clinkers, or granolithic concrete and should be drained by laying the paving to fall to shallow surface channels, connected to a main channel leading to a gulley outside the building.

In larger buildings the main channel may be of iron, and covered with a grating, as shown in section in Fig. 67. The channel and grating should, of course, be protected against corrosion. The form of gulley used for stable

[1] These are also often fitted when private sewage disposal installations involving filter beds are used. Grease even in relatively small quantities reduces filter bed efficiency (See Chapter 11 for details of filter beds, etc.)

work differs from the ordinary yard gulley. It should have a perforated iron bucket to intercept particles of straw, horse dung, etc. The bucket is readily removable, like the tray of a grease trap (Fig. 67). It would have the usual iron grating over. In other respects the drainage of stables and similar buildings follows the general principles already described.

Petrol interceptors. In the case of garage buildings the danger of petrol washings finding their way into the drainage system, and possibly leading to explosions, arises. By the Public Health Act, 1936, it is illegal to discharge into a sewer any petrol, or any other oil which gives off an inflammable vapour at a temperature of less than 73° F. In a small garage, attached to a building having a fair amount of land, surface drainage of the garage is sometimes run to a soak-away pit, dug well away from the building, but in the case of garages in built-up areas this is difficult if not impossible.

The requirements of the London County Council may be given as an example of what should be done in other cases. Figure 67 shows a section and plan of a special form of interceptor which is acceptable as meeting the case, the example given being suitable for a garage taking six cars.[1] It will be seen to consist of three chambers, each 3 ft sq. and 4½ ft deep, built of brickwork on a concrete floor.

As the diagram shows, the only connection between chambers is through pipes submerged to points only far enough from the floor to avoid sludge passing. By this arrangement the petrol, lighter than water, rises to accumulate at the top of the sewage in each chamber, any vapour being carried off by the ventilating pipes (shown by dotted lines).

Petrol gulleys, suitable for use with private garages for 1 or 2 cars, are marketed by many manufacturers of drainage fittings. In these, by means of deep seals and removable perforated buckets, water passing through them is forced to follow a circuitous route so that any petrol it carries has ample opportunity to float to the surface, where it evaporates.

The increased demand for "parking only" garages, as integrated parts of new buildings erected in central city areas, has led to some relaxation of interception standards. Where no petrol is stored or sold, a single chamber interceptor—arranged as the first chamber of the example in Fig. 67—is often accepted for the interception of petrol from surface drainage from parking spaces for up to 12 cars.

Acid wastes. Many industrial processes produce waste which is corrosive in character. Local authorities now have powers to require the pre-treatment of industrial wastes to reduce their alkaline or acid content to a level not likely to be harmful to the public sewers. (Public Health (Drainage of Trade Premises) Act, 1937.) Public Health Act, 1961 (Part V).

[1] Some Authorities will accept two-compartment interceptors for more than 6 cars.

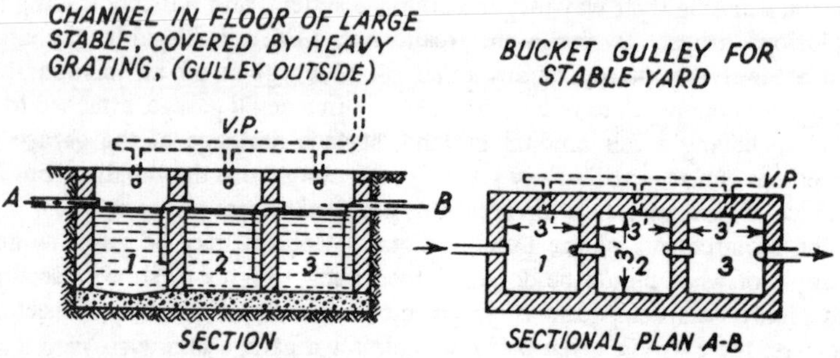

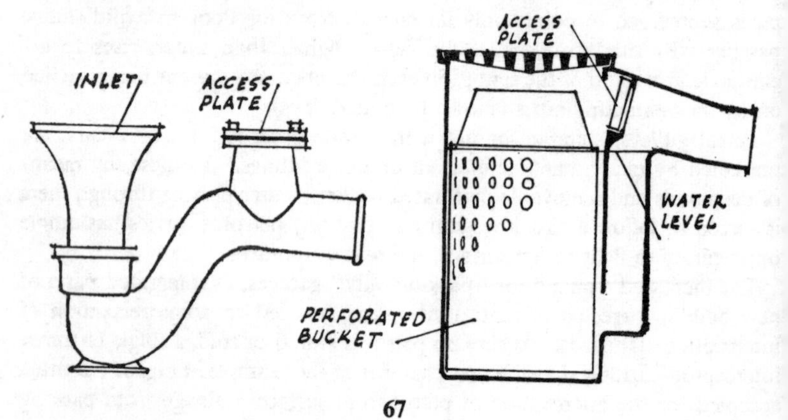

67

67 *Drain fittings*

(*Top*) Specialised fittings referred to in the text.
(*Centre*) Petrol interceptor for larger installations.

The dip-pipes between chambers are usually of cast iron—marketed as standard fittings. Depth of liquid in each chamber should be not less than 3 ft and each chamber should have a sealed access cover over it.
(*Below*) A standard cast iron accessible gulley, *left*, and a garage gulley, *right*.

To preserve internal pipework against corrosion, polythene and even glass are often used for waste pipes and, although neutralising treatment installations are sited to avoid running of corrosive effluents through as much as possible of the drains installation, special drain materials are often necessary.

Cast iron as normally treated is not very resistant to chemical attack and where its use for carrying acid waste is necessary for other reasons pipes with interior surfaces coated with glass vitreous enamel are available.

Stoneware pipes are reasonably resistant to corrosive wastes but a special grade of pipe, "salt-glazed ware pipes with chemically resistant properties", are manufactured (covered by B.S. 1143). Fireclay, glass enamelled pipes are generally more resistant to chemical corrosion than salt-glazed stoneware pipes.

Acid soils. Some soils, in particular heavy clay soils and made-up ground containing clinker, ashes, etc., are chemically corrosive. Cast-iron pipes in these soils need protection—usually provided by bituminous coatings or bituminous impregnated wrappings.

Drains below buildings. Where drains are necessarily laid below buildings they may be constructed of stoneware with the precautions of double covers to inspection points or covers at drain inverts within chambers as described earlier. The additional protection against fracture and leakage given by the bylaw requirement to completely encase them in concrete is not generally regarded as making them suitable for use in cases where the major part of a drainage system lies within or beneath buildings or for use where vibration or pressure are likely. In these circumstances cast-iron drains are used.

Cast-iron drains. For normal drainage work pipes to B.S. 437 are used. B.S. 78 and 1211 C.I pipes for sewage, water and gas cover material and dimensional standards for "vertically cast" and "spun" pipes respectively. Several grades are specified according to the pressures they are to withstand. B.S. 437 gives a heavy grade of cast-iron and spigot and socket jointing is specified. Bolted flanged or spigot and socket joints can be obtained under B.S. 78 and 1211. Spigot and sockets pipes to B.S. 1211 are being increasingly used instead of 437 as they are dimensionally more accurate and are obtainable

---

The inlet piece to the gulley is interchangeable for any of a range of inlet pieces with one or more horizontal or vertical branch inlets.

The garage gulley is suitable for the interception of petrol from waste water from domestic garages. Water passing through the gulley must reach the outlet through the perforations in the bucket and then around the narrow annular space between bucket and gulley walls. In the process petrol separates to float to the surface of the large volume of water in the gulley and evaporates. (Petrol gulleys have an overall depth of about 2 ft 6 in.)

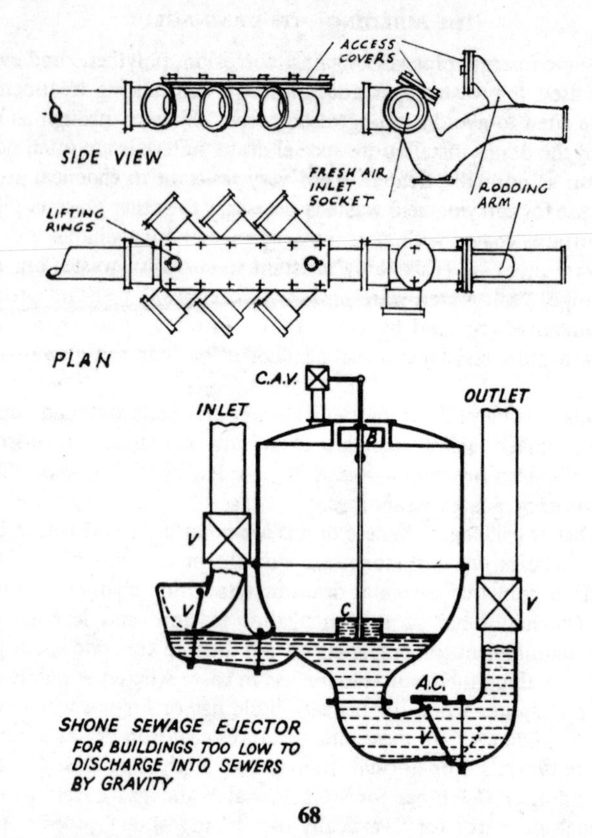

68

68 *Drains within buildings*

(*Above*) A cast-iron inspection chamber and intercepting trap assembly. The same fittings are used for setting within brick or similar chambers below floors of buildings or for suspending within buildings.

The chamber illustrated has six branches but standard chambers can be obtained with as little as one branch or as many as eight.

All branch sockets are set at 45° to the flow, changes in direction between this angle and branch angle being made with standard bend fittings.

(*Below*) A diagrammatic section through a "Shone" sewage ejector. Lifting power is provided by compressed air produced by a compressor, usually driven by an electric motor. The action of the apparatus is as follows:

The sewage gravitates through the inlet pipe into the ejector and gradually rises until it reaches the underside of the bell, B. The air at atmospheric pressure inside this bell is then enclosed and the sewage, continuing to rise outside and above the rim of the bell, compresses the enclosed air sufficiently to lift the bell, and spindle, which opens the compressed air admission valve, C.A.V.

in 18 ft lengths. Joints for spigot and socket pipes are caulked lead joints similar in all respects to those described in Chapter 7 for cast-iron soil pipes above ground. An extensive range of standard traps, gulleys, bends, junctions and inspection chambers are available for use with cast-iron drains, dimensional and material requirements for which are covered by B.S. 1132.

Pipes are available in diameters up to 24 in. and standard protection is by means of bituminous coating. Standard pipe length is 9 ft, so that far fewer joints than for stoneware pipes are required.

The great strength of cast-iron pipes and of their jointing makes them secure enough against leaks and damage to be run above ground or suspended within buildings. To provide for the necessary access in the latter case bend and junction fittings are made with removable plates. These are bolted to the fittings with gun-metal bolts and seated on impregnated felt washers to ensure airtightness. One-piece inspection chambers for which any necessary number of branch socket inlets required can be specified are used at major inspection points and these are made accessible in the same way by means of covers bolted into position over impregnated gaskets. These covers are sufficiently secure against leaks for no other closure of drains within buildings to be required, e.g. if drains are suspended. Typical cast-iron fittings are illustrated in Figs. 67 and 68.

Although cast-iron drains may be constructed with open channels these are rare. When drains run beneath buildings with access provided by

---

The compressed air, thus automatically admitted into the ejector, presses on the surface of the sewage, driving the whole of the contents before it, through the bell-mouthed opening at the bottom, and through the outlet pipe, to the high-level gravitating drain. The sewage can only escape from the ejector by the outlet pipe, as the instant the air pressure is admitted on to the surface of the liquid, the valve on the inlet pipe falls on its seat and prevents escape in that direction. The sewage passes out of the ejector until its level reaches the cup, C, and still continuing to fall, leaves the cup full. The weight of the liquid in the portion of the cup thus exposed, i.e. no longer unsupported by the surrounding liquid, is sufficient to pull down the bell and spindle, thereby reversing the compressed air admission valve, which first cuts off the compressed air and then allows the air within the ejector to exhaust down to atmospheric pressure. The outlet valve falls on its seat, retaining the liquid in the outlet pipe, and sewage is free to flow into the ejector once more, driving the free air before it through an air valve as the sewage rises; and so beginning a new cycle of operations.

N.B.—The positions of the cup and bell floats are so adjusted that compressed air is not admitted to the ejector until it is full of sewage, and the air is not allowed to exhaust until the ejector is emptied down to the discharge level.

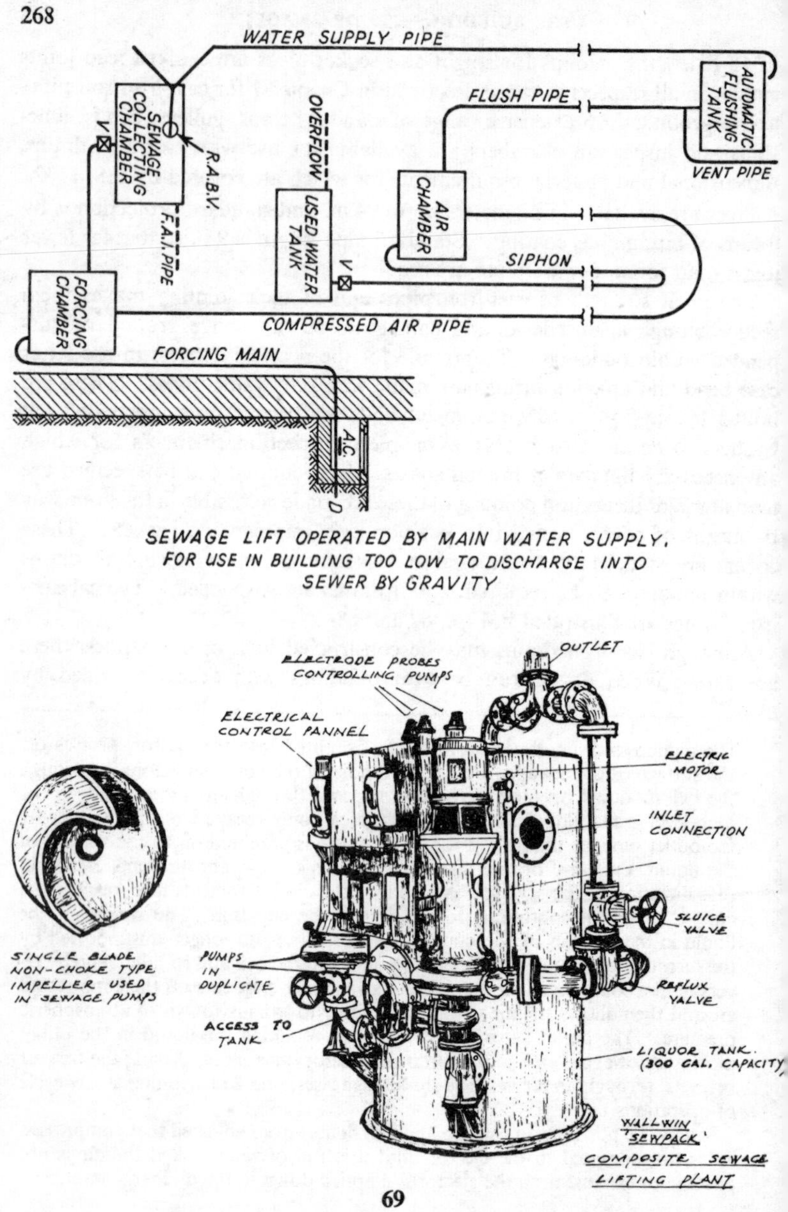

SEWAGE LIFT OPERATED BY MAIN WATER SUPPLY. FOR USE IN BUILDING TOO LOW TO DISCHARGE INTO SEWER BY GRAVITY

69

inspection chambers built with access covers set at the lowest floor level the standard inspection chambers with bolted covers described above are almost invariably used at the drain level.

Suspended drains. Suspended drains are often resorted to within buildings when their lowest floor levels are below sewer level. If often happens that all sanitary accommodation can be planned on the upper floors of the building so that sewage collection can be run to the sewer by gravity by suspending the drains within the building, for example, at high level in the basement or sub-basement.

Sewage lifting. When the positioning of sanitary accommodation below the level of the sewer cannot be avoided, it becomes necessary to collect this part of the building's drainage to a convenient point at the lower level for raising to a level from which it can be discharged by gravity to the sewer. Figure 68 illustrates and describes a sewage ejector which raises sewage by compressed air and Fig. 69 illustrates and describes a "sewage lift". The latter found considerable use in the days when electricity was not freely available or so reliable as it is to-day. The space required for the apparatus cannot be easily found or spared when compared with that required for the ejector or the small sewage pump. Also most water authorities object to the use of sewage lifts when the running of mains water to waste is involved.

Pumps for raising sewage in domestic buildings have been slow in finding favour due to using them with open sumps. Now that composite plant consisting of a sealed sump with pump and motors in duplicate are available as a single unit (Fig. 69) their greater efficiency and space saving advantages are being recognised.

---

69 (*Top*) *A Sewage lift*

Lifting power is provided by compressed air produced by water falling from high level. The operation is as follows:

The flushing tank is placed fairly high up in the building, and the other chambers in approximately the positions shown. The drains discharge into a sewage-collecting chamber, from which the sewage flows to the forcing chamber, being prevented from returning by a non-return valve. When the sewage reaches a certain level in the collecting chamber, it opens the reverse action ball valve, R.A.B.V., and allows the automatic flushing tank to fill. The latter in due course discharges, expelling and compressing the air in the air chamber, which exerts a pressure on the sewage in the forcing chamber and drives it up through the forcing main to the high level drain D. (*Bottom*) The composite sewage lift plant consists of the liquor tank and pumps in duplicate. These are operated by the electrode probes which enter the tank. When the liquor rises in the tank and makes contact with an electrode an electrical circuit is made which brings the pump in action. Another electrode at low level breaks the circuit in a similar way. The third electrode shown is to bring in the stand-by pump should the first not operate or prevent the level in tank from rising. Non-choke impellers of the type illustrated are used in the pumps.

9

The Building—its Drainage: II

Layout of drains. Having considered the principles underlying the design of drainage schemes, their application to specific circumstances can be considered.

An accurate block plan of the building is prepared, and the position of all soil, waste and rainwater pipes marked on it, together with the position of any W.C. on the ground floor which is to be connected directly to the drain. The arrangement of the drainage will, of course, depend on the character of the building, the nature of the site and the local bylaws.

The local authority may require rain and surface water to be kept separate from waste water and "soil" or may permit all to be delivered into a "combined" sewer. It may require an intercepting trap and F.A.I. or its bylaws may forbid them or make them permissible. Again, with a terrace house, the main drain may need to pass under the building if the sewer is in the road in front, whereas in the case of a semi-detached or detached house the drains can usually be kept quite outside the building. A few typical examples are illustrated.

Figure 70 shows block plans of two small terrace houses of different plan. In these the heads of the gulleys under the rainwater pipes are not shown owing to the smallness of the scale.

In both examples it is assumed that the local bylaws require an intercepting trap and F.A.I., and the intercepting chamber is placed in the front garden and the fresh-air inlet carried up behind the pier which carries the front railings. Back inlet gulleys are shown taking the bath and sink wastes, although in current practice gulleys with back inlet sockets to discharge wastes below the gulley grating are preferred.

In the left-hand diagram the drainage from a yard gulley at the back is turned into the drain from the W.C., to assist in flushing it. The vent pipe is shown connected to the manhole at the back.

In the diagram on the right the running of the W.C. branch below the building avoids two additional changes in direction in the drain and two additional inspection chambers. The vent pipe taken from the branch drain

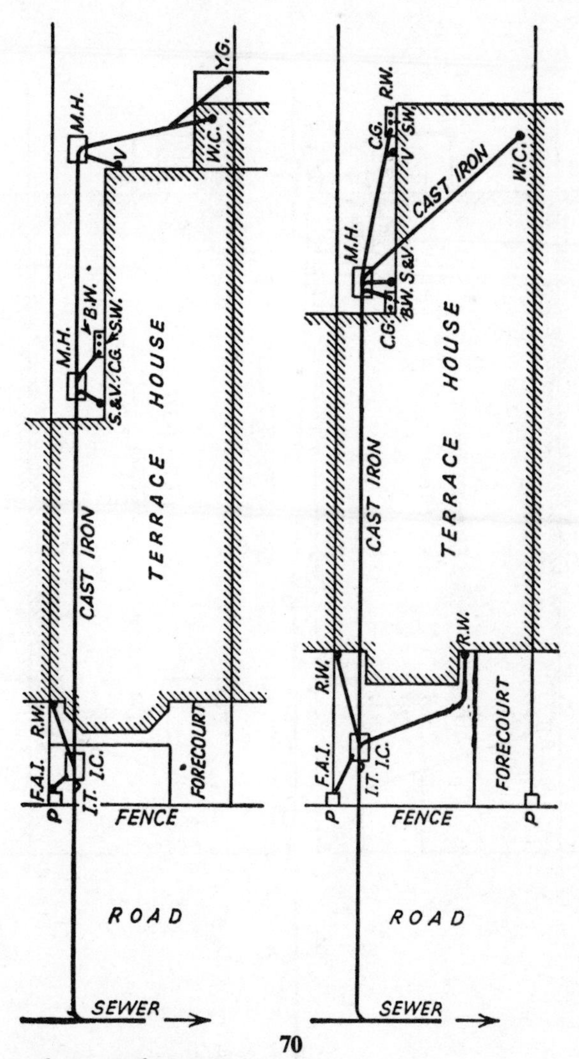

70 *Drainage for terrace houses*

Examples of drainage from terrace houses when a combined sewer is in the road fronting the terrace.

Key to letters used on the plan:
R.W., Rainwater pipe and gulley; S. and V., Soil and Vent pipe; V., Vent pipe; S.W., Sink waste; B.W., Bath waste; B.I.G., Back inlet gulley; Y.G., Yard gulley; I.T., Intercepting trap; I.C., Intercepting chamber; M.H., Manhole; P., Pier.

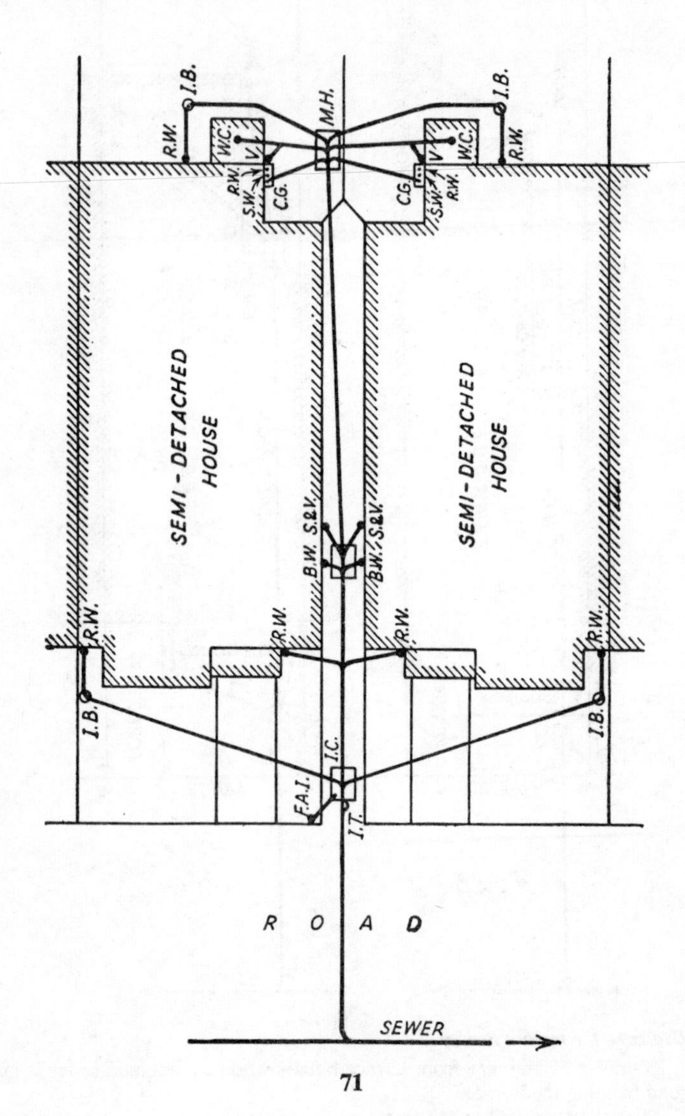
I.B.
R.W.
W.C.
V.
M.H.
R.W.
S.W.
C.G.
SEMI - DETACHED HOUSE
B.W.
S.&V.
I.C.
F.A.I.
I.T.
ROAD
SEWER

71

to the sink gulley is not essential but shows the method of arranging such a pipe when a soil pipe is not near enough to the head of the drain to ventilate it adequately.

Figure 71 illustrates and describes a typical arrangement of drains from semi-detached houses and Figs. 72 and 73 the arrangement of drains from detached houses.

Working sections of drainage schemes. Having prepared the plan of the drainage scheme, working sections of the drain runs are often required. The levels along the lines of the proposed drains are taken and the sections plotted, showing the existing surface of the ground. (The method of taking the levels and plotting the sections is beyond the scope of the present work.) Figure 74 gives examples of completed sections after the lines of the proposed drains, positions of manholes, etc., have been added.

As these sections show the gradients which result in the "branch" drains, those between M.H.4 and M.H.6 and between M.H.3 and M.H.5. are excessive. This condition can be corrected by deeper digging for these drains. This would probably be the more economic method in an installation of the size under consideration but an alternative method—one which would be preferred when drain runs of considerable length are involved—would be to introduce "ramps" or "drop-pipes". Figure 75 shows the arrangement of a ramp to eliminate steep gradient.

Setting out drains. From the prepared plan and sections, the drains are

---

71 *Drainage for semi-detached houses*

The plan shows a pair of semi-detached houses drained together. A common passage leads to the tradesmen's entrances at the back of the houses and the main drain is laid under this. Its course is not quite straight from end to end—to make it so would bring the back manhole under the fence. Inspection bends are placed on two of the rainwater drains in each case. By placing the back manhole farther from the street, the rainwater drain at the back of each house might have been given one change of direction instead of two, but in this case the foul drains would have had to enter the manhole with a very sharp curve and the lesser evil has been chosen.

It is better to connect the vent pipe to the drain from the W.C., a foul drain, as shown, rather than to the longer drain taking rainwater only.

Key to letters used on the plan:

B.I.G., Back inlet gulley; I.B., Inspection bend; M.H., Manhole; R.W., Rain-water pipe; S.W., Sink waste; B.W., Bath waste; V., Vent pipe; S. and V., Soil and Vent pipe; I.C., Intercepting chamber; I.T., Intercepting trap; F.A.I., Fresh-air inlet.
The sewer is a combined sewer and it has been assumed that local practice calls for the use of intercepting traps.

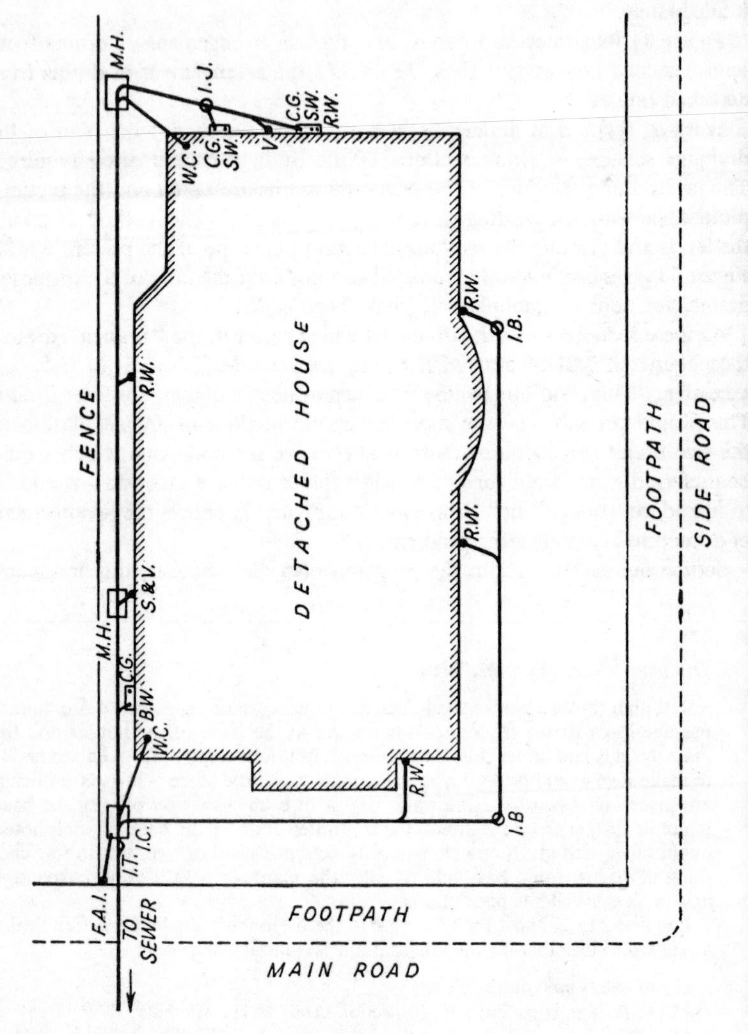
FENCE
DETACHED HOUSE
FOOTPATH
SIDE ROAD
FOOTPATH
MAIN ROAD
M.H.
I.J.
C.G.
S.W.
R.W.
V.
C.G.
S.W.
W.C.
R.W.
R.W.
I.B.
R.W.
S.&V.
M.H.
C.G.
B.W.
W.C.
R.W.
I.B.
I.C.
I.T.
F.A.I.
TO SEWER

72

set out. The lines of the main drain and branches are pegged out on the ground and the gradients set out before any excavation is commenced.

Sight rails and boning rods. The only accurate method of securing a perfectly regular gradient is by the use of sight rails and boning rods. On either side of the proposed drain, at the upper and lower end of each length of drain, a drain pipe of good diameter, say 9 in., is set up as shown at D.P. in Fig. 75. In each of these an upright post is planted, well packed round with earth or sand. Sight rails, S.R., are then fixed to the posts at each end of the length of drain, at such a height that their upper edges will set out in the air an imaginary line parallel to the intended drain, and at a convenient height above ground for a man to sight (see caption to Fig. 75). Sight rails are always fixed first at the point at which the drain commences. (This is the lower end, since it is the outfall level which is usually more or less rigidly fixed by circumstances, such as the level of an existing sewer, and because drains are invariably laid uphill.) Rails are fixed next, at all changes of direction or gradient, at any convenient intermediate points, and finally at the top end of the drain. The posts should be well away from the edge of the trench to prevent disturbance by falling earth. The sight rail is a wooden straight-edge, fixed level from one post to the other.

The boning rod or traveller. Figure 75 shows the elevation and a side view

---

72 *Drainage for a detached house*

A detached corner house is shown separated from an adjoining house by a narrow passage. The placing of the sanitary fittings makes an economical arrangement difficult because of the narrowness of the passage. The bath waste and soil-pipe might have communicated with the same manhole by placing the latter nearer the street, but the small space available between the manhole and the building would then have caused very awkward junctions and the method shown is considered the better for this reason. It will be seen that the ground-floor W.C. is not under that on the floor above, and the drain from the former is therefore taken direct to the intercepting chamber. An additional manhole might have been put at the back to take the two sink wastes and the rainwater, but the increase in cost, over that of the arrangement shown, would hardly be justifiable. An inspection junction, I.J., is used at the connection of the second sink waste.

N.B.—For key to letters used on the plan, see Fig. 71.

A modification of the arrangement shown would be to make the long rain-water drain from the right-hand side of the house an "air-disconnected drain" by putting in, close to the intercepting chamber, a trapped yard gulley with side inlet for the drain and using untrapped gulleys at the feet of the rainwater pipes.

(See Figs. 50 and 67 on pp. 204 and 264.

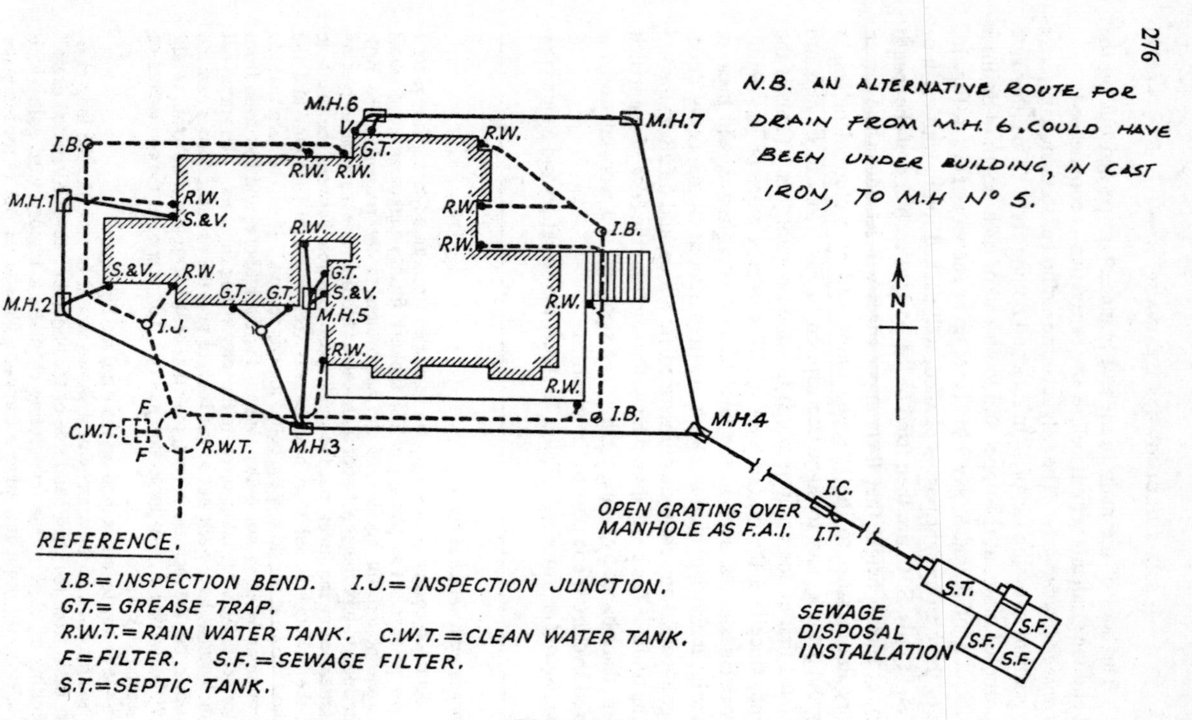
N.B. AN ALTERNATIVE ROUTE FOR
DRAIN FROM M.H. 6. COULD HAVE
BEEN UNDER BUILDING, IN CAST
IRON, TO M.H Nº 5.
M.H.1
M.H.2
M.H.3
M.H.4
M.H.5
M.H.6
M.H.7
I.B.
R.W.
S.&V.
G.T.
V.
I.J.
C.W.T.
F
R.W.T.
N
I.C.
I.T.
OPEN GRATING OVER
MANHOLE AS F.A.I.
S.T.
S.F.
SEWAGE
DISPOSAL
INSTALLATION
REFERENCE.
I.B.= INSPECTION BEND. I.J.= INSPECTION JUNCTION.
G.T.= GREASE TRAP.
R.W.T.= RAIN WATER TANK. C.W.T.= CLEAN WATER TANK.
F= FILTER. S.F.= SEWAGE FILTER.
S.T.= SEPTIC TANK.

73

of an adjustable boning rod, or traveller. It is in fact an elongated T-square, having the blade in two pieces, and capable of adjustment to any desired length by means of iron bands and clamping screws at S.S. At the foot is an iron shoe, projecting so as to enable it to be rested on the invert of the pipe.

Adjustment for line and gradient. For the purpose of laying the pipes to the exact line, the centre of the trench should be marked on each sight rail, and a plumb-bob suspended from this point by a fairly stout cord. Each pipe must be firmly bedded in the line joining these cords, its exact level being secured by the pipe layer inserting the shoe of the boning rod upon the invert of the pipe and keeping the rod upright. The overlooker then sights over the lower sight rail to see whether the top edge of the cross head of the boning rod is above or below the line of sight from rail to rail. If it is above, the ground must be trimmed away and the pipe lowered until the true grade is reached. Should it be below, it should be gently raised and packed with concrete.

The trench should not be cut wider than is necessary to allow sufficient room for the pipe layer to work at the bottom and the length of trench opened up at one time is governed by the number of men at work, the nature of the ground and the interference with access to the premises. Where the ground is bad from wet sand or other causes, or when drains pass close to walls and buildings (where the foundations may be liable to disturbance by reason of the trench being kept open), trenches should be cut in short lengths and with especial care.

Timbering trenches. As the excavation of the trench proceeds, the sides should, unless the soil is very firm and the depth of the drain small, be supported by proper timbering. A method applicable to ordinary cases of moderately firm earth is to place vertical boards about 9 in. × $1\frac{1}{2}$ in. in section, "poling boards", at frequent intervals, or close together, according

---

73 A "*Separated*" *System of Drainage*

The diagram illustrates the drainage of a fairly large bungalow with its own system of sewage disposal, the latter installation being situate some three or four hundred yards from the house. The drains would be of 4-in. pipes throughout.

As the septic tank is used, grease traps are provided instead of gulleys. (These are of the lifting tray type, a flushing grease gulley would not be permissible owing to the necessity of keeping grease out of the septic tank.)

The intercepting chamber, being some considerable distance from the house, is covered by an iron grating to act as a fresh-air inlet. It will be seen that a vent pipe is provided to the head of each of the principal branch drains.

The rainwater collection, which should be kept out of the septic tank installation, is shown connected to a storage tank.

N.B.—Septic tank installations are described fully in Chapter 11.

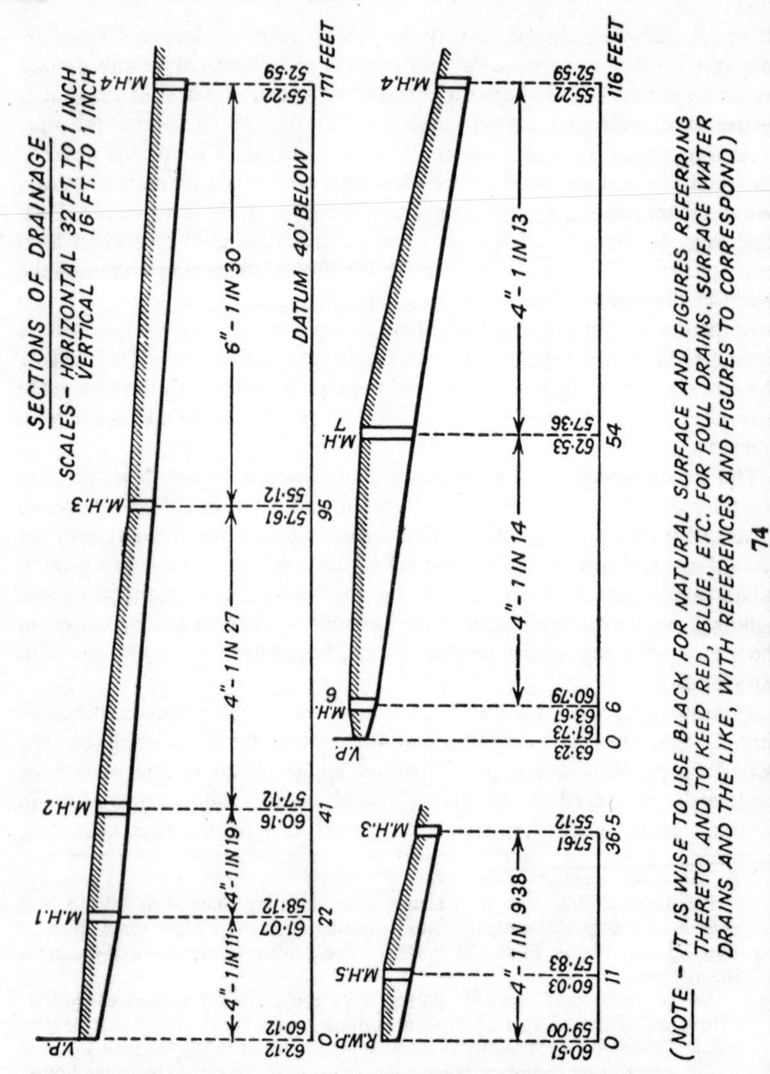

74 *Drainage sections for some of the bungalow drains shown in Fig. 73.*

It will be seen that against each ordinate on the sections two heights are figured, the greater being the existing surface level, and the lesser the level of the invert of the proposed drain at that point. (The "invert" of a drain is the lowest point of its interior.) The upper end of the drain should be about

to the nature of the ground, supported by horizontal timbers about 9 in. × 3 in. in section, "walings". The walings are kept apart by struts, about 4 in. square, wedged tightly between them. The struts should not be nearer together than about 6 ft or they will interfere with the work of the pipe layer.

In the method described the timbering cannot be placed in position until the ground has been excavated to the depth of the poling boards and if the ground is too loose for this to be done safely, it is necessary to increase the thickness of the boards to 2 in. and to sharpen their ends so that they may be gradually driven down as the excavation proceeds. Boards driven in this way are usually called "runners".

In a very deep trench, the method of timbering is best carried out on the lines shown in Fig. 76, in which two settings of runners are pointed at the foot and driven in. If the ground is very bad, the walings can be omitted, the trench being timbered by means of horizontal planks or sheeting, placed close together and secured by vertical polings about 9 in. × 3 in. in section, and about 6 ft apart, braced by strong struts as before described. In cases of this kind it may be advisable to leave the lower timbering in permanently.

Concrete under pipes. Reference should be made to page 238 on the research carried out on bedding of drain pipes. Local authorities have in the past required concrete bedding under pipes. If this is still required the method used should be carefully revised in accordance with B.R.S. recommendation.

The practice of putting down a 3 in. bed of concrete and packing a drain on bricks from this foundation concrete, leaving the bricks as part of the final bed, is most unsatisfactory; the bricks form hard spots and cause bearing fractures. In cases where Class B bedding is not adequate the trench should be deep enough to allow first a bed of selected material of 6 in. depth to be placed and tamped. This should be followed by 1½ in. to 2 in. of 1 – 5 – 10 concrete as a blinding layer—to give clean firm trench bottom. From this the drain can be laid on temporary packings 4 in. deep (flexible joints) 2000 lb/in.^{2} test strength concrete should then be packed under the pipe (Fig. 76) and before the concrete has hardened, the temporary packings should be removed and the concrete cleared 1 in. from the face of the socket to allow movement of the flexible joint. The first 12 in. of back filling should consist of selected material lightly tamped in 6 in. layers.

In cases where greater pipe strength is required the above procedure may be followed but the pipes completely surrounded with concrete, which must be placed without horizontal construction joints, to obtain increased strength.

---

2 ft below the surface, and the line of drain drawn in such a position as will give a reasonable gradient, without coming nearer to the surface than about 2 ft

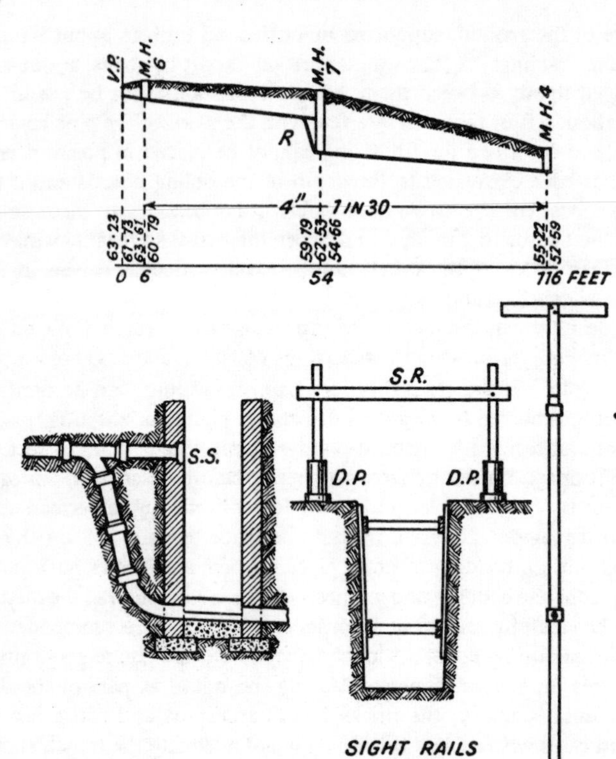

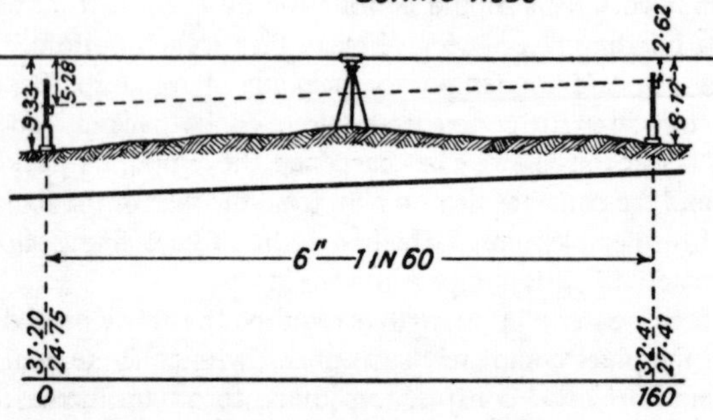

EXAMPLE TO SHOW USE OF SURVEYORS LEVEL TO SET UP SIGHT RAILS TO GIVE CORRECT GRADIENT

75

75 *Drain ramps*

(*Top*) The drain section between M.H. 4 and M.H. 6 from Fig. 74 shown with a ramp, R, introduced to decrease the general gradient of the drain. The arrangement of the ramp in more detail is shown below (*centre, left*).

A stopper is sometimes placed at S.S. (the rodding eye), but better drain ventilation is obtained without it. If the ramp is not more than about 18 in. in depth, it can be formed in the channelled floor of the manhole.

Arrangements of this sort are sometimes described as "tumbling bays" or "drop manholes", and they may be used, with small modifications, to connect a branch drain at a higher level to a main drain or private sewer at a lower level. The B.S. Code of Practice on Building Drainage shows a preference for a vertical drop pipe to connect the two levels instead of the sloping ramp, and in this case it is wise to carry the drop pipe up to the surface and provide a hinged access cover in case the lower section should get blocked. (See Fig. 85, p. 310.)

Pipes of "ramps" and "drops" should be encased in concrete.

(*Centre*) Arrangement of site rails and typical "boning" rod used in setting out of drains (see text).

(*Below*) LEVEL CALCULATIONS. The method of fixing the sight rails at the correct height can be explained by the aid of the lower diagram. It is assumed here that a drain 160 ft long has to be set out at a gradient of 1 in 60 from a length of drain, already laid, whose invert level is 24·75 ft above datum. At a gradient of 1 in 60 the rise in 160 ft will be $\frac{160}{60}$ = 2·66 ft, so that the level of the invert at the upper end of this length of drain will have to be

$$24{\cdot}75 + 2{\cdot}66 = 27{\cdot}41,$$

as figured in the illustration. Two sight rails are shown in the section, and the level should be set up midway between them to eliminate any error of collimation in the instrument.

The levels figured on the section show that the depth of the invert of the drain below ground at the lower end of this length is 31·20 — 24·75 = 6·45 ft, whilst at the upper end it is 32·41 — 27·41 = 5·00 ft. If the sight rails are set 10·50 ft above the invert of the drain the height of the sight rails above the ground will be 10·50 — 6·45 = 4·05 ft at one end, and 10·50 — 5·00 = 5·50 ft at the other end. This will be a convenient height for sighting in the manner which will be described later. It should be noted at this point that the ground level is of interest only in finding out what will be a convenient height for the sight rails above the drain. Having selected this height the "ground" levels are disregarded in what follows. They are likely to be changed slightly, by falling in of stones, or by earth thrown up, and are therefore quite unreliable as a basis from which to set out the levels of the drain.

USE OF SURVEYOR'S LEVEL. In the present instance, having decided that the sight rails are to be 10·50 ft above the drain, they must be set up at reduced levels of 24·75 + 10·50 = 35·25 ft at the lower end, and 27·41 + 10·50 = 37·91 ft at the other end. Suppose that when the level has been set up properly it is found, by sighting upon a bench mark, or other point whose level has previously been determined, that the height of the line of collimation of the telescope is 40·53. Then the sight rail at the lower end must be set up, quite level, so that a staff held oni ts upper edge reads 40·53 — 35·25 = 5·28 ft, while at the upper end of the drain the sight rail must be fixed so that a staff held on it reads 40·53 — 37·91 = 2·62 ft. The boning rod is then adjusted, by its clamping screws, so that its length is exactly 10·50 ft.

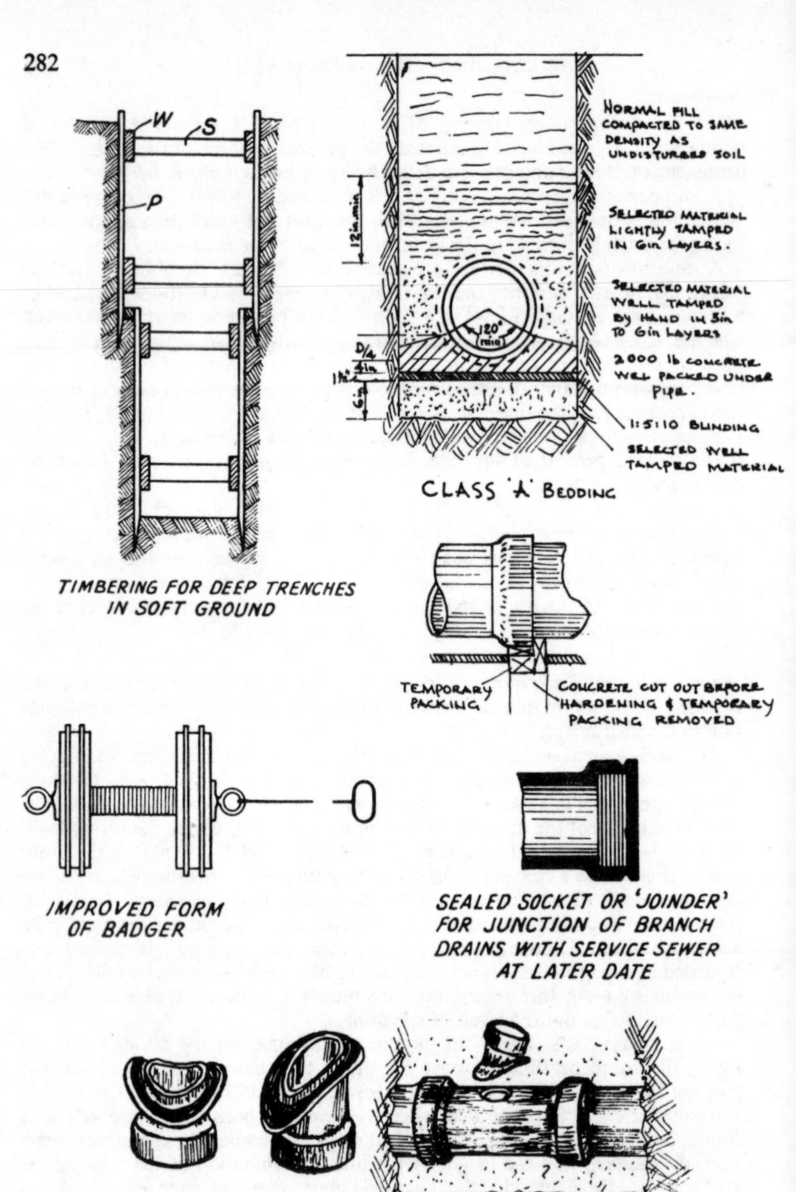

TIMBERING FOR DEEP TRENCHES IN SOFT GROUND

CLASS 'A' BEDDING

IMPROVED FORM OF BADGER

SEALED SOCKET OR 'JOINDER' FOR JUNCTION OF BRANCH DRAINS WITH SERVICE SEWER AT LATER DATE

Temporary packings and clearances must be dealt with as previously described.

These new methods of laying drains may not be readily accepted by some contractors. Supervision of the work will have to be more rigorously carried out to ensure that the work is according to specification at least until the practices are familiar to the industry.

Bad ground. Where the ground is exceptionally bad or wet it will assist to confine the movement of the earth or water by the use of sheet piling which should be left in. Cast-iron piping is generally more suitable but if the soil is aggressive or contains sulphates C.1 may need special protection.

Use of badger. In the laying of stoneware pipes (traditional method) care must be taken to prevent fouling their interior with cement. As each pipe is jointed, a "badger" should be drawn through, in order to remove any mortar which may have found its way through the joint. In its ordinary form, a badger consists of a semicircular piece of wood having, preferably, a rubber ring projecting from its curved edge. A handle about 3 ft long completes its construction. An improved form of this appliance is shown in Fig. 76 consisting of two circular discs of wood, edged with rubber and connected by a steel spiral spring, which enables the badger to be drawn through a bend.

Testing new drains. The drain having been laid and jointed, it should be inspected and tested, first by visually inspecting both pipes and joints, marking any defects with chalk and then, after the work has been completed not less than twenty-four hours, by applying the water test, in order to

---

76 *Installation and arrangement*

(*Top, left*) A section showing the arrangement of poling boards, P, walings, W, and struts, S, in supporting trench walls in soft earth and, *right*, Class A bedding for drains where the loading is greater than that suitable for Class B bedding (page 240) and below—removal of temporary packing to allow flexible joint to function.

(*Centre, left*) A "badger", a tool for keeping drain interiors clean during laying (see text), and, *right*, a diagram showing the arrangement of the capping to the socket of a "joinder" junction, i.e. a junction left in a line of drain for connection of a branch drain at a later date. The use of a joinder junction is not approved unless the connection of branch at a later date is definite and trench is being left open for it, or position marked. If a trench is backfilled because a connection is not required within the same contract it is unlikely that it will be found by excavation and the usual method of saddling will be adopted.

(*Below, left*) Saddles of different angles used for making connections to existing stoneware or concrete drains or sewers.

(*Below, right*) Inserting a saddle on a stoneware pipe in which a hole has been cut to receive it. The saddle is bedded and jointed with 1:1 cement mortar.

determine the water-tightness of the drain.[1] The method of doing this is dealt with under the heading of sanitary surveys.

Filling in trenches. If drains are found to be in order the trenches can be filled in. This is a matter requiring careful supervision, as damage is easily done by falling stones or brickbats. For the first foot of depth over the pipes, the earth used should be freed from stones; after depositing it in the trench it should be well but carefully rammed or consolidated. The filling should then be completed in layers of not more than 1 foot in depth, each layer being well rammed. On completion, the drain should be again tested in order to detect any damage during the filling in. It is sometimes arranged to make the contractor responsible for the drain standing the water test three months after completion, in order to ensure the use of cement in proper condition and a good quality.

Connection to sewer. The connection of drains to the sewer is carried out in a number of ways. In developing an estate, junctions for future use are often put in the sewer opposite the various plots. The mouth of the branch of these junctions are sometimes closed by means of a piece of slate, but this is an unsatisfactory practice. Proper junctions sometimes called "joinders", can be obtained for the purpose. These have the branch temporarily but securely closed, as shown in Fig. 76. In this example a cap is formed as part of the junction, a fairly deep triangular groove being formed round so that a few taps with a cold chisel readily detaches it, leaving the socket free for the connection of the drain.

If a junction has not been put in, it is a frequent practice to remove two or three pipes in order to build one in. Alternatively use can be made of the saddle shown in Fig. 76.

Drain repairs. In the ordinary way, on finding that a drain is leaky, the ground is opened up in order to expose the drain and so trace the leaky joint or cracked pipes. This necessitates the ground remaining open for at least a day or two, and often means taking up floors and so on.

A system of repair, in use for many years by a London company, avoids this nuisance. The drain is first cleaned out and disinfected, the disinfectant being applied under pressure, so that it will pass through any defect and so disinfect the surrounding soil. An appliance is then passed through the drain, charged with Portland cement grout, which, by means of compression, is forced into every flaw in either pipes or joints. The inside of the drain is said to be left free from any roughness due to this process, and the company is said to guarantee the drains to stand the water test on completion. The

[1] It is usually required that drains are tested in the presence of the local authority's inspector.

system has much to commend it where a drain is only slightly leaky, and the uncovering of the drain is a matter of great inconvenience.

Remodelling old drains. The remodelling of old drainage systems presents no additional problems. The principles which a new system should satisfy have been fully described, but it should be pointed out also that where, in remodelling a system, an old drain is discarded, the drain should be taken up and the trench disinfected before returning the earth. The extent to which an existing system is remodelled is a matter dependent entirely on the circumstances of each individual case. In some cases, sound but moderate proposals would be certain to be carried out, and sanitary progress thereby furthered, while an elaborate proposal might lead to nothing much being done, and progress thereby retarded.

Drain rods and fittings. For the cleansing of drains and the removal of stoppages, various tools are used, fixed to drain rods. The latter are of red malacca cane or of spiral and flexible steel spring, the usual length of each section being 3 ft with a total length in the complete set or bundle of anything from 30 to 90 or 100 ft. The rods are fitted with screws and sockets, so that they may be put together to form a long rod. Various tools are used for fixing to the end of the rod, including fixed and hinged badgers, double "corkscrews", spring hooks, etc., for the purpose of removing obstructions.

After the removal of a stoppage the drain can be finally swept out by a circular brush of either brass or whalebone, affixed to the end of the rods.

Maintenance of drains. Systems of drains should ideally be cleaned and inspected at regular intervals. Gulleys and manholes should be washed out, drains rodded to remove deposits and the whole system flushed with clean water. Stoppers and covers should be checked for seal, of course, and defects revealed should be corrected. Good practice is to do this every third year.

Cesspools. In some country districts there are no sewers and the installation of a sewage-disposal installation may not be justified or possible. In these circumstances cesspools are often used.

The usual official requirements as to cesspools are that they shall (1) be not less than 50 ft from a dwelling; (2) be not less than 60 ft from any well, spring, or other source of water supply; (3) be readily accessible for cleansing, and in such a position as to make it unnecessary for the contents to be carried through a building; (4) have no connection with a sewer or watercourse; (5) be disconnected from the drains by means of an intercepting trap; (6) be of brickwork built in cement mortar on a bed of concrete or equivalent construction cement rendered or asphalted inside, and backed with not less

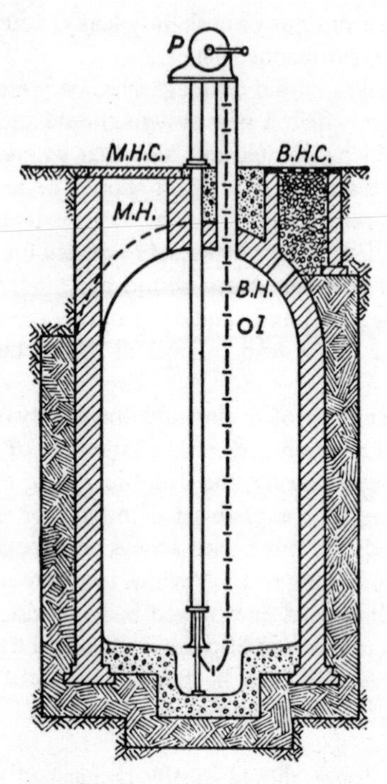

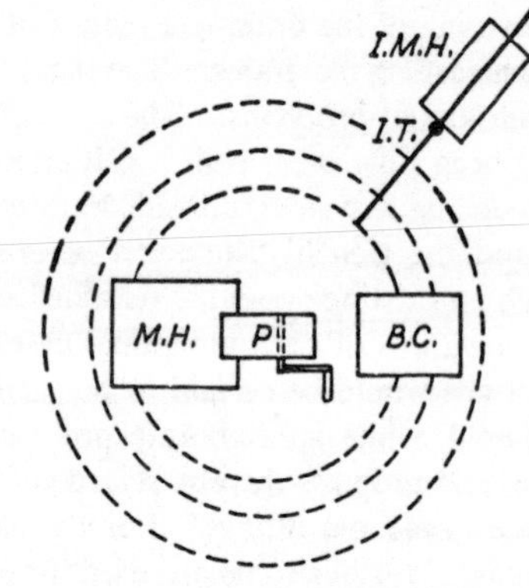

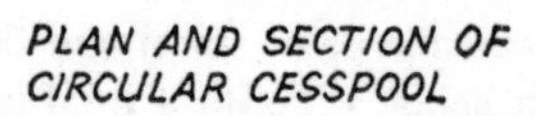
PLAN AND SECTION OF CIRCULAR CESSPOOL

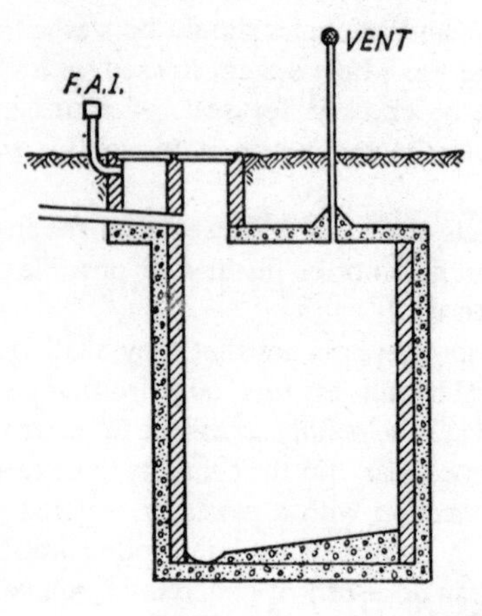

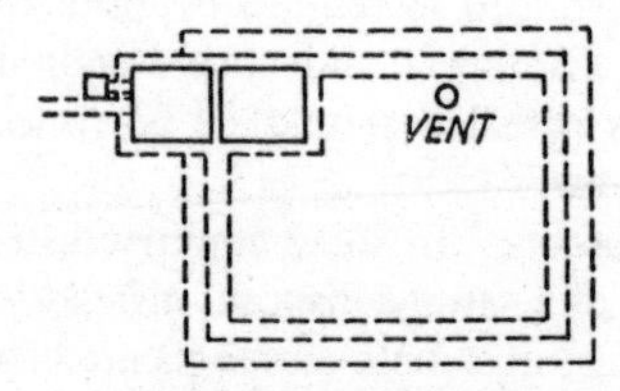

PLAN AND SECTION OF RECTANGULAR CESSPOOL

77

than 9 in. of clay puddle if the soil is waterlogged; (7) be covered, ventilated, and have means of access.

Cesspools may be either rectangular or circular on plan. Size will depend on the number of persons served and on the emptying service available. Good practice is to allow for at least 28 days' storage at a rate of 25 gallons per person per day. Capacity required can be reduced by running waste water to a soakaway but this is not good practice and often not permitted by local authorities.

Figure 77 shows a section through a cesspool found sometimes in remote districts where there is no public cesspool emptying service. It is of circular plan, built of brickwork, cement rendered, and backed by clay puddle; the floor is of concrete, falling to a sump or sinking in the middle. It has an access shaft covered by a stone slab or manhole cover, M.H.C., and is ventilated by a breathing chamber having a grating over it at B.H.C. This chamber is about 18 in. square on plan, and is constructed as follows: A short length of 9-in. pipe is built into the dome to form a breathing hole, B.H. Over this is placed a galvanised iron grating. The chamber is then filled with broken stone, such as road metal, and completed by a grating. The inlet to the cesspool is at I. Emptying is accomplished by the provision of a chain pump, as shown at P. The essential part consists of the pump tube and an endless chain carrying circular iron discs at intervals of about 9 in. These discs carry the sewage up the pipe when the handle is turned and discharge it from the mouth of the pump. The plan shows the relative positions of the parts. It will be seen that an intercepting chamber is provided close to the cesspool. If some distance from any building, the cover of the intercepting chamber can be in the form of a grating, to act as a fresh-air inlet to the drains.

If the local authority undertakes to empty the cesspool at regular intervals by means of a motor tanker provided with a suction pump and several lengths of armoured hose, which is usual nowadays, the chain pump is omitted. Emptying by chain pump calls for suitable land adjacent to the cesspool and after sewage discharge the ploughing of the fouled land.

---

77 *Cesspools*

(*Above*) A traditional form of cesspool built of brick surrounded with clay puddle and fitted with a chain pump for discharging sewage over adjacent farm land.

(*Below*) A rectangular cesspool of reinforced concrete construction.

10

Sewerage

"Sewerage" and "sewage". The term sewerage means the system of sewers for the collection from a district not only the wastes from the various sanitary fittings, but also the rainwater which falls on the area sewered and is not absorbed by the ground. The dirty water carried by the sewers is "sewage".

Little is known of the early history of sewerage in Britain, but sewers are undoubtedly of ancient origin. Some of the main sewers constructed by the Romans can still be seen in Rome.

Sewer layout. In designing a system of sewerage the engineer gives consideration to the position of the outfall of sewage, i.e. the location of the disposal or purifying plant; the patterns of the streets on plan; the area of the land to be drained; its possible population; the nature of the surface soil; the configuration of the ground; the rainfall and the water supply. (Students and others who need a deeper knowledge of detail are referred to the British Standard Code of Practice on Building Drainage (CP 301) and Civil Engineering Code of Practice (No. 5) on Sewerage.)

Position of the outfall. The position of the outfall, the site chosen for the purification processes should preferably be at a low level, so that the discharge to it may be by gravity and the cost of pumping may be avoided. Land of low value would naturally be preferred, remote from habitations so that nuisance is avoided, and ample in extent, to provide for possible future extensions. These considerations may, of course, conflict with one another; for instance, it is possible that the low-lying land to which a gravitational discharge is practicable may have a high value for industrial purposes. In this case a careful comparison would have to be made between the economy of utilising such a site, or of using some other site in an unobtrusive position of less value, to which the sewage would have to be pumped.

Tributary sewers. Working backwards from the outfall, the main outfall sewer will rise at a small gradient and branch off into different districts by smaller sewers, which will receive tributary sewers serving particular streets or estates. Many of these will, in turn, receive tributary sewers from other treets. The plan form of the complete sewerage scheme will therefore lepend upon the layout of the town and upon the estate planning.

Size of sewers. The size required for any particular sewer will depend ıpon:

1 The area of the district to be drained by it, chiefly because the amount of storm water to be carried off will depend largely on this. The maximum rate of run-off will, however, not be *proportional* to that area, because in a large area the flow will be spread over a longer period of time, as will be explained later.

2 The density of the population: firstly, because the discharge of foul sewage will depend upon this, and secondly, because the more dense the population the greater will be the proportion of impermeable surfaces, in the way of streets, roofs and paved yards, and therefore the larger will be the run-off of storm water to the sewers. In calculating density consideration is given not only to the present population, but also to the population expected when the land is fully developed, or during the next 30 years or so. It is not an expensive matter to make a sewer a little larger than is needed for present requirements, but it is very costly to take up one sewer and replace it by a larger one. In most cases the density provisions of a town-planning scheme will be of very great assistance in estimating future population and the likely area of roofs and paved surfaces.

3 The nature of the surface soil and its degree of cultivation: some soils are more permeable than others and water falling upon them will percolate to form underground streams. Even on relatively permeable surfaces, if not paved, much of the storm water will run into ditches and streams and will not enter the sewers.

4 The physical features of the land. Other things being equal, water will percolate into steep land to a less degree than into flat land, because it will have less time to soak in. Also, since on steep land the water will travel at a greater velocity, the flow from distant parts of the drainage area will not lag much behind that from the nearer parts, so that the run-off will be more concentrated.

5 The amount of rainfall in the district. The mean annual rainfall is, however, of less importance than might at first be supposed, because in the design of a sewerage system the concern is not with the total flow in a year, but with the magnitude of short storms. It is by no means always the case that districts subject to the heaviest annual rainfalls are subject to the heaviest storms.

6 The water supply of the district, since all the water which goes into a building will normally emerge as sewage. Water consumption per head of population tends to increase, in some districts because of the growth of the number of motor cars and consequently of water used in washing them, and in other districts through the more universal provision of baths and water closets. This tendency should be provided for. In the estimate of the water supply water (if any) coming from other sources than the town mains; for example, from private wells, springs and rain-water tanks should be included. In some places, even where there are water closets, the use of cesspools may be general, in which case some of the water supplied to the houses will not be discharged into the sewers. Cesspools, however, are regarded as a temporary expedient, likely to be dispensed with when the sewerage system becomes available. Sewers are usually made large enough to accommodate the sewage which is, for the time being, discharged into cesspools.

7 The gradient available for the sewers. It is obvious that velocity of flow will be increased by an increase in the gradient, so that a smaller cross-sectional area is needed to obtain the same discharge. (See also later in this chapter.)

There are three methods of arranging a system of sewers, known respectively as the combined, separate and partially separate systems.

Combined system. The combined system involves only the provision of a single sewer in each street, there being also a single system of drains to each building, i.e. the sewer takes all the domestic sewage, rainwater on roofs and backyards, and the road drainage.

Separate system. In the separate system there are two sewers, one for foul sewage and one for surface water. Each building has two sets of drains, one for sewage and one for rainwater.

Partially separate system. The partially separate system is a compromise between the two just described, and consists of two sewers; one sewer takes all the drainage from buildings (i.e. the "soil" sewage, the waste water from baths, basins, scullery sinks and rainwater from roofs and private paved spaces). The other sewer takes the surface water from road gulleys and sometimes the rainwater from the roofs of public buildings and public paved spaces. The rainwater from the roofs of private buildings is sometimes described as the "unavoidable rainfall". The partially separate system (like the combined system) involves the house owner in only one set of house drains.

Each of the systems possesses certain advantages and disadvantages when one is compared with the other, but individual preference and local conditions enter largely into the choice of system.

Quantity of rainwater. The quantity of rainwater to be dealt with per day is very variable, and it is difficult to design a foul sewer satisfactorily if it is liable to enormous fluctuations of volume of flow. If two sewers are used, the foul sewer can be relatively small, and the smaller a sewer is, so long as it is large enough for its work, the cleaner can it be kept. Again, if pumping has to be resorted to, the quantity to be pumped is reduced to a minimum by the exclusion of rainwater. (It becomes unnecessary to lay down a pumping installation of sufficient capacity to lift all the rainwater, as well as sewage, to a higher level. If proper precautions are taken it is possible to run the surface water to the nearest natural watercourse.)

Objections to separate sewers. In rural districts, generally speaking, the rainfall is comparatively pure and so can be safely taken direct to a watercourse. In other cases, however, this is not so. The first washings of a busy street, after a dry spell, give a liquid that could only be fairly regarded as foul sewage. Another consideration is that if there are two sewers in the street instead of one, there must be proportionately greater obstruction to traffic by repairs. It has been said that another drawback of the separate system is the possibility of house drains, conveying foul sewage, being connected to the rainwater sewer. This is hardly a valid argument, however, as the local authorities have ample powers of supervision.

The reason that the separate system has not been extensively adopted is that, generally speaking, local authorities have no power to compel the provision of two sets of drains to buildings. This fact has led to the fairly extensive adoption of the partially separate system. The sewage from the higher levels of a district is collected into subsidiary sewers of relatively small diameter, say from 9 in. upwards, and is discharged into main sewers at the lower levels.

Intercepting sewers. Where the levels of the district vary considerably it may be necessary to use intercepting sewers, that is to say, subsidiary main sewers running on different contours and draining the areas above but all discharging ultimately into the main outfall sewer. It often happens that the sewage from a low-level intercepting sewer has to be pumped up into the outfall sewer. Assume a town laid out on a hill sloping rapidly down to a river. If there were only one sewer, at the lowest level, it would be liable to be flooded by the surface water from the high levels; further, the sewer might be at such a level that the whole volume of sewage passing through it would have to be pumped up at the outfall. The method then adopted is to have one or more sewers to intercept the drainage above that level. Thus, in

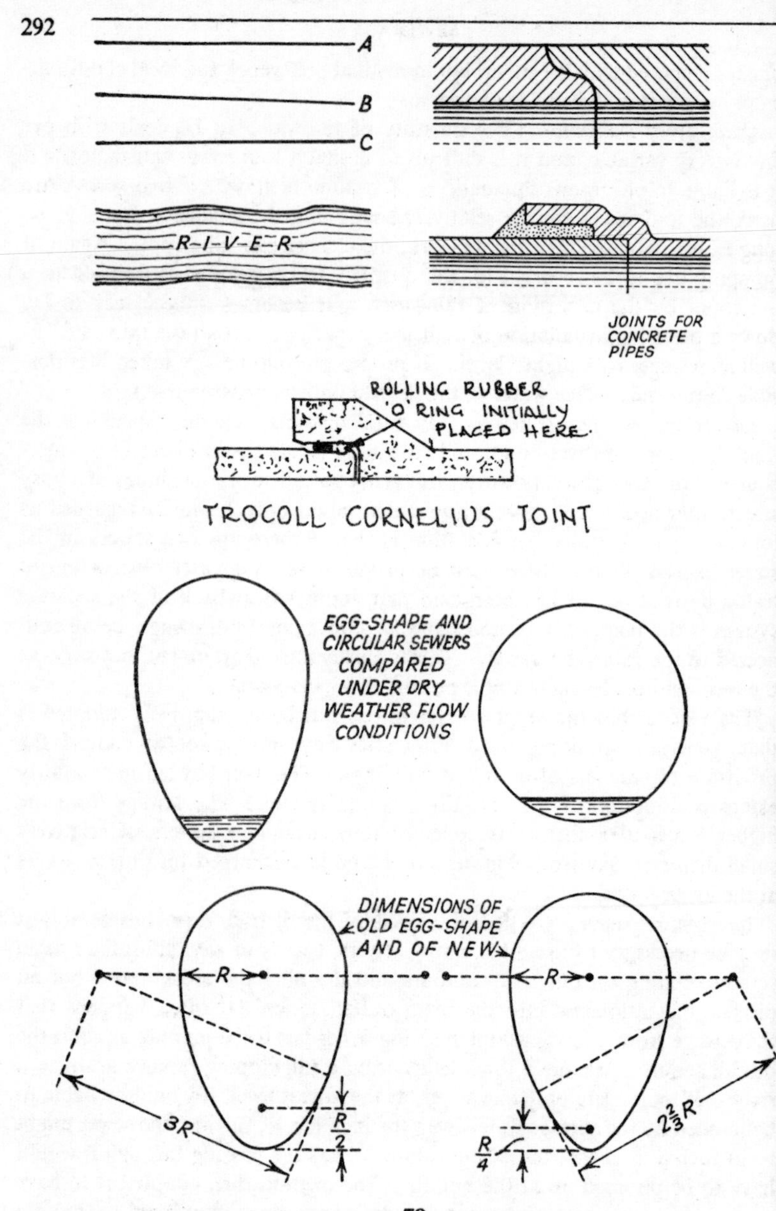
A
B
C
R-I-V-E-R
JOINTS FOR CONCRETE PIPES
ROLLING RUBBER 'O' RING INITIALLY PLACED HERE
TROCOLL CORNELIUS JOINT
EGG-SHAPE AND CIRCULAR SEWERS COMPARED UNDER DRY WEATHER FLOW CONDITIONS
DIMENSIONS OF OLD EGG-SHAPE AND OF NEW
R
R
3R
R/2
R/4
2⅔R

Fig. 78 the sewer on contour A would take the drainage from above its level, he sewer on contour B the drainage between the levels A and B, and sewer C the drainage between B and the river. The three sewers would then converge at some distance from the town and the whole combined volume would be carried in the main outfall sewer. This is the arrangement in London, north of the Thames. Assuming, in Fig. 78, that it is necessary to keept the main outfall sewer at about the level of B, sewer A would discharge nto B by gravitation, and the volume passing through C would be pumped up into B.

SEWER CONSTRUCTION

Pipe sewers. Small sewers are generally constructed of iron pipes with caulked lead joints or of stoneware pipes with cement joints. (One of the patent forms shown in Fig. 61, p. 240, is sometimes used.)

Stoneware pipes for sewers may be obtained in 3-in. rises up to 30 in. diameter, though the larger sizes are easily damaged in transit and are not very popular.

Iron pipes, on the other hand, are available from 6 in. in the same rises up to 4 ft diameter and larger.

---

78 *Sewer lines and sections*

(*Top, left*) A diagram showing a typical arrangement of sewers on sloping ground. Sewer lines follow the contours of the ground in the collecting area to meet eventually, without excessive gradient, for the run to the disposal centre (see text).

(*Top, right*) Joints used for concrete pipes. The flexible joint, *below*, is to be preferred for obvious reasons.

(*Centre*) Comparison of egg-shaped and circular sewer sections showing the greater depth of liquid in the egg-shaped section for a similar quantity of sewage.

(*Below*) Diagram showing, *left*, the method of drawing the section of the ordinary, or old egg-shaped type. The depth is one and a half times the greatest horizontal diameter. The top is a semicircle of radius R; the invert, or bottom, is a circular curve of $\frac{1}{2}R$ in radius, and the top and bottom are joined up by circular curves of radius $3R$. The sketch shows the centres from which the arcs are struck. The diagram, *right*, shows, in the same way, the method of drawing the new egg-shaped type, which is also known as the metropolitan. The bottom is more pointed, giving still better hydraulic mean depths for small flows. As in the last case, the depth is one and a half times the greatest horizontal diameter, but the radius of the invert is only half as great as in the previous case (i.e. $\frac{1}{4}R$). This necessitates, of course, a different radius for the connecting arcs; $2\frac{3}{4}R$ instead of $3R$.

Precast concrete sewers. Although large sizes in cast-iron socketed pipes are available, most engineers choose prefabricated concrete pipes for big intercepting or trunk sewers. They are more costly than stoneware pipes in the small sizes, 12 in. diameter and smaller, but in the larger sizes (up to 6 ft in diameter) they prove more economical, in addition to having greater strength.

JOINTS FOR PIPE AND CONCRETE SEWERS. The least satisfactory feature of the concrete tube, as ordinarily made, is the joint (78). The commonest form is known as an "ogee" joint and it will be seen that the moulded ends of the pipes are simply put together with a little cement mortar between. Another form is that using spigot and socket with cement joint, but the better form is the flexible joint, for reasons similar to those given for stoneware drains. One of the many flexible joints available is shown in Fig. 78.

Foundations for sewers. Stoneware pipes and concrete tubes may be supported by concrete, as for drains (Fig. 76). This is essential if the subsoil is soft, to distribute the weight of the sewer over a larger area of subsoil; it is also necessary if the subsoil is a hard rock, to form a surface smooth enough to give an even bed for the pipes. If a sewer is under a carriage-way it is always advisable to support it by concrete in this way, whatever the nature of the subsoil, and if the depth is shallow so that the sewer may be damaged by heavy vehicles, the concrete should be extended over the sewer to form a covering arch.

When the diameter required for a sewer is greater than the largest size made in iron or stoneware, choice lies between concrete tubes and sewers built up of brickwork or concrete in situ. Concrete tubes[1] are normally much cheaper and are much more rapidly laid, an important point in view of the inconvenience caused to traffic by sewerage works in streets.

Subsoil water. Difficulty sometimes occurs by the rise of subsoil water as work of sewer laying is being carried out.

Sometimes special invert blocks are used, having holes to admit the subsoil water to the spaces left in the hollow blocks, which form channels conducting the water to the lowermost end of the system. Another good method is that shown in Fig. 79. Below the concrete foundation a small trench is cut to take a land drain of from 3 to 6 in. in diameter. The pipes are unglazed and are merely butt-jointed, without sockets. The trench is filled with broken stone.

A third method, adopted where springs occur, is to sink a pair of drain pipes on end, one on either side of the sewer, and fill them with gravel, leaving small openings in the sewer to allow the water to escape laterally to

[1] Concrete tubes are obtainable in sections which can be bolted together and lined usually with bricks.

the top of the pipes and so down through them. The openings in the sewer are closed as the work proceeds.

The methods of setting out the course, and gradients, of a sewer are similar to those adopted for a drain. (Described in Chapter 9.)

"Grips" for pipe sewers. In the case of pipe sewers, grips are cut under the sockets to permit the joint to be properly made and to permit the pipe to be supported throughout its length.

Egg-shaped sewers. The shape in cross-section of sewers is usually either circular or egg-shaped. Egg-shaped sewers are not so popular as they once were, probably because a circular sewer of similar capacity is stronger. Nevertheless, there are, as will be seen, certain qualities inherent in the egg-shape which are not found in the circular cross-section. Stoneware pipes are usually obtainable only in the circular form, but concrete tubes can be obtained in either shape; brickwork can of course be built to either form (79).

Egg-shaped and circular cross-sections compared. The respective advantages and disadvantages of the two shapes may be briefly stated. Circular sewers of brickwork are stronger than egg-shaped sewers and slightly less expensive to construct, but the egg-shaped has advantages from a hydraulic point of view. Figure 78 shows sections of two sewers, both having the same sectional area and both containing exactly the same quantity of water. It will be seen that the water is of greater depth in the egg-shaped sewer than it is in the circular one. The greater the depth of the flowing liquid, the greater its velocity, therefore the egg-shaped sewer will, when compared with one of circular section, equal in area, and containing the same volume of liquid, be the more self-cleansing.

A basic requirement in designing a sewer is to give it the greatest possible hydraulic mean depth for small volumes of flow, and this condition is more easily met in egg-shaped sections.

Timbering for sewer trenches. The timbering of the trenches will generally follow the same line as given earlier for drains (Figs. 75 and 76), but for bad ground the sizes of the timbers must be increased. When the ground is very treacherous it may be necessary to leave in the lowermost set of timbering, to prevent collapse as the timber is removed.

Running sand. When laid in running sand, small sewers should be of iron pipes supported as shown in Fig. 76. Similar support should be given where pipes pass above ground, with additional strengthening given by a cross timber above the pipe, and longitudinal timbers connecting the heads of the piles.

Tunnelling for sewers. Where sewers are very deep below the surface, it is not always economical to lay by means of open cuttings. In such cases

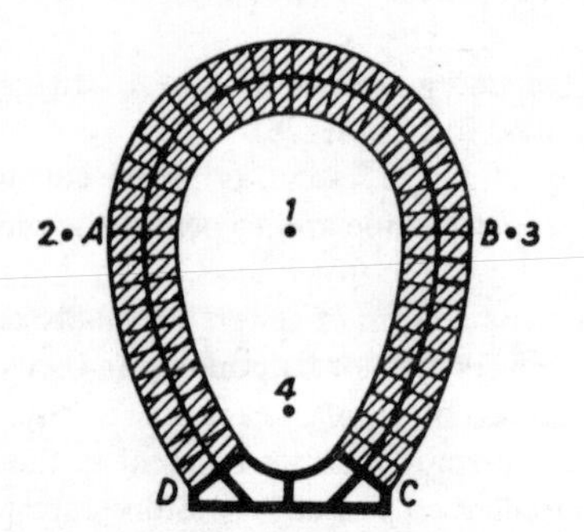

TERRA-COTTA INVERT BLOCK USED IN BRICK EGG-SHAPE SEWER

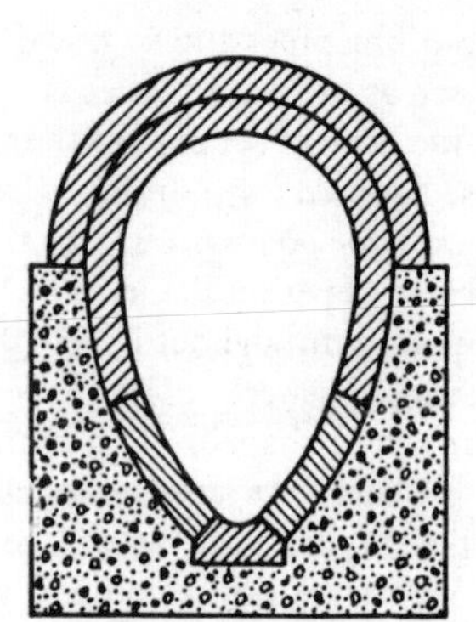
ALTERNATIVE EGG-SHAPE CONSTRUCTION

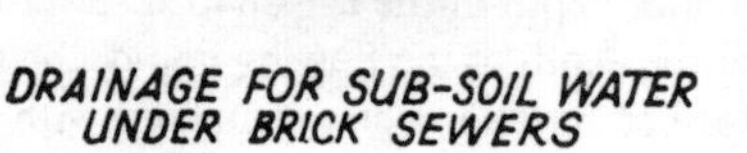
DRAINAGE FOR SUB-SOIL WATER UNDER BRICK SEWERS

TIMBERING FOR SEWER IN TUNNELLING

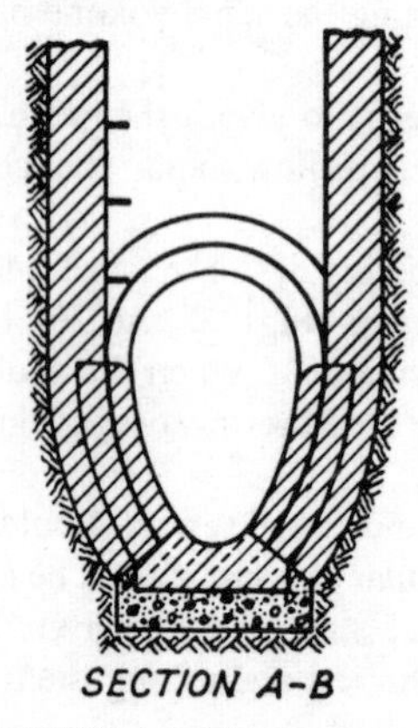
SECTION A-B

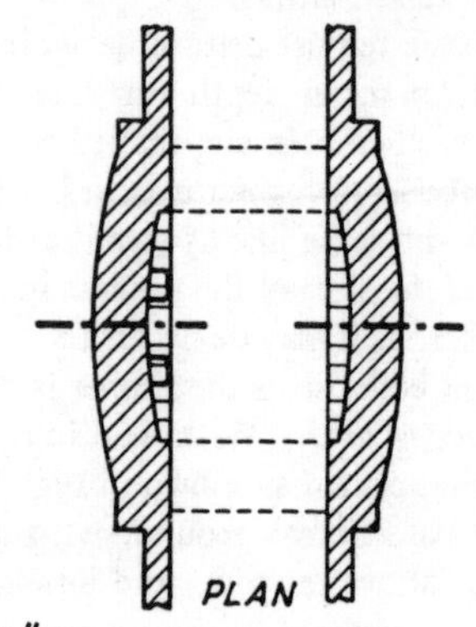
PLAN

BRICK MANHOLE FOR 30"x45" EGG-SHAPE SEWER

tunnelling is resorted to. For a simple case, the tunnel might be formed by excavation, timbering the work as shown in Fig. 79. The timbers shown would be of about the following sizes: longitudinal members 9 in. × 3 in. or 9 in. × 4 in., other members 9 in. × 9 in., at horizontal intervals of about 5 ft. If the tunnel is large, it is often constructed by means of a compressed-air shield of the type used in the construction of tube railways, the tunnel being lined by cast-iron[1] sections built up to form a circular lining, bolted together and well grouted, between and behind, with Portland cement grout. Such tubes are completed to form the sewers by lining with fine concrete washed with neat cement, or the sewers are constructed inside it in the ordinary way.

[1] Reinforced concrete sections are now frequently used in a similar way.

---

79 *Sewer brickwork*

(*Above*) EGG-SHAPED SEWERS IN BRICKWORK. The diagram, *left*, shows one method of constructing an egg-shaped sewer in brickwork. The invert is formed of terra-cotta blocks, which give a minimum of joints at this important point. They are hollow, as shown, and are usually made with rebated joints at their ends, to secure perfect alignment; they are usually filled with fine concrete before laying, to increase their strength. The inner ring of brickwork should be of blue Staffordshire bricks, which form a non-absorbent lining. The bricks are specially made and moulded to the proper radius, to permit of thin joints of uniform thickness, instead of wedge-shaped joints as they would otherwise be. Between the inner and outer rings of brickwork a thick line is shown. This represents a collar joint, consisting of a layer of cement mortar, about ½ in. in thickness, the object being to give a second line of defence against leakage. Sometimes the sewer is only lined with Staffordshire bricks up to the commencement of the covering arch, A–B, the arch being of ordinary pressed, or engineering, bricks. The outer ring of brickwork is of pressed bricks set in cement and it is less important that the bricks be moulded to the proper radius.

If the sewer is very large, the invert blocks may be built up of three pieces in the width.

N.B.—The diagram also shows the centres from which the arcs are struck, and from which the joints of the brickwork radiate. Concrete would be put under the invert blocks, and up the sides of the sewer to form a support on which the brickwork can be laid.

The diagram, *right*, shows an arrangement in which the outer ring of brickwork is replaced by concrete on the lower part of the sewer.

(*Centre*) Arrangement of a subsoil drain below the sewer foundation, *left*, and the usual arrangement of timbering to tunnelling for sewer works, *right* (see text).

(*Below*) MANHOLES FOR LARGE SEWERS. Manholes for larger sewers are of specialised construction. The diagrams show the plan and cross-section of a manhole on an egg-shaped sewer. It will be seen that, without making the base of the manhole of exceptional size, there is no appreciable benching, merely enough to give a foothold. The curved shape of the walls on plan is to give greater strength.

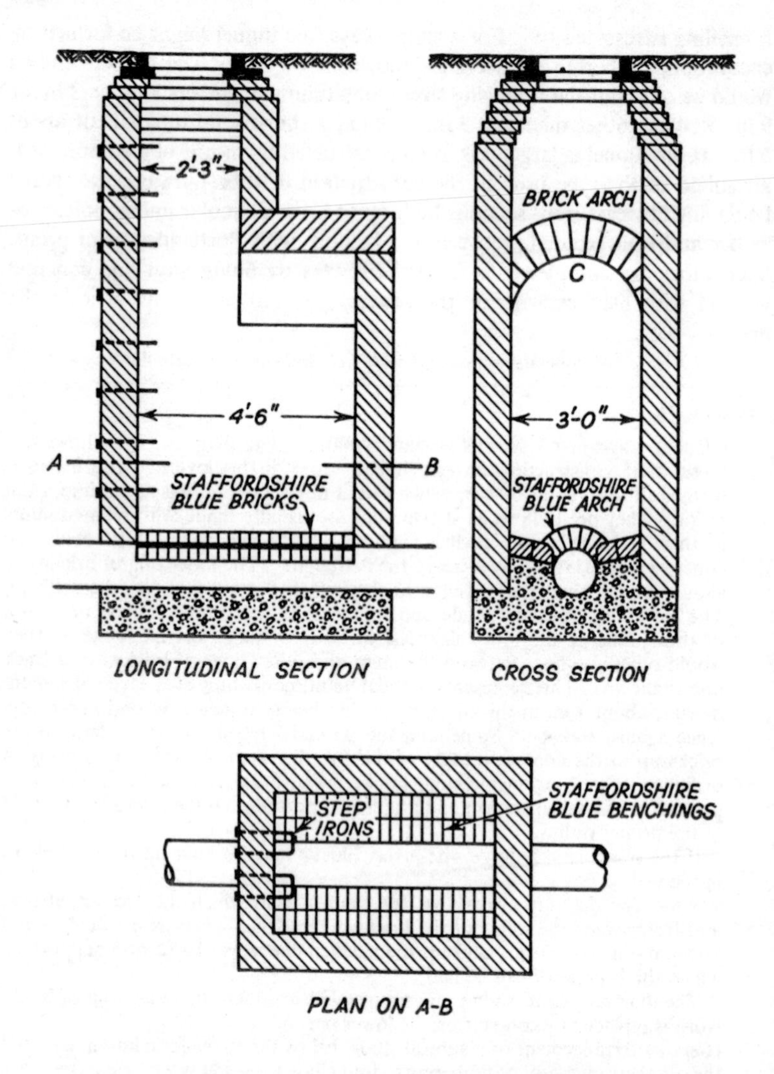

BRICK MANHOLE FOR 12 INCH CIRCULAR PIPE SEWER

80

Sewer manholes. Sewers are laid in straight lines between points of inspection, manholes being placed at all changes of direction and gradient. Manholes should also be put at the junctions of main and branch sewers, and also at storm overflows, and, on straight lengths, at intervals of about 100 yards. Bends in small sewers are formed entirely in manholes, but in sewers of large size, this is, of course, impossible. The forms of manholes vary with the size and type of sewer, and also with individual preference.

Manholes may be built of brickwork or formed of concrete tubes, the latter being much the cheaper. Figure 80 shows details of a brick manhole on a 12-in. pipe sewer, and Fig. 81 typical arrangement of the access to a sewer below a busy street.

Manholes of circular plan. Some engineers prefer manholes of circular plan, on the ground that they are stronger, but they are rather more costly to construct, unless of precast concrete. If circular they usually taper in section to give adequate working room at the bottom and not too large a cover at the top.

Lampholes. Manholes should be from 75 to 120 yards apart; if for any reason two manholes must be placed at a rather greater distance apart than this, a lamphole should be provided between them.

Lampholes are formed of 12-in. or 15-in. pipes leading vertically down from the street to the crown of the sewer, cased round in concrete and covered with a slab of the same material, or stone at the top, in which is set a removable cover. A lamp can be lowered down the shaft thus formed, and from the next manhole on either side the condition of the inside of the sewer examined.

---

80 *A brick manhole to a pipe sewer*

From the plan and sections it will be seen that the lower part of the manhole is 4 ft 6 in. by 3 ft internally, the upper part being reduced, by arching over, to a shaft of considerably smaller size. The benching is formed by means of Staffordshire blue bricks. Over the manhole shaft is a heavy iron frame with removable cover.

In all manholes step-irons must be built in as shown. They should be protected against corrosion by a thick bituminous coating or by heavy galvanising. The benchings should be at, or slightly above, the level of the top of the pipes and should have enough crossfall for condensed water to run off them into the sewer, but not enough to make it difficult for a man to stand on them.

The brick arch at C on cross section is often replaced with a reinforced concrete slab.

To prevent the weight of the walls cracking the pipes small arches are formed over the latter.

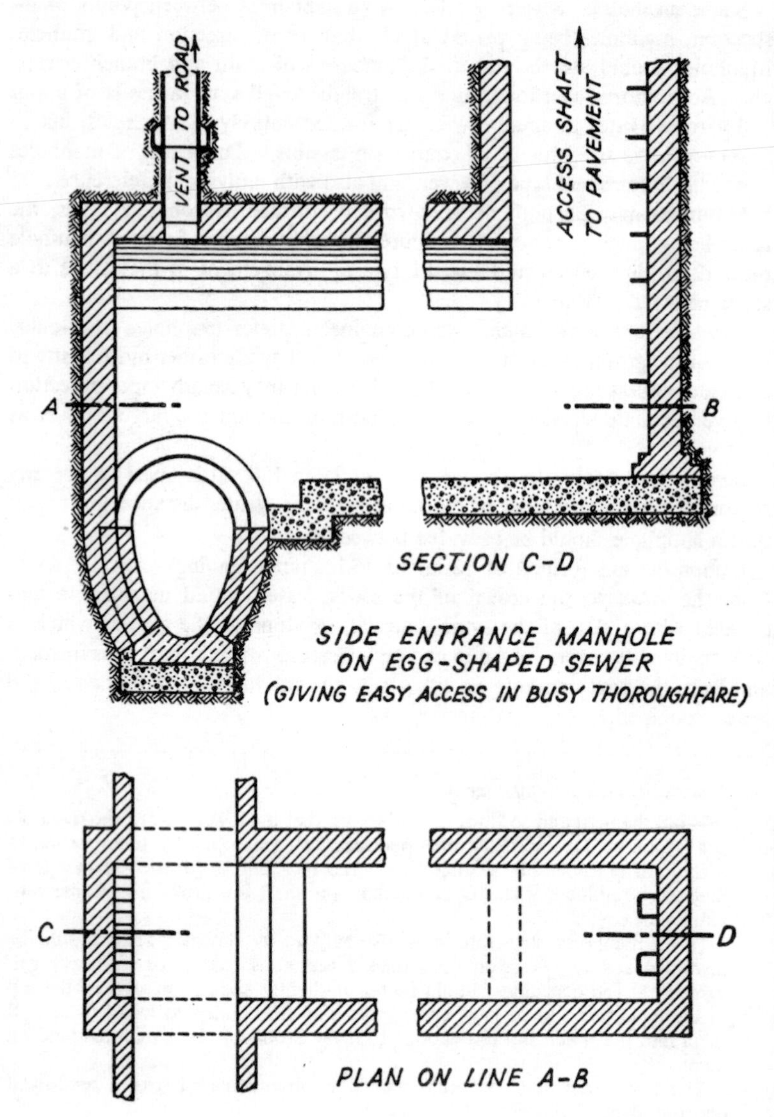

SIDE ENTRANCE MANHOLE ON EGG-SHAPED SEWER (GIVING EASY ACCESS IN BUSY THOROUGHFARE)

81

Sewer gradients. While a sewer should, if possible, be laid with sufficient gradient to ensure the flow through it being a self-cleansing one, it should not be given an excessive fall; it is often said that excessive fall causes undue wear and tear on the pipes, but there does not seem to be any real evidence of this.

Ramps. Where falls are considered too great, a ramp similar to that shown in Fig. 75 is sometimes used but it is more usual, in the case of a sewer, to form the ramp as Fig. 82.

The incoming sewer, at the higher level, is fitted with a specially made vertical junction bend of easy radius, and is discharged into a vertical pipe, which should be of smaller diameter because the velocity in it will be so high. The energy of velocity is dissipated by eddying in its fall and its flow around the bend leading into the manhole. The junction bend at the top of the vertical pipe is also extended through the manhole wall at A; to give access and ventilation to the upper pipe. No stopper should be put at A, as this would impede ventilation. It will be noted that the vertical pipe is cased in concrete.

Ramps are to be avoided as far as possible. They add considerably to the cost of a sewer (manholes must be deeper than if the sewer were laid at a uniform gradient) and they also tend to churn up the sewage and liberate gas. They can in most cases be avoided by the judicious use of intercepting sewers.

Prefabricated manholes in concrete. Figure 82 also shows details of a concrete tube manhole. It will be seen that whilst the shaft tapers, so as to secure good working room at the bottom with a cover of reasonable size at the top, the upper and lower shafts are tangential to one another on one

---

81 *Access to sewers below streets*

In a street in which traffic is heavy, manhole openings in the roadway are apt to cause considerable interference with the traffic; and it is then a common practice to provide manholes with side entrances, the latter being accessible from the pavement. The diagram shows details of such a manhole. An access shaft leads down from the pavement to a short tunnel leading to the side of the sewer. The tunnel is best formed by arching over, or using reinforced-concrete construction. The whole manhole can be formed of either brickwork or concrete, or partly the one and partly the other. A vent shaft is carried up to the roadway, in the form of a pipe, preferably to a ventilating column, but often in the past to a ventilating grating at street level. (Ventilation is essential in the case of a side entrance manhole, however much one may object to sewer openings at street level. Its large size makes it a considerable receptacle for the accumulation of foul air.)

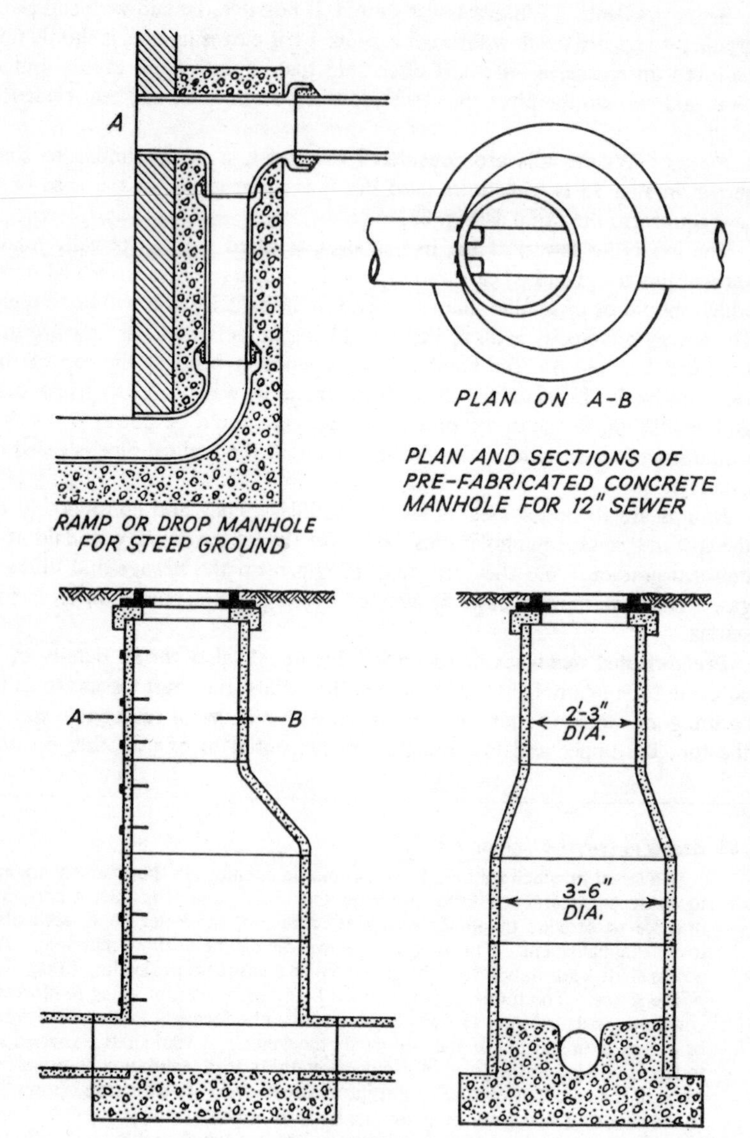

A
RAMP OR DROP MANHOLE
FOR STEEP GROUND
PLAN ON A-B
PLAN AND SECTIONS OF
PRE-FABRICATED CONCRETE
MANHOLE FOR 12" SEWER
A
B
2'-3"
DIA.
3'-6"
DIA.

82

vertical line. The step-irons are, of course, fixed on this straight side. Shafts are built up from precast rings, from 2 to 3 ft long, having "ogee" joints, as described for concrete tube sewers. The sewer inlet and outlets are formed in one with the bottom ring, with either ogee or socketed joints, or, if preferred, the bottom ring is supplied with stoneware pipes inset. The channel and benchings are formed in cement concrete and cement mortar after the bottom ring has been set in position.

Increased gradients at bends. Where a bend occurs in a sewer, it should have a rather greater fall in its length than the uniform fall of the straight lengths it connects, to allow for increased friction.

Sewer junctions. Where a small sewer discharges into a larger one, their inverts should not be at the same level. That of the smaller is set above that of the larger, in order to prevent sewage standing in the smaller with a consequent check on the velocity of its flow. There must be no right-angled junctions on a sewer, just as there should be none on a drain. All branch sewers join the main with a bend pointing in the direction of flow. In the case of pipe sewers, this is easily effected inside the manhole by the use of proper stoneware channel junctions. In the case of an egg-shaped or other form of brick or concrete sewer, the junction is effected by the use of specially made stoneware junction blocks, built into the sewer at the required positions.

Bell-mouth junctions. Where large main sewers join, a special form of construction becomes necessary, the form depending on the special condition to be met in each case. Figure 83 gives details of what is known as a bell-mouth junction between three egg-shaped sewers.

Road gulleys. Road gulleys are placed at intervals of from 40 to 75 yards, according to the longitudinal fall of the road. They can be of iron, stoneware, artificial stone, concrete or brickwork. They can also be either circular, square or rectangular on plan, but the general principle of design of any sanitary fitting applies—there should be a minimum of angles and corners. Figure 83 shows a section through a well-known type of stoneware gulley and one built of brickwork, lined inside with cement mortar, covered by a stone slab, and surmounted by the usual heavy iron grating.

---

82 *Manholes*

(*Above, left*) An arrangement of a "drop" or "ramp" in a sewer—used to maintain shallow gradients when sewers are laid in steep ground (see text).

(Another "drop manhole" is illustrated in Fig. 85.)

(*Below and above, right*) Arrangement of a typical precast concrete sectional manhole of the type described in the text.

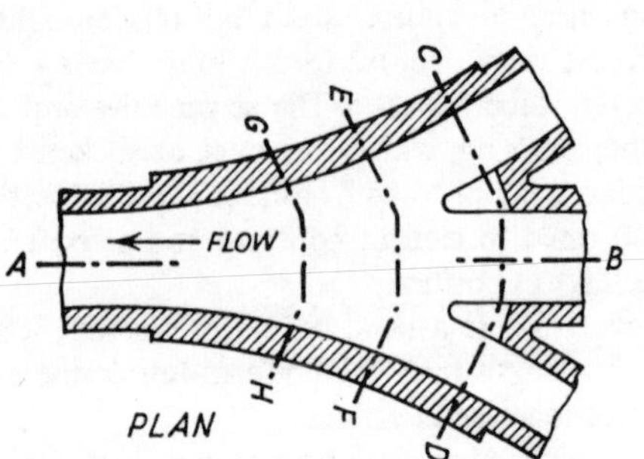

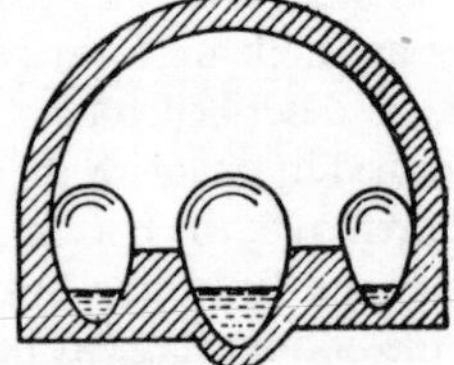
SECTION C-D

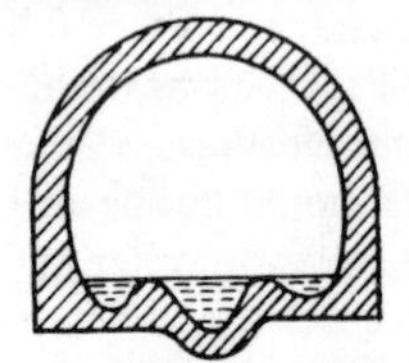
SECTION E-F

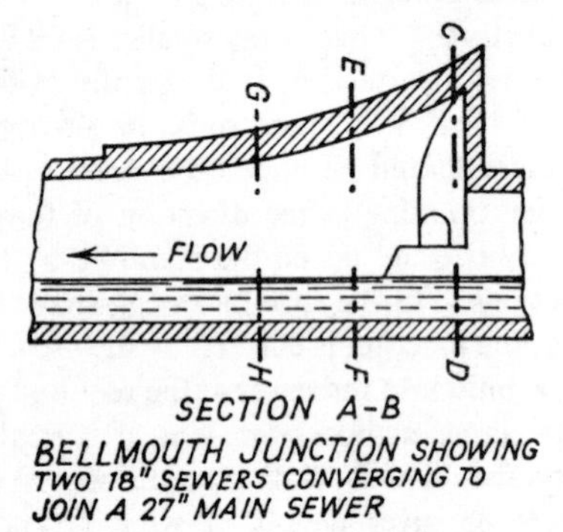

SECTION A-B

BELLMOUTH JUNCTION SHOWING TWO 18" SEWERS CONVERGING TO JOIN A 27" MAIN SEWER

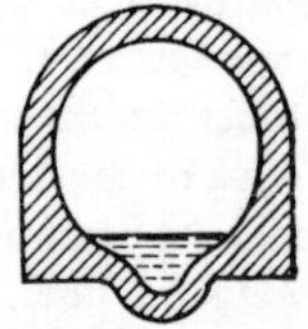
SECTION G-H

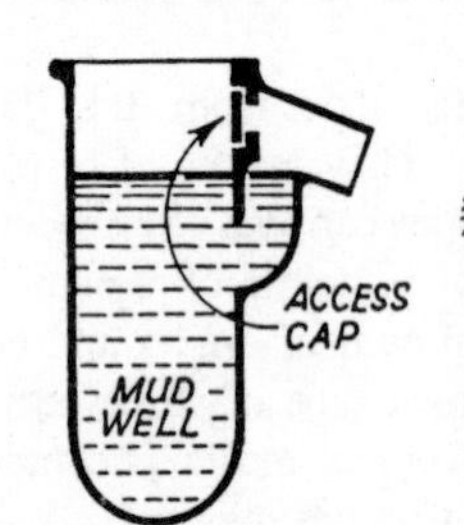

STONEWARE ROAD GULLEY
NEEDS SETTING ON CONCRETE AND SURROUND OF SAME TO TAKE HEAVY IRON GRATING AT GUTTER

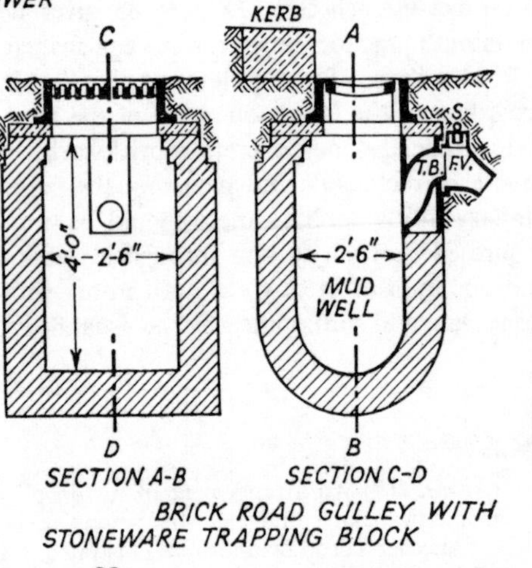

SECTION A-B SECTION C-D

BRICK ROAD GULLEY WITH STONEWARE TRAPPING BLOCK

83

FLUSHING SEWERS

Flushing is often necessary for sewers. For example, when a sewer is designed for prospective requirements and will, for some time, receive much less than its ultimate quantity of sewage means of flushing are often required. Flushing is also required whenever gradients are insufficient to produce a self-cleansing velocity of flow.

There are many means of flushing. Automatic flushing tanks are described in Chapter 9, and large tanks of that kind, built of brickwork and placed underground, are often used. Such tanks are placed at the upper, dead ends of each section of sewers that need flushing.

Flushing arrangements aim simply at creating an effective velocity through the sewers, for a sufficient time to remove any deposits and cleanse the sewer, and one of the simplest ways of flushing is to dam the sewage at manholes and then liberate it when it has attained a sufficient head or depth. Special flushing gates, sluices, are fixed in manholes for this purpose. An old-fashioned method was to use a board across the outlet of the manhole, fitting into grooves at its ends and lower edge, but a few inches away from the mouth of the outlet. The sewage accumulated behind the board, which was then pulled up by means of chains in order to liberate it. The arrangement had the advantage that if the sewage was allowed to rise above the top edge of the flushing board, it simply flowed over and through the sewer. If a sluice or gate is used, a form of inverted ramp is usually provided as an overflow in

---

83 *Bell-mouth junction: Road gulleys*

(*Above*) A "BELL MOUTH" JUNCTION FOR "EGG-SHAPED" SEWERS. The construction will be fairly evident from the illustrations. The walls of the sewer are thickened around the junction, as shown in plan and longitudinal section. The remaining illustrations show cross-sections of the junction at three different points. This example is typical of the method of construction in any similar situation.

(*Below*) ROAD GULLEYS. In the cast-iron gulley, shown *left*, the trap is formed in one piece with the main body of the gulley, and an access stopper is provided to the drain leading to the sewer. The stopper is of iron, fitting into an iron frame with an airtight joint and secured by means of gunmetal thumb screws. The depth below the trap is to intercept mud, which settles to collect in the mud-well for removal at intervals.

In the brick gulley shown in long and cross section on the *right*, the trap is formed by means of a stoneware trapping block, T.B., in two pieces, a light flap valve being added at F.V. if desired. There is no direct access to the sewer from the gulley, but an access stopper exists just under the roadway surface as shown.

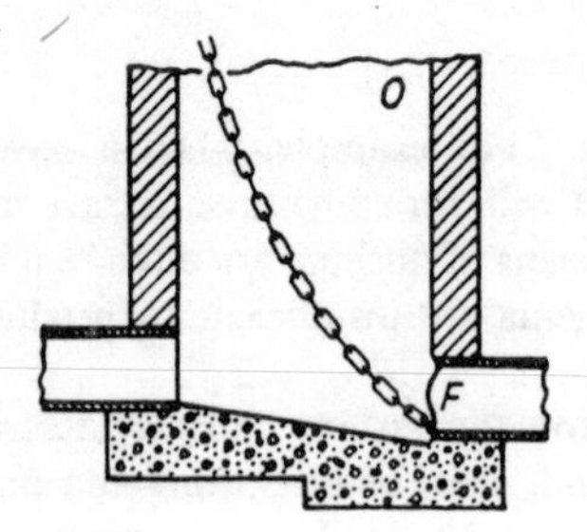

FLAP VALVE TO AID FLUSHING

STORM WATER OVERFLOW

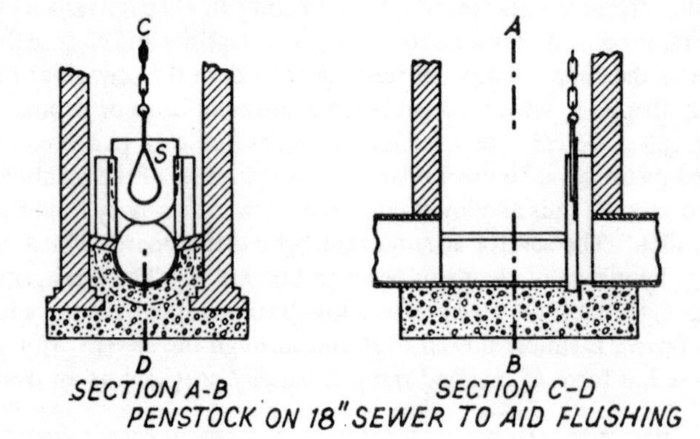

SECTION A-B

SECTION C-D

PENSTOCK ON 18" SEWER TO AID FLUSHING

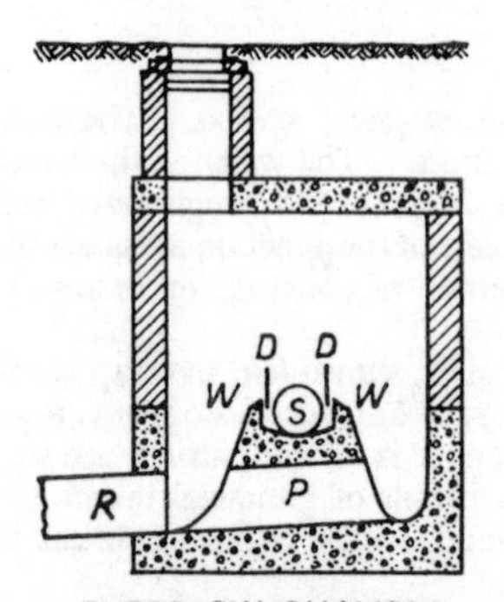

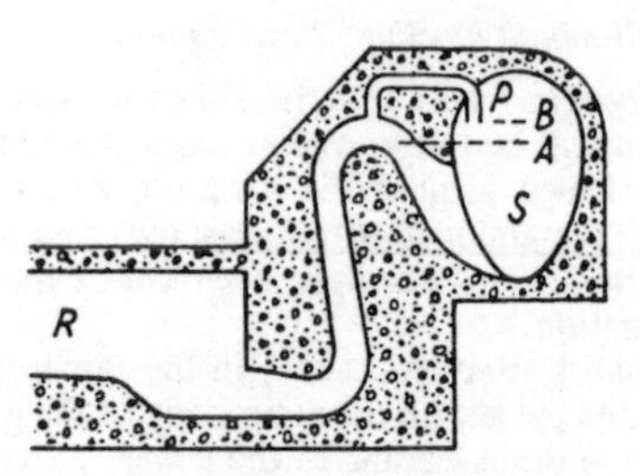

OVERFLOW CHAMBER WITH DOUBLE SPILLWAYS OR WEIRS FOR STORM WATER

SIPHON SPILLWAY TO REMOVE SURPLUS STORM WATER BUT RETAIN SOLIDS AND FLOATING DEBRIS

84

case of neglect to open the sluice, the manhole end of the ramp being always open.

An alternative method is to use a "flap valve" operated by chain from ground level (84).

84 *Sewer flushing: Stormwater overflows*

(*Top, left*) The arrangement of the base of a manhole when a flap valve, F, is used as an aid to flushing. The floor is slightly sunk in front of the outlet, to permit of the flap readily opening, and a strong chain is attached to the flap and fastened loosely near the top of the manhole. (The chain shown in the sketch is unnecessarily heavy, but a strong one is essential.) The overflow mouth is indicated and the pipe from it would pass down to join the outlet sewer a few feet from the manhole.

Flap valves sometimes have floats attached to them, which are intended to lift them automatically when the sewage reaches a certain height, but such arrangements have not proved reliable.

(*Centre*) A penstock valve or sluice. This is merely an iron plate or door, fitting into a grooved frame of iron and capable of being rapidly opened by the pull of a chain from above. The frame in the example shown is fixed a little away from the outlet to allow the sluice to form an overflow. (The sections show the sluice open.)

(*Top, right*) A storm water relief sewer built from the main sewer to a river. A flap valve is shown at its outlet, to prevent back flow when the level of the river is unusually high. The level of the invert of the relief sewer at its upper end is such that when water is at this height the main sewer is carrying six times the dry weather flow.

(*Below, left*) A WEIR TYPE STORM-WATER OVERFLOW. In the illustration S is the main sewer leading out of the chamber. (This is of less diameter than the sewer flowing in, because of the help given to it by the relief sewer.) Inside the chamber the water flows in a nearly flat channel, at each side of which is a weir, W. The sewage which falls over the left overflow passes directly to the relief sewer, R, whilst that which falls to the right does so after flowing through the passage, P. It is often, but not always, the practice to provide "dip plates", D, to prevent floating solids from being carried over the weirs to the relief sewer. Sometimes the tops of the weirs are in the form of adjustable iron plates.

(*Below, right*) A SIPHON SPILLWAY OVERFLOW. This is arranged so that when the main sewer, S, is carrying six times the dry weather flow the water level in it is at A. Any small rise above that level causes water to flow over the throat of the spillway. At this stage there is no siphonic action, because the throat is kept at atmospheric pressure by the air pipe, P. If, however, the water level rises to B, the mouth of the air pipe will become sealed, with the result that air will be carried away from the throat by the flow of water and siphonic action will begin. The siphon will then discharge full bore, the head on the siphon being the difference between the water level in the main sewer and that in the relief sewer, R. Because the siphon inlet is well submerged, except at the tail end of the discharge of storm water, very little of the light floating matter will enter, whilst, because it is so high above the invert of the main sewer, none of the heavy solids will do so.

Tipping tanks. Tipping tanks are also used for flushing sewers, but they are only suitable for small volumes of flow.

Penstocks. Yet another method of flushing is shown in Fig. 84, which shows a longitudinal and cross-section of the base of a manhole fitted with a penstock or sluice.

For properly cleansing the sewers it is necessary to introduce plentiful supplies of water, and to do it systematically. In dry weather, more frequent flushings are, of course, necessary, and in times of epidemics disinfecting liquids are sometimes added to the flush water.

Other flushing methods. Where a river is near, it is generally possible to obtain an ample supply of water for flushing, and many sea-coast towns use sea-water with more or less beneficial results. Water may be taken from the street hydrants and admitted to the sewers through manholes or lampholes. Storm water may be collected and used with advantage. Before the use of automatic flushing tanks became general, an ordinary tank was often used. It was constructed of brickwork or concrete, with cement lining, with a capacity of from about 1500 to 1800 gallons. It could be filled from hydrants in about twenty minutes and its contents were then allowed to pass out through a 9-in. pipe, this taking only about three minutes, and producing a powerful scouring effect. Automatic arrangements for flushing are now more usual and much more satisfactory than those requiring manual attention.

Storm water. When the combined system of sewerage is in use, it would be very costly to construct long lengths of main sewer large enough to carry away all the rainfall which finds its way into the sewers during a heavy storm while it would also be a severe tax on the sewage disposal plant to deal with such large volumes. It is usual, therefore, at selected points not far removed from streams or other watercourses, to put in storm overflows, by means of which excess of rainfall is discharged into relief sewers leading directly to watercourses.

Provided that each overflow is at a suitable level, the watercourse will not be unduly polluted. This is because during the early part of the storm when the street washings and other objectionable matter are carried into a sewer, the volume of flow will not have risen to the overflow level. By the time overflow level is reached the storm water is running clear and sewage in the sewer will be so diluted by it as to be unlikely to cause a nuisance in a stream to which it is discharged, especially if care is taken to avoid taking light floating debris and heavy solid matter over the storm-water overflow.

The Ministry of Health requires that the storm-water overflow level sha be at such a height that it will not function unless the discharge of the sewer is more than six times the mean dry weather flow.

A simple method of arranging an overflow by means of a simple relief sewer is shown in Fig 84. This arrangement, however, will seldom be satisfactory, because it is unlikely that sufficient water could get into the relief sewer, in a heavy storm, to prevent the main sewer getting completely full and surcharged and much more than six times the dry weather flow would pass to the outfall, or to the next overflow.

It is therefore usual to install a long overflow weir, or two such weirs, in a special manhole called an overflow chamber. The object of having two side weirs is, of course, to reduce the size and cost of the chamber (84).

Whilst the provision of a storm-water overflow of this type can be made, by placing it at the correct height, to function only when the inflow in the main sewers exceeds six times the dry-weather flow, it would be wrong to suppose that all that excess will pass over the weirs. As the water level rises higher above the sill of the weir the discharge of the overflow will increase, but so will the discharge of the outgoing main sewer.

Siphon spillways. To overcome this objection, in some recent schemes siphon spillways, such as that shown in Fig. 84, have been used.

Leap weirs. One defect in the separate system of sewerage is that the first washings of streets, roofs and yards in a storm, especially after a drought, are apt to be very foul and therefore unfit for discharge into a river without treatment. To provide against this, leap weirs, illustrated diagrammatically in Fig. 85, are sometimes used.

(The leap weir is not suitable for use as a means of getting rid of excess of flow in a combined sewer, because when the velocity of the stream is high all the flow would be carried to the river, whereas the Ministry of Health require that six times the dry-weather flow shall remain in the sewer.)

A modified form of leap weir is also shown in Fig. 85.

Surface water separator. An appliance introduced at Birmingham many years ago, which attempts to divert the excess over six times the dry-weather flow in a manner different from those described is also illustrated in Fig. 85.

Inverted "Siphons" at stream crossings. Where a sewer has to cross a stream, railway cutting or other similar obstacle an inverted siphon is often necessary, although these are objectionable features and avoided wherever possible. They usually consist of two sloping pipe lengths meeting a flat length between them. They are usually formed of cast iron or steel pipes, treated with the Angus Smith or other process, and should be laid in duplicate. Manholes are provided at each end, and if the length is very great it is wise

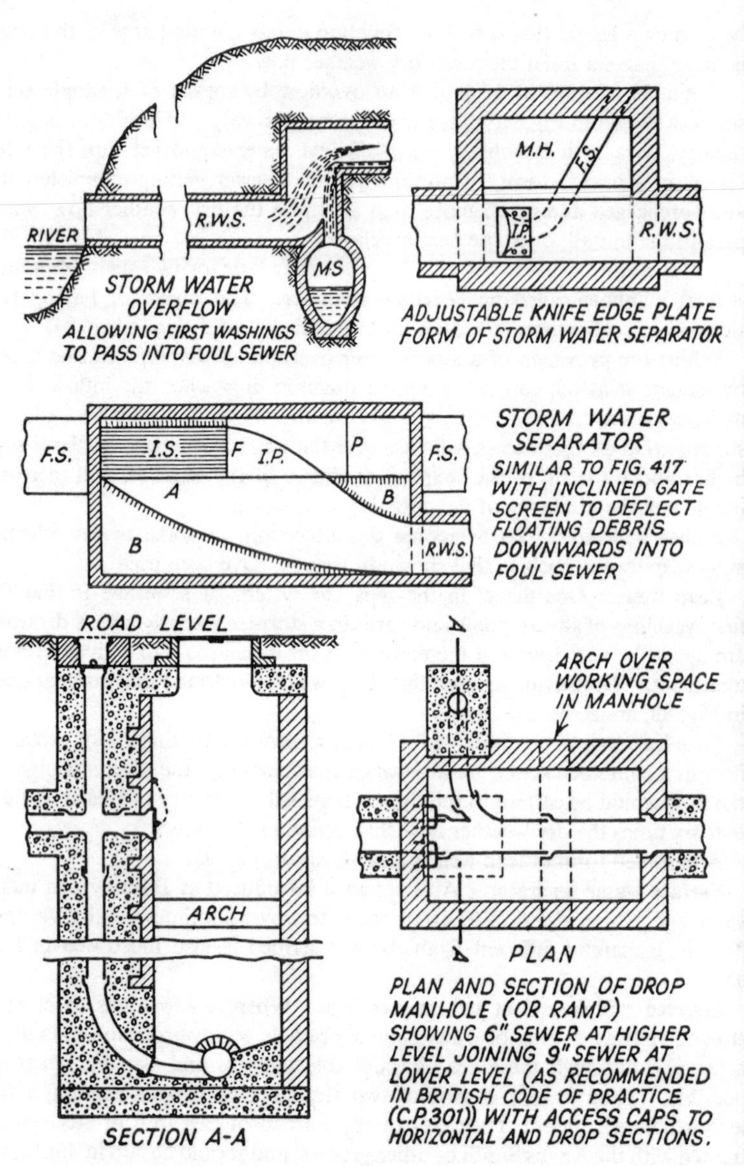
RIVER
R.W.S.
MS
STORM WATER
OVERFLOW
ALLOWING FIRST WASHINGS
TO PASS INTO FOUL SEWER
M.H.
F.S.
I.P.
R.W.S.
ADJUSTABLE KNIFE EDGE PLATE
FORM OF STORM WATER SEPARATOR
F.S.
I.S.
F
I.P.
P
F.S.
A
B
B
R.W.S.
STORM WATER
SEPARATOR
SIMILAR TO FIG. 417
WITH INCLINED GATE
SCREEN TO DEFLECT
FLOATING DEBRIS
DOWNWARDS INTO
FOUL SEWER
ROAD LEVEL
ARCH
SECTION A-A
A
A
ARCH OVER
WORKING SPACE
IN MANHOLE
PLAN
PLAN AND SECTION OF DROP
MANHOLE (OR RAMP)
SHOWING 6" SEWER AT HIGHER
LEVEL JOINING 9" SEWER AT
LOWER LEVEL (AS RECOMMENDED
IN BRITISH CODE OF PRACTICE
(C.P.301)) WITH ACCESS CAPS TO
HORIZONTAL AND DROP SECTIONS.

85

to carry up a vent shaft at the middle to prevent the siphon becoming air-locked.

There is always a tendency to blockage in the flat length, and it is usual to adopt some device to check this, such as putting a permanent large chain through from end to end, so that it can be pulled backwards and forwards to stir up the silt. The object of laying siphons in duplicate is so that sewage can readily be diverted from one to the other in the event of stoppage.

Bridge crossings. Where sewers cross bridges, they are usually of iron or steel pipes to resist vibration. Sometimes they are accommodated between the girders of the bridge or, if this is impossible, fixed to brackets at the side.

SEWER VENTILATION

Methods of ventilation of sewers have given rise to much controversy in the past.

If sewage is of domestic character and the sewers are well constructed with good gradients, foul air should not be generated in any appreciable quantity and sewer air should not be dangerous to the health of those who happen to

---

85 *Weirs*

(*Top, left*) A LEAP WEIR designed to separate first washings from streets from storm flow in a surface water only, sewer. When only a small quantity is flowing in the sewer, the velocity will be low and the water will fall almost vertically into the main sewer, M.S., of the foul sewage system. If the rain-water sewer is fairly fully charged the velocity will be much higher and the water will leap across the gap to the lower rainwater sewer, R.W.S. It is obvious that the success of this method depends on the proper proportioning of the width of the gap and the amount of fall to the lip of the weir.

(*Top, right*) A MODIFIED LEAP WEIR. In this an adjustable iron plate, I.P., is fixed over the mouth of an opening in the sewer invert. When only a small quantity of water is passing along the rainwater sewer, all of it goes through the opening to the foul sewer, but when there is considerable velocity very little will be intercepted in this way.

(*Centre*) A SURFACE WATER SEPARATOR. Its operation is as follows:

A horizontal flat plate, F.P., is fixed across the foul sewer, F.S., at the required height to cut the flow into two parts; one that below six times the dry-weather flow, and the other, that above it. On the flat plate is fixed a vertical curved plate of iron, I.P., which diverts the upper flow into the rainwater sewer, R.W.S. At the entrance to the manhole is an inclined wire screen, I.S., with an upright triangular side at A. This screen forms a sort of basket, which prevents rags, paper, and other rubbish collecting at the edge of the flat plate, or passing into the rainwater sewer.

(*Bottom*) A DROP MANHOLE for connection of two sewers at different levels.

inhale it. In such cases all that seems necessary is sufficient means of ventilation to allow air to escape from the sewer, when the water level rises through heavy rainfall, and to allow air to enter the sewer when the water level subsides.

If the sewers are so flat in gradient, however, that the discharge is much delayed and solid matters settle and decompose, gases will be given off which are highly offensive, and even dangerous to health. How noxious sewer air becomes depends also on the character of the sewage. Decomposing sewage will always give off carbon dioxide, marsh gas and ammonia, which should be classed as asphyxiating, rather than poisonous gases, but some sewage also gives off sulphuretted hydrogen, which is definitely poisonous. Trade effluents often contain chemicals which, on mixing with one another, may react chemically and form gases of a poisonous character. The possibilities of coal gas, leaking from gas mains, and of petrol from garages entering sewers with consequent formation of explosive mixtures with air, must also be considered. In all such cases adequate ventilation is essential for the general health of the community, for the safety of men who occasionally have to enter the sewers, and for the prevention of damage to the sewers by explosion.

That the danger resulting from inadequate ventilation is in some cases a very real one is illustrated by the report of a Committee, appointed by the Home Office and the Ministry of Health in 1933, to enquire into the precautions that should be taken for the safety of persons entering sewers. It recommended that, before a man enters a sewer by way of a manhole, the cover thereof and those of the manholes on either side should be removed for at least half-an-hour, at the end of which time tests shall be made for sulphuretted hydrogen, for asphyxiating conditions, and for inflammable gases, and that unless these tests proved satisfactory no one should enter the sewer without a special respirator.

It is clear that a certain amount of ventilation is essential and that in some cases a thoroughly efficient system is desirable. It is, however, often difficult to secure this result without causing a public nuisance.

Combined sewer and drain ventilation. For many years, a section of municipal engineers have agitated for the prohibition of the intercepting trap between house-drains and the public sewer until, to-day, many local authorities, encouraged by the Model Bylaws, have altered their local bylaws so as to make the use of the intercepting trap optional to the householder or to forbid its use and that of the mica flap air inlet.

When the sewers are modern and are provided with a reasonable fall, the sewer air is very little worse than that in a well-constructed house drain, and there seems little reason to object to the sewers and the drains being ventilated as a single unit. When this is done, the local authority provides large fresh-air inlets at intervals along the sewer and air flows along the sewer, entering the many house drains along the route, to discharge well above eaves level, through the many soil-pipe vents of the houses served. When conditions are good, the benefit to the sewer ventilation is inestimable and that of the many private drains is satisfactory. The disadvantage, in the view of many surveyors and architects, is in the loss of individual control of the separate house drain units. Their view is that where the local authority's air inlets are widely spaced, nearby house drains get a plentiful supply of air and drain ventilation is good, but house drains farthest from the air inlets have the air flow through them reduced almost to vanishing point. This is a problem, however, for the local authority's surveyor or engineer, not for the individual householder, and if the local authority sees that air inlets are placed at sufficiently close intervals along the sewer, the combined sewer and drains ventilation scheme appears to be satisfactory.

Gratings at street level. The use of open gratings at manholes is the easiest method of sewer ventilation and has been greatly used in the past. The use of open gratings dates from about 1834. The system is open to considerable objection owing to the more or less frequent offensive emanations from the gratings. Complaints on this ground led in many areas to gratings being closed one by one, and the substitution for them of vertical shafts, it being thought that the high shafts would act as outlets and the remaining gratings as inlets.

Investigations by Mawbey and De Courcy Meade. Some valuable investigations in this field were carried out by E. G. Mawbey, formerly Borough Engineer of Leicester, and by T. De Courcy Meade, formerly City Engineer of Manchester.

Mawbey carried out thousands of tests, at all times of the year, in Leicester, and came to the conclusion that surface gratings are unnecessary, vertical shafts alone being sufficient. He found that the shafts gave both inward and outward air currents, but usually the latter, which were in all cases the more vigorous. In a thousand tests, he found the average upward current to be 162 ft per min, and the average downward current to be 34·6 ft per min.

De Courcy Meade's experiments corroborate the results obtained by Mawbey, Meade pointing out that the shafts act indifferently as both inlets and outlets, the air currents being governed by the difference in temperature between the internal and external air, the rise and fall of the sewage, the construction and character of the sewer, etc. All the conditions are liable to be neutralised and reversed by the direction and force of the wind, while the heat of the sun, of course, affects the draught through any particular shaft.

In the face of these results there has been a growing tendency, in recent years, towards the use of vertical shafts alone. These may be erected against the sides of buildings, but local authorities often find difficulty in obtaining the necessary permissions. An owner runs a serious risk in granting such a permit, since, if the shaft is not thoroughly well constructed and maintained, there is the possibility of nuisance by reason of defective joints. Further, the settlement of the building, and consequent settlement of the shaft, may lead to a fractured pipe or broken joint at the foot of the shaft, allowing the soil around to become impregnated with sewer air. In some few instances shafts have consequently been erected against buildings, but not attached to them. All iron vent shafts should have rust pockets at their feet.

Sewer vent shafts should preferably be carried up independently of buildings, either beside the kerb or in the centre of the roadway, to a height at least equal to that of the ridges of the roofs of the abutting houses. High lamp standards have been used as vent shafts in some places, notably at Southport. In some cases the shafts have been carried up beside, and attached to, telegraph poles, but there is a risk here of damage to the joint at the pipe base by motion of the pole in a high wind.

The sizes of the shafts depend on the size of the sewer, but they range from 6 to 9 in. in diameter as a rule, and are put at about 200 yards apart. The system of ventilating by detached shafts is simple, sound, calls for a minimum of attention, and, compared with more elaborate systems, is inexpensive.

Deodorising systems. Systems of deodorisation are of many forms, the two best known being the "Reeves" and the "Caink" systems. In the former, recesses are formed, i.e. manholes to the sewer in which are placed two vessels, charged with chemicals which mix continuously, forming gases which purify the sewer air. In the Caink system the apparatus used is in the form of an air filter and deodorant. These systems have never been very popular among local authorities and are little used.

Use of mill chimneys. In some few towns the connection of the sewer to mill chimneys has been tried, but with little success. The draught proved so great near the chimney that it tended to unseal neighbouring traps, but 200 yards away it had little ventilating effect. The application of such a system would obviously be limited by the inadequate supply of mill or factory chimneys suitably placed even in industrial areas. It is interesting to note that the first experiment of this kind was made on the main sewers of London by Sir Joseph Bazalgette, who used a furnace chimney in the tower of the Houses of Parliament but with poor results.

The Shone and Ault system. An interesting experiment in ventilating sewers and house drains as a single unit was the Shone and Ault system. In this system, invented when intercepting traps were compulsory in all districts, powerful suction fans at selected points on the sewerage system drew out the air from both sewers and house drains and discharged it, after filtering and deodorising in quiet spots where no nuisance could be caused. Air inlets were provided by the hundreds of house soil and "vent" pipes, their intercepting traps being by-passed by special adjustable valves on the cleaning arms of the interceptors. There was thus no risk of building up suction or vacuum which would endanger the trap seals.

The system was expensive to install and needed constant supervision to keep the by-pass valves in adjustment and perhaps for that reason never became popular.

VOLUME OF SEWAGE

Determination of the volume of sewage to be carried by the sewers and their size calls for careful investigation and calculations.

Dry-weather flow. The volume of dry-weather flow in any sewer, if only sewage be admitted, may be assumed to be equal to the amount of the water supply, say 25 to 30 gallons per head per day. The rate of flow is not, however, uniform throughout the day, owing to the variation in quantity of water used at different times of the day. In making provision for the maximum dry-weather flow of sewage, it is usual to assume that one-half the daily quantity is discharged over a period from six to eight hours. If, therefore, a daily quantity of 25 gallons per head is assumed the maximum flow will be at the rate of 12½ gallons per head in, say, six hours. About 2 gallons per head per hour.

Surface water or rainfall. The amount of rainfall which it is necessary to provide for in the sewers is a difficult matter to determine and is often underestimated. The minimum amount the sewer should receive below storm overflows is fixed by the Ministry of Health at six times the dry-weather flow, but the amount to be received above such overflows must be estimated. As excessive rainfall is relatively rare, it is unusual to provide against possible damage by sewers overflowing except in cases where such damage would be great and the initial expense justified.

Storm water. For purposes of design, a method first proposed by Mr Lloyd Davies is usually adopted for estimating the amount of rainfall to be provided for in sewers. The basis of the method is as follows:

Rain storms of abnormally high intensity do not last for a long period and are not such a heavy burden on the sewers as storms of rather less intensity lasting for a long period. (This is because a large volume of rain is used in filling up the sewers to their greatest capacity.) On the other hand, very prolonged rainfall is not of great intensity and the sewers are able to carry away the water, as it falls, without difficulty. Between the extremes there is a type of storm which proves the greatest burden upon any particular sewer under consideration.

This is the storm which lasts just so long that the first drops of rain, falling on the uppermost part of the drainage area, reach the sewer at the same moment as the last drops are falling in its immediate vicinity. This period of time is known as the "time of concentration" and is calculated by dividing the distance between the uppermost part of the drainage area and the sewer, by the probable velocity of the water in the sewers between these points and adding to it an allowance of about five minutes for the time which is required for the water to get into the sewers by way of rainwater gutters, downpipes, gulleys, etc.

It is also necessary, of course, to determine the greatest intensity of the storm which will last for a period equal to the time of concentration. Careful observation of storms, over a period of years in many localities, show that this can be determined with reasonable accuracy by one of the following formulae:

If the time of concentration is not more than 20 minutes,

$$R = \frac{30}{T + 10}.$$

If the time of concentration is not less than 20 minutes,

$$R = \frac{40}{T + 20}.$$

In the above formulae R is the rainfall in inches per hour, and T is the time of concentration in minutes.

Impermeable surfaces. The amount of impermeable surface in the drainage area above the point in question is next ascertained. The volume of storm water to be provided for is then calculated by the following formula:

$$Q = A \times R,$$

where Q = volume in cu. ft per sec,
A = impermeable area in acres,
R = rainfall in in. per hr.

EXAMPLE. Find the diameter to be given to a circular sewer, to be laid at a gradient of 1 in 500, at the lower end of a drainage area of 400 acres, which will eventually house a population of 20,000 persons, drainage being on the combined system. The general gradient of the drainage area is such that the sewers above the new length have a velocity of flow of about 4 ft per sec when discharging at maximum rate.

First determine the volumes to be carried.

Dry-weather flow. Assume that the sewage proper is 25 gallons, i.e. 4 cu. ft /head /day.

Mean discharge = 20,000 × 4 = 80,000 cu. ft/day.

About one-half of this is estimated to pass through the sewer in six hours; this means that the maximum dry-weather flow is twice the mean rate.

$$\text{Max. D.W.F.} = 2 \times 80{,}000 = 160{,}000 \text{ cu. ft/day.}$$

$$= \frac{160{,}000}{24 \times 60 \times 60} \text{ cu. ft/sec.}$$

$$= 1{\cdot}85 \text{ cu. ft/sec, or say}$$
$$2 \text{ cu. ft/sec.}$$

Storm water. It will be assumed that a study of the map of the drainage area shows that some parts of the area are 6000 ft from the sewer which we are considering.

This length is divided by the velocity of 4 ft/sec (= 240 ft/min) and 5 minutes is added for time of entry:

$$\text{Time of concentration} = \frac{6000}{240} + 5 \text{ min}$$

$$= 25 + 5 = 30 \text{ min and}$$

$$\text{Rate of rainfall} = \frac{40}{T + 20} \text{ in./hr}$$

$$= \frac{40}{30 + 20} = \frac{4}{5} \text{ in./hr.}$$

In order to estimate the probable area of impermeable surface, when the land is fully developed, it would be necessary to examine estate plans, provisions of town planning schemes, etc. Comparison of the figures of the population and the area, given in the question, suggest however that the whole of the land will be developed for building at about ten or twelve houses per gross acre, under which conditions the area of roads will amount to about

15 per cent of the whole land, and the area of roofs and paved yards to about the same percentage. Thus

Impermeable area $= 30$ per cent of 400 acres

$= 120$ acres

Volume of storm water to be accommodated $= A \times R$

$$= 120 \times \frac{4}{5} = 96 \text{ cu. ft/sec.}$$

Adding to this the maximum D.W.F. we find we have to provide for a total discharge in the new sewer of 98 cu. ft. per second. This should be carried by the sewer when flowing not more than two-thirds depth, under which condition the cross-sectional area of the water is $0{\cdot}556d^2$ and the hydraulic mean depth is $0{\cdot}29d$, where d is the diameter in feet. (See p. 256.)

Using the formulae, already given for drainage, $Q = AV$ and $V = C\sqrt{RS}$ (see p. 254) and combining these into the formula $Q = AC\sqrt{RS}$,

where $V =$ Velocity of flow in ft/sec:

C is a coefficient: R is the Hydraulic Mean Depth and $S =$ fall/length (the "sine" of slope of the sewer)

$$98 = 0{\cdot}556d^2 \times 100\sqrt{0{\cdot}29d \times \frac{1}{500}}$$

$$= 55{\cdot}6d^2 \times \sqrt{0{\cdot}00058d}$$

$$= 55{\cdot}6d^2 \times 0{\cdot}024\sqrt{d}$$

$$= 1{\cdot}33d^2 \times \sqrt{d},$$

$$\therefore d^2\sqrt{d} = \frac{98}{1{\cdot}33} = 73{\cdot}5$$

A few trials of likely values of d show that

$$\text{If } d = 5 \text{ ft., } d^2\sqrt{d} = 25\sqrt{5} = 56.$$

$$\text{If } d = 6 \text{ ft., } d^2\sqrt{d} = 36\sqrt{6} = 88.$$

The correct value of d seems therefore to lie about midway between 5 and 6 ft. Try $d = 5\frac{1}{2}$ ft.

Then $$d^2\sqrt{d} = (5{\cdot}5)^2 \times \sqrt{5{\cdot}5}$$

$$= 30{\cdot}3 \times 2{\cdot}34 = 71.$$

The diameter should therefore be 5 ft 6 in.

Using Crimp and Bruges formula

$$V = 124\, M^{\cdot 67} I^{\cdot 5}$$

in a similar manner gives a requirement of a 5 ft diameter sewer. Comparison with the tables produced by Hydraulics Research Station (Hydraulic Research Paper No. 4 obtainable from H.M.S.O.) based on the more complicated Colebrook-White formula and using the linear roughness coefficient for spun concrete pipes of ·002 gives an answer approximately equal to the Crimp and Bruges figure.

Gradients for sewers. The gradient to be given to sewers is usually fixed with certain limits by the physical features of the district and the level of the point of outfall. Every effort is made however to ensure that gradients shall be such that the sewer is self-cleansing, not only when carrying its maximum quantity of sewage, but also in dry weather. If the flatness of the district makes this impossible, the inclination should be at least sufficient to give a self-cleansing velocity when the sewers are being flushed, and automatic flushing tanks should be provided.

Self-cleansing velocities for sewers. For sewers with intermittent flows the aim should be to obtain a minimum velocity of 2½ ft per sec. for the average rates of flow. (Too frequently self-cleansing velocities are based on maximum carrying capacities and this usually represents the most serious storm occurring once in a year.) Where sewers have a continuous flow a velocity of 2 ft per sec. will be adequate and keep small solids (grit) in suspension, but it is insufficient to pick up those which have settled.

The smallest-sized sewer should not be less than 6 in.[1] in diameter, and then only where there is no likelihood of its being extended.

There is always difficulty in sewering a district, when levels are such that a gravitation system is not possible. Pumping stations can in such cases be provided, or requirements met by the provision of a series of Shone ejectors, or sewage lifts, both of which are described in Chapter 9. (N.B.—The sewage lift is seldom economical for use on a large scale, owing to the large volume of water required to operate it.)

[1] The Byelaws now permit 4 in. diameter.

11
Sewage Disposal

A vital part of any system of drainage is the provision for the disposal or purification of sewage. The problems raised are by no means simple, and effective purification can only be accomplished by the earnest collaboration of the engineer, the chemist and the bacteriologist. It is from such close collaboration that current sewage disposal techniques have developed.

Pollution of rivers. Many years ago the condition of our streams and rivers was exceedingly bad, owing to the discharge of crude or only partially purified sewage, and it became necessary to pass the Rivers Pollution Prevention Act of 1876. Section 3 of this act provides that local authorities and other parties shall use the best practicable and available means to render harmless the sewage discharged into streams and rivers. And, later, the Rivers (Prevention of Pollution) Act, 1951, gives River Boards the right to control the discharge of trade effluents into streams, and insists on a minimum standard of purity before the effluent of sewage purification plant and apparatus or plant for dealing with liquid trade waste can be discharged into streams and rivers.

It has thus been necessary to see that sewage, before being discharged into streams, is purified and not simply clarified; that is to say, not only is matter in suspension removed, but organic impurities in solution are stabilised so that secondary decomposition is not set up after the effluent has mingled with the water in the stream.

Composition of sewage. Sewage is a very complex substance, its composition varying tremendously. It is obvious that there must be a great difference, for example, in the composition of the sewage from a purely residential district and that from a large manufacturing town, where sewers receive waste liquids from trade and manufacturing processes which themselves differ from town to town.

It is difficult, therefore, to give definite information as to the chemical composition of sewage. The Rivers Pollution Commissioners, in 1876, published a table of compositions of sewage for both water-closet towns and privy midden towns. (The latter are so rapidly becoming obsolete that they hardly call for notice now.) An abstract of the table referring to water-closet towns, i.e. towns discharging principally ordinary domestic sewage into the sewers, is given in Table 20.

TABLE 20.—*Average Composition of Sewage*

Total Solid Matters in Solution	Organic Carbon	Organic Nitrogen	Ammonia	Total Combined Nitrogen	Chlorine	Suspended Matters		
						Mineral	Organic	Total
In Parts per 100,000[1]								
72·2	4·696	2·205	6·703	7·728	10·66	24·18	20·51	44·69
In Grains per Gallon								
50·54	3·287	1·543	4·692	5·410	7·462	16·926	14·357	31·283

Since the above table was compiled it has been discovered that a part of the solid matters formerly supposed to be in solution is in reality in a state intermediate between solution and suspension. These matters are known as "colloids" and they are particles of a jelly-like character. The purification of colloidal matter is one of the most difficult problems in sewage treatment.

Bacteria. Sewage is highly charged with various kinds of bacteria, some of which are made use of in certain processes of purification (see later). An appreciation of the nature of bacteria is essential to the proper understanding of sewage treatment.

Bacteria are minute vegetable growths, varying in size from about one-fifteen-thousandth to one-twenty-five-thousandth of an inch in diameter; they increase usually by division, occasionally by spore formation; their multiplication is exceedingly rapid and is interfered with by cold. Moisture is necessary for their successful working.

They are of two distinct types, namely, the parasitic, needing a living host, and the saprophytic, living on dead matter, but some exist indifferently as both parasites and saprophytes. Sewage disposal involves the saprophytic organisms, which are subdivided into anaerobic, living without air, and aerobic bacteria, living with air.

Crude sewage contains enormous quantities of anaerobic bacteria and

[1] The internationally adopted method of expression is parts per million.

relatively very few aerobic, but it is possible largely to destroy the former and to cause the latter to multiply, by prolonged aeration of the sewage. The effect of anaerobic bacteria is to cause the sewage to decompose, in which process part of the organic solids are liquefied and gasified. The effect of aerobic bacteria is to enable the organic matters to combine with the oxygen present in the sewage and so to form stable and harmless compounds, such as nitrates. The quantity of nitrates present in a sewage effluent is indeed an indication of the amount of purification by oxidation that has occurred in the treatment. It is, however, no indication of whether the effluent is fit to be discharged into a stream, for its fitness depends not on how much purification has been done, but on how much is left undone. A good criterion of this is the amount of oxygen which will be absorbed by a sample in a certain standard time, from a standard solution of potassium permanganate.

It is difficult to define the meaning of the word "harmless" as used in Section 3 of the Rivers Pollution Prevention Act, 1876. The old Local Government Board was often asked to prescribe a standard of purity for sewage effluents. The Board, however, always refused to do so, on the ground that each case should be dealt with on its own particular merits.

Development of disposal standards. In 1898 a Royal Commission was appointed to investigate the question of sewage disposal, and this Commission issued many reports. The eighth, issued at the end of the year 1912, deals with the question of standards of purity of effluents.

A brief summary of the conclusions of the Commission on this point is as follows:

"The law should be altered, so that a person, discharging sewage matter into a stream, shall not be deemed to have committed an offence under the Rivers Pollution Prevention Act, 1876, if the sewage matter is discharged in a form which satisfies the requirements of the prescribed standard, this prescribed standard being either the general standard, or a special standard which shall be higher or lower than the general standard, as local circumstances require or permit.

"An effluent, in order to comply with the general standard, must not contain, as discharged, more than three parts per 100,000 of suspended matter and, with its suspended matters included, must not take up, at 65° F., more than two parts per 100,000 of dissolved oxygen in five days. This general standard should be prescribed either by Statute or by Order of a Central Authority, and should be subject to modifications by that authority after an interval of not less than ten years.

"In fixing any special standard, the dilution afforded by the stream is the chief factor to be considered. If the dilution is very low, it may be necessary for the Central Authority, either on its own initiative or on application of the Rivers Board, to prescribe a specially stringent standard, which should also remain in force for a period of not less than ten years.

"If the dilution is very great, the standard may, with the approval of the Central Authority, be relaxed or suspended altogether. Relaxed standards should be subject to revision at periods to be fixed by the Central Authority, and the periods should be shorter than those prescribed for the general or for the more stringent standards.

"With a dilution of over 500 volumes, all tests might be dispensed with, and crude sewage discharged, subject to such conditions as to the provision of screens and detritus tanks as might appear necessary to the Central Authority."

Since the report of 1912, much research has taken place and quite a number of statutes (some of which will be referred to in Chapter 12) have been added to our legislation.

Prevention of river pollution. The Rivers Boards Act divides the country into areas, each under the care of its own local River Board. The Rivers (Prevention of Pollution) Acts of 1951 and 1961 give River Boards duties and powers to control discharges of sewage and trade waste into rivers in their respective areas. No discharge may be made to a river without the consent of the River Board and the 1961 Act specifies the information which must be given to the Board when making an application. Standards vary from area to area, and no national standard of purity exists and river boards are guided mainly by the character of the rivers in their charge.

Insufficiently purified sewage effluent discharged into a river increases the proportion of organic matter, the number of bacteria and reduces the number of parts of dissolved oxygen per 100,000 parts of water in the river. The bacteria and other micro-organisms (apart from their power to propagate disease if allowed to contaminate drinking water) use for their living processes some of the oxygen held by the water. The amount of oxygen so utilised or absorbed is generally referred to as the "Biochemical Oxygen Demand" (or B.O.D.). A well-purified sewage effluent should have a B.O.D. of 0·5 parts per 100,000 or less, and most sewage works managers try to maintain a standard for suspended matter of not more than 2 parts per 100,000, which, when taken into the stream of a river with a reasonable volume and velocity of flow, will dilute to safe conditions for fish life and the tiny animal or vegetable organisms which form its food. B.O.D. is also a good indication of the number of bacteria likely to be found in an effluent and so, indirectly, of its effect on the river as a source of domestic water supply.

The field of sewage disposal is one in which there has been a vast amount of experimental work in recent years, and whilst the prompt and effectual removal of the excremental and other refuse is of the utmost importance, no one system of disposal can be applied indiscriminately. The system which is applicable to one district may not be by any means the best for another, differently situated or conditioned.

Disposal methods. The chief methods of treatment for the disposal of sewage may be classified as:

1 Discharge into the sea or a tidal estuary.
2 Land treatment (aerobic).
3 Some suitable combination of any of the following:
(*a*) Sedimentation tanks, with or without the use of chemical precipitants (mechanical treatment); (*b*) Septic tanks or hydrolytic tanks (anaerobic treatment); (*c*) Activated sludge tanks (aerobic); (*d*) Percolating filters (aerobic).

Whatever treatment method is adopted, the primary object is purification. Sewage works should be kept free from nuisance; the expenditure, both capital and annual, should be kept as low as possible consistent with efficiency.

Discharge into sea or tidal estuary. In the case of towns on the sea-coast, discharge into the sea or a tidal estuary furnishes an efficient and economical means of disposal. Great care is necessary in selecting the position for the outfall, and careful observations of the nature of the prevailing currents should be made over a fairly large area. The observations are made with the help of floats, the directions taken being carefully recorded with the aid of a theodolite or prismatic compass, so that the course of the current may be plotted on a plan. The sewage will in most cases have to be discharged into favourable currents on the ebb tide, tanks, of course, being provided for storage during high tide. In a few exceptional cases it is possible to discharge the sewage at all states of the tide without causing a nuisance, in which cases storage tanks are unnecessary.

Land treatment. Land treatment as a sole method of treating sewage is obsolete, the main reasons being that the cost of land is too high, there is likelihood of nuisance (unless exceptionally well managed) and the amount of manual labour required is expensive and difficult to obtain. The description of the treatment is included as it provides useful background on previously used methods and on the principles underlying the disposal of a treated effluent to the land for isolated premises. There are two methods of applying sewage to land for the purpose of purification, known as irrigation and filtration respectively.

Irrigation. Irrigation is the system in which the sewage is made to flow over an area of land continuously for a certain time, the area being then rested while agricultural operations proceed. The land is not underdrained. This system is best carried out by using land which has a fall of about 1 in 100 and passing the sewage over it in a thin sheet.

Land filtration. Filtration is generally carried out on flat or levelled land. Plots are underdrained and enclosed with earth walls or banks. These are flooded with sewage which is allowed to soak away before reflooding, thus passing alternate layers of sewage and air through the soil. In both systems ridges and furrows, as shown in Fig. 86, are sometimes used, the advantage being that the roots of the crops on the ridges absorb the sewage without the crops themselves being fouled.

The sewage carriers require to be carefully arranged and constructed. The main carriers or channels can be of concrete, and the minor carriers can either be similarly constructed, or may consist of grips, or channels, just cut in the ground. Fig. 86 shows what is known as the catch-water system, applied to an area of rough and irregular surface. The minor carriers are carefully formed along contours, at vertical intervals of about 2 ft 6 in., as shown. The inlet to the main carrier is controlled by a meter chamber, to measure the quantity applied at one time. The entrance to the minor carrier, at its junction with the main, is controlled by a small sluice. The land drains should not be of less diameter than 3 in., and there is no advantage in putting them deeper than from 4 to 5 ft below the surface. A manhole is shown on the subsoil drain, for the purpose of sampling the effluent passing through the drains.

SOIL FOR LAND FILTRATION. A most important factor in filtration treatment through land is the nature of the soil. A good loamy soil is best, sands or gravels having relatively limited capacity for treatment.

Peat and clay should only be used when there is vegetable soil above them, of at least 6 or 9 in. in depth.

Good soils for purification purposes are alluvial drift and gravel, oolitic limestone, Bunter sandstone, magnesian limestone, chalk and old red sandstone.

IMPORTANCE OF TOP SOIL. The bulk of the purification is effected in the first foot or so of depth, but it is necessary to have an underlying soil of a porous nature in order to carry off the effluent. The action of an earth filter is partly mechanical, partly chemical and partly biological. The destruction of organic impurities in sewage is brought about by a process of active fermentation, termed nitrification, caused by aerobic bacteria, the organic matters being resolved into soluble nitrates, products having no smell, colour or injurious properties. Nitrification ceases if the treatment of the land with sewage is not conducted intermittently and, if irrigation or filtration is carried on without care and without regard to the scientific

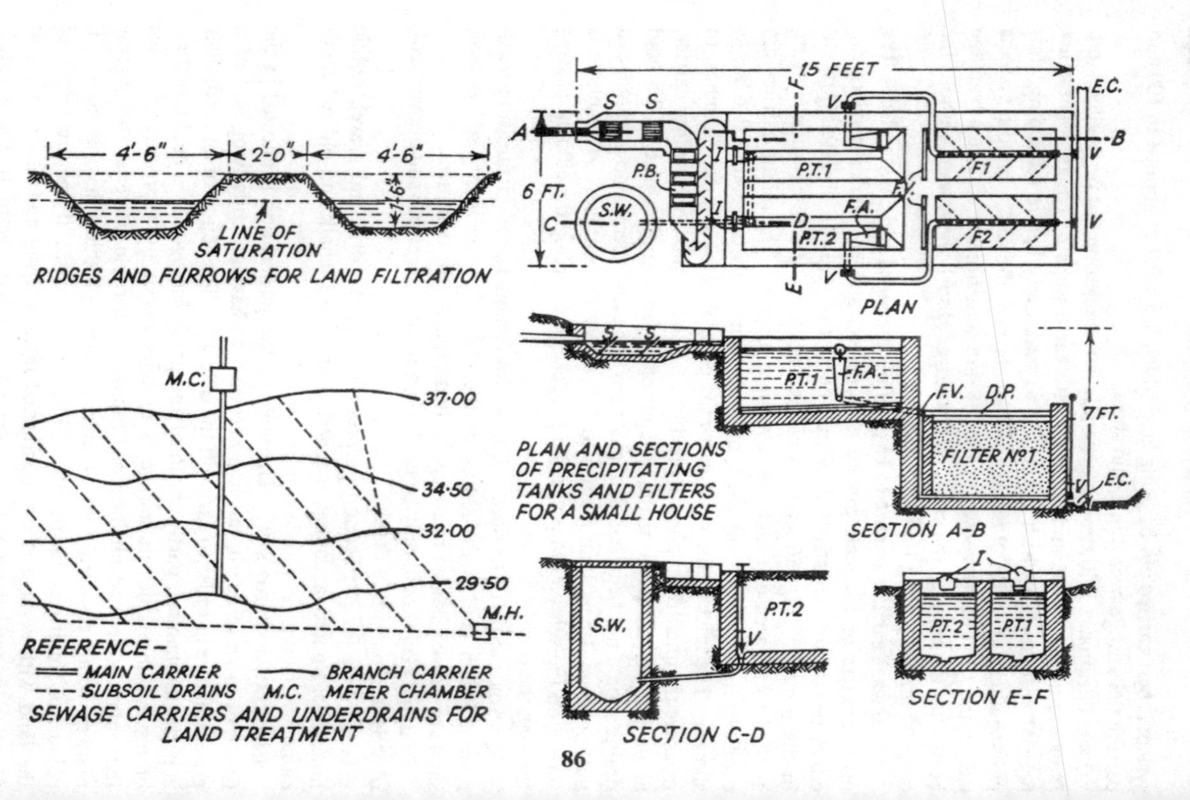
4'-6"
2'-0"
4'-6"
1'-6"
LINE OF SATURATION
RIDGES AND FURROWS FOR LAND FILTRATION
M.C.
37·00
34·50
32·00
29·50
M.H.
REFERENCE –
MAIN CARRIER
BRANCH CARRIER
SUBSOIL DRAINS
M.C. METER CHAMBER
SEWAGE CARRIERS AND UNDERDRAINS FOR LAND TREATMENT
15 FEET
6 FT.
A
B
C
D
E
F
S
P.B.
S.W.
I
P.T.1
P.T.2
F.A.
F.V.
F1
F2
V
E.C.
PLAN
D.P.
7 FT.
FILTER No 1
SECTION A-B
PLAN AND SECTIONS OF PRECIPITATING TANKS AND FILTERS FOR A SMALL HOUSE
SECTION C-D
SECTION E-F

86

86 *Sewage disposal* (*older methods*)

(*Above, left*) LAND FILTRATION. Arrangement of ridges and furrows used in purification of sewage by land filtration. Vegetable crops or herbs are often grown along the ridges.
(*Below, left*) Layout of a "catch-water" system of land filtration (see text).
(*Right*) A SMALL-SCALE PRECIPITATION INSTALLATION. The overall dimensions indicated on the plan and sections are approximate but they give a rough idea of the scale.

The sewage enters at A and passes through two screens; and then along an iron channel containing three precipitating boxes or cages, P.B., containing, say, blocks, of alumino-ferric. It passes along a further length of channel, in which are a series of baffle plates to mix thoroughly the precipitant with the sewage, which then enters, through either of two inlets, I., precipitating tanks, P.T.1 or P.T.2. The effluent from these is conveyed by floating arms, F.A., to distributing pipes lying over the centres of the filters. Each filter is ventilated by a filter vent, F.V., and the effluent passes down through the filter and out through a valve, V., into the effluent channel, E.C. The sludge from the precipitating tanks passes to a sludge well, S.W., the entrance to which is controlled by the valve, V., shown on section C.D. The inlets to the precipitating tanks are in the form of sluices, that of the precipitating tank P.T.2 being shown closed and that of P.T.1 being shown open.

The sludge can be removed from the sludge well by means of an ordinary farmyard or chain pump and conveyed to the kitchen garden by a trough or channel. If the garden is small, it may be necessary to transport the sludge, in a water barrow, and to empty it into shallow trenches, 12 to 18 in. deep. These are topped with garden soil as soon as the sludge is hard enough. The soil bacteria quickly transforms the sludge into fertile plant food.

CHLORINE TREATMENT. If the disposal plant has to be rather near the building served or on the side of the prevailing winds, there may be some nuisance and it may be worth while to install an automatic chlorination equipment. An expert in chlorination should be consulted, for overdosing would kill bacteria and stop the bacterial action, but correct dosing (either in liquid or gaseous form or as sodium hypochlorite and bleaching powder) reduces odour without interfering with the bacterial action. Chlorination also helps to keep the filtering material in a clean condition and prevents the film of green slime (due to algae) which often forms on the surface of the filter beds, holding up the effluent in large puddles (or ponds), and allowing the effluent to run too fast through the filter bed in the remaining parts which are not so affected. Public sewage-disposal plants sometimes cure this tendency of the filter beds to "pond up" by inoculating the surface with a few pieces of clinker from a nearby sewage works where the beds are known to be clear. This inoculation introduces a few specimens of a small grey-blue insect, known as a "springtail" (*Achorutes subviaticus*). These soon multiply and feed upon the algae, thus keeping the surface clean. In small bacteria beds for private houses, it is generally enough to rake over the surface occasionally.

N.B.—The action and construction of filter beds are described later in this chapter as are other arrangements for small-scale private sewage disposal installations.

principles involved, there is a risk of the pollution of subsoil waters and streams.

It is easy to see why a non-porous soil is unsuitable for sewage purification—although the sewage may be mechanically strained, the absence of free oxygen in the soil prevents purification.

Given a suitable soil and good management, filtration through land results in an effluent as pure as can be obtained by any other means; it must not be forgotten, however, that a sewage farm cannot be free from smell and should therefore not be near built-up areas.

INTERCHANGE IN LAND TREATMENT. A general practice was to work a sewage farm on the basis of alternate sections being given up to irrigation and to filtration, and to change them over once a year. This enables the land to be well worked up and aerated, especially if the ridge and furrow system is adopted, and the ridges and furrows levelled once a year. Italian rye grass is a favourite crop on sewage farms, the reason being that it grows so rapidly and closely that weeds are kept down—an important point to land treatment. Mangolds and other crops are also grown.

It will be obvious that, if the areas are interchangeable for both irrigation and filtration, the whole must be underdrained.

That no hard-and-fast rule, or definite figure, can be given as to the area required for any particular case of land treatment will be evident from the following extract from the Fourth Report of the Royal Commission on Sewage Disposal:

"We doubt whether the most suitable kinds of soil, worked as a filtration farm, should be called upon to treat more than 30,000 to 60,000 gallons per acre per 24 hours at a given time (750 to 1500 people per acre), or more than 10,000 to 20,000 gallons per acre per 24 hours calculated on the total area of irrigation (250 to 500 people per acre). Soil not so well suited, worked as surface irrigation, or combined surface irrigation and filtration, 25 to 50 persons per acre." (The sewage in the foregoing cases is assumed to have been settled in tanks before it is applied to land.)

It is impossible to lay down any hard-and-fast rule as regards the proper proportions between the area being irrigated at one time and the surplus resting or aerating, but the Commissioners suggested that four-fifths of a surface irrigation farm and two-thirds of a filtration farm should be at rest. The Commissioners in effect also expressed their inability to say whether slow or rapid alternations of work and rest are advisable.

The Commissioners laid much stress on the fact that the success or failure of a sewage farm lies largely with the management. It pointed out that there is much temptation to try and grow remunerative crops but that the farming operations should be relegated to the background, and the production of a good effluent be placed before everything else.

"STANDBY" FILTER FOR SEWAGE FARMS. When land treatment is adopted it is usually advisable to have a filter, such as will be dealt with later, as a standby for emergency; if one is provided it should be given a dose of sewage regularly to keep it in good condition. It is also the practice, before applying sewage to land, to pass it through screens, and often through sedimentation tanks as well.

SEWAGE "SCREENS". Various things, such as road metal, rags, brushes, corks, etc., find their way into sewage, and it is desirable in all cases (except in very small plants), whatever the nature of the subsequent treatment, to remove them by screening. There are many forms of screen, the commonest form consisting of a framework carrying a series of flat bars at intervals of about ½ to ¾ of an in., the screen being inclined at an angle of 30° or more to the vertical and the bars bent over at the top in the direction of the sewage flow. The screen is kept clear by frequent raking, either by hand or machine. In large works mechanical devices are almost always used for keeping the screens clear. Where the screens are at a good depth below the ground, they are generally in duplicate, sliding vertically, so that they can be readily raised and cleaned.

Other forms of screen are endless bands of copper-wire netting, and circular, revolving, perforated plates.

The screenings should frequently be removed, covered with lime or ashes, as they are often offensive, allowed to drain and dug into land or used as manure.

Screens are omitted in very small works, such as those for a country-house, or a group of houses, as they need frequent attention or become completely blocked.

Alternatives to land treatment Some earlier methods are still in common use. These fall into two stages: (1) the removal of suspended solids, by sedimentation or digestion, and (2) the oxidation of organic matters.

Detritus tanks. Some of the suspended solids in sewage are inorganic, i.e. of mineral origin; these settle more rapidly than organic matter and therefore can be separated by passing the sewage through a tank, at a velocity sufficiently great to prevent organic substances from settling, but slow enough to enable grit to be deposited. (For this purpose the velocity is about 1 ft/sec.) Such tanks are called "Detritus Tanks" or "Grit Chambers" and are long and shallow. There must be at least two of them, to enable them to be cleaned out in turn. They are usually constructed of concrete with floors sloping toward the inlet, at which end the greater part of the grit will be deposited. The combined capacity, of the two or more tanks provided. should be about half-an-hour's dry weather flow.

Mineral matter is removed to make subsequent treatment easier.

There is some difference of opinion as to whether grit chambers should be placed before the screens or after, but it is probably the better plan for them to precede the screens.

Settling tanks. Sedimentation or Settling Tanks differ from Detritus Tanks in that they are intended for settling out the organic solids. The velocity of flow through them must therefore be very low. They may be worked on a continuous or intermittent principle; that is the sewage may flow continuously through them at an imperceptible velocity, or they may be filled and allowed to stand for a time before being emptied. The advantage of the continuous flow tank is the smaller amount of head difference required between the tank and the filter and that being continuous there is not the need for switching from one tank to another as they become full (a cycle on intermittent flow would require 3 tanks) thereby reducing the amount of labour and attention required. The use of continuous flow tanks is now so general that reference to settling tanks implies continuous flow.

Tanks are usually built of concrete with floors sloping towards a sludge outlet. Their usual depth is from 6 to 8 ft and the total capacity of the tanks (including spares) should be from ten to eighteen hours' dry-weather flow.

Continuous-flow settling tanks. The inlet and outlet can be weirs, about 6 in. from which are scum boards extending into the sewage for the whole width of the inlet weir, to induce vertical movement and thus prevent the incoming sewage passing straight along the surface from the inlet to the outlet weir.

Intermittent-flow settling tanks. If the intermittent-flow principle is adopted the inlet can be a weir, but the outlet must be a telescopic pipe or a floating arm which falls as the tank is emptied. The sludge is removed from intermittent tanks at about every third emptying; in continuous-flow tanks it is removed every few days in summer time, but less frequently during winter, the object always being to remove it before it becomes septic. Sludge can be removed, without emptying the tank, by opening the sludge outlet and allowing the pressure of the water above to force it down the sloping floor, the process sometimes being aided by squeegees, either hand-operated or mechanical.

Precipitation tanks. There is no doubt that the precipitation of suspended solids can be effected more quickly and thoroughly by adding chemicals to the sewage.

One of the oldest methods is to add about 6 or 10 grains of lime per gallon of sewage, but more efficient precipitation is obtained by reducing the quantity of lime to something under 5 grains to the gallon and by subsequently adding from 5 to 15 grains of sulphate of alumina or sulphate of iron, or of a mixture of sulphate of alumina with iron and silica, known as "aluminoferric". The effect of lime and a sulphate, in forming a flocculent precipitate which, in settling, brings down with it the finest of suspended particles, has already been referred to in Chapter 6, relative to methods of water filtration.

The effluent from a chemical precipitation tank will be clear and free from smell, but in no sense are the organic matters in solution purified; such an effluent, therefore, if passed into a stream, may later decompose and give rise to a nuisance; the effluent ought, therefore, to be subjected to further treatment before being passed into a stream. A further disadvantage of the method is the large quantity of sludge produced, which needs frequent removal and is difficult to dispose of. This sludge is a mixture of 5 to 10 per cent of solids and 95 to 90 per cent of water.

The application of precipitation to a small-scale installation is illustrated and described in Fig. 86.

Chemical treatment. Chemical treatment was much used during the latter part of the nineteenth century; it is now seldom used except for sewage of a special character, as where it contains a large amount of waste from breweries and tanneries, in which case the chemicals may be of particular value in keeping down smell at the disposal works.

The construction of tanks generally used for chemical precipitation will in no way differ from those used for ordinary sedimentation.

Horizontal- and vertical-flow precipitation tanks. Settlement tanks, whether chemicals are used or not, are by no means always of the "horizontal-flow" type described above. Sometimes a "vertical-flow" type is used. These are square or circular in plan and often as deep as 30 ft. The upper part has vertical sides, but the lower part is an inverted pyramid or cone converging to a sludge outlet at the bottom. The sewage is admitted low down in the tank, but above the highest sludge level. The outlet is a peripheral weir at the top. After admission the sewage rises very slowly, but the sludge carried in it first stops and then begins to fall to the sludge outlet. If a place for its deposit is available below the level of the outlet the sludge can be disposed of, without the tank being emptied, by opening the valve controlling the sludge outlet and allowing the hydrostatic pressure of the overlying sewage to force the sludge along an outlet pipe. As, however, a fall as great as the depth of the tank is seldom

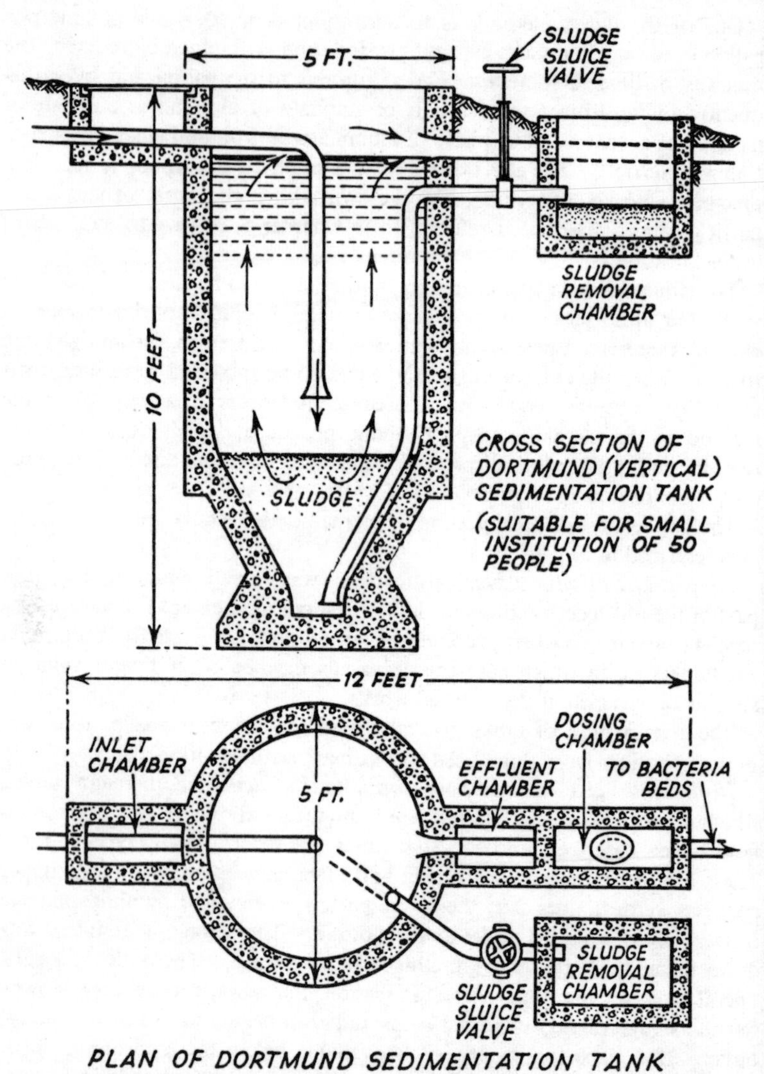

PLAN OF DORTMUND SEDIMENTATION TANK
SHOWING ARRANGEMENTS FOR SLUDGE REMOVAL AND DOSING CHAMBER LEADING TO CONTACT BEDS OR CONTINUOUS FILTERS

87

available, the sludge usually has to be pumped from the outlet pipe to a higher level.

Vertical-flow tanks can be of smaller capacity than horizontal-flow tanks, but their great depth makes them more costly to construct. They are often called DORTMUND TANKS, as they were first used at Dortmund in Germany (87).

Septic tanks. Septic tanks, first introduced by Mr Cameron at Exeter, resemble sedimentation tanks in that their purpose is to get rid of solids in suspension, which would clog the filter or "bacteria" beds. Unlike sedimentation tanks, however, the intention is to liquefy or gasify the suspended solids as far as possible, rather than to remove them as sludge. With this object the sludge is left in the tank until it putrefies, a portion only of it being removed when it has accumulated to such an extent as to fill the tank to about one-third of its capacity. At least three tanks should be provided, except on small works, and the capacity of all the septic tanks provided should be about twenty-four hours' dry-weather flow. Their depth is usually about 10 ft.

The inlet may be by a weir with scum board, or by a vertical inlet pipe carried down to about half the depth of the tank. The outlet is usually a weir provided with a scum board.

ACTION OF SEPTIC TANKS. The satisfactory action of septic tanks depends upon the sludge being left long enough on the bottom for all air to escape, so that the anaerobic bacteria thrive and cause decomposition. Bubbles of gas then come through to the surface, carrying solid particles with them, thus forming a scum which helps to keep air from direct contact with the sewage. The decompositon, in addition, liquefies some of the solids and breaks up the remainder into fine particles. At one time it was thought necessary to roof in these tanks, in order to preserve the anaerobes from light and air. It is now known, however, that this is effectively done by the scum, so that the cost of a roof can be avoided unless it is necessary to prevent a nuisance from smell.

As compared with sedimentation tanks, septic tanks have the advantage that much less sludge has to be disposed of, and this will, if well digested, be far less offensive than the raw sludge from settling tanks; further, it contains a much smaller proportion of water, so that it is more easily dealt with and more useful as manure. Their disadvantages are, firstly, that the ebullition of gases liberated from the sludge carries particles of sludge upwards, so that the effluent contains large numbers of suspended black particles, which need

---

87 *Dortmund tank*

A vertical flow or "Dortmund" tank for sewage sedimentation. Tanks are often square in plan and arranged in groups of four with a common peripheral weir outlet.

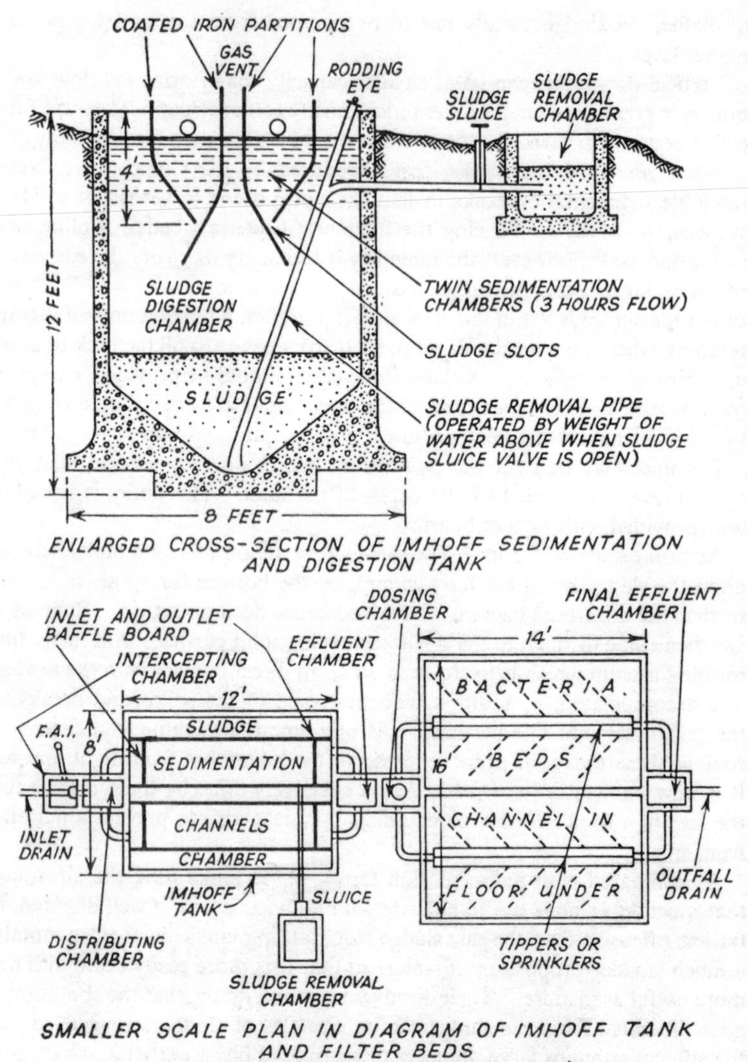

88

88 *Imhoff tank*

Typical arrangement of an Imhoff tank for the reduction of sludge by digestion (see text).

to be settled in an additional settling chamber before the effluent is passed on to bacteria beds; secondly, the effluent contains a great deal of carbon dioxide and practically no oxygen, a state which is unfavourable to subsequent aerobic treatment, so that it is advisable to aerate it by allowing it to fall from a trough into channels, if the necessary fall is available; a third disadvantage is the objectionable smell which arises from these tanks. They are seldom installed now in any large new plants, but covered tanks of this kind are the most used type for isolated country houses owing to the small attention needed.

Hydrolytic tanks. An improved form of septic tank, known as a hydrolytic tank, was introduced by Dr Travis at Hampton. He was the first to realise that a large part of the solids in sewage were of "colloidal" or jelly-like character, and that these, though not ordinarily deposited in sedimentation or septic tanks, could be made to settle if the sewage was brought into contact with a sufficient area of solid surfaces.

USE OF COLLOIDERS. He therefore divided his tanks into compartments. The sewage was first admitted to settlement compartments in which were fixed a large number of vertical splines, or strips of wood, known as colloiders, to which colloids and fine suspended particles adhered, to drop off subsequently in flakes to the bottom of the chamber. A further innovation was that this falling mass gravitated through outlets to a liquefying chamber, in which the decomposition took place. The rising sludge particles, carried by the gases of decomposition, could not get into the settlement compartments, the effluent from which was therefore remarkably free from suspended solids and colloids. This effluent passed over weirs from the settlement compartments for subsequent aerobic treatment, whilst the sewage from the liquefying chamber, containing a large amount of sludge particles, was passed over a separate weir to a hydrolysing chamber; this was simply an additional settlement chamber fitted with colloiders.

The Imhoff tank. The Imhoff tank, largely used in Germany and America, works on the same principle as the Travis tank, but differs from it chiefly in that the main chamber (that for liquefying and digesting the sludge) has no outlet except that for sludge removal. Solid matter reaches the digestion chamber from twin sedimentation chambers set above it and there is left to digest and liquefy, only the residual sludge is drawn off, the offensive gases passing out through the gas vent between the two sedimentation chambers, as shown in Fig. 88.

(*Below*) The tank shown in relation to the filter or "bacteria" beds over which the effluent is passed. (The action of the dosing chamber and of the bacteria beds are described in this chapter.)

TREATMENT OF THE EFFLUENT. Before considering other methods of sewage treatment it should once more be emphasised that screens, detritus chambers, sedimentation tanks, chemical precipitation treatment, septic tanks, hydrolytic and Imhoff tanks are all merely means of depositing or liquefying suspended solids, and hence clarifying the liquid and making it more suitable for subsequent purification. The effluent from these tanks contains large amounts of organic solids in solution, which, if not oxidised, will subsequently decompose and give rise to a nuisance.

Methods of oxidising effluents vary considerably. Land treatment described earlier is one method. Other methods have to be used where it is desired to treat large volumes of sewage on a comparatively small site. Such treatment is often carried out in what are called "bacteria beds". These may be on the intermittent principle, in which case they are called "contact beds", or on the continuous-flow principle, in which case they are called "percolating filters" or "trickling filters". In either case the aerobic bacteria are used to promote purification.

Bacteria beds. The beds are filled with pieces of stone, clinker or similar material. Though rough porous material is generally preferred to smooth impervious ones, quite good results are obtainable with the latter; in fact it may be said that the nature of the material is relatively unimportant as long as it is clean and free from dust, is not so soft as to crumble, and contains no constituents which will cause it to disintegrate. Broken clinker is mostly used because it presents a maximum of surface area and is usually cheaper than stone. It is not so durable, however.

Aerobic bacteria. Aerobic bacteria are not common in sewage, and a new filter gives little or no purification. With repeated dosing and aeration, however, the aerobic bacteria multiply and in a few weeks or months, according to the temperature, form into spongy growths on the clinker or stone.

Dibdin's slate beds. Contact beds were first used by Mr Dibdin, then chemist to the London County Council, in 1893. They are not now used and in the same way that continuous flow is implied when speaking of sedimentation tanks so percolating or trickling filters are implied when referring to bacteria beds, the advantages in this case being similar to those of the sedimentation tank. The description of contact beds is included as they have formed an important phase in the development of sewage purification.

The submitting of an effluent to one contact bed is only termed a single contact process, and does not give a sufficiently high degree of purification. If the effluent is passed through two contact beds in succession the process is known as double contact, which is usual, and if through three beds, triple contact, which is fairly rare. A very common depth for contact beds is about 4 ft, although they may be found to vary from about 2½ to 6 ft. A very satisfactory discharge after each filling is about one-third of the gross capacity, the other two-thirds being occupied by the filtering medium, bacterial growths, deposits of solids and colloids and by water which never drains away. This is equivalent to a discharge of 56 gallons per cubic yard of filling material.

Two hours may be taken to fill a bed, after which the sewage is allowed to stand in it for one hour; alternatively filling can be done in one hour and two hours allowed for standing; in either case a further five hours is allowed for the effluent to drain away and for air to penetrate between the stones. The beds can thus be filled only three times in twenty-four hours, giving a maximum capacity of 168 gallons per cubic yard per day. As the double contact process is generally used this is reduced to 84 gallons per cubic yard of total contact bed capacity.

Such a rate would be satisfactory in practice but could not be kept up for long, unless the sewage were weak or the suspended solids had been removed, by chemical precipitation or a hydrolytic tank. The usual rate worked to in practice is 40 to 50 gallons per cubic yard per day. (Should it fall below the lower of these figures it is a sign that the beds have become unduly choked with solids through overwork.)

CONSTRUCTION OF CONTACT BEDS. The floor and walls of the beds are usually built of concrete and must be watertight; the total area should be divided up so that the maximum size of a single bed does not exceed about two hours' dry-weather flow, which ensures quick filling and emptying and satisfactory working generally. In the case of double contact, it is usual to place the second bed at such a level that the first bed can be readily discharged on to it. A finer material is used in the second than in the first, since the object of the first is to "take the rough off", so to speak. A common practice is from 1½ to 2 in. gauge for the material in first beds, and ¾ to 1½ in. for the second, although finer material is sometimes used.

Beneath this material and above the concrete floor is a system of drains, which may consist of some form of false floor made of specially shaped tiles; semicircular channels in the floor, covered by tiles; these tiles are sometimes perforated, but this is not essential; semicircular tiles with perforations on the crown; interlocking tiles forming drains in section like an inverted V.

In all cases the drains are laid to fall to main effluent channels.

The inlets and outlets of contact beds are usually controlled by means of

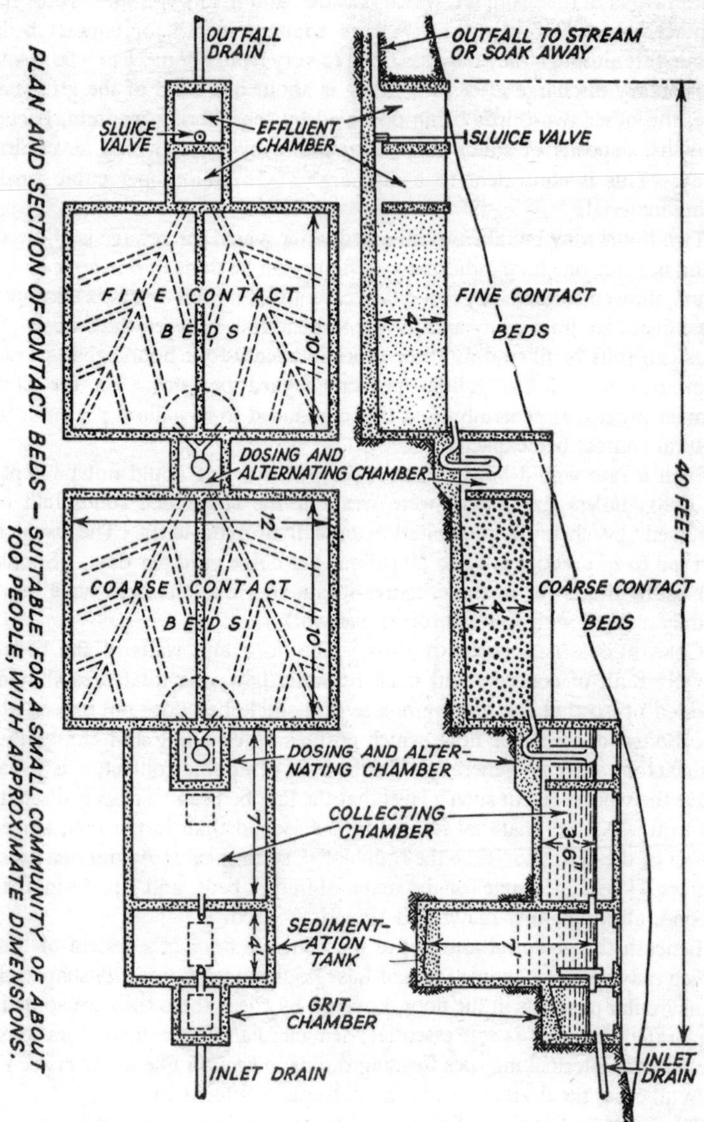

PLAN AND SECTION OF CONTACT BEDS – SUITABLE FOR A SMALL COMMUNITY OF ABOUT 100 PEOPLE, WITH APPROXIMATE DIMENSIONS.

89

siphons operating in collecting chambers. A general arrangement of this and contact beds given in Fig. 89.

CONSTRUCTION AND WORKING OF CONTINUOUS BACTERIA BEDS. The percolating filter is distinctly different from the contact beds so far as the method of working is concerned. The outlet is allowed to remain open, and the effluent is applied evenly and continuously, usually in the form of a fine spray, by automatic or other means, so arranged that alternate layers of sewage and air pass through the filter. Such beds are usually circular or rectangular in plan, the construction being formed in much the same way, except that the treated effluent is allowed to flow away freely through an opening at floor level at the lower end. Since there is no hydrostatic pressure in the beds the walls need not be of watertight construction; they are, in fact, sometimes made honeycombed, with the idea of securing better aeration of the beds. This is not now considered a desirable proceeding as it causes the beds to become unduly chilled in cold weather, in addition to which the holes in the walls become a breeding place for flies. An example of smaller filter beds is included in Fig. 91, p. 348.

It is important that the sewage shall be applied evenly to every part of a filter bed. For very small plants, where economy is of great importance, this may be done sufficiently well by allowing the sewage to overflow from a large number of cast-iron troughs, or from W-shaped gutters with notches in their central ridge, although distributors of a simplified form are now available for the smallest of plants. For large plants, which are more likely to be used intensively, a more precise method is desirable and the following are methods which are in general use:

1 For circular beds—rotary distributor.
2 for rectangular beds—moving pipes or trough from which the sewage is allowed to trickle from holes or notches in the side.

It is always possible for moving pipes to be driven by motors, but it is

---

89 *Contact beds (obsolete)*

General arrangement of contact beds and sedimentation tanks forming the sewage purification installation for a small community. A site with substantial slope as shown is necessary if elaborate and expensive pumping equipment is to be avoided. (Ground with less fall can be utilised by separation of the items of the installation.)

obviously economical to allow the sewage to drive them, when enough head to give the requisite pressure can be arranged.

REVOLVING SPRINKLERS. When beds are circular in shape the pipes are in the form of two or four arms, radiating from a central column where they are fed with sewage. The holes in the pipes are closer together, or else of larger diameter, near the pipe ends than nearer the centre, because they have a greater area to feed. The sewage, issuing from holes in the side of the pipes on one side only, exerts a reaction on the pipe, which drives it in the opposite direction, on the same principle as in the lawn sprinklers in common use. The pipes are of wrought-iron or steel and usually the holes are bushed with gunmetal or brass to prevent corrosion. Even so the holes tend to become choked at times with suspended solid particles, so that they require occasional clearing.

To avoid this trouble, the sewage is sometimes made to pass from wide notches in the feed tube into buckets of a long waterwheel, the weight of the sewage driving the wheel forward, the sewage itself being then spilled on to the bed. In other cases the water-wheels are quite short and spill their contents into perforated troughs from which the sewage trickles on the bed. In large beds the radial arms are usually steadied by support at their extremities in the form of wheels running on rails.

DISTRIBUTORS FOR RECTANGULAR BEDS. When beds are rectangular the same principles can be adopted, but it is necessary for the distributors to be fed from troughs running alongside the beds by siphons. Some of the most modern distributors for rectangular beds have water-wheels at their ends only, which discharge into pipes which span the bed. The direction of movement of the distributors has to be stopped and reversed when they reach the ends of the bed. This is done quite simply by fixed buffers, which actuate levers.

The above description gives only a general indication of the nature of the many automatic sprinklers produced by various manufacturers.

Dosing chambers. Filters should work at a more or less constant rate for the best efficiency, and it must be borne in mind also that automatically operated distributors will not move at all unless they are fed with a certain minimum of sewage. It is usual therefore to provide a tank called a "dosing chamber", through which the sewage passes before reaching the filter. This will store up sewage when the flow is small and automatically discharge the whole of its contents when it becomes full. The filter will then work only intermittently but at its optimum speed. As a certain amount of sedimentation will occur in the dosing chamber it should have a sludge outlet. (See Fig. 90.)

Depth of beds. There are differences of opinion as to the best depth for percolating filters, but 4 ft of material is essential and many authorities on the subject prefer from 6 to 10 ft. Deep filters obviously need less area and smaller distributors for the same capacity, so that they are usually less expensive, even when allowance is made for the extra cost of deep excavation. Deep filters involve, however, a big loss of head, since the sewage must go in at the top and out at the bottom.

Filter-bed material. The gauge of the filtering material is usually rather less than that commonly adopted for contact beds, from 1 in. to 1½ in. being fairly normal practice. There is, however, no unanimity of opinion as to the best gauge—in fact it is probable that the gauge should be regulated according to the nature of the sewage and of the preliminary treatment—a sewage which may have a quantity of suspended solids requiring a considerable depth of relatively coarse stone, and one which is fairly free from suspended solids and colloids having a less depth of finer material.

"*Ponding*" *on the surface of bacteria beds.* It is sometimes found that gelatinous fungoid growths occur on the surface of the filters, so that ponding of the sewage occurs. This can generally be checked by resting the beds. If circumstances prevent the resting of the beds, or if this proves ineffectual, the addition of a dose of chlorine to the sewage may have the desired effect. A more drastic remedy is to apply caustic soda or copper sulphate to the growths.

A certain amount of fine suspended solids will usually pass through percolating filters, whilst colloidal matters, after collecting on the filtering medium, will periodically break away in flakes, usually in early spring. These solids may at times amount to more than the 3 parts per 100,000 which the Royal Commission on Sewage Disposal regarded as the limit which should be discharged into rivers. In works of any size, therefore, a tank, called a "humus tank", is provided for their settlement. Its capacity is about four hours' dry-weather flow and it resembles an ordinary sedimentation tank, except that the flow through it is more rapid.

Rate of filtration. The general rate of filtration of a sewage of average strength, previously passed through settlement tanks or septic tanks, will be about 70 to 50 gallons per cubic yard of filter per day respectively, which is about twice the rate of passing through contact beds.

Contact beds and percolating filters compared. The relative merits of contact beds and of percolating filters were summarised many years ago by Dr Barwise as follows:

With contact beds the sewage need not be so carefully distributed,

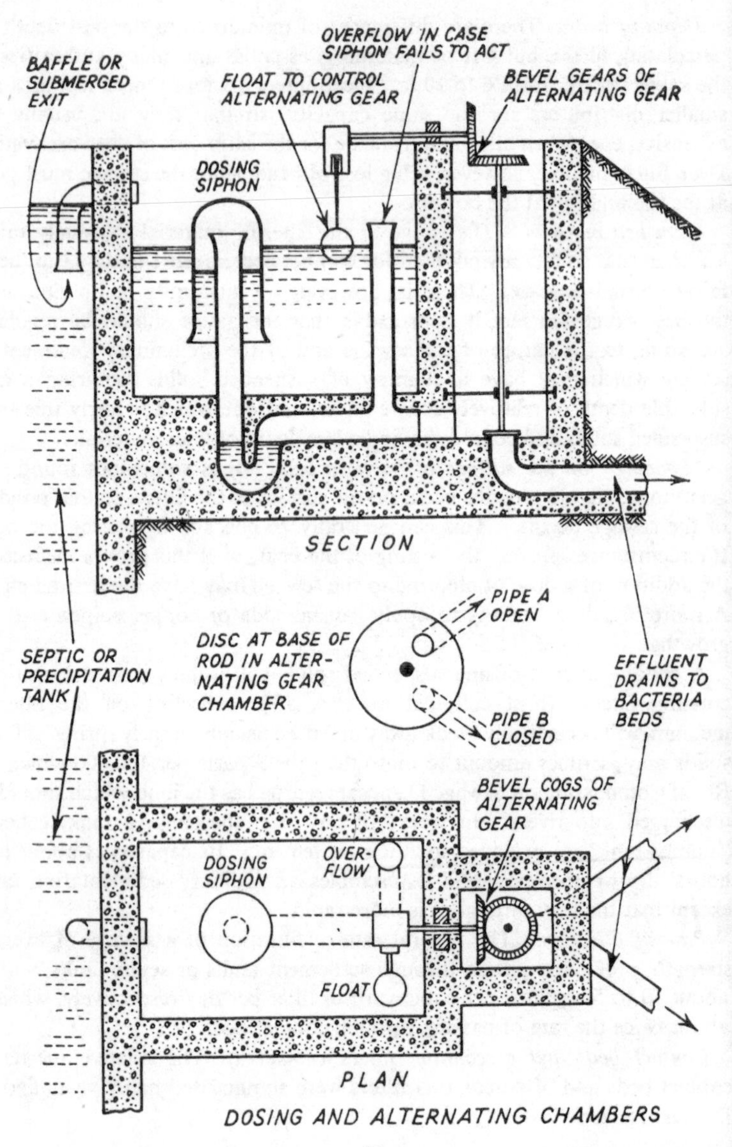

DOSING AND ALTERNATING CHAMBERS

90

whereas with percolating filters the sewage must be carefully and intermittently distributed by expensive means.

With contact beds the size of the filtering medium need not be so carefully graded, whereas in the other case it needs careful grading.

Contact beds must have watertight walls, whereas percolating filters are often formed with walls of very open construction, often above ground, or with no walls at all.

Double contact is required to give results approaching that obtained from one percolating filter.

With contact beds the oxidation is limited, as the air supplied only equals the volume of sewage treated, while the air supplied to percolating filters may be as much as five or six times the volume of sewage, thereby giving greater oxidation.

With contact beds the sewage, being stagnant, has a greater tendency to clog the bed, while, in the other case, such clogging as does occur is on the surface, and the filter does not deteriorate if well made.

Lastly, percolating filters will do more work per day than can be done by contact beds of equal area.

For these reasons contact beds are now not used.

Activated sludge. The use of activated sludge in sewage purification is a development in which dissolved impurities in the effluent of the sedimentation tank are oxidised by the addition of air whilst in a tank, as opposed to a

---

90 *Dosing chamber*

A dosing chamber used to ensure that flow of liquid to bacteria beds is adequate to operate distributing gear and that the rate of application of sewage to the beds is at the optimum rate for purification (see text).

In action the rise of sewage in the chamber compresses air beneath the siphon dome which in turn depresses the level of water in the trap below, allowing air to escape. Water eventually overflows the bell-mouth inlet to the pipe beneath the siphon dome to start the emptying of the chamber by siphonage.

In larger installations it is usually practicable for the direction of sewage to one or other of a series of filters or contact beds to be carried out manually.

In smaller installations, however, duplicate filter beds are often employed and it may be thought desirable to use automatic alternating gear in or alongside the dosing chamber. This can be done simply, as shown in the diagram, by arranging a copper float which rises and falls with the effluent in the dosing chamber, at the same time turning bevel gears, arranged to turn the vertical rod in the alternating gear chamber shown. To the bottom of this rod is attached a circular disc (contrived with a ratchet and the gearing) which alternately opens and closes the entrances to pipes A and B, leading right and left, to the duplicate filter beds.

bacteria bed, the suspended matters being utilised in the process, to distribute aerobic bacteria about the whole bulk of the liquid. The suspended solids are removed by sedimentation after oxidation.

For many years in the nineteenth century experiments were carried out by blowing air through sewage with the object of oxidising impurities. The results were invariably disappointing, owing to the difficulty of keeping the air in contact with the impurities long enough before it escaped.

Eventually Dr G. J. Fowler discovered that if sludge is repeatedly aerated, the anaerobes, which are present in it in great abundance, are destroyed and aerobes take their place. Such sludge is then said to be "activated" because, if circulated in fine particles in sewage, whilst air is being passed through it, the aerobes will bring the oxygen into chemical combination with the dissolved organic matters and nitrify them at a greatly increased rate.

To get the best result the particles of sludge must be moved about in the sewage with a velocity of about $1\frac{1}{2}$ ft/sec., this movement being generally created by means of the air which is needed for oxidation.

If air is blown through nozzles or perforations it rises quickly as bubbles and escapes without doing much good. It is therefore forced by air compressors, or rotary blowers driven by an electric motor, through porous tiles, known as diffusers, which form part of the floor of the aeration tank—generally about $\frac{1}{18}$th part of the whole floor. The air should preferably be filtered before it is drawn into the blowers, to eliminate particles of dust which would gradually choke the diffusers. Aeration tanks operated in this way are usually 10–12 ft deep.

When the tank is in action the ascending air drives up the liquid and sludge lying over the diffusers and eventually escapes from the surface, but the liquid and sludge move laterally to places where there is no rising column of liquid, the unsupported sludge then falling to the bottom of the tank once more. As more and more sludge accumulates in heaps in those parts of the floor where there are no diffusers, it slides down upon the diffusers and is blown up once more. During all this time sewage is flowing very slowly in and out of the tank, passing through the whirling particles of sludge in its passage. The sewage leaves the tank clear and inoffensive, but carrying with it a large amount of the sludge particles. It is therefore passed into settling tanks, where it remains for one-and-a-half to four hours. A part of the settled sludge is returned to the sewage, at its inlet to the aeration tank, to replace that which has been carried away in the effluent. It appears that the amount of sludge in the aeration tank should be about 7 per cent of the volume of the tank.

It has been pointed out that the amount of air actually utilised in oxidation is only about 5 per cent of the air admitted, the remainder being required only for the purpose of agitating the sludge. The question naturally arose as to whether some cheaper method of agitating the sludge and of aerating the liquid could be devised.

It has been shown by Mr Haworth at Sheffield that the activated sludge process can be carried out, without the introduction of compressed air, by passing the sewage along channels in which its surface is churned up by paddles, or even simply disturbed by giving the channel a slight slope, the sludge being given a spiral movement by putting baffle walls in the centre of the channel at an angle to the direction of the flow.[1]

More recently methods of using activated sludge have been developed for smaller scale installations. These employ a circular tank which narrows at the base for the aeration process. In this is set centrally a hollow shaft with its base just clear of the tank bottom and its top, of bell-mouth shape, set just above the sewage surface. An impeller set just within the sewage at the top of the shaft draws sewage up the shaft to spew it out at the surface. This thoroughly aerates the sewage and sets up a circulatory movement throughout the contents of the tank. In a typical installation sewage reaches the aeration tank described via a weir inlet from a detritus chamber and flows from it via a baffled inlet to a settling tank. This latter is also tapered at the base to facilitate sludge draw-off by gravity.

Installations are fully automatic. The impeller is readily arranged for intermittent operation by means of a time switch, and a connecting pipe from the sludge well of the settling tank to the central shaft of the aeration tank enables the suction set up by the impeller to draw back just enough activated sludge to balance that carried away by the sewage passing through the aeration tank.

Advantages of activated sludge process. The advantages of activated sludge treatment are as follows:

It requires little space, causes remarkably little smell, and is a very flexible form of treatment. The time of aeration, quantity of air and proportion of sludge can all be varied to give the desired result.

Its disadvantages are that working costs are higher than those of sedimentation and filtration works, that skilled management must be in attendance. It is very sensitive to changes in the character of the sewage and enormous quantities of sludge are produced. It may also be mentioned that occasionally there is a sudden increase in the sludge in the aeration tank to more than twice its normal volume, and that this is accompanied by a deterioration of the effluent. This is known as "bulking" and is due to presence of protozoa

[1] This method, known as the Sheffield Channel Bio-aeration system, was another stage in the development of sewage purification, but it is now seldom used.

and other growths, brought about apparently by insufficiency of air. The condition can be remedied by prolonged aeration.

A most noteworthy fact, relative to the activated sludge process, is the rapidity with which organic matters are oxidised when the sewage is first brought into contact with the sludge and the slowness with which it is improved by more prolonged treatment. For example, at Birmingham it was found that 60 per cent of the impurities were oxidised in one hour and that only a further 32 per cent were oxidised in the next five hours.

It seems therefore that, although it is possible to effect satisfactory purification by sufficiently prolonged activated sludge treatment and settlement alone, it is more economical to aerate for about one hour only and to complete the oxidation of organic matters in percolating filters. After the one hour's aeration and subsequent settlement of sludge, the sewage will be quite free from colloidal matters and well charged with oxygen, and can be passed through the percolating filters at twice the ordinary rate. When this arrangement is adopted it is, however, necessary to reactivate the settled sludge, before returning it to the sewage entering the aeration tanks, since the sludge has more work to do, as it were, when it is brought into contact with fresh sewage every hour, than it would be required to perform if it remained in the same sewage for six or eight hours—the time required for full purification.

Disposal of sludge. One of the greatest troubles in sewage disposal works of any size is the disposal of sludge. Formerly it was sometimes possible to dispose of it in a crude state by sale as manure, but this is now practically impossible and the problem is to get rid of it at the least possible cost. The principal methods of doing so are as follows:

1 Barging it out to sea—a cheap process for places conveniently situated for so doing. This is done in the case of London, Manchester, Southampton and other places.
2 Covering flat land with a layer of a few inches of the wet sludge. This rapidly dries, but the system is unsuitable for strongly smelling sludge.
3 Shallow burial in the ground. Wet sludge is run into trenches about 24 to 30 in. wide and 12 to 18 in. deep, spaced about 3 ft apart. When the sludge has dried to a firm state it is covered with a thin layer of soil. After a period of not less than one month the land is ploughed up and planted with crops. Land should not be sludged in this way more than once a year. The objection to the method, in large works, is the very great area of land needed.
4 Lagooning or air drying. In this method earth tanks, from 2 to 4 ft deep, are made by excavation and by forming banks with the excavated

material, and under-drained with 3 in. or 4 in. diameter agricultural land drains, spaced at intervals of about 9 ft. The bottom of the tank is then covered with a layer of 6 in. or more of clinker or ashes. Sludge is run or pumped in, and allowed to remain there for some months. When moisture has drained and evaporated sufficiently for the sludge to be dug out it has shrunk to about one-half its original volume. When dug out the sludge may be used as manure, or for filling up low-lying land. The objection to the method is that nuisance arises from smell and flies, making it unsuitable for use near inhabited areas. Its advantage is its cheapness as compared with most other methods.

5 Pressing it into cakes in special presses. This process reduces moisture content to about 50 per cent and the bulk to about one-fifth. If the district is agricultural the cakes may be saleable; in other cases they are used for filling low land, dug into land, barged to sea or mixed with house refuse and burnt in refuse destructors. This is an excellent method of treatment, but unfortunately it is a very expensive one.

6 By digestion in tanks. This is a process which has been developed greatly in recent years at Birmingham and elsewhere. It is a septic tank treatment applied to sludge after its separation from sewage, the sludge being usually inoculated with an admixture of already digested sludge.

Sludge digestion. The digestion or decomposition of sludge is effected in two stages, in primary and secondary digestion tanks, In the first, it is kept only so long as it is digesting vigorously and evolving gas, the process being aided by maintaining a temperature of about 75°F; the gas given off in this stage can be used to drive gas engines, as it has a far higher calorific value than town gas. The sludge is then passed to secondary tanks, where a certain amount of liquefaction occurs, the liquid given off being taken away and returned to the raw sewage for treatment. The final sludge, which is inert and unobjectionable, is pumped to drying beds which are under-drained, and is later dug out and disposed of by sale or for filling land. At Birmingham the process is carried on near thickly populated areas, there being practically no smell. Perhaps the first example in the country of the activated sludge process was at West Middlesex Sewage Disposal Scheme at Mogden, about ten miles west of London. There is a ready sale in that area for the digested sludge as a fertiliser and the sludge-gas which is produced, first used for power production on the works, has been found to have valuable industrial uses, and is now compressed into gas cylinders and sold to firms like Fords at Dagenham (with a saving in the county rates), while the machinery on the works has gone back to diesel oil, petrol, etc., on the score of economy.

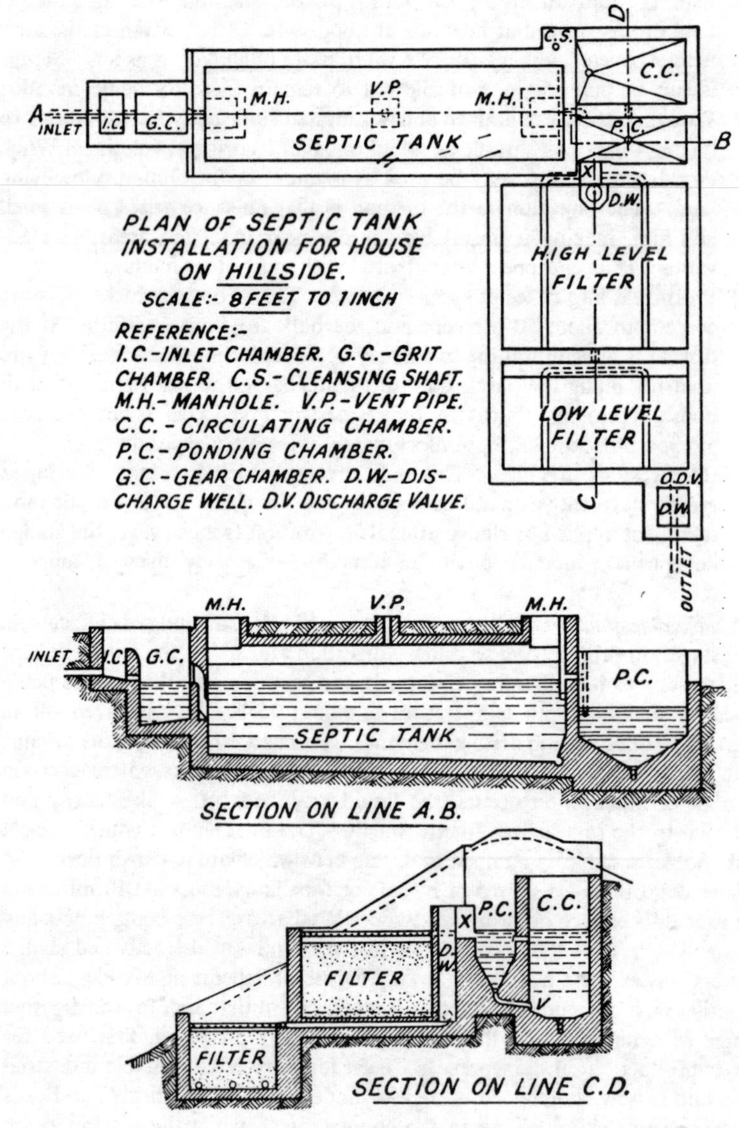
A
INLET
I.C.
G.C.
M.H.
V.P.
M.H.
SEPTIC TANK
C.S.
C.C.
P.C.
B
D
X
D.W.
HIGH LEVEL FILTER
LOW LEVEL FILTER
C
O.D.V.
D.W.
OUTLET
PLAN OF SEPTIC TANK INSTALLATION FOR HOUSE ON HILLSIDE.
SCALE:- 8 FEET TO 1 INCH
REFERENCE:-
I.C.-INLET CHAMBER. G.C.-GRIT CHAMBER. C.S.-CLEANSING SHAFT.
M.H.-MANHOLE. V.P.-VENT PIPE.
C.C.-CIRCULATING CHAMBER.
P.C.-PONDING CHAMBER.
G.C.-GEAR CHAMBER. D.W.-DISCHARGE WELL. D.V. DISCHARGE VALVE.
M.H.
V.P.
M.H.
INLET
I.C.
G.C.
P.C.
SEPTIC TANK
SECTION ON LINE A.B.
X
P.C.
C.C.
D.W.
FILTER
V
FILTER
SECTION ON LINE C.D.

Disposal schemes for country houses. The methods and principles described above can be and are applied in smaller scale private treatment installations. Figures 91 and 92 illustrate and describe small-scale septic tank installations designed for sloping and flat ground respectively.

It should be pointed out that an architect requiring sewage-disposal plant and having decided on the type of disposal scheme most suitable to the conditions, usually leave the design of the details in the hands of a specialist firm. A number of these operate in London and most large towns.

---

91 *A septic tank installation on sloping ground*

A purification installation involving the use of a covered septic tank and successive filtration arranged to exploit steeply falling ground. Operation is as follows: The sewage enters at A, passing through the inlet chamber, I.C., and the grit chamber, G.C., from which it enters the septic tank. The tank, as shown in section AB is covered and ventilated, and has two manholes for access. Both inlet and outlet are submerged, and the sewage passes into the ponding chamber, P.C., from which it can circulate through the circulating chamber, C.C., as shown in section CD. (There are non-return valves, V.V., between the ponding and circulating chambers.) From the ponding chamber liquid passes through the automatic gear in the chamber X., into two distributing pipes over the top of the high-level filter. The effluent from this filter is collected in drains on its floor, leading to the discharge well, D.W., adjoining the ponding chamber. From there it runs to the low-level filter, from which the final effluent is discharged into the nearest water-course.

The sludge from the septic tank is collected through a special form of perforated pipe, and led to a cleansing shaft, C.S., the floor of the circulating chamber connecting with the same pipe. From the cleansing shaft the sludge can be run off in any required direction for disposal.

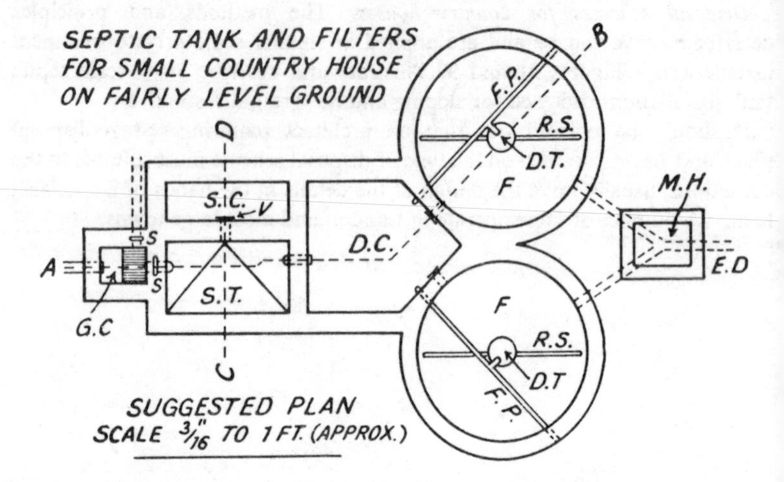
SEPTIC TANK AND FILTERS
FOR SMALL COUNTRY HOUSE
ON FAIRLY LEVEL GROUND
B
F.P.
R.S.
D.T.
F
M.H.
D
S.C.
V
S
S
A
D.C.
S.T.
G.C
E.D
F
R.S.
D.T
F.P.
C
SUGGESTED PLAN
SCALE 3/16" TO 1 FT. (APPROX.)

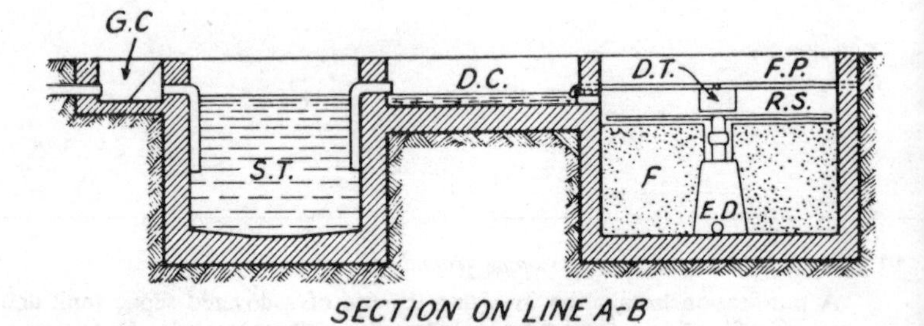
G.C
D.C.
D.T.
F.P.
R.S.
S.T.
F
E.D.
SECTION ON LINE A-B

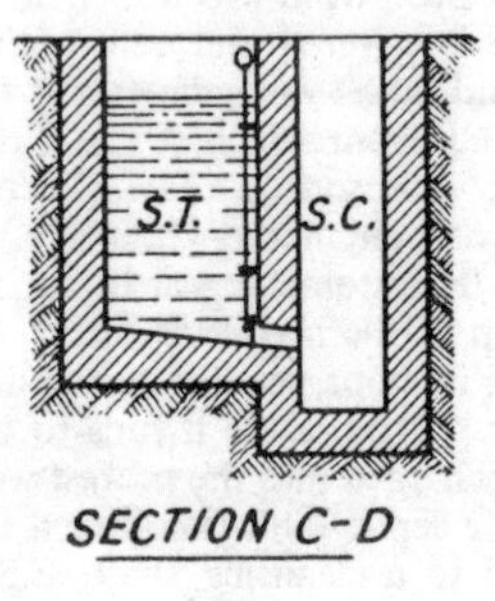
S.T.
S.C.
SECTION C-D

92

92 *A septic tank installation on flat ground*

The septic tank is shown uncovered, it being assumed that it can be placed far enough from the house and road to avoid nuisance from smell. Operation is as follows:

The sewage enters a grit chamber, G.C., in which is a screen. An overflow from the grit chamber is shown in dotted lines, the entrance to it being controlled by a small sluice, S. The sewage passes from the grit chamber via a sluice S, and a submerged inlet to the septic tank, S.T., the floor of which slopes to the sludge chamber, S.C. (section C-D). (Sludge is removed by pumping or other means from the sludge chamber.) The outlet for liquid from the septic tank is also submerged, and leads to a very shallow distributing chamber, D.C., (section A-B).

Adjoining the distributing chamber are two circular filters, F. In the centre of each is a collecting or dosing tank, D.T., which actuates a rotary sprinkler, R.S. The dosing tank is fed from the distributing chamber by feed pipes, F.P., and the chamber can be flushed out by means of a valve leading direct to the filter.

The filtered effluent passes from the bottom of the filters into the effluent drain, E.D., a manhole being placed near the filters to enable the effluent from them to be sampled.

12

Sanitary Surveys and Reports

A fundamental principle in making surveys or examinations of any kind is that nothing should be taken for granted. This is particularly so in the case of sanitary surveys which form a vital part of the examination of buildings prior to occupation or purchase.

The conditions to be fulfilled by a building's sanitary arrangements have already been discussed in detail and there would be no useful purpose served by repeating them here. It will be clear, however, that in making a sanitary survey there are many points which require consideration; the general arrangement of the building, and in particular the relation between the positions of sanitary fittings, living rooms and bedrooms; ventilation, dampness, water supply, sanitary fittings and drainage.

The surveyor may find a plan of the drainage on the premises. He may accept this as information, but should satisfy himself as to its accuracy. He often finds a gardener or caretaker who is most anxious to give him information on such matters as the courses of the drains, but again such evidence should be verified. If in inspecting, say, the water supply he finds a casing over some of the pipes, such casing should be removed and the pipes traced from end to end.

The following is an outline of the procedure of making the inspection, booking the notes, and writing the report on such information as is obtained.

Testing the drains. One of the most important things incidental to the survey is the testing of the drainage system. There are four principal methods of doing this.

1 By olfactory or odour test.
2 By smoke test.
3 By water or hydraulic test.
4 By air or pneumatic test.

The odour test. The odour test is not a very satisfactory test, but occasionally circumstances are such that other tests cannot be applied. The test, which is only suitable for soil and waste pipes and the joints around fittings, can be applied in either of two ways. One way is to use a chemical drain tester. There are many varieties of these, consisting of packages of phosphorus compounds or other evil-smelling substances. They are put up in many forms, and consist of receptacles from which pungent vapours are ejected after they have been passed through the trap. They are furnished with fairly long lengths of string, usually coiled round them, by means of which the receptacle can be withdrawn after use. An example of this kind of appliance is shown in Fig. 93—that known as a Kemp tester, one of many similar products.

The other method of applying the odour test is to place oil of peppermint in a bucketful of boiling water, about one and a half ounces of the oil to a quart of water, and pour this into the system. Mixing and handling should be done by an assistant, the surveyor himself keeping away during the process. The smell produced is very pungent and readily clings to one's clothes. A room to room search for traces of the smell, which come from leaky joints in the pipes or fittings or from an insufficiently sealed or unsealed trap, is then made.

The smoke test. The smoke test can be used for pipes below as well as those above ground, but it is not generally a satisfactory test for underground drains. In the case of defects above ground the smoke is readily visible, apart from its smell, and in the case of a defective drain having only a shallow covering of porous soil the smoke will readily issue at ground level. With a considerable depth of earth over the pipes, or earth of a dense, damp nature, such as clay, however, smoke will not find its way to the surface. To help it to do so, a probing iron is sometimes used. This consists of a pointed iron rod a few feet long, with a handle, used by walking over the course of the drain and forcing the rod down into the soil at frequent intervals to leave holes through which the smoke may rise. (The probing iron is also used for the purpose of probing the ground to locate the course of drains whose position is unknown or uncertain.)

The smoke is produced in two ways: by smoke rocket or smoke case; by a smoke machine. Figure 93 illustrates and describes a typical example but a basic disadvantage of smoke rockets is that smoke cannot be produced under pressure. To overcome this difficulty many forms of smoke machines have been introduced. These differ in detail but the broad principle underlying them all is the same, the forcing of smoke produced by burning oily cotton waste, thick brown paper steeped in creosote oil, and other substances, into the drain. Figure 93 shows, diagrammatically, the essential parts of a smoke machine.

DRAIN PLUGS. When testing a soil or waste pipe with a smoke machine

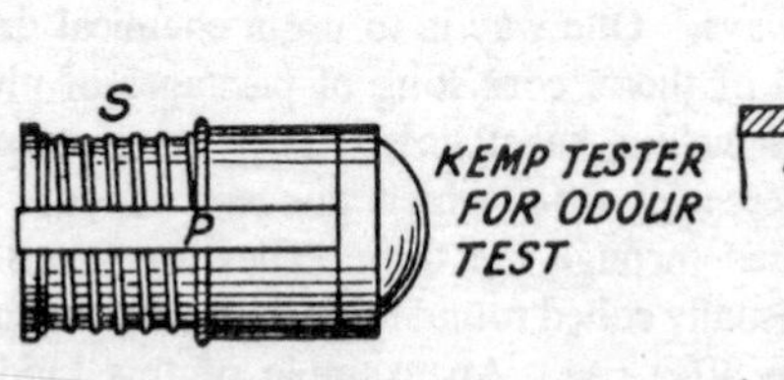

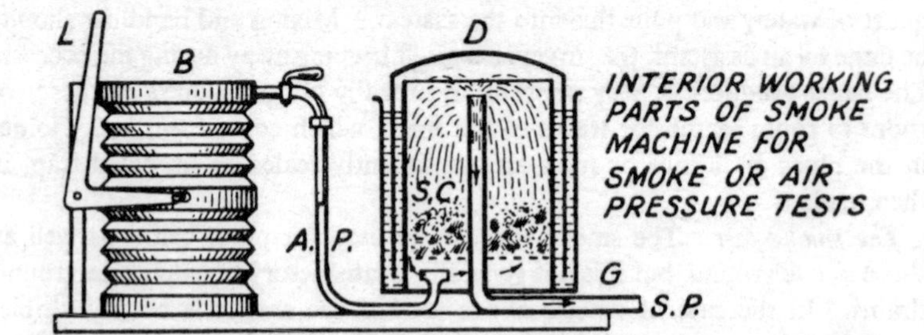

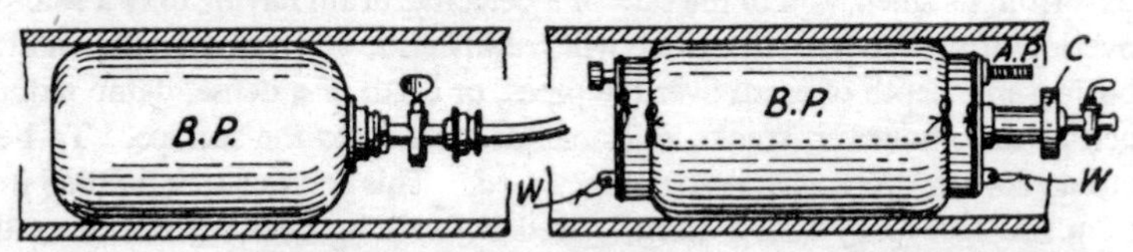

TWO FORMS OF BAG PLUG FOR WATER, AIR OR SMOKE TESTS

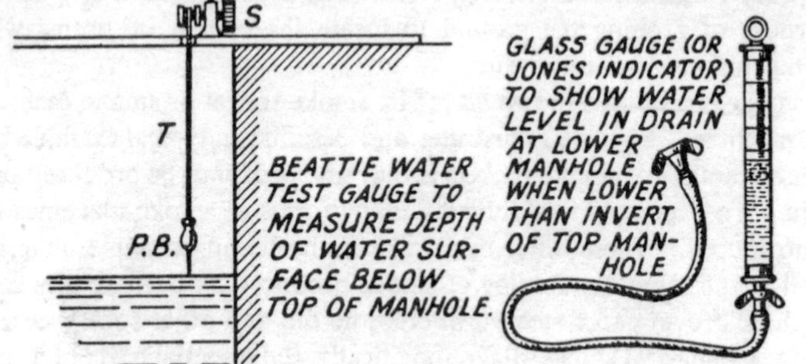

93

93 *Testing the drains*

(*Top, left*) THE KEMP TESTER FOR DRAINS. This consists of a thin glass tube containing a chemical compound. The substance is kept in the tube by a cap and rubber washer, a spiral spring, S, around the tube tending to force the cap off. This is prevented, before use, by a strip of paper, P, which passes over the cap and down the two sides, to which it is fastened. The whole appliance is only about 2 in. long. In use it is flushed through the trap by a bucketful of water, hot if available. The wetting rapidly softens the paper strip and releases the contents.

(*Below*) A TYPICAL SMOKE ROCKET. This consists of a cardboard tube about 8 in. long and 1½ to 2 in. in diameter, the end being closed with paper. It has two wooden strips or fillets, S.S., fixed to it by nails through their centres, These are turned so that they are at right angles to the case, in order to keep the rocket off the invert of the drain, and clear of sewage. On lighting the paper fuse at the end, a dense volume of smoke issues. (The case should be removed from the drain after use.)

(*Centre, above*) A SMOKE MACHINE operation is as follows: S.C. is the smoke chamber which has a water jacket round it, a dome, D, fitting well down into this to provide a seal against the escape of smoke. Near the bottom of the chamber is a grating on which the smoke-producing substance is placed. The pipe for the conveyance of the smoke to the drain (S.P.) passes down the centre of the chamber, the inlet being near the top as shown. Alongside the smoke chamber is a double bellows, B, actuated by a lever, L, by means of which air is pumped through the air pipe, A.P., to the under side of the grating. (The lever must not be worked too rapidly or it may cause the material to blaze instead of smoulder, with a consequently diminished amount of smoke.) A pressure gauge is sometimes added at G in order to register the pressure applied.

(*Top, right*) A RING OR DISC PLUG. This comprises a rubber ring set between two circular discs of iron which can be forced together by means of a wing nut, W.N., thus causing expansion of the ring, R.R. A screw cap, C, is provided at the outer end, which can be readily removed by means of the projecting lugs shown, either for the purpose of attaching a smoke pipe or for releasing water when the ring is used for the water test.

(*Centre, below*) TWO FORMS OF BAG PLUG. A simple plug, left, and a better form, right, which has two brass ends, with means of attaching a string or wire, W, to enable it to be pulled either up or down the drain, before it is inflated. A brass tube passes right through the bag, with a connection at C which can be used for attaching either the nozzle of the smoke machine, or a small tap to let the water out after a water test. The bag is inflated through a small pipe, A.P., and is closed after inflation by leaving on the tap of the pump.

(*Bottom, left*) The BEATTIE GAUGE for measuring water level in drains. This consists of a horizontal bar carrying a support for a small horizontal spindle, S, on which are mounted a milled turning wheel and a small drum on which is wound a tape measure. At the end of the tape, T, is a plumb bob, P.B., with a long point. This is allowed to fall slowly until the point touches the water surface. The spindle is then clamped by a small set-screw, S.S. The apparatus can be lifted up from the side of the manhole and put in its case, no one but the observer knowing the water level. (*contd. overleaf*)

the drain should be plugged at the nearest manhole. This sometimes may be roughly done by means of wet cloths placed around the flexible pipe which is attached to the outlet of the machine, but it is far better to use a proper drain plug. There are two principal types of plug, those which consist of a rubber ring capable of being expanded, and those which consist of a rubber bladder encased in coarse canvas, to strengthen it and give it gripping power, which can be inflated by means of a small hand pump.

There are many varieties of each type. The earlier forms of rubber ring were of circular section, but this did not give a good grip to the pipe, and later developments of this type have all tended towards giving greater gripping surface, Fig. 93. The best ring plugs, however, do not give such an effective closure to the drain as a good type of bag plug.

The earlier forms of bag plug were of spherical shape, but these are not now so extensively used as those of cylindrical shape. Figure 93 shows a simple form of bag plug in position. It is inflated by means of a hand pump similar to a bicycle pump, and after inflation the small tap shown can be turned off. It will be obvious that such a plug will not only accommodate itself to any irregularities in the pipe better than a rubber ring, but will also give a much larger gripping surface and therefore a firmer hold. Figure 93 also illustrates a more elaborate plug and describes its use.

APPLYING THE SMOKE TEST. In applying the smoke test the drain is plugged at either end so as to form a closed chamber into which the smoke may be pumped. In the case of a soil, ventilating, or waste pipe it is a good plan to test first with the top of the pipe open, and then, if possible, with it closed by means of wet cloths. The first test makes it possible to see if there is any blockage in the pipe, and the second puts a certain amount of pressure on the joints. The smoke test may be regarded as satisfactory for an uncovered drain, but it is not sufficiently severe for a covered one, whether new or old.

Care is necessary in the use of smoke rockets, as fumes of a suffocating nature are liable to accumulate at the bottom of manholes.

The water test. It has often been argued that the water or hydraulic test is an unfair one, in that it puts a greater strain on the lower end of the drain than it does on the upper end. This argument has some justification, but any

---

(*contd. from previous page*).

(*Bottom, right*) The JONES INDICATOR for measuring water level in drains. This consists of a glass graduated tube, marked in inches and decimals which can, by means of a flexible tube, be connected to the drain plug at the lower end of a drain. Once the water is at rest in the drain, its level can be recorded and noted, a lower reading later betraying any leakage.

drain may become blocked and is most likely to do so at the intercepting trap, in which case the water test will be at once applied naturally, the only difference being that the water in this case will be foul, with consequent danger in case of leakage.

It is also argued that the water test is not a fair one for other than new drains. The bylaws of local authorities, however, all require new drains to be watertight, the inference being that unless they are so there is risk of danger to health. If it is necessary for a new drain to be watertight in the interests of health, it is equally so for a drain which is no longer new. The argument that the water test is not a fair one for old drains raises the proposition that while it is necessary for a drain, when new, to be watertight, there comes a time in the life of the drain when this is no longer necessary. Exactly how long after construction that time occurs no one has yet had the courage to state.

It is unavoidable that drains will deteriorate. There are many reasons why this is so. Some are subjected to traffic vibration, others to settlement or other disturbance. However true this may be a surveyor who allows a client, on the strength of his report, to enter into occupation of a house, the drains of which are not watertight, incurs a grave responsibility.

APPLYING THE TEST. Broadly speaking, the water test is applied by plugging the lowest point of the drainage system and filling the drains with water until it stands at a depth of, say, not less than 2 ft in the upper manhole, a subsidence of the water indicating a leakage. The "head" of 2 ft mentioned should be looked upon as a minimum, local bylaws may require a greater head and the B.S. Code of Practice on Building Drainage (which is advisory only) advises a head of 5 ft at the upper end of the glazed ware drain under test, maintained for at least 10 minutes.[1]

If there is considerable fall on the drainage system it is wise to test it in sections, i.e. wherever the system has several manholes it is advisable to test the length from one manhole to another, working downwards from the upper end. (This enables the water from the upper lengths to be used for testing the lower.) In any case in which there are gulleys at a lower level than the

[1] Confusion may arise from the use of the terms "Head of Water" and "Water Pressure".

"Head of pressure" is simply the height of a column of water, in lineal feet, above the point at which the internal strain or pressure is to be recorded. Thus, provided the water is not flowing, the pressure in the supply pipe, at the point just behind the bathroom tap, is dependent on the number of feet, measured vertically, from the tap to the water surface in the service tank in the cistern room or loft. If this height is 10 ft, then the pressure at the tap, when shut, may be said to be 10 ft head. This may be translated to pressure per square inch by multiplying the "head" by 0·434, so "10 ft head" may be described as 4·34 lb/sq. in., and owing to the laws of hydraulics, this pressure operates in every direction. The 5 ft head mentioned above thus indicates a pressure of 2·17 lb/sq. in.

water in the manhole, they must be plugged in order to prevent the water issuing from them.

MEASURING SUBSIDENCE. Great care is necessary in observing the water level and noting whether it subsides. If the sides of the manhole are of absorbent material, there is bound to be a drop in the water level owing to the absorption. In such a case the production of exact results is a matter of difficulty, considerable experience being needed in reference to the allowance for absorption. If the manhole sides are of non-absorbent material, the depth of the water surface below the top of the manhole can be accurately measured and noted. A chalk mark, or piece of stamp paper, as an indication of the original level of the water are often made use of but either can be easily tampered with. The depth is best accurately measured down from the top and the figure booked. A neat contrivance for this purpose is that known as the Beattie water test gauge—shown in Fig. 93.

Another way of safeguarding records of water level is to use a "Jones Indicator" (or glass gauge), also shown in Fig. 93. This appliance is also useful for determining the fall of drains. If a drain is filled so that the water is just half-way up in the mouth of the pipe in the upper manhole, the total fall on that length of drain will be the depth from the water level in the gauge to the centre of the drain plug below it. Yet another use for the glass gauge is in determining the approximate position of a leakage. When there is no longer any lowering of water in the gauge, the height of water level above invert of manhole is read (say 15 in.) and the horizontal distance back to the leakage can be calculated by proportion, if the gradient of drain is known. For a drain laid at 1 in 40 with the gauge reading as above of 1·25 ft the

$$\frac{\text{distance}}{1{\cdot}25} = \frac{40}{1}$$

$$\text{From which distance} = 40 \times 1{\cdot}25$$

$$= \underline{\underline{50 \text{ ft.}}}$$

A variant of the glass gauge is the "bucket gauge" in which a metal canister or "bucket" holding about a quart of water replaces the glass tube.

This can be used for completing the "filling" of an unfinished length of drain at its upper end, while the glass gauge indicates water level and leakage at the lower end.

Another method of applying the water test is to attach a short length of 1½-in. pipe to the plug by means of an elbow or bend, having inside it a small bore pipe to permit the escape of air as the water enters the drain. The water can be allowed to rise in the pipe nearly to the top, and the depth of the surface below the top can be measured and noted.

If there are no manholes, the ground must be opened up at both ends, for the purpose of inserting a plug at the lower end, and of connecting a vertical bend at the upper, in which the water level can be noted. During testing, plugs should be examined from time to time to see they are watertight.

DRAIN BEYOND THE INTERCEPTOR. It is by no means a common practice to test the length of drain from the interceptor to the sewer, but this can be readily done by floating a bag plug through the interceptor, attached to a wire or cord, and then inflating it. This length of drain should be as watertight as the remainder of the system.

The procedure of floating the bag plug along the drain and then inflating it can prove of very great value. By its use one is able to localise a leak in the system. Knowing that a length is leaking, float the plug down for a length of, say, 10 ft and then test that short length. If the result is satisfactory, deflate the plug and float it on for, say, another 10 ft, and again test.

PIPES ABOVE GROUND. It is a common practice to test soil and vent pipes by means of the water test, though it is considered too severe a test by many sanitary engineers. In passing new work it should certainly be done, but a smoke test under pressure is regarded by some authorities as sufficient for pipes which have been standing some years. The arguments in reference to the fairness of the water test for old drains also apply to testing of above-ground pipework. N.B.—The application of the water test is essentially a matter for a fine day, as in wet weather there is a danger of rainwater finding its way into the drain. During the testing of any drain care should be taken that the sanitary fittings are not used, for the same reason.

The air test. The air or pneumatic test is one of which the merits have been much urged in recent years, by the oppponents of the water test, on the grounds that it applies a uniform pressure to all parts of the drainage system. (As already pointed out this does not indicate what happens if a drain becomes blocked at its lowest point, when the pressure to which the drain is subjected increases progressively as the drain fills.) Another argument in favour of air testing is that it exposes leaks not detected by water testing.[1]

The test is applied by closing all openings on the system and pumping in air by means of a small pump to which a pressure gauge is attached. If the traps on the system are not also plugged, no appreciable pressure can be applied, since a pressure of about 0·036 lb/sq. in. or 1 in. head of water will be liable to upset the equilibrium of the water seal. If the traps are plugged, any desired pressure can be applied.

[1] An air test is more searching for above ground pipes, but below ground the low pressure may be held by a waterlogged clayey soil surrounding the pipe.

PRESSURE FOR TESTING. It is generally accepted that stoneware drains should safely stand a pressure of 3 lb/sq. in. (about 7 ft head of water), while properly constructed iron drains should safely stand 10 lb/sq. in. (about 23 ft head). The air having been pumped in to a pressure of, say, 3 lb per sq. in. as indicated on the pressure gauge, the tap of the pump is closed. Any decrease in pressure recorded by the gauge will indicate leakage. It will be seen that the method does not lend itself to the localisation of leaks.

Drain mirrors. Other appliances used in the testing of drains are drain mirrors and electric lanterns. In inspecting a straight length of drain between two manholes, a mirror may be placed in one of the manholes, and a small electric lantern in the other. The mirror is mounted on a stand like an easel, and, if set up at a convenient angle, the observer can, by the aid of the light, note the internal condition of the drain by looking into the mirror. The effect should be like looking through a tube. If the lantern is a powerful one, its light will be strong enough to illuminate the drain round a slight bend, in which case, although the reflection of the globe containing the light cannot be seen, there is sufficient illumination of the interior of the drain for its interior condition to be observed for an appreciable distance from either end.

Need for testing. A drainage system requires maintenance in just the same way as other parts of buildings, although this is a fact which is often overlooked. Any system of drainage should be inspected and tested, at regular intervals—ideally every 2 years.

Need for system in sanitary surveys. Whenever a full-scale sanitary survey is undertaken arrangements should be made for the surveyor to be met on the site by a plumber, or preferably a plumber and a labourer, to act as assistants. (In London some of the large firms of sanitary engineers keep men who are experienced in this particular work, and send them out with all the necessary apparatus to assist surveyors. The expense is inconsiderable, and the value of an assistant accustomed to the work is great.) On arrival at the site, the surveyor should first make a preliminary examination of the exterior of the house, and its surroundings. Having done so, he is in the position to instruct his assistant as to the removal of manhole covers, opening up the ground where necessary, plugging the drains, applying the tests, and so on. While this is being done, he is free to turn his attention to the inside of the house until called out by his assistant in reference to points incidental to the tests.

Nothing is more important than that he should be systematic in his inspection.

The survey notebook. Let us assume that the inspection to be made is that of a fairly large house with a basement, and that the surveyor intends starting at the lowest floor and working upwards. His notes should be made in a systematic way in notebooks kept for this particular purpose. (Special books are obtainable, with the various headings printed in, and with sheets of squared paper at intervals for the purpose of making sketch plans. Plain notebooks are usually preferred as no printed notebook can give all the headings likely to be required for every possible case.)

Having entered the descriptions of the property and the date, the surveyor proceeds to the basement and takes notes of all matters coming under the heading of sanitation at this level before proceeding upwards. As to items which are satisfactory his notes need only be the briefest description, but unsatisfactory items should be noted in detail. In dealing with each room he should have regard to its lighting, ventilation and signs of dampness, if any, and locate the cause. He should look for gulleys in the floor, making a careful search, and having any lumber removed in order that he may do so.

Water closets. If a room contains sanitary fittings they should be thoroughly inspected; if quite satisfactory the only note necessary is, say, "W.C. quite satisfactory", but before making such a note regard should be had to the following points: floor and wall surfaces, type of apparatus, its condition and cleansing properties, trap, its form and condition, means of flushing, capacity of cistern, condition, ball-valve, overflow, flushing pipe, and all the joints around the apparatus and cistern.

Sinks. In the case of a sink, the surveyor should have regard to its material, condition, trap, waste pipe, point of discharge, its situation as regards light, and the nature and condition of the water fittings supplying it.

Having gone through the basement in this way, he should then go to the ground floor and follow a similar procedure; then on to the upper floors, each floor being completed before another is commenced.

At the top of the building cisterns will usually be found and the surveyor should have regard to their situation, accessibility, lighting, ventilation, material, capacity, condition, connections, overflows and all other details.

Hot-water service. The hot-water service should not be overlooked and, unless satisfied that the service is efficient and sufficient, the matter should be settled by lighting the fire and noting the time taken to get hot water and the approximate temperature obtained.

Cold-water supply. Enough has been said above to indicate the general manner of proceeding, but special features will frequently occur. If, for example, there is any reason to doubt the quality of the water, samples should be taken for tasting. If filters are found, they should comply with the requirements for a satisfactory filter discussed in Chapter 5.

Testing the gas supply. If gas is used in the building examined, some sanitary surveyors make a practice of testing the soundness of the gas piping. This is done by means of a small machine consisting of a pump, pressure-gauge and safety-valve. Gas pipes should withstand a pressure of about 2 lb per sq. in., the method of applying this being as follows.

Shut off the gas at the meter, and connect the pump to a gas bracket by means of a flexible tube attached to the machine. Pump until the gauge registers the desired pressure. The finger of the gauge should then remain stationary. Should it not do so, the leakage can be traced by putting a small quantity of liquid ammonia in the machine and proceeding in the following way.

Open the tap of a gas-fitting, preferably the farthest from the meter, to allow the air to escape, and then pump the fumes of the ammonia into the pipes. If a chemically prepared paper is then passed over the surface of the pipes, the ammonia fumes which are escaping at any leak will change its colour.

Exterior of house. On completing the inspection of the interior of the house, attention is given to the exterior. Should there be an open area, the condition of its paving and the facilities for draining it are noted. If there are timber floors to the rooms inside, provision of air bricks for the ventilation of the space below it are noted. In the case of non-basement houses one often finds air bricks blocked up by the banking up of flower beds, or formation of rockeries. The condition of the walls and evidence of dampness; of the roof and cracked or broken slates or tiles, defective or blocked gutters or defective flashings, should all be examined and recorded.

Waste and soil pipes. Waste pipes on the faces of the walls are examined to determine the following points: size, material, jointing, fixing, and treatment of their upper and lower ends, particularly as regards disconnection in cases in which it is desirable. Whether the open ends of soil and vent pipes are in too close proximity to windows or skylights is of particular importance.

Gulleys, grease traps, manholes, etc. Gulleys, grease traps, etc., are examined to see whether they are of satisfactory type, properly set, in clean condition, with sound covers and so on. This being done, the manholes, their construction, arrangement, condition and covers are examined. (Incidental to this item will be the sufficiency or otherwise of the diameters of the drains discharging into them.)

The disconnecting trap. The surveyor will have acquainted himself with the requirement of the local bylaws, and whether a disconnecting tap is required by them. Bylaws are not retrospective, so the date of erection of the building may have some relevance. Although most bylaws are fairly strict these days, it should be remembered that building bylaws set out to give the *minimum* that will satisfy the local authority concerned, and mere compliance does not of necessity connote a healthy dwelling.

However that may be, the surveyor should investigate the existence or otherwise of an intercepting trap between drain and public sewer, cesspool or private disposal plant and, if it exists, whether the interceptor is in a satisfactory state, of a good type, and whether the stopper of its cleaning arm is secure.

Drain ventilation. The method of ventilating the drains must be investigated, though the actual test of efficiency will be carried out in conjunction with the drain tests.

Inspection of water levels. While the surveyor is giving the bulk of his time to the foregoing items, he will be from time to time interrupted by the necessity of measuring the water levels in manholes, inspecting plugs and booking results of tests, but there is, of course, no need for him to stand alongside a manhole while the test is in operation. If a leak is found in the drains, its position should be located by floating the bag plug through and inflating it at various points or by use of the glass gauge as described earlier. In the case of pipes above ground, a defective joint or pipe can be readily seen and its exact position booked.

Plan of drains and building. A rough sketch plan of the outline of the building and the courses of the drains should be made, if none is available, to enable any proposed alterations to be shown on a plan attached to the report. If any alterations are to be suggested, the approximate dimensions should be figured on this plan.

In many cases the courses of the various drains will be fairly obvious from the inspection of the manholes and a comparison with the positions of the gulleys and other features, but in any case of doubt the course of the drain should be traced by pouring coloured liquid through the gulley or fitting. The water may be coloured by adding whiting, or cork dust of various colours is obtainable for the purpose.

The length of drain from the interceptor to the sewer should be tested, or, if there is no sewer, the cesspool should be carefully examined and notes made of any defects or objectionable features.

Example sanitary survey. The following is an example of notes which might be taken when making a sanitary survey of a good-sized house sixty or seventy years old and assuming, for convenience, that plans of the building and its drainage are available. (The plan of the basement and its drainage is shown in Fig. 94.)

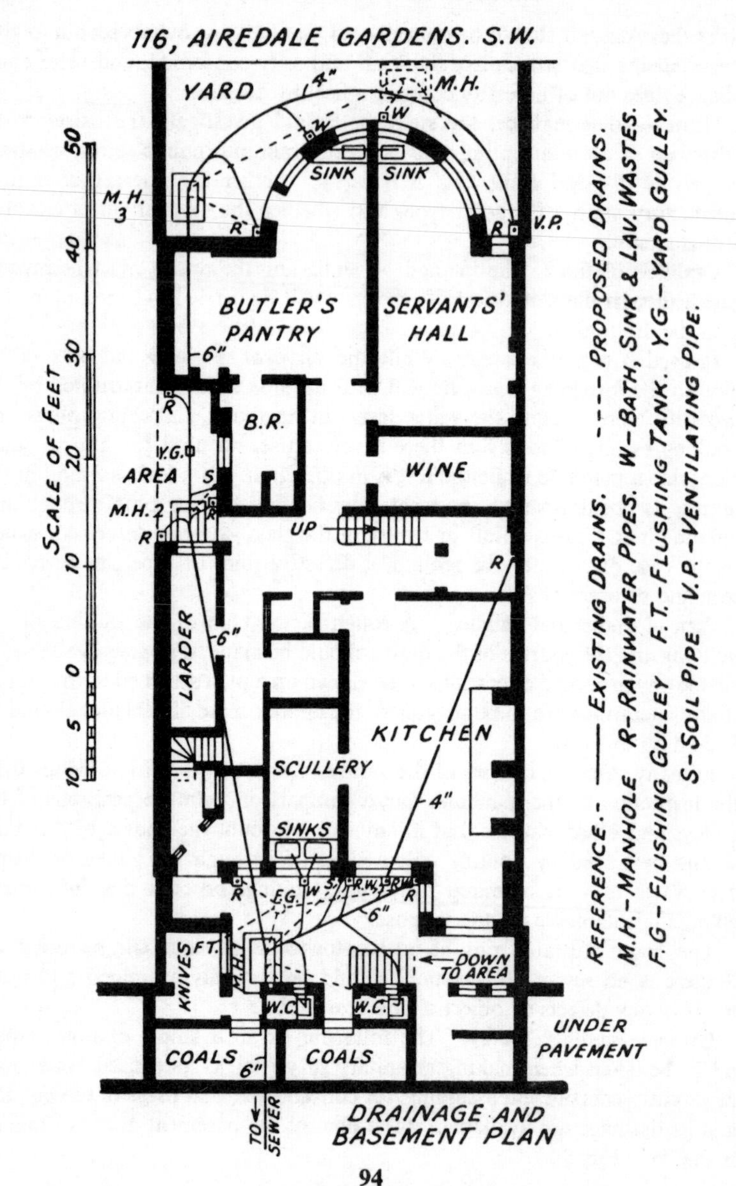
116, AIREDALE GARDENS. S.W.
YARD
4"
M.H.
W
SINK
SINK
M.H.
3
R
R
V.P.
BUTLER'S
PANTRY
SERVANTS'
HALL
6"
R
B.R.
Y.G.
AREA
S
WINE
M.H.2
R
R
UP
R
LARDER
6"
KITCHEN
SCULLERY
4"
SINKS
R
F.G.
W
S
R.W.
R.W.
R
6"
KNIVES
F.T.
M.H.1
DOWN
TO AREA
W.C.
W.C.
UNDER
PAVEMENT
COALS
COALS
6"
TO
SEWER
DRAINAGE AND
BASEMENT PLAN
SCALE OF FEET
50
40
30
20
10
0
5
10
REFERENCE.- —— EXISTING DRAINS. ---- PROPOSED DRAINS.
M.H.-MANHOLE R-RAINWATER PIPES. W-BATH, SINK & LAV. WASTES.
F.G.-FLUSHING GULLEY F.T.-FLUSHING TANK. Y.G.-YARD GULLEY.
S-SOIL PIPE V.P.-VENTILATING PIPE.

94

SANITARY SURVEY OF 116 AIREDALE GARDENS, S.W., FOR C. JONES, ESQ. 12TH SEPTEMBER, 1961

INTERNALLY. *Basement.* Well lighted and ventilated. No internal gulleys. Internal r.w. pipe at back of central staircase. Iron shoe at foot with screw-down cover in good order.

Servants' Hall. White-glazed sink, cracked; grating outlet. One and a quarter inch lead waste discharging into trap of butler's pantry sink near by. Waste blocked. H. and C. supply. C.W. tap wants new washer.

Butler's Pantry. White-glazed sink, sound; plug outlet and overflow. Lead-covered draining board. One and a half inch lead trap and waste through wall and over gulley. H. and C. supply. Taps in good order.

Scullery. Two white-glazed sinks side by side, badly chipped and worn. One with plug outlet and overflow, other with grating. One and a half inch lead wastes, one discharging into trap of other. Waste through wall and over gulley. H.W. taps want new washers.

Knife House. Draw-off tap in good order, no drip sink but cement floor with good fall to doorway.

Servants' W.C.s. W.C. adjoining area steps. Hopper pan and trap, trap broken. Seat badly broken. Two gal W.W.P. in good order but handle missing. Other W.C., pedestal washdown, broken. Seat has balance weights, which have been cause of breaking pan. Two gal. W.W.P. in good order but handle missing.

Cement floors to both W.C.s, good windows, and ventilated by space below door also.

GROUND FLOOR. *Cloakroom.* White glazed tip-up lav. basin. One and a quarter inch lead trap and waste through wall and over gulley. H. and C. supply. Taps in good order.

W.C. adjoining. Wash-out apparatus, dirty condition. Dished marble safe, no waste pipe. Two gal. W.W.P. in good order. Well lighted and ventilated.

FIRST FLOOR. *W.C.* Exactly as last, otherwise in good order.

Bathroom. White porcelain enamelled bath. Fixed enclosure, pol. mahog. top. Lead safe under with waste through wall. Two-inch lead trap and waste through wall and over hopper head. H. and C. supply—taps in good order.

---

94 *House plan*

The house plan used as a basis for the example notes and reports described in this chapter.

Draw-off tap beside bath, with lead-lined drip sink under waste through wall, all in good order.

White glazed lav. basin, weir overflow. One and a quarter inch lead trap and waste through wall and over hopper head. H. and C. supply—taps in good order.

SECOND FLOOR. *W.C.* Exactly as for first floor and ground floor.

Bathroom. Exactly as first floor, but no lav. basin.

THIRD FLOOR. *Slop Sink.* Brown's patent, properly trapped and discharging into soil-pipe. Two gal. W.W.P. over, also H. and C. supply. All in good order. Well lighted and ventilated.

Cistern. Large G.S. cistern, with overflow through wall. Ball-valve in good order. Supplies all taps except the one in Knife House, which is off main.

HOT-WATER SERVICE. Large G.S. cylinder beside range in kitchen. Service very efficient, but no safety-valve to boiler.

EXTERNALLY. *Area Pavings.* Cement, with good falls to gulleys.

Dampness. Slight dampness on wall adjoining M.H. No. 2 in central area, due to split length of R.W. pipe.

Roof. Slate, about half-dozen cracked. Lead flashings sound. Parapet gutters require cleaning out.

Waste Pipes. R.W. pipes all in good order except one just referred to.

Hopper heads taking wastes from baths and lavs. rather fouled.

Soil-pipes. Centre area, near M.H. No. 2, 4-in. light lead with wiped joints. Badly bent and bruised. Takes W.C.s on first and second floors. No anti-siphonage pipes. Carried well above roof. Grating perished. Joint at foot sound.

Front area, facing street, lower portion 4-in. light lead, square section, somewhat dented. From about 12 ft above paving to near eaves in 4-in. iron, circular, and then 4-in. light lead, circular, to well above ridge.

Gulleys. All ordinary stoneware yard gulleys in fair condition. One grating broken in yard at back and one in front area.

Manholes. Three in all. No. 1 (front area) brown glazed stoneware channels. Bottom not benched and very defective. Walls cement rendered and in good order. Hinged iron cover, broken. Intercepting trap, stopper to arm missing.

No. 2 (central area) similar construction and benching defective as before. Cover badly rusted. No. 3 (at back) ditto, and cover broken.

Diameters of Drains. Main from M.H. 3 to M.H. 1 of 6-in. pipes also 6-in. from angle of kitchen to M.H. 1. All others 4-in. All under floors and pavings, ground not opened up, but appear to be stoneware socketed pipes and cement joints throughout, judging from manhole connections.

Ventilation of Drains. Outlet ventilation provided by S.P. in front and centre areas only. No V.P. at back. F.A.I. to M.H. 1 in chase in wall of W.C. Mica flap valve, grating broken, flap missing.

RESULTS OF TESTS. *Smoke Test on Soil-pipes.* One in centre area quite sound. Other, front area, weak at joint near eaves, between lead and iron.

Water Test on Drains. R.W. drain under kitchen discharging into back of gulley, quite sound. Drains under yard slightly leaky. All other drains very leaky, particularly that from M.H. 2 to M.H. 1.

Recommendations to be considered on site. The surveyor should not leave the site until he has considered the recommendations he intends making. It is most important to check on the feasibility of suggestions he intends to make. There are often obstacles which are not obvious from a sketch plan, and it would not be to his credit to suggest amendments which cannot be carried out.

The report. Having made the survey, the next step is the writing of the report. This is a matter calling for the exercise of considerable care and judgment. When making recommendations, all the circumstances of the case must be taken into consideration. It is, perhaps, easy to say, if the system of drainage is generally unsatisfactory, "remove the whole system and begin again", but if the client is a lessee with a fairly short unexpired term, this would probably lead to nothing being done at all, whereas moderate recommendations would probably be carried out. Counsels of perfection, if injudiciously given, tend to set back the clock of sanitary progress. The surveyor should take his client entirely into his confidence, and tell him frankly, if such is the case, that while a suggested alteration would be a great improvement, there would be no danger to health, under ordinary circumstances, in leaving that particular item as it is.

Avoid technical terms. When reporting to a lay client, care should be taken to keep the report as free as possible from technical expressions which a layman would not be likely to understand. A report written in plain language gains in intelligibility, and certainly loses none of its professional value if properly done.

Forms of report. There are many ways of writing a report, and individuals choose the form they prefer. The following are typical alternative methods:

1 A formal report, headed as such, and free from any personal comment, the various items being dealt with under subheadings. The report on each item can be immediately followed by any recommendations which

it is desired to make, or all the recommendations can be left until the end of the report. The former is usually the more convenient way, and the recommendations can then be briefly summarised at the end.

2 An informal report, written in a personal manner, in the form of a long letter. Marginal subheadings should be used in this case also, to help the client to find any particular item. The recommendations can be dealt with in the same way as above. Reports should of course be dated, and headed with the name of the property, after the opening words "Dear Sir".

3 A formal report, headed as such, arranged in, say, three columns, the first being headed Item, the second Report, and the third Recommendations, the report being signed and dated as before.

Example report (formal type). Assuming that a surveyor prefers the type of report described at (1) above his report, based on the notes already given, might read as follows:

REPORT ON THE SANITARY CONDITION OF 116 AIREDALE GARDENS, LONDON, S.W., FOR C. JONES, ESQ. 15TH SEPTEMBER, 1961.

GENERAL NOTE. The sanitation of this house is not of recent date and is, generally speaking, in an unsound condition. Considerable remodelling and overhauling are necessary.

THE WATER SUPPLY

The water supply is derived from the mains of the Metropolitan Water Board, but there are no taps off the main except one in the Knife House. All the sanitary fittings are supplied from a large galvanised steel cistern on the third floor. This cistern is in good order, and has an overflow pipe carried through the external wall.

It is very desirable that the taps over all sinks where water will be drawn for drinking or cooking purposes should be supplied direct from the main.

The hot-water service is in an efficient state. There is a large storage cylinder in the kitchen, near the range, but there is no safety-valve on the boiler. It would be well to provide one and to overhaul and clean out the boiler and cylinder.

Hot- and cold-water supplies are laid on to all the baths, lavatories and sinks. The water fittings are of good quality, but several taps require new washers.

THE SANITARY FITTINGS

Water-closets. There are internal closets on the ground, first and second floors. They are well lighted and ventilated, but each is equipped with a pedestal wash-out apparatus. This is a bad form of apparatus, the force of the flush from the cistern being expended in clearing out the basin, leaving no scouring effect for the trap. They should be replaced by a good type of wash-down apparatus.

Each closet is flushed by two-gallon water-waste preventing cistern and these are in good order. Each of the pans stands on a dished marble slab, intended to act as a safe, but to do so these slabs should be provided with waste pipes passing through the external wall.

There are two servants' closets under the pavement, the apparatus in both being in a very insanitary state. In both, either the pan or the trap is broken, and in one the seat is badly broken. The flushing cisterns are quite efficient except that the handle of each is missing. Both these closets should be overhauled, and a good type of pedestal wash-down apparatus installed.

The paving, lighting and ventilation of these W.C.s are satisfactory.

Sinks. There are five sinks. That in the *Servants' Hall* is white glazed, with a grating outlet, the waste pipe discharging into the trap of the *Butler's Pantry* sink nearby. This sink is cracked and should be renewed. At the same time a trap should be provided and a new waste pipe taken direct through the wall to discharge over a gulley.

The present method of dealing with the waste is unsatisfactory and the waste pipe is now blocked.

The *Butler's Pantry* sink is white glazed, but with plug outlet and overflow. It is in good order and is fitted with a lead-covered draining board. The sink is trapped and the waste pipe discharges through the wall over a gulley.

The *Scullery* has two sinks, side by side, both white glazed, one with grating outlet and the other with plug and overflow. Both are badly chipped and worn and should be replaced. The waste pipe from one passes into the trap of the other. When replacing the sinks this should be altered, and each sink separately trapped and provided with its own waste pipe, passing through the wall and discharging over a gulley.

A *Slop Sink* is provided on the third floor, properly trapped and discharging into a soil-pipe. This fitting is of good quality and in sound order. The small apartment in which it is placed is well lighted and ventilated.

The tap in the *Knife House* has no drip sink under it, but the floor is of cement and has a good fall towards the doorway. There is, therefore, no harm in not providing one.

Baths. There are two baths, on the first and second floors respectively. Both are white porcelain enamelled in good condition but have fixed enclosures and polished mahogany tops. Fixed enclosures are not desirable, but otherwise the baths are all in good order. Each has a lead safe under, with proper waste pipes. The baths are trapped and provided with good-sized waste pipes discharging through the walls, over hopper heads.

In each bathroom there is a draw-off tap beside the bath, with a lead-lined drip sink and proper waste pipe from it.

Lavatory Basins. There are two of these. That in the cloakroom, on ground floor, is an old-fashioned tip-up basin of white glazed ware, with properly trapped waste pipe carried through the wall and discharging over a gulley. This fitting is not very sanitary, and should be replaced by a good modern type of basin, such as is provided in the first-floor bathroom.

The lavatory there is in excellent order. Its waste pipe is trapped and discharges over a hopper head.

THE DRAINS

The courses of the existing drains are shown on the accompanying plan by firm lines, their diameters being figured. They were not uncovered during the inspection, being all under floors and pavings, but from the connections with the manholes they appear to be of ordinary stoneware socketed pipes, jointed in cement. The water test was applied to the whole of the drains. The rainwater drain under the kitchen is quite sound, but all the other drains are defective. The length under the yard at the back is slightly leaking and is very badly planned. The other drains all leaked badly, but particularly the length between manholes Nos. 1 and 2.

It is strongly urged that the whole of the drains, except the length under the kitchen, be taken up, the trenches properly disinfected, and the drains relaid using heavy cast-iron pipes, protected against corrosion by the Angus Smith process, and with caulked lead joints, the pipes being laid on concrete. The plan shows the suggested modifications by means of dotted lines. These modifications occur under the yard at the back, and under the front area, the courses of the remaining drains being kept as at present. The complicated junctions under the front area should be done away with, the two W.C.s and the soil taken separately into the manhole, and the various other wastes collected into a large gulley between the scullery window and manhole No. 1. The provision of a 30-gallon automatic flushing tank, fixed in the Knife House, and discharging at least once a day, would be an advantage.

Manholes. There are three manholes for inspection. They are all of defective construction at the bottom, which is formed of glazed stoneware channels set in concrete, the remainder of the floor being practically flat and badly broken up, instead of being well benched up in cement. These should be remodelled on up-to-date lines, preferably with white glazed channels and proper benching. The walls are rendered in cement and are in fairly good condition. The iron covers to Nos. 1 and 3 are broken, and that to No. 2 is very badly rusted. All three manholes should have new heavy galvanised steel airtight covers. An intercepting trap is provided to manhole No. 1. It is of satisfactory type, but the stopper to the cleaning arm is missing and there is nothing to shut off the air of the sewer to which the drains are connected. It is important that a proper airtight stopper be provided forthwith. It is suggested that another manhole be added in the yard at the back, which will greatly improve the arrangement of the drainage at this point.

Gulleys. The gulleys are all ordinary stoneware yard gulleys. In remodelling the system, channel gulleys would be more suitable for the outlets of waste pipes from baths, lavatories, and sinks, the ordinary form being retained for the rainwater pipes. If the system is carried out in iron, the new gulleys should be of iron. Two of the present gulleys have broken gratings.

VENTILATION OF THE DRAINS

Outlet ventilation is provided by means of the soil-pipes in the front and centre areas respectively. There is no outlet ventilating pipe at the head of the system and one should be provided as shown on the attached plan. The inlet for fresh air is placed in a chase in the wall of the W.C. adjoining manhole No. 1 and is fitted with a mica flap valve which is badly broken. If the new vent pipe is added at the back, this fresh-air inlet can be removed entirely, sufficient inlet being provided in such case by the soil-pipe in the front area.

RAINWATER PIPES

The rainwater pipes are all in good order, except for a split length on the wall adjoining manhole No. 2, which has caused slight dampness on the exterior of the wall. This length should be removed and a new one provided.

WASTE PIPES

The wastes from the baths and lavatories above the ground-floor level are discharged into hopper heads of rainwater pipes. These heads are all rather fouled and the practice of using them for this purpose is no longer permitted in the London area. Main waste pipes should be provided, carried well above the roof and finished with open ends for the purpose of ventilating them. Where two fittings discharge into the same waste pipe, their traps should be properly ventilated to protect them against siphonage.

SOIL-PIPES

The soil-pipe near manhole No. 2 is of light lead, 4 in. in diameter, with wiped soldered joints, but is badly bent and bruised. The joint at the foot is sound, and the pipe is carried well above the roof, but its otherwise defective condition makes it desirable to remove it and provide a new pipe of 3½ in. diameter, together with 2-in. anti-siphonage pipes to the traps of the W.C.s discharging into it. The soil-pipe in the front area is partly of lead and partly of iron, partly square and partly circular in section. It is somewhat dented and the tests disclosed a leaky joint. The square section is particularly insanitary. This pipe should also be replaced by a proper one as just described, and both should have domical wire gratings at the top to prevent obstruction by birds.

ROOF AND GUTTERS

There are about half a dozen cracked slates, which should be removed and replaced by new ones.

The lead flashings are in good order, but the parapet gutters are badly in need of cleaning out.

SUMMARY OF RECOMMENDATIONS

The foregoing recommendations may be briefly summarised, as follows:

Additional draw-off taps to be provided from the main water supply pipe.

Hot-water service to be overhauled and safety valve added to boiler.

New washers to be provided to taps where needed.

Present closet apparatus to be removed throughout and new pedestal wash-down closets provided.

Waste pipes to be put to the marble safes in W.C. compartments.

Handles to be provided to cisterns where missing.

New sinks to be put in Servants' Hall and Scullery, and waste pipes remodelled in both cases.

Lavatory basin in Cloakroom to be replaced by one of modern type.

The drainage to be remodelled, involving relaying nearly the whole in iron pipes, including remodelling manholes and building one new one, overhauling and renewing gulleys, etc.

New soil-pipes to be provided in place of existing ones, with anti-siphonage pipes.

New outlet vent pipe to be provided at the upper end of the system, and old fresh-air inlet removed.

Rainwater pipes to be overhauled, and new waste pipes provided, ventilating any traps where necessary.

Roofs and gutters to be overhauled.

(*Signed*) A. SURVEYOR, F.R.I.C.S.

20 *Blank Street,*
London, S.W.

The plan shown in Fig. 94 would be attached to the report. It will be seen that technicalities can be largely avoided in writing the report and that care is taken to avoid writing the report as a specification of the suggested work. The specification is a separate matter entirely, and, being intended for a builder or sanitary engineer, can be in technical language. It would also give much more detailed information as to sizes and materials.

A formal report such as the foregoing would be accompanied by a letter acknowledging receipt of instructions, and stating that the survey has now been made, etc.

Report in informal style. If the foregoing report had been written as an informal report, it might be somewhat as follows:

20 *Blank Street, London, S.W.,*
15*th September*, 1961.

DEAR SIR,

116 AIREDALE GARDENS, LONDON, S.W.

In accordance with the instructions contained in your letter of the 10th inst., I inspected this property on the 12th inst., and now have pleasure in reporting to you as follows:

GENERALLY. The sanitation of the house is not of recent date and is, generally speaking, in an unsound condition. Considerable remodelling and overhauling is necessary.

THE WATER SUPPLY. The water supply is derived from the mains of the Metropolitan Water Board, but there are no taps off the main except one in the Knife House. All the sanitary fittings are supplied from a large galvanised steel cistern on the third floor, which is in good order, etc., etc., etc.

Yours faithfully
A. SURVEYOR, F.R.I.C.S.

To C. Jones, Esq.

Report in tabulated style. If, on the other hand, the tabulation method is adopted for the report, a covering letter would be needed, and the report might read as follows:

REPORT ON THE SANITARY CONDITIONS OF 116 AIREDALE GARDENS, LONDON, S.W., FOR C. JONES, ESQ. 15TH SEPTEMBER, 1961

Item	Report	Recommendations
Water supply.	From mains of Metropolitan Water Board. Large galvanised steel cistern on third floor, in good order. It supplies all sanitary fittings. No draw-off taps on main supply pipe except one in the Knife House.	The taps over all sinks at which water will be drawn for drinking and cooking purposes should be supplied direct from the main.
Hot-water service.	etc. etc.	etc. etc.

(*Signed*) A. SURVEYOR, F.R.I.C.S.

20 *Blank Street,*
London, S.W.

The importance of drawing up the report after the fullest consideration of all the circumstances, economic and otherwise, must always be borne in mind, the conditions under which sanitary surveys are made being so very diverse. As already pointed out, moderate recommendations are often justified and often lead to the improvements being made, whereas counsels of perfection may well lead to nothing being done at all.

13

Refuse Collection and Disposal: Street Cleansing: Disinfection and Smoke Abatement

Refuse collection

The disposal of refuse is a most difficult but important part of the work of local authorities. The nature and quantity of refuse to be dealt with varies with the locality, particularly that part of it which comes from trade and industry.

Composition of refuse. An average composition of house refuse, expressed as percentages of weight, would be about as follows:

Fine dust 28 per cent, cinders 26 per cent, paper 15 per cent, putrescible matter 14 per cent, cans and other metal 4 per cent, glass and crockery 3 per cent, rags 2 per cent, bone 1 per cent, unclassified matter 7 per cent.

Calorific value of house refuse. The calorific or heating value is usually between one-fourth and one-seventh that of good steam coal. It should be borne in mind, however, that the composition and calorific value vary considerably according to the season, mainly because coal fires are more general in winter than in summer. It is interesting also to note that, owing to the greater use of gas stoves, electric cookers, and such appliances, house refuse is changing in character. It often contains much less cinders and ashes than hitherto, causing the calorific or fuel value to be lower. A natural corollary of this is that the cost of destruction is increasing far more steeply than increase in wages would justify. In some places refuse destructors, which used to be worked entirely by refuse, have now to be assisted by means of small coal, coke breeze or cheap oil.

When it is pointed out that the average amount of refuse collected per annum is about a quarter of a ton per head of population, it will be seen that dealing with the waste matters of a large population is a big undertaking.

The most sanitary method of dealing with refuse is to cremate it. This is done, in a well-administered locality, in special furnaces, known as refuse destructors. Much could be done to reduce the difficulty and cost of destroying it if householders realised that they had some personal liability in the matter, burned as much refuse as possible in their stoves or grates, and deposited waste vegetable matter in compost heaps in their gardens.

Storage of refuse by householder. Fixed ashpits are fortunately a thing of the past and for dwelling-houses portable galvanised iron bins, of a capacity not exceeding 2 cu. ft, are usually insisted on. (These are usually made of sheet of No. 20 B.W.G. and are sometimes, but not always, corrugated to give increased strength. A seating hoop is provided at the base, to keep the floor of the bin off the ground, and the top edge is strengthened by a stout galvanised iron hoop, to help preserve the shape; two strong galvanised iron handles are riveted to the body. Bins are covered by lids with deep rims which fit loosely over the body—bins often get rough usage by the dustmen and some distortion in shape may occur.) The bin should be kept on an impervious floor, such as in a paved yard and it should be strongly impressed on householders that they should not put liquids or very wet refuse in bins and they should not burn refuse in them. Dustbins moulded from both plastics and rubber are now available. Both have the advantages of quietness in use and resistance to distortion arising from rough handling. Both are considerably more expensive than steel bins and for general use have not as yet supplemented the latter to any serious extent. A system being introduced which has much to recommend it is the disposable paper bag – secured to a stand, removed and replaced by the Local Authority.

Collection of refuse. The usual practice in large towns is for refuse to be collected from dwelling-houses once in each week, with a more frequent call (perhaps daily) at hotels, restaurants and large blocks of flats. A weekly collection is by no means an ideal arrangement, for it is not desirable that putrescible matter should be kept so long in the immediate neighbourhood of dwellings and some towns have instituted a bi-weekly, or even daily, call with conspicuous success and at no great increase in cost.

If bins are provided for flats and tenements they should be much smaller than those used for dwelling-houses and they should be emptied each day into large "property containers", placed outside the building at ground level. This daily removal from flats is necessary because the bins will usually be kept indoors; for the same reason bins of pleasing appearance are available enamelled inside and out, with a hinged lid which in some types is made to open by pressing a lever with the foot.

Dust chutes for flatted dwellings. An alternative method of removing refuse from flats is by its discharge to the ground floor through chutes 12 to 14 in. in diameter, with a well-fitting door at each flat. The inlets to the chute should not be placed inside the flats if it can be avoided, as some nuisance from smell and dust is unavoidable. The chute should extend upwards above the roof, like a chimney, for ventilation purposes, and there should be facilities for washing it down with water periodically.

The property container for a block of flats will be a solidly-built steel box, capable of holding 2 or 2½ cubic yards of refuse. Containers are fitted with dust-proof sliding lids and wheels which enable them to be removed to the collecting vehicles, a cleansed container being substituted below the chute.

Property containers from hotels and blocks of flats can be carried conveniently by a motor lorry, of which the body can be tilted to form a sloping platform. The containers run on their own wheels and are drawn up the platform by a cable worked from the engine, after which the platform is returned to the horizontal.

Standardised chutes built up from large diameter glazed stoneware sections are now available complete with hygienic inlet hoppers and provision for ventilation and cleansing access (95).

The Garchey system of refuse disposal. This is a system of water carriage collection for refuse designed for use in large blocks of flats and tenements in place of ordinary dust chutes which are apt to cause nuisance from dust and smell, especially in hot summer weather. It was first used in Paris, but has been used with success at Leeds and elsewhere in this country.

The method involves the use of a special type of kitchen sink with a 6-in. diameter outlet. This is normally closed by a metal cap in the centre of which is the ordinary waste outlet. A trapped refuse container set below the sink receives refuse which is flushed from the fitting by waste water from the sink. The system is illustrated and described in Fig. 96.

Refuse and waste water are carried by a system of pipework to a centrally positioned receiving tank or tanks from which they are lifted together by compressed air to a feed tank from which they gravitate to a hydro-extractor, where water is removed by centrifugal action. The residual refuse falls into an incinerator, the heat from which can be used for a laundry or similar purposes.

It should be added that it is made impossible for tenants to pass into the receiver from the sink articles so large that they might cause an obstruction. Large articles, if they cannot be broken up, must be disposed of in some other way.

The advantage claimed for the Garchey method, relative to discharge to a container by chutes, is that dust and smell are avoided. The capital outlay involved is, however, far greater and the system can only be applied with efficiency on large-scale undertakings.

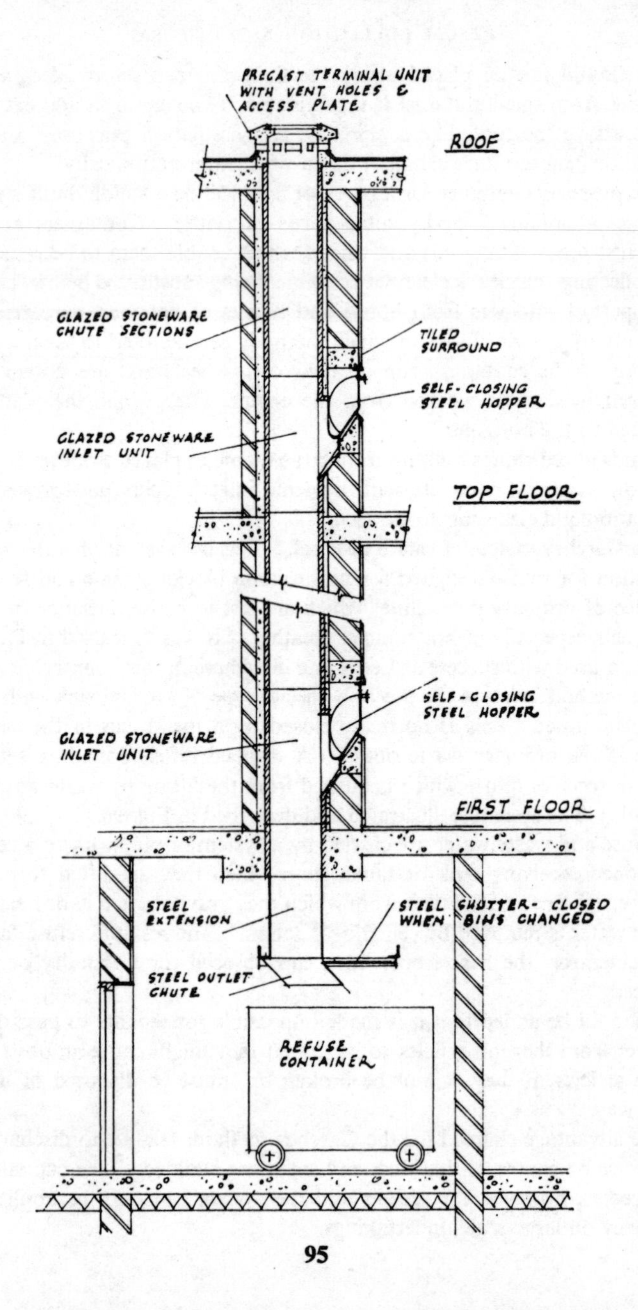
PRECAST TERMINAL UNIT
WITH VENT HOLES &
ACCESS PLATE
ROOF
GLAZED STONEWARE
CHUTE SECTIONS
TILED
SURROUND
SELF-CLOSING
STEEL HOPPER
GLAZED STONEWARE
INLET UNIT
TOP FLOOR
SELF-CLOSING
STEEL HOPPER
GLAZED STONEWARE
INLET UNIT
FIRST FLOOR
STEEL
EXTENSION
STEEL SHUTTER- CLOSED
WHEN BINS CHANGED
STEEL OUTLET
CHUTE
REFUSE
CONTAINER

95

Waste disposal units. To enable the advantages of water carriage refuse disposal to be applied to individual cases or small-scale undertakings waste disposal units for domestic use have been marketed in the years since the Second World War. These consist of electrically powered grinding or pulverising machines which are placed below the outlets from normal sinks.

Waste is fed to the unit via a removable plate in the sink and solid matter passing into it is ground finely enough to be safely carried away through normal waste pipework. Units will cope with all forms of food waste, including smaller bones, and paper. Larger articles, tins, etc., must of course be collected and disposed of in the usual way.

The fitting of the unit requires a waste opening in the sink about 3½ in. in diameter but sinks in all usual materials are now manufactured with waste outlets of this size.

When the unit is not in use the sink is used in the normal way, a normal trap being fitted on the outlet from the disposal unit. (Provision of an electric supply point and switch are required in the vicinity of the sink.)

Vehicles used for collection. At the beginning of this century the vehicles used for dust collection were horse-drawn wooden carts with open tops and high sides and the dustmen had to mount a short ladder with the bin, before tipping, in a cloud of dust, into the cart. Today vehicles are usually motor-driven and controlled. Vans are enclosed so that the contents of bins can be discharged without the dust being blown about.

There are many good designs of van, covered by close-fitting steel shutters. In some of these shutters at the sides are raised and lowered by pedals, operated by the dustmen before and after emptying the contents of a bin. They have small wheels and a long low body to avoid the use of ladders. A more recent development is the moving floor type of vehicle. This has a floor which resembles a rolling shutter shopblind in appearance, carrying a barrier about 3 ft high extending across the whole width of the vehicle. Loading is done at the rear end of the van. When the refuse reaches the level of the top of the barrier the floor and barrier are moved forward a little and loading is continued, the floor being moved forward at intervals until the barrier reaches the driver's end.

---

95 *Refuse chute*

Typical arrangement of a communal refuse chute. The chute is 15 in. diameter internally and built up of specialised standard glazed stoneware sections.

"Service" to the ground floor can be arranged by fitting a hopper in the refuse chamber wall—positioned to discharge directly into the refuse container.

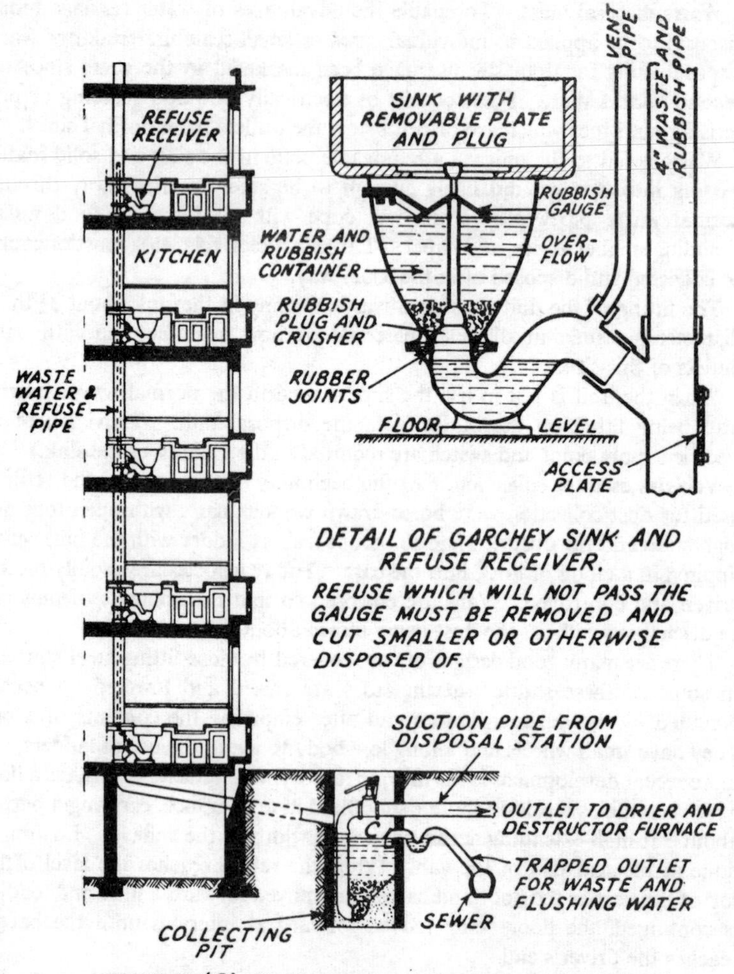

THE GARCHEY METHOD OF REFUSE REMOVAL FOR LARGE BLOCKS OF FLATS.

96

Most modern collecting vehicles have devices by which the body can be tipped to a steep angle for discharging the contents quickly and completely at the place of disposal, the tipping mechanism being actuated by gearing from the engine which normally propels the vehicle.

Another excellent modern vehicle has inside it a helical screw which gathers the refuse, as it is shot into the body, passes it forward and compresses it. Tipping gear is not needed, as the load is emptied by reversal of rotation of the screw. An advantage of this type is that a much greater weight can be carried in equal space, due to the compression of refuse by the screw.

Method of locomotion. It is not possible to generalise as to the best method of propelling collecting vehicles. Whilst today the petrol engine is most commonly used, it is not at its best when used in a service which requires frequent stopping and waiting; on the other hand it is most efficient when long distances have to be travelled to the place of disposal. Where houses are rather scattered and there is no great length of haul to the tip, horse-drawn vehicles may still be the best proposition and there are today horse-drawn vehicles of quite satisfactory design. In general however and wherever

---

96 *The Garchey system of refuse disposal*

This is a water carriage system of collection using enlarged waste water pipework and normal sink waste water for flushing. The specialised sink has a 6 in. diameter outlet plate through which rubbish is passed and in which is set the normal sink outlet. The sink is used for ordinary purposes with the plate fixed in place, whilst solid refuse can be disposed of through the large outlet when the plate is removed. Under the sink is a cast-iron pear-shaped receiver whose outlet is closed by a plunger, fitted with an overflow, and into this both liquid wastes and solid refuse pass. Below the receiver is a trap, with 2-in. water seal and anti-siphonage pipe, connecting it to a vertical cast-iron gravitation pipe, extending from below ground to a level above the roof, being open at the top like a soil-pipe for ventilation purposes. The contents of the receiver are from time to time discharged to this by pulling up the plunger which normally closes the outlet of the receiver.

The gravitation pipe leads to an airtight collecting chamber, placed underground outside the building. This has a trapped overflow, leading to the main drain or sewer, for continuous discharge of liquids, but the solids at the bottom are removed intermittently. This is done through a suction pipe which leads to the receiving tank of a disposal station, discharge being controlled by a hand-operated valve. The suction is effected by a motor-driven vacuum pump placed at the disposal station and it is claimed that discharge can be obtained for a distance of 5 miles by this means although, for obvious reasons, the receiving and destructor station is usually an adjunct to the block or series of blocks of flats in which the system is installed. At the disposal station refuse is dried and incinerated to provide heat for heating or similar services.

development is more dense, or longer hauls to tip are necessary, the petrol-driven vehicle is preferred. Some districts find it an economy to use a fleet of tractors with a larger number of trailers which can be moved quickly to strategic points for filling and then transported (two or three at a time) to the place of disposal.

Electrically-driven vehicles are occasionally used and they have some distinct advantages. There is little or no loss at stopping and starting and no power is used when the van is stationary. The main objections to them are that the accumulators, which are used to drive them, are a considerable dead weight, that maintenance of accumulators is a serious item and that the speed of such vehicles in the travel to the tip is invariably low.

Methods of disposal. While the best method of disposal is by burning, many other methods are in use. In the case of some towns on the coast, refuse is barged out to sea in special barges and dropped into deep water. This method has its drawbacks; in winter the weather is often such that the barges dare not go out for sometimes a week at a time, which necessitates storage and consequent nuisance. Again, the tide will often bring a quantity of the lighter particles of refuse back to shore.

"Controlled tipping." In many districts refuse is tipped on low-lying land, sand wastes, moorland, disused quarries, etc. There has in recent times been much criticism of this practice, on the grounds that such tips are unsightly, form breeding-places for rats and flies, and cause unpleasant smells, sometimes increased by combustion of the refuse. To prevent these results the following precautions are now usually taken.

Before tipping is begun the surface soil of the site is removed and set aside for covering the refuse; the refuse is spread evenly to a depth not exceeding 6 ft and neatly banked; tins are raked to the foot of the bank, placed upright and filled with earth; carpets, linos, rags, etc., are laid flat at the foot of the bank and covered; glass and china is broken up and paper consolidated by ramming; cinders and ashes are brought to the top; each day's tippings are covered with a layer of earth at least 9 in. thick.

Whilst "controlled" tipping of this character is not as satisfactory, from the health point of view, as burning, it will generally be much less costly. The refuse is quite harmless after two or three years and the site is then suitable for agricultural purposes or for use as a public open space.

Salvage. When refuse is to be burnt it is sometimes found that it is profitable first to salvage from it such articles as cinders, rags, tins and bottles. This practice also has the advantage of diminishing the amount which has to be incinerated.

Salvaging is done partly by screening, partly by hand-picking, and partly by the use of electro-magnets to pick out iron.

Cinders may be saleable for brick-making, rags for paper-making. Tin and solder can be recovered from cans by chemical or electrolytic methods, and the remaining iron in the cans will be saleable if compressed into bales.

The prices obtained in pre-war years for these by-products seldom repaid the cost of their separation, but during the Second World War special efforts made to salvage metals, paper, rags and other useful materials were well repaid. Householders were asked, in the national interest, to keep these items clean and separate from other refuse and (in many districts) to take them to depots or dumps, from which the salvaged materials were collected by the local authority.

Refuse can sometimes be sold, or given away, to farmers as manure, and it much improves heavy clay soils. Disposal in this way will, however, be impossible unless the larger articles have been removed by salvaging, or pulverised.

Pulverising. Pulverising is done by heavy hammers, swinging in a revolving drum, the material falling as dust through a screen. Tins, and other articles which cannot be broken, must first be removed. The object of pulverisation is to make the refuse more suitable as manure.

Refuse destructors. In the early days of destructors objections were raised on the grounds that they were nuisances to a neighbourhood by producing offensive smells, and that fine ash or dust was carried up the chimney shaft and scattered for a considerable distance around. Before scientific principles were applied to their construction there is little doubt that such complaints were well founded, but such great advances have been made that sanitarians are now agreed that disposing of towns' refuse by burning is the only really satisfactory method.

Essentials of a destructor. The essentials of a satisfactory destructor installation are that its position should be fairly central, to economise cost of cartage; it should convert organic matter to harmless and useful inorganic matter; there should be no nuisance from smell, smoke, dust or other cause.

In early types of destructor the furnace was at a comparatively low temperature and fed by a natural draught of air. Modern destructors have forced draught, causing a high furnace temperature, with consequently more thorough combustion of gases and less liability to the causing of a nuisance.

Early destructors. The design of refuse-destroying furnaces has developed from those invented by Fryer and first installed in England at Manchester in 1876. A brief description of the original Fryer destructor is given (97).

The Horsfall destructor. It will be seen from Fig. 97 that in the Fryer

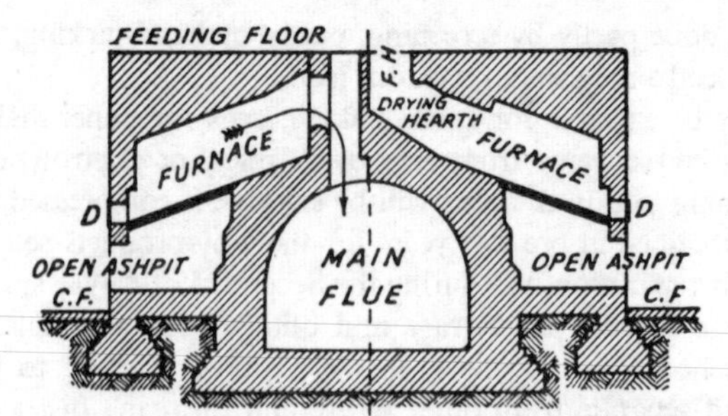

EARLY TYPE OF DESTRUCTOR WITHOUT FORCED DRAUGHT AND OPEN ASHPIT.

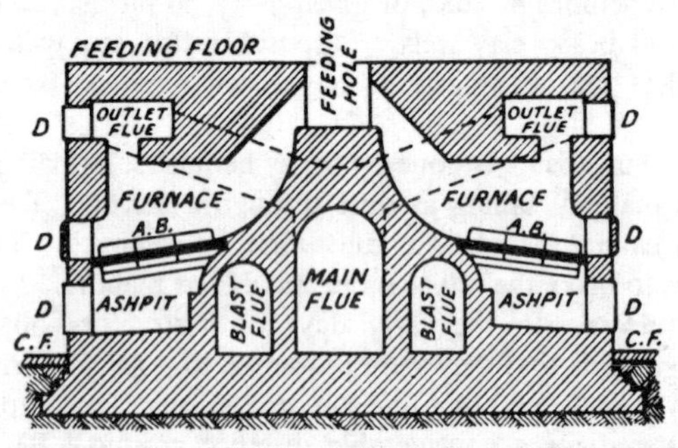

HORSFALL DESTRUCTOR WITH FORCED HOT DRAUGHT CLOSED ASHPIT AND TOP FEED.

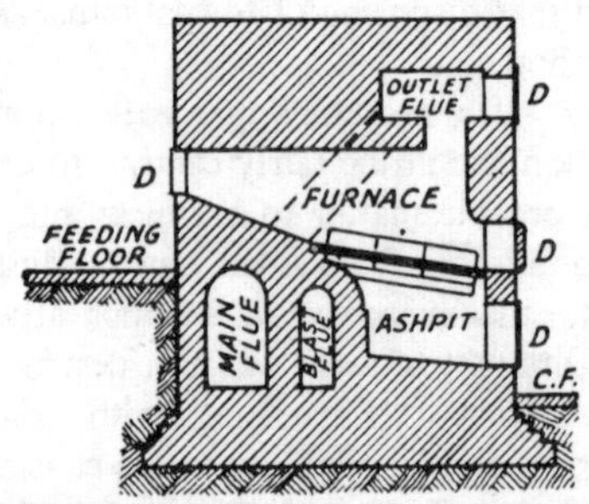

FORCED HOT DRAUGHT DESTRUCTOR WITH BACK FEED FROM LOW CHARGING FLOOR.

destructor the gases given off by the burning refuse pass straight into the main flue and are not in fact cremated as is so desirable. The first great advance was made by the Horsfall destructor, in which gases produced were made to pass over the hottest part of the fire to an outlet flue in front and above the furnace (97).

---

97 *Refuse destructors*

(*Top*) THE FRYER DESTRUCTOR. It consists of a group of cells, each of which constitutes a separate furnace, consisting of a wide but shallow arch with inclined fire bars below it. The disposition of the cells is largely a matter of convenience, depending on the exigencies of the site, but they were usually placed in two rows, back to back, as shown in the diagram. Each cell was about 9 ft front to back, and about 5 ft wide. The front of the furnace was formed by the fire bars with the arch over them, the former being of very heavy section and set to an inclination of about 1 in 3. The back of each furnace was divided into two parts, one in the form of an opening through which the gases, given off by the burning refuse, pass to the main flue, as shown, *left*, and the other in the form of a charging opening or feed hole, F.H., with an inclined drying hearth below, as shown, *right*. The top of the destructor forms a platform on to which the vans bring the refuse by means of an inclined road. The opening for the entry of refuse is divided from the opening for the exit of gases by a wall, and the refuse is prevented from getting into the main flue by the round-topped low wall shown in the section. In this original form of destructor the main flue was made very large, so as to act as a dust catcher, and the ashpit below the fire bars was open at the front, adjacent to the clinkering floor, C.F., the clinker being removed through doors formed at D.

Furnace cells were provided with special openings, for introducing infectious bedding, diseased meat, dead animals, etc., arranged to allow these to fall directly into the furnace.

(*Centre*) THE HORSFALL DESTRUCTOR. In this form the ashpit was enclosed and a forced draught provided for. This was done by means of a blast flue for each row of cells, placed alongside the main flue to achieve a fairly high temperature. Air was driven through the blast flue by means of a powerful steam jet at the end and entered the ashpit through air boxes, A.B., at the sides of the cell. The sides of the cells were particularly liable to damage and the clinker very liable to adhere to them, and air boxes were arranged with plates which were readily renewable. It will be seen that there was no drying hearth in this form. There are three doors to each cell, the top one for cleaning the outlet flue, the next for clinkering, and the lowest for access to the ashpit. The fire grates to each furnace varied in area from 25 to 42 sq ft.

(*Bottom*) A BACK-FEED DESTRUCTOR with furnace cells arranged in a single row; a modification of the Horsfall type shown above. The furnace is fed from a feeding floor, below the top of the destructor. This method is quite sound, there being no great loss of heat by opening the charging door, owing to the front situation of the outlet flue. Front feeding, on the other hand, is open to objection on the grounds of heat loss during charging.

The addition of the forced draught, and the alteration of the position of the outlet flue, led to the cells being able to consume about twice as much refuse per day as was possible before, and at a lower cost.

As in the Fryer destructor, cells were usually arranged in two rows placed back to back.

One advantage of placing the cells back to back is that the main flue can be placed between them and its high temperature thereby be preserved.

Not all destructors are arranged in this way, however, and designs also vary in other respects. Some destructors are fed at the top, some at the back, and some from the front. An example of a back-fed destructor with cells arranged in a single row is also illustrated in Fig. 97.

For obvious reasons refuse should have as little handling as possible, and in large installations systems of mechanical feeding are now widely adopted. The refuse is first tipped into a large hopper, from which it travels on a belt conveyor to small hoppers, placed over each furnace.

Tub feeding destructors. As an alternative the Horsfall Tub Feeding system may be installed. A large container or tub is lowered, by an overhead travelling crane, into a charging pit, so that the lorries can tip their contents directly into it at ground level. Each tub holds about two tons of refuse, and enough tubs are provided to receive the refuse collected at each collection. The tubs are lifted to the high level by the crane and placed on a platform to await charging. When a furnace has to be charged, a tub is lifted by the crane and lowered into a cradle over the furnace. The descent of the cradle opens the charging door and its ascent, when the tub is lifted after charging, closes the door. The operation of charging the two tons into the furnace takes less than a minute and the system effects a great saving of labour and increases the working capacity of the cell. Further, it ensures the maintenance of a high temperature.

Heat utilisation. It is usual to utilise the heat from the furnaces to generate steam, which is used for various purposes such as the generation of electricity, pumping water or sewage, and so on.

Further improvements have been made in recent destructor practice. Thus, the air is heated to a high temperature before admission to the blast flue, the heated air raising the temperature of the furnace by an amount equal to nearly twice as much as its own temperature. Not only does the hot air raise the temperature of the furnace, it also helps to absorb the moisture in the burning refuse.

The air heater is arranged in the form of tubes, through which the waste gases pass after serving the boilers, thus raising the temperature of the air around the tubes. Such air is then driven to the ashpit by means of either steam blowers or fans. Both fans and blowers have their advocates, but blowers seem to be better where pressure has to be overcome.

Temperature created. The temperature of the waste gases of a good destructor is far higher than that of the gases from an ordinary boiler furnace. Under the old natural-draught system a temperature of about 900°F was seldom exceeded, but in the case of a good modern high-temperature furnace the figure ranges from about 1500° to 2000°. The gases, after serving a boiler and being utilised for heating the air for the forced draught, can be further used to warm the water which is on its way to the boiler. This is done in what is termed an economiser, an apparatus somewhat like a hot-water coil, the waste gases playing round the pipes.

Dust chambers or interceptors. An important feature in a destructor is the combustion chamber, generally arranged at the end of a row of cells, the object being to reduce the velocity of the gases travelling to the chimney shaft, and ensure the deposit of dust in a position at which it is easily accessible. Alternatively the gases are passed through a whirling chamber, where they are made to rotate rapidly, so that the dust is separated by centrifugal force.

While the cellular plan was the original one for destructors some types of destructor are not arranged in this way, but have a continuous fire grate from end to end, with undulating arches over them to deflect the gases over the fire on their way to the flue. Both arrangements have their advocates and good examples of both can be found.

Woodall-Duckham destructor. A type of destructor with novel features is the rotary furnace of the Woodall-Duckham Co. In this the refuse is dried on a moving inclined and stepped hearth and moves continuously to the ignition stage, in which it is partially burnt upon an inclined grate, of which alternate fire bars are mechanically rocked to move the refuse forward. Combustion is aided by a blast of air from below. The refuse falls from the end of this grate into the upper end of an inclined rotating kiln, lined with firebrick. As it cascades down the inclined kiln the refuse is completely consumed. The gases from the ignition grate and from the kiln pass into a large combustion flue, from which they pass to the boilers. Dust is extracted from the gases leaving the boiler flues before they pass to the chimney.

It is claimed for this plant that labour cost is reduced, that less ground space is required to deal with an equal quantity of refuse, and that there is complete absence of dust and fumes from the chimney.

Ventilation of destructor buildings. The building in which the destructor installation is housed requires careful ventilation. If possible air inlets are provided to replace used and tainted air withdrawn by the combustion flues.

One of the best ways is to provide an air duct high up in the building and communicating with the air supply to the forced draught fans so that they pull part of the air they require out of the building.

Capacity of cells. The quantity of refuse consumed per cell in twenty-four hours varies according to the make of furnace, method of stoking, nature of draught, etc., and can be anything from 8 to 20 tons. The percentage of clinker left, after burning the refuse, averages from 25 to 33 per cent.

Residuals. The composition of the clinker also varies greatly, but it was stated by H. P. Boulnois to be, generally:

Silica	69·4 per cent
Iron and alumina oxides	21·4 ,,
Carbonate of lime	9·2 ,,

the composition of the fine ash being much the same, but containing more silica.

Many destructor installations have, in the past, been failures by reason of the fact that efforts were being made to get too much out of them. The complete destruction of the refuse must always come first and foremost in any satisfactory installation, and the raising of steam, etc., be an after consideration. There are, however, certain residuals incidental to any such process. As has been seen, waste gases are utilised for raising steam; bottles and tin cans can be rescued and, lastly, there is the clinker. When finely crushed, clinker can be used instead of sand in mortar and plaster (if of good quality), for sanding slippery roads and for bedding paving slabs. It is also used for fine concrete, for paving slabs and paving laid *in situ*. The slabs are generally of three parts fine clinker and one part Portland cement, moulded under a pressure of about 60 tons per sq. ft.

In some places bricks have been made from the clinker. Thus pressed bricks have been made of one part of Portland cement to nine parts of finely crushed clinker. The resulting brick is only very slightly absorbent and is strong; it is grey in colour and is used for fixing bricks, since it will take nails.

Other uses for clinker are for filter beds for sewage, filling up low-lying land, and under the foundations of concrete roads and paved footpaths. Unfortunately destructor clinker is often of too poor a quality to be useful for any purpose.

Street cleansing

The cleansing of streets is a matter which, generally speaking, is quite distinct from the destruction of house refuse, though part of the street refuse is often mixed with it and taken to the destructor. Street refuse consists of dust, mud, rubbish, road-scraping, ice, snow and filth.

Streets must be kept clean primarily for sanitary reasons, but also for appearance, comfort and convenience. Dust carries organic impurities, and is a means of spreading the germs of disease. (That from wood pavements is especially injurious to the lungs and eyes.)

From the point of view of cleanliness, the materials used for road surfaces may be placed in the following order: (1) Asphalt. (2) Concrete. (3) Wood paving. (4) Tar macadam. (5) Granite setts, and (6) Macadam. In this classification it is assumed that all are in good condition. (It is obvious that an old and worn wood surface, for instance, would be more difficult and costly to cleanse than a new surface of, say, tar macadam.)

Comparison of different types of road surface. A little consideration will disclose why some types of surfacing are more costly to cleanse than others. Thus, asphalt is non-absorbent and jointless, therefore such garbage as collects on it can be readily removed. Granite setts, however, though practically non-absorent, have a multiplicity of joints in which garbage can collect. Water-bound macadam is easily worn down and produces dust and mud. On the other hand it should not be overlooked that very smooth materials, such as compressed rock asphalt, may have to be gritted in wet or icy weather and that this increases the amount of material which has to be scavenged.

Method in organisation. The secret of success in cleansing streets is method. A definite system should be mapped out and strictly adhered to. Not only should the local authority cleanse the main and side streets, they are often responsible also for cleansing courts and alleys. In a well-regulated town the main streets are swept or cleansed at regular intervals, once a day for preference, gathering the dust or debris into heaps along the gutters, or into slots at kerb level, leading to small bins under the kerb or footpath. From there the dust may be transferred to a hand barrow.

Suburban streets do not need such frequent cleansing as the busy streets of the town, and it is usually sufficient to cleanse them about twice a week.

Asphalt and wood-block roads should be frequently washed, but in many cases one hears of the difficulty of obtaining the necessary supply of water. In most places there is only one supply for all purposes, public and private, and it is a matter for consideration whether an unfiltered supply for washing streets, fire extinction, and such purposes, could not advantageously be provided.

In rainy weather the street orderly boys should be armed with squeegees, with which to push the slop which forms on the surface into the side channels. This tends to keep the road surface clean and safe for traffic.

Macadam and granite sett roads are best cleansed by sweeping, either by hand or machine.

Hand sweeping. Hand sweeping is still largely done, and possesses the advantage that effort can be confined to those places which need it. A machine will sweep all the road, whether it needs it or not, and is liable to leave mud and dirt in pot-holes. Motor sweepers, however, are extensively used in large towns.

Machine sweeping. One much used machine comprises a four-wheeled motor vehicle, with a rotary broom fixed between the two axles at an oblique angle. The broom is turned in direction opposite to that of the wheels of the vehicle, being driven by a chain from the gear box. The road is swept in two halves, the mud and dust being brushed into the channels. Other vehicles follow for its removal, after the channels have been swept by hand. Other designs of sweeper have water tanks and sprays, in order to wet the surface in front of the brushes and so facilitate the removal of dried mud.

Another type of vehicle is provided not only with water tank, spray and brush, but also a collecting bin into which the sweepings are brushed by three further rotating brushes. Another machine similarly sweeps the refuse into a bin mounted on a trailer.

Disposal of street sweepings. The disposal of street sweepings is generally a troublesome matter. The scrapings from macadamised roads can generally, if washed, be used with lime or cement for mortar. Mud is often tipped on waste land, but it should not be placed on possible building sites. It can also be mixed with house refuse and burned in a destructor.

Street watering. An adjunct to street cleansing is the need to water streets in order to keep down the dust in dry, windy weather. In the case of wood-paved roads the watering is also beneficial to the wood itself, making it less subject to injury by abrasion. In crowded districts, or in times of epidemics, disinfectants are often added to the water. A typical mix is 1 lb of permanganate of potash and half a pint of sulphuric acid to 100 gallons of water. Blocks of a disinfectant termed pynezone are also used for this purpose.

Roads may be watered by hoses or by means of water carts. In England the latter method is the more usual. The water either issues through a perforated pipe or is distributed by falling on two rotating discs or spreaders. A good cart or wagon will spread the water over a width of 20 ft, the quantity used varying from one-tenth to one-fifth of a gallon per square yard of surface.

Snow cleansing. In the case of snow, it is difficult to do anything until the fall has ceased, when all available men should be set to work, dealing with the streets in the order of their importance. The snow should be banked up at the sides of the road, clear of the channels and gulleys, with gangways through where desirable. Snow ploughs are also used. Disposing of the snow is often difficult. Sometimes it is tipped down manholes into the sewer, but this is only possible with very large sewers and the usual plan is to cart it away to the parks and open spaces and tip it on the land. If the town is on the banks of a river, the snow can be thrown into the river.

An application of salt greatly facilitates clearance, since it lowers the freezing temperature of water and therefore causes the snow to melt. The resulting slush, however, must be promptly swept away.

The expense of completely clearing streets of snow is very great. For example, it has been said that to clear a 6-in. fall of snow from the streets of London would require more vehicles than exist in that area. To do more than clear the principal streets of large towns after a heavy fall of snow involves sums of money quite disproportionate to the benefits effected.

Disinfection. A few brief notes on the subject of disinfection will not be out of place in the present volume.

The principal infectious diseases are: cholera, chickenpox, diphtheria, erysipelas, influenza, measles, mumps, scarlet fever, smallpox, enteric fever, typhus fever, tuberculosis, and whooping cough. Most diseases are caused by bacteria or micro-organisms, hence the urgent necessity for disinfectants and antiseptics.

Distinction between disinfectants, antiseptics, deodorants and disinfestants. A *disinfectant* is an agent which will kill the germs of disease, e.g. hot air, steam, formaldehyde, sulphur dioxide, chlorine, chloride of lime, perchloride of mercury, carbolic acid and many proprietary preparations mainly derived from coal-tar.

An *antiseptic* is an agent which will prevent the multiplying of bacteria, e.g. refrigeration, desiccation, alcohol and, in many cases, a weaker dilution of a disinfectant.

A *deodorant* is an agent which will absorb disagreeable odours—sometimes the term is applied also to agents which will mask or hide such odours and which are not true deodorants. Dry earth of suitable type forms a good deodorant, so, too, do proprietary preparations containing a good concentration of chlorophyl. Oxygen and ozone are also excellent in this respect.

A *disinfestant* is an agent which will destroy disease-carrying pests like rats, mice, fleas, lice, bugs, mosquitoes, flies, etc. Hydrocyanic gas, mentioned later, is one of the best, but is a deadly poison and must be used by experts and with extreme care.

Value of fresh air and sunlight. Fresh air and sunlight have considerable germicidal properties, but quick and complete destruction of germs, or true disinfection, can only be brought about by either chemical means or heat. In most districts there is a public disinfecting station, where articles can be sent for disinfection. Such a station will be described later.

Disinfection of clothing. Where articles of clothing and bedding cannot be sent to a disinfecting station they should be burned if possible; otherwise they should be boiled or soaked for twenty-four hours in some disinfecting liquid, such as a solution of Izal, 5 parts to 100 parts of water; chloride of lime, 2 oz. to a gallon of water; carbolic acid, 5 parts to 100 parts of water; or perchloride of mercury, ½ oz.; hydrochloric acid, 1 ounce; and aniline blue, 5 grains to 3 gallons of water. Perchloride of mercury, or corrosive sublimate as it is often called, is a cheap and very powerful disinfectant, dangerous to use on account of its being colourless, and a very deadly poison; the object of mixing the above ingredients with it is to tint it and make it offensive, so as to avoid mistake.

Formaldehyde and formalin. Coal-tar is the original source of most of the patented disinfecting liquids which are on the market. One of the most powerful disinfectants is that known as formaldehyde. It is generally supplied to the public in the form of solution containing 40 per cent of formaldehyde, the solution being known as formalin. In the same way that the destructive distillation of coal produces coal-tar, so a similar treatment of wood produces wood-tar. In both cases other materials are produced, including, in the latter case, what is known as wood naphtha or methyl-alcohol, from which, by an oxidising process, the formaldehyde is produced. The use of formaldehyde is apt to produce a painful irritation of the skin and nails, and it is very desirable, therefore, to prevent the hands being wetted by it.

Use of heat and steam. In the case of articles of small value, the safest way is to burn them, but disinfection may also be secured by exposing them to either dry or moist heat. Exposure to hot air at a temperature of 284°F for four hours is about equal to the effect of exposure for five minutes to steam at a temperature of 212°F. Steam is therefore much more widely used.

Steam disinfectors. There are many forms of steam disinfecting apparatus. One of the oldest and best known is the "Washington-Lyons". The disinfecting chamber is of oval section, encased by a steam jacket, the outer casing being covered with asbestos to assist in retaining the heat. The apparatus is built into a wall which divides a large room into two, and which has no door or other means of communication except a fixed window, through which signals can be given. The infected articles are brought into the room on one side, hence distinguished as the "infected" side, and are put in a cradle or hung on hooks in a light frame on wheels, which is then run into the disinfecting chamber, the door of which is screwed up to airtight closure against a rubber gasket. Steam, at a pressure of 30 lb to the square inch, and a temperature of 273°F, is then turned into the outer jacket, so as to raise the temperature of the inner chamber high enough to prevent condensation of moisture, from the clothes, etc. Next, the air is exhausted from the chamber as far as possible, to give space for the steam. This is done by the suction created by a jet of steam passing over a pipe and at high velocity, a two-thirds vacuum being obtained in about ten minutes. Steam is then admitted for ten minutes, until a pressure of 30 lb per sq. in. is registered, corresponding to a temperature of about 250°F. It is then shut off to see if the pressure gauge shows any fall, due to particles of steam condensing; if so, steam is turned on again until the pressure remains constant. In bad cases, the steam is turned on a second time for a further ten minutes.

After the steam is cut off, dry air is passed in through tubes on which steam is playing, in order thoroughly to dry the articles, the cradle being then drawn out through the opposite door of the apparatus, the "clean" side of the disinfecting station. The whole process takes from thirty-five to forty minutes.

Great care has to be exercised in regulating temperature, as the sanitary authority disinfecting is held liable for any damage done to the articles.

It is essential that saturated steam should be used, superheated steam having little greater power of penetration than hot air. (Saturated steam is water vapour at the boiling temperature which is normal to the prevailing pressure. Superheated steam is steam whose temperature has been increased above the boiling-point by passing it through a coil in a furnace, in which form it behaves like other gases.)

There are a large number of patterns of steam disinfector, and it is difficult to say that one is better than another. One of rather a different type from that just described, however, is the "Thresh" disinfector. In this, the lower part of the enclosing jacket of the cylinder acts as the boiler, and has a small furnace under it. The steam passes continuously through the disinfecting chamber, escaping up a chimney, i.e. is not under pressure, as in the case of the Washington-Lyons apparatus. Heated air is afterwards admitted and the articles rapidly dried.

Infected articles should be brought to the disinfecting station in proper vans lined with sheet metal and airtight, kept solely for the carriage of infected articles, separate vans, kept for that purpose only, being used for carrying away the clean articles.

Public disinfecting stations. A public disinfecting station consists principally of two rooms, the infected and disinfected side, separated by a wall with no possibility of the passage of air from one to the other, such as a door or opening window. The apparatus is built into this wall. The van used for the carriage of infected goods should be housed at the infected end of the building, and the clean van at the other end. An incinerator, or small refuse destructor, should be installed at the infected end for the destruction of things which are too filthy to clean. Bedclothing and similar things require to be soaked in water and washed before passing through the disinfector—the steam fixes stains permanently. It is therefore usual to install a certain amount of laundry apparatus, such as a washer, hydro-extractor (or centrifugal wringer), drying chamber and mangle, etc.

Some things cannot be subjected to steam at all. It is therefore a good plan to provide a formalin chamber, that is to say, a room kept exclusively for submitting articles to the action of formaldehyde gas, generated by special types of lamp.

Verminous persons. Bathrooms should be provided, one for men and one for women, for the cleansing of verminous persons. The bathrooms should adjoin the infected room, and have special hoppers, locking each side, in which the person can place his clothes, which are then put through the disinfector and made fit for use again.

In some cases, a bottle-washing room is added with special washing machines, sinks, etc.

It perhaps need hardly be said that any such building should be exceptionally well lighted and ventilated, and that the walls and floors should be jointless and non-absorbent, the walls being preferably of glazed tiles to facilitate cleansing. All angles should be rounded, with the same object.

Disinfection of living rooms. The disinfection of rooms or buildings can be effected in many ways. Assume sulphur dioxide is to be used: Open all cupboards, drawers, boxes, etc., saturate the walls, floor and woodwork with water, and seal up all openings, such as fireplace, windows, doors and ventilators, with brown paper. Place the sulphur on a tin plate, say 2 lb to every 1000 cu. ft of space and support it in a larger vessel containing water, to guard against fire. Put this in the middle of the room, ignite the sulphur, and make a speedy exit. Shut the door and seal it up by pasting strips of paper round its edges. Leave the room thus for twenty-four hours. Then open the doors and windows, strip the paper off the walls and burn it, wash off the ceiling with limewash, and scrub the floor and all woodwork, furniture, etc., with a solution of perchloride of mercury, 1 part to 1000 parts of water.

Sulphur dioxide can also be obtained in tins under pressure, which is a convenient form, as all that is necessary is to cut off the top of the tin and allow the gas to escape. Gilt picture frames, or steel goods, should not be allowed to remain in the room, as the sulphur dioxide attacks these materials.

Formaldehyde is also largely used for the fumigation of rooms, being either vaporised by means of special lamps, or sprayed over the surfaces of walls, ceilings, floors, etc.

Vapour-producing lamps and sprays. Many forms of lamp and spray have been introduced, but it is deemed beyond the province of this volume to deal with them. Some important experiments in reference to the spraying of disinfectants were carried out by Drs Thresh and Lowden, who arrived at the following conclusions:

1 That for spraying to be efficient, every portion of the surface to be disinfected must be thoroughly moistened with the disinfecting solution; merely passing the spray into a room and trusting to its settling upon the surfaces is utterly unreliable.
2 Whitewashed surfaces require particular attention, being far more difficult to disinfect than surfaces of wood and paper.
3 Solutions containing under 2 per cent of formaldehyde are not absolutely reliable. Solutions, therefore, of not less than this strength should be used.
4 A proper spray, properly used, effects room disinfection in the minimum of time and with the minimum of expense, and is more reliable than disinfection by sulphur or formalin vapour.

Some of the forms of disinfecting equipment are arranged so that they can, if desired, work from the outside of the room by spraying through the keyhole.

Hydrocyanic gas for disinfection and disinfestation. Hydrocyanic acid gas, which in solution is commonly known as prussic acid, is a most effective means of fumigation, and destroys bacteria, vermin, bugs, lice and even the eggs of bugs, etc. It does no damage to metal, wood or paintwork, is relatively cheap and there is no danger of fire. The disadvantage of the method is that it is a most deadly poison, so that its application needs skilled operators and the evacuation of the house on either side. The destruction of pests (or "Disinfestation") is often particularly important, owing to the diseases which many of them carry, and in this connection, insects such as flies, bugs, lice, beetles, etc., can be conveniently dealt with by a dust or spray containing D.D.T. or by a dust, fumigation or spray of Gammexane, both of which have a valuable residual action lasting some weeks and which act by paralysis rather than direct poison.

Smoke abatement

Another aspect of drainage and sanitation on which attention is now being focused is smoke abatement.

In large boiler furnaces the chief cause of smoke is improper stoking and an insufficient air supply. If the furnace is regularly stoked with small quantities of fuel at short intervals, and is provided with proper draught, either natural or forced, there should be no nuisance. A chimney is not, in fact, solely intended to let smoke out, its main purpose is to produce a draught through the furnace and assist combustion.

As hot gases rise up a chimney, air enters the furnace to take their place. If a forced draught is used injudiciously, it is apt to be productive of considerable smoke, but forced-draught systems should be capable of regulation, and be put in the hands of competent stokers.

The Clean Air Act, 1956, gives local authorities power to designate smoke control areas.

Such designations require confirmation of the Minister and in "designated areas" owners or occupiers of existing private dwellings may apply for grants towards the cost of adapting or replacing grates and stoves so as to enable smokeless fuel (gas coke, hard coke, Phurnacite, anthracite. Welsh dry steam coal, Coalite and Rexco) to be used.

The Act makes it an offence in a Smoke Control Area for new furnaces to be installed which are incapable of operating without emitting smoke when burning fuel for which they were designed, the maximum penalty for infringement being £100. This requirement applies to all new furnaces installed after 31st December 1956, with the exception of domestic plant with a capacity of less than 55,000 btu's per hour and certain movable furnaces.

A person proposing to install a furnace to which the Act applies is required to notify the local authority of his intention, and failure to comply with this requirement may involve a maximum fine of £10. It is not an obligation to submit plans or specification, and where plans and specifications are not submitted the local authority is not required either to give or withhold its consent, the application then being merely to inform the local authority of the exact location of the proposed new installation.

If plans and specifications are submitted to and approved by the appropriate local authority, the furnaces, when subsequently installed, will be deemed to comply with the Act. It is therefore desirable in all cases to submit plans to ensure that no offence under the Act will be committed.

It should be borne in mind that approval of an installation by the local authority pursuant to the Act will not be a bar to the institution of proceedings under the Act in respect of other matters, for instance, the emission of dark smoke following improper operation of the plant.

N.B.—In any proceedings in respect of the emission of smoke in a Smoke Control Area, it will be a defence to prove that the smoke was not caused by the use of any fuel other than an authorised fuel. Authorised fuels are defined as follows:

Anthracite
Briquetted fuels carbonised in the process of manufacture
Coke
Electricity
Gas
Low temperature carbonisation fuels
Low volatile steam coals

Information on smokeless zones and the appliances and fuels conducive to clean air is available from the Solid Smokeless Fuels Federation (S.S.F.F.), 74 Grosvenor Street, London, W.1.

Domestic fireplaces. In the case of domestic fireplaces (see details of construction in Chapter 4), stoking should be regular; one should not let a fire go almost out and then heap it up with coal; such a procedure is bound to lead to smoke, not necessarily in the house, it is true, but every such addition helps to pollute the air of our towns.

Further improvement might be made by the provision of better linings to chimney flues. These are often of very rough construction, i.e. they are not properly parged and cored and obstruct air passage through them. The use of unglazed tubes of clayware for lining flues is no new idea, and has much to recommend it.

APPENDIX I

The Materials used in Sanitary Work

The following are brief descriptions of the composition, properties and manufacture of the principal materials used in sanitary work.

Asbestos cement. Asbestos cement products are made of a mixture of asbestos fibres and Portland cement, moulded or "spun" to form. Asbestos is a naturally occurring silica compound which is crushed and shredded prior to mixing with the cement. The resulting material is highly resistant to corrosion, alkalis and sewage. Its strength increases with age, but with age it also becomes brittle. For this reason lowest lengths of exposed soil pipes are often protected against damage or a length of cast-iron pipe is inserted.

New asbestos cement, like other cement surfaces, attacks paint and must be weathered or treated with an alkali-resisting primer before it can be satisfactorily painted.

Pipes used for sanitary installations are supplied coated with bituminous composition unless specified otherwise.

Bricks. The principal use of bricks in sanitary work is for the construction of manholes and sewers, and for these items bricks should fulfil the following conditions:

1 They should be non-absorbent unless protected by a non-absorbent facing.
2 They should be well baked throughout.
3 They should be uniform in size, shape, and texture.
4 They should have sharp arrises or edges.
5 They should be free from flaws, stones and lumps of lime, the last named being liable to expand and split the brick.
6 They should ring well when two are struck together.
7 They should be strong and require repeated blows before breaking.
8 They should stand handling and cartage well without injury.

Brick earth. Bricks are formed of clay or shale, baked or burned. Their quality depends on the chemical composition of the earth used, the amount of preparation it has undergone, the temperature at which burned and the care with which the burning is carried out.

A good brick earth is generally composed of silica and alumina, together with a small quantity of lime or iron, or both, which act as a flux to fuse the particles together, giving silicate of alumina. Small percentages of other substances are also contained, such as magnesia, potash, soda and manganese, which give the colour to the brick. Colour is also dependent on the temperature of burning. For example, the well-known Staffordshire blue brick owes its colour to a fairly large proportion of oxide of iron, which is converted from the red oxide to the black by the high temperature. A small proportion of iron, and a moderate temperature, give bricks from orange to a deep red in colour, while bricks free from iron burn white. Magnesia gives a yellow colour.

Brickmaking. Brickmaking involves four stages, the preparation of the earth; moulding; drying; and burning.

PREPARATION. The clay is first exposed by unsoiling or removing the earth above it, then dug, freed from stones, ground in some cases, and tempered, which consists practically of kneading.

MOULDING. Bricks may be moulded by hand or by machine. Those used in sanitary work are usually machine made.

Machine moulding is carried out in three ways:

1 By forcing the plastic clay continuously through an opening and cutting off the brick lengths by means of descending wires, which of course give a brick without a frog. The marks of the wires can always be seen on a wire-cut brick.
2 By moulding the brick from powdered clay under great pressure, such bricks usually having frogs.
3 By moulding the bricks in the ordinary way and then subjecting them to compression under a piston.

Pressed bricks of the last two classes have very true surfaces and hard edges.

Before the bricks are ready for burning they must be dried, which is usually done naturally either indoors or out.

BURNING. The burning can be accomplished in two ways, either in a clamp or in a kiln. A clamp consists of a stack of raw bricks built up over a rough system of flues formed by bricks already burned, on a properly drained floor covered with burned bricks. Combustible material is mixed with the clay from which bricks are formed and bricks are burned by setting fire to the clamp. The quality of the bricks produced is often very uneven.

Brick kilns. Kilns are of two principal kinds, the intermittent and the continuous. The former is known as the Scotch kiln, and consists of a low, rectangular, roofless building, with a wide doorway at each end, and fire holes along each side. Flues are formed with bricks from side to side, the kiln is loaded, and the doorways bricked up. The whole charge of bricks is then burned, allowed to cool, and then the kiln is emptied. The best-known type of continuous kiln is the Hoffmann, of which there are many forms, differing only in detail. All are chamber kilns, circular, oval or rectangular on plan, having chambers which are separated by removable doors. In some chambers the bricks are being placed, in some they are drying, some burning, some cooling, and some being unloaded. This system is now in use in all the large brickyards, and gives a regular supply independent of weather, the kiln being roofed.

Bricks for sanitary work. The best bricks for sanitary purposes are pressed red bricks, blue Staffordshire bricks, and hard bricks salt-glazed on the exposed faces, like the surface of a drain pipe. Glazing is effected by the vaporisation of common salt in a special kiln, which covers all exposed faces with a thin film of glass.

Staffordshire blue bricks have a crushing strength as high as 16,600 lb/sq. in. and are almost completely impervious to water. They are therefore eminently suitable for engineering or sanitary work where these qualities are necessary, particularly in underground work in wet or waterlogged soil. In positions involving exposure to sand-laden winds or alternate wet and frost they are ideal.

Pressed red engineering bricks (such as Accrington reds) have crushing strength up to 10,300 lb/sq. in., but are not quite so impervious to moisture as Staffordshire blues.

Brown salt-glazed bricks and white vitreous-glazed bricks are used where a smooth easily cleansed surface is required or where their light reflecting qualities will be useful. When the body of glazed bricks is absorbent and the bricks are used in a position where they are exposed to moisture from the rear (as in facing a retaining wall) it may be found in frosty weather that the glaze will craze or flake off—pushed off by ice forming behind the glaze.

Useful data is available on the behaviour of clay engineering bricks in B.S. 1301, which calls for Class A engineering bricks to stand a minimum crushing test of 10,000 lb/sq. in. and a maximum water absorption (after a 5-hour boiling test) of 4·5 per cent of their dry weight, and for Class B engineering bricks to withstand 7000 lb/sq. in. and not exceed 7 per cent water absorption.

Stone. Stone is occasionally used in sanitary work, in the form of slabs for the tops of manholes and similar situations. York stone is the best fitted for these purposes.

Terra-cotta. This material is made by burning certain clays and is sometimes used for special invert blocks to egg-shaped sewers. Items are coated with glaze so that burning produces a hard vitrified outer skin, which is usually indestructible by acids but which must not be interfered with, e.g. by chipping adjoining edges to make them even in surface, as this exposes the softer inside structure of the material. Terra-cotta is almost always moulded hollow, with diaphragms or webs connecting the outer walls of the blocks, to reduce firing shrinkage. Cavities are usually filled with fine concrete before items are positioned.

Cement. Cements are of two kinds, natural and artificial. The former are burned from natural lumps of a clayey or stony nature, and the latter are burned from a mixture of materials. Cements can be further divided into those suitable for internal and for external use.

The principal cements for outside or underground work are Portland and Roman cements and for inside use plaster of Paris, Keene's, Parian, and similar cements. The best and strongest cement is Portland, so called from its supposed resemblance in colour to Portland stone. It is made from a mixture of chalk and clayey materials. In some parts of the Medway, and on the Thames side, a mixture of chalk and river mud is used, the mixture being regulated so that the finished product contains about 60 to 65 per cent of lime, 20 per cent silica, 10 per cent alumina, and a small amount of other constituents.

Manufacture of Portland cement. Measured proportions of chalk and clay are thoroughly combined by passing them through a set of three wash mills to form slurry which is passed through very fine screens. The slurry is next elevated, by pumping, to storage and mixing tanks, in which it is kept in motion by mechanical stirrers. It is sampled and chemically tested to check its composition and then conveyed to a special form of rotary kiln, to be dried and burned.

The kiln is about 6 ft in diameter and 130 ft long and fixed with its length inclined to the horizontal. The slurry enters at the upper end, and is dried by the rising hot gases, probably in about the first sixth or seventh of the length of the kiln, and issues at the lower end in a stream of fine clinker. A temperature of about 2800°F is kept up at the lower end of the kiln, the flames being fed by pulverised coal injected by an air or steam blast. The clinker falls into coolers, and is afterwards taken to a grinding mill. This is of cylindrical form, lined with plates lapping one over the other like roof tiles, and contains a number of hard steel balls. The rotation of the cylinder reduces the clinker to a fine powder which passes through perforations in the mill and is ready for further grinding. This is effected in another cylindrical mill containing specially hard pebbles, and known as a tube mill. This grinds the cement to a degree of fineness permitting over 90 per cent of it to pass through a sieve having 28,900 holes to the square inch. To make the cement ready for immediate use, a special apparatus is attached to the end of the tube mill, which subjects the cement to a charge of superheated steam at great pressure, a method superseding the old-fashioned method of spreading the cement over a wooden floor for a month or so to aerate it.

British Standard Portland cement. The best way to ensure that Portland cement is satisfactory is to require that it shall comply in all respects with the requirements of the latest specification of the British Standards Institution (B.S. 12), which covers "normal" or "quick-setting" grades.

B.S. 12 prescribes tests for fineness, chemical composition, strength, setting time and soundness. "Normal" cement does not begin to set for 30 minutes after mixing with water, setting being complete in something under 10 hours. "Quick-setting" cement begins to set 5 minutes after mixing and completes setting in something less than 30 minutes. In any specification for sanitary or building work it should be stated which of these classes of cement is to be used; normal setting should always be specified unless there is some special reason for requiring a quick-setting variety, e.g. where it is difficult to keep subsoil water from the work for more than a very short period.

Rapid-hardening cements. Of late years efforts have been made to produce cements which, whilst not beginning to set any more quickly, will harden more rapidly once setting has started. To understand their action it must be realised that the setting of cement depends on the combination of lime with alumina and silica in the presence of water, and that lime combines with alumina much more rapidly than it does with silica. Acceleration of the hardening can be obtained by finer grinding of the cement, so that the particles of lime are in more intimate contact with those of the other materials, and by increasing the proportion of alumina and reducing the proportions of lime and silica. (Rapid-hardening cements produced by fine grinding are known as "Ferrocretes" and it is claimed for them that in 3 days they will have the same strength that ordinary Portland cement has in 28 days.)

High-alumina cements are variously known as "Ciment Fondu", "Bauxite Cement" and "Aluminous Cement". For them it is claimed that in one day they will have twice the strength ordinary Portland cement has in 28 days. Of greater importance however is the resistance of High Alumina cements to sulphate attack. In many areas of the country sulphates of calcium and magnesium are present in the soil and if ordinary Portland cement is used for underground work in these areas it soon suffers loss of strength. High Alumina cements are not so affected. They are also preferable in marine areas and where brackish sub-soil water is present. They are covered by B.S. 915.

The cost of Ferrocrete is about 15 per cent greater than that of Portland cement and that of Ciment Fondu 100 per cent greater. The use of the latter is therefore usually confined to cases where considerable economies can be effected by the early removal of timber shuttering, the quick filling in of trenches, or diminution of a period of pumping.

Blast-furnace cement (B.S. 146). This is a comparatively new addition to the list of cements available. It utilises slag from blast furnaces in which limestone has played its part in the treatment of the iron. It may be obtained more cheaply than ordinary Portland cement—especially in blast-furnace areas It is somewhat more resistant to acid attack than Portland cement.

USE OF CEMENT. Cement should not be used neat except as a cement wash. Neat cement is more likely to expand or shrink on setting than a mortar made of 1 part of cement to 1 or 2 parts of sand.

Bylaws sometimes compel the use of neat cement for drain or sewer jointing with the idea that it will make the joint stronger and more watertight. Not only is this a needless extravagance, but involves risk that the cement on setting will expand fracturing the sockets and with subsequent contraction will become loose in the sockets and leaks result. (See page 238.) An admixture of at least an equal quantity of sand with the cement will prevent this and will at the same time reduce the cost of the work. The B.S. Code of Practice on Building Drainage recommends equal parts of sand and cement.

Roman cement. Roman cement is burned from calcareous nodules found in the London clay. It is used to a limited extent, its rapid-setting properties fitting it for work between tides or similar cases, but it has no great ultimate strength. It is said that even before setting it resists water, and the tendency to be washed away, better than other cements.

Keene's, Parian and similar cements. Keene's, Parian and similar cements are suitable only for such purposes as wall linings for inside work, since they contain a large amount of gypsum, which is soluble in water. Both are manufactured from plaster of Paris, Keene's cement by the addition of alum, and the Parian cement by the addition of borax. Both are very suitable for filling in cracks, because they expand in setting.

Sand is obtained from sand pits, river beds and the seashore. Pit sand is often angular, sharp and gritty, and on this account has generally been preferred for making mortar or concrete, to river sand, the grains of which are usually rounder and smoother. Of late years careful experiments seem to have shown, however, that angular grains are not superior to round grains; whether this is the case or not, the point is of small importance compared with that of obtaining a material which is free from any admixture of clay, loam, earth or organic matter. Sea sand contains a large amount of salt, and mortar and concrete containing it hold damp and effloresce. It should not, therefore, to be used in mortar for brickwork above ground, or for any other purpose where dampness or efflorescence would be a disadvantage. For other purposes there appears to be no valid objection to its use.

SUBSTITUTES FOR SAND. When sand is not available crushed stone may be substituted, or even crushed furnace ashes, or blast-furnace slag. Such materials, however, should not be crushed too small, and with stones—notably granite—it is difficult to avoid crushing it to fine dust, which results in a weak concrete. If any furnace residue is used it must contain no trace of coal dust. Unburnt coal expands when wet and, if present in mortar or concrete will cause it to crumble. Slag is a material which varies very much in quality and should not be used on important work without expert advice.

Mortar. For sanitary work cement mortar is almost always used, composed of Portland cement and sand. It should be mixed dry, the ingredients being carefully turned over together two or three times before the water is added. Proportions of mixes range from one part of cement to one of sand, to one of cement and four of sand. For jointing drain pipes, joints of brick sewers and similar work, one of cement and two of sand is a good proportion. Not more should be mixed than is immediately required, as mortar which has commenced setting cannot satisfactorly be re-mixed.

Concrete. As will have been seen, concrete, which is really an artificial stone, is largely used in sanitary work. There are two chief varieties of concrete, lime concrete and cement concrete; but the former is now little used, cement concrete being desirable for any work required to be waterproof. Bituminous concrete is also sometimes used, this being a compound of bitumen with broken stone, the former taking the place of cement.

Cement concrete consists of three materials, Portland cement, sand and a larger aggregate, such as broken stone. The cement and sand together form a matrix or mortar which binds together the aggregate. The aggregate may be of broken stone, broken bricks, gravel, Thames ballast, coke breeze or furnace slag. (Remarks made above about the two last-mentioned materials apply with equal force to their use as aggregates. They are not generally used in sanitary works.) If unscreened gravel or Thames ballast is used no sand will be needed in addition to that which is contained in the ballast. This material is, however, of uncertain quality. It used to contain a reasonable amount of sand for the making of concrete, but now very often contains far too much. It should be used with caution.

Whatever the nature of the aggregate chosen, it should be free from clay, loam and earth, or freed from these by washing. If stone or brick is used, it should be broken to a size suitable to the character of the work to be executed, only pieces which are capable of passing through a screen of specified mesh being used, whilst small stuff, which passes through a much smaller screen, should be rejected.

Gauge of aggregate. For heavy retaining walls or foundations the material should be capable of passing through a screen of 2 in. or 2½ in. mesh; for work which is to be watertight, such as the walls of a sedimentation tank, a gauge of 1 in. would be reasonable, whilst for thin slabs of concrete and for reinforced concrete the maximum gauge should be about ¾ in.

Proportions. The proportioning of the materials is of great importance, the ideal proportion for strength and watertightness being that in which the cement completely fills the voids between the grains of the sand, and the matrix so formed completely fills the voids between the pieces of the larger aggregate.

This proportion can be determined roughly in the following manner. A watertight box of known capacity is filled with the broken stone and water is poured in until the spaces between the stone are completely filled; the volume of water is carefully measured as it is poured in and this will be an indication of the amount of sand required. A similar test can be conducted on the sand, the amount of water added in this case being an indication of the amount of cement required.

It will generally be found that the proportions arrived at by these means will be about one part of cement, two parts of sand and four parts of stone, so that in reinforced concrete and other work which has to be watertight, these proportions can be used if great care is taken in the mixing. To allow for uneven mixing the proportions may be 1, 1¾ and 3½ in important work. For the foundations of ordinary buildings, for support of sewers and other work in which watertightness is of no importance and only moderate strength is required, the proportions are commonly made 1, 3 and 6 respectively.

Watertight work. Where a strong or watertight concrete is required the proportion of water added is of great importance and should be carefully controlled. It should be as little as is possible to produce a concrete which is easily workable. This proportion will vary with different aggregates and sands according to their initial wetness and their porosity. Only clean water should be used.

Concrete mixing machines. Concrete is preferably mixed in machines, in which there are fittings for measuring the various materials, including the water. In cases where a mixing machine cannot be used the ingredients should be carefully measured in gauging boxes and tipped on to a board platform. They should then be turned over carefully at least twice, to mix them thoroughly, in the dry state. After this, clean water should be added through a rose, and the whole turned over again at least twice in its wetted condition. Concrete should not be tipped from a height, or the heavier particles will separate from the lighter, but should be gently lowered into position, deposited in layers not more than 1 ft thick, and each layer well rammed. If any layer has set before the next is added, it should be allowed to set hard and should then be roughened, brushed, wetted and coated with cement and water, a mixture known as "cement grout", before a fresh layer is placed.

Glazed pipes. The relative advantages of stoneware and fireclay for the manufacture of drain pipes have already been referred to. They are both manufactured, by machine, in the same way. The machine is arranged so as to extend through two floors of the building.

On the upper floor is a steam cylinder, working a steel ram. Below the ram is a hopper or funnel, formed in the floor and into which the clay is charged. Connected to the outlet of the hopper, in the room below, is a steel pipe mould, with a core inside it, the socket being lowermost. There is a space between the core and the mould, which, if filled, and the mould and core then removed, would leave the partly finished pipe. At the lower end of the mould is a small platform which can be readily raised or lowered, and on this is the socket part of the core. The clay is charged into the hopper and the ram allowed rapidly to rise and fall, to compactly fill the mould. Clips, holding the platform to the base of the mould, are then released, and the ram allowed to descend slowly to remove the pipe from the mould and on to the lowering platform. When a sufficient length of pipe is through the mould, it is cut off by a thin steel wire to a length rather greater than its ultimate length. It is then taken to a revolving table, cut to its true length, trimmed and the grooves on the socket and spigot formed. The platform is brought up to its original position, re-clamped, and the operation repeated. Bends are formed by the pipe moulder taking the lower end of the pipe, as it issues from the mould, and pulling it round to the desired curve. Junctions are formed of two pipes moulded as just described, a hole being cut in the side of one, and the other cut to fit, the moulding being carefully completed by hand. More complicated pieces of stoneware are moulded in two halves and then put together, the joint being carefully made good.

DRYING AND BURNING. Drying is generally done in a drying shed, often over a kiln. Items are then stacked in a dome-shaped kiln, having fire holes around its base, and burned for about 3 to 4 days, according to the composition of the clay. While in the kiln they are, when sufficiently burned, glazed by the vaporisation of common salt, applied either at the fire holes, or at the top of the kiln. The heat transforms the salt into a vapour which coats every exposed surface in the kiln, and combines with the surface of the clay. (Salt glaze cannot be chipped off a pipe without taking off a piece of the pipe itself.)

An alternative method of glazing, of greater expense, and with many disadvantages, is that known as lead glazing. The glaze is applied after the pipes or other articles have been burned and removed from the kiln. It consists of a mixture containing, among other things, oxides of lead and tin, silica, china clay, and borax. This forms, when burned in another kiln at a temperature of about 1000°F, a thin surface coating of a glassy nature, but one which does not combine with the material of the pipe, and can be readily chipped off.

Stoneware pipes, if required to be of "tested" quality, are tested by means of a hydraulic press, the objects of the test being to determine resistance to absorption, percolation and pressure. (See Chapter 8.)

Cast iron, wrought iron and steel. The manufacture of these materials is too large a matter to be dealt with fully in a work of this kind, but differences in composition and properties are worth noting. The main difference in composition is in the proportion of carbon contained. Cast iron contains from about 2 to 6 per cent, wrought iron from 0 to 0·15 per cent, and steel from 0·12 to 1·5 per cent.

Cast iron is obtained by smelting the ore in blast furnaces and running the metal into moulds termed pigs. Pig iron is remelted to obtain good quality material. There are three kinds of cast iron, white, grey and mottled, which contains both the grey and white varieties. White and mottled cast iron are less liable to rusting than the grey variety, but the last mentioned is the material which, because of its greater strength, is used for structural castings.

Cast iron is crystalline in structure, has relatively little resistance to tension, but great strength in compression. It is lacking in elasticity and is hard and brittle.

Wrought iron is obtained from cast iron by a series of processes, the object of which is to remove the carbon and the impurities which made the cast iron brittle. Wrought iron is of fibrous structure, very tough and ductile, easily forged and welded but not fusible. It has high resistance to tension and to compression.

Steel may be produced by adding carbon to wrought iron, or by removing a portion of the carbon from pig iron. There are a large number of processes by which this may be brought about. Mild steel is a material which is superior to wrought iron for all ordinary structural uses, principally in that it is stronger and more uniform in texture. It has great tensile strength, and has greater resistance to compression than wrought iron, and a harder surface. It is also more elastic in nature. Mild steel is forgeable and weldable, like wrought iron. Given pieces of the same bulk, cast iron of good quality will withstand exposure longer than wrought iron, because of the rapid way in which commercial wrought iron goes to pieces by flaking, a process which does not apply to cast iron.

Iron pipes. Cast-iron pipes are formed in a mould usually having a core in the middle. They can be cast horizontally, vertically or in an inclined position. All three methods are in use, but the vertical method is best, though perhaps less convenient to adopt. It gives pipes of more uniform thickness and greater density. The inclined method, in which the mould is placed at an angle of about 45° with the horizontal, also gives a good quality of pipe. The horizontal method is used chiefly for the lighter kinds of pipe, and does not give such a good pipe as either of the other methods. In vertical casting the pipe is cast with the socket downwards, to give maximum density at that part, and cast of greater length than needed, by from 6 in. to a foot, so as to allow the dross and air bubbles to rise to the top. (This part is afterwards cut off.)

"Spun" iron pipes. An alternative method of manufacture is that in which the iron is "spun" by centrifugal force against a rotating mould, no core being used in this process.

B.S. 78 specifies vertically cast-iron pipes for pressure purposes and B.S. 437 similar pipes for drains. B.S. 1211 specifies spun iron pipes for pressure purposes. The fittings to be used in conjunction with cast-iron drain pipes are covered by B.S. 1130.

Wrought-iron pipes. Wrought-iron pipes are made in three alternative ways. The strongest pipes, such as are required for high-pressure hydraulic mains, are formed by winding a bar of iron spirally around a core, the abutting edges being then welded together. Pipes of this variety are of very great strength, and have been made to stand a stress of several tons per square inch without injury. The second method consists of bending a bar round a core then welding together the abutting edges, thus forming a longitudinal joint. The third method is similar, but the adjoining edges are welded by the electrical resistance method. This process produces a very high grade of tube which may be used for boiler and super heater tubes, refrigeration plant tubes, etc.

PROTECTION FROM CORROSION. As has been pointed out in earlier chapters, it is necessary to protect iron pipes from corrosion. The Angus Smith method, galvanising and Bower-Barff process have already been described. Another process is that of glass enamelling the inside of the pipe. This consists of coating them internally with lead glaze, as described for stoneware, and then firing them in a kiln. The great trouble with pipes of this kind is the difficulty of cutting them without removing part of the internal lining of glass and so exposing the iron to oxidation. Steel pipes are specified in B.S. 534.

Lead. This material is of great importance in sanitary work. Not only is it used for gutters, flashings, flat roofs, cisterns, damp courses, etc., but also for much sanitary pipework.

Lead is produced by smelting ores, the ores from which it is principally obtained being galena and cerussite. It is a very malleable material and can be readily worked to almost any shape without applying heat.

Sheets of lead can be either cast or milled. Cast sheets are now little used, having several drawbacks. They can be obtained up to about 16 ft long by 6 ft wide, but are of uneven surface and thickness and liable to flaws and sand holes. Milled lead sheets are generally used both for flats and gutters, and also for all other sanitary work. They are obtained by first casting a large, thick block and then rolling and re-rolling it in a mill, having two very heavy steel rollers, until it has been reduced to the desired thickness. Milled lead is obtainable in sheets up to about 35 ft long and 9 ft wide, though rather smaller sizes are more usual. Milled lead sheet is described by its weight per superficial foot. Standards for sheet lead are set by B.S. 1178.

Alloys of lead. One defect of lead is that under long continued strain, especially when subjected to vibration, it crystallises and becomes brittle. It has been found that this does not occur if the lead is alloyed with small quantities of certain other metals, and the resulting alloys are considerably stronger than ordinary lead. These alloys are referred to in Chapter 6.

Red and white lead. Lead is also used in sanitary work in the form of so called red and white lead. Red lead is obtained by oxidising metallic lead in a furnace, when exposed to the action of air. A coating of oxide is formed, and this is removed to expose a fresh metallic surface, this process being continually repeated. The oxide is then ground in water between stone rollers, and again exposed to the action of air in another furnace.

This enables it to take up more oxygen and gives it its red colour. It is then re-ground in water and dried.

White lead is made by exposing metallic lead to the action of the fumes of acetic acid in the presence of carbonic acid gas. The lead is suspended in jars over the acid, the jars being usually stacked in tiers between permanent and temporary floors covered with tan. A stack formed in this way is left for about three months to ferment, when the heat vaporises the acid and causes the tan freely to give off carbonic acid gas. This forms a coating of carbonate on the lead, which is then removed and ground. To bring it to its commercial form, as used by the painter, it is then re-ground in linseed oil.

Lead in contact with Portland cement. It is now known that lead is affected chemically by damp Portland cement, and for this reason lead placed in contact with cement should be previously coated with bitumen.

Lead pipes. At one time lead pipes were made by bending the lead around a core and soldering the joint, and pipes of this kind are still sometimes found in old houses. Nowadays, however, solid drawn seamless pipes are used. They are made by forcing semi-molten lead through a die by means of a hydraulic press, or by the use of a ram actuated by steam. Over the head of the ram a thick cylinder of lead is enclosed in a very strong casing. At the top of the casing interchangeable dies can be fixed, varying of course with the size of the intended pipe. The ram works around a rigid pillar, to the top of which a short length of core is fixed, having a diameter equal to that of the pipe. Around this is fixed the die, which is larger in radius by an amount equal to the thickness of the pipe. Through the opening so left, the ram forces the lead in the form of a continuous tube.

Tin-lined lead pipes. In somewhat the same category as lead pipes are tinned-lead pipe and tin-lined pipe. The former is of drawn lead thinly coated with tin by the simple process of pouring a little molten tin into the lead pipe as it comes from the pipe machine, the pipe being sufficiently hot to keep the tin in a molten state. The tin amalgamates to some extent with the lead to form a surface alloy, but the coating is far from uniform, and the resulting pipe little better than one of ordinary drawn lead. The tin-lined pipe is an article of quite a different nature, there being a definite tube of tin inside the lead. The construction of the pipe is simple. In the casing of the pipe machine, instead of merely a thick cylinder of lead, is a cylinder in two parts, the inner one of tin and the outer one of lead, the ratio of their thicknesses corresponding with the ratio of the thickness of the tin and lead in the finished pipe. The pipe therefore issues from the machine as a tube of tin inside a tube of lead. The object of tinning or tin lining a pipe is to make it suitable for the conveyance of soft water without injuring its quality, but there is often considerable trouble in jointing, the lining being destroyed and the surface of the lead exposed.

Bends and traps in lead. Bends and traps can be formed from drawn-lead piping by means of special bending appliances, but the solid drawn-lead bends and traps can be made in a pipe machine very similar to the one described already. The difference lies in the fact that, in place of the vertical ram, two horizontal rams are used. By setting them to work at varying speeds the lead is forced through the die at a faster rate on one side than on the other, thus giving a bend of radius depending on the relative velocities of the rams.

Lead wool or leadite. This substance consists of fine threads or shavings of lead, twisted to form a sort of rope. It is used instead of ordinary molten lead for caulked lead joints and is particularly suitable for work under water or in positions difficult of access.

Polythene. This is a thermoplastic synthetic material which is strong and extremely light. It is highly resistant to corrosion and to attack by most acids and alkalis.

Tubes are extruded from it in many grades of material and wall thicknesses —those suitable for plumbing being covered by B.S. 1972 which covers tubes of two thicknesses—one thick enough for screw jointing and one thin enough to require other jointing methods. Tubes are easily formed and the lighter grade can be satisfactorily jointed in a variety of ways (Chapter 6).

Polythene's principal disadvantages are its low melting point (about 110–115°C), which makes it unsuitable for tubes carrying hot water, and its need for frequent fixing to prevent sagging or bowing.

Polythene is also used for the manufacture of moulded traps and larger size pipes and fittings suitable for soil and waste installations. Tubes and pipes have the advantage of very smooth internal surfaces.

P.V.C. See pages 171 and 234.

Copper. This material is used for roofing and flashings, damp-proof courses, hot and cold water services (including back boilers, cylinders and tanks), soil and waste pipes, rainwater gutters and downpipes.

A reddish-brown metal, it is obtained by smelting ores, such as pyrites and malachite. It is tough, malleable and ductile and can be forged hot or cold. Cold working gradually hardens the metal, so that annealing is needed to restore a dead soft temper if the working is to continue past the hard stage.

For roofing purposes copper is obtainable in two forms, sheet and strip, the former being in basic sizes of 4 ft × 2 ft and 6 ft × 3 ft (though larger sizes are obtainable) and the latter in long rolls of any width up to 2 ft. When exposed to the atmosphere it takes on a protective coating or patina, which may vary in colour from a rich grey-green to brown, or even black, and may be either a carbonate, sulphate or chloride of copper, according to the impurities of the atmosphere.

For damp-proof courses it is obtainable in long coils in all the usual wall widths (B.S. 743).

Copper tubing may be obtained in half-hard temper in straight lengths up to 18 ft and in soft temper in coils of length up to 60 ft. When water comes into contact with the interior of the tube a protective coating is formed, unless the water is very acid, in which case the water will acquire a green tinge. The corrosion-resisting qualities of the metal, smoothness of bore, ease of jointing and neatness of appearance make it a first-class plumbing material. Standards for light-gauge copper tubes are set by B.S. 659.

Zinc. Zinc is used in roof work, for lining cisterns in some cases, as a constituent of various alloys, and also for galvanising. Most of the zinc used in this country comes from Belgium, and its thickness, when in the form of sheets, is customarily measured by means of the Belgian zinc gauge. It is very brittle when cold, and also when raised to a temperature of about 400°F, but at about 220°F it is very malleable and can be rolled into sheets, which retain their malleability. Zinc sheets are soon destroyed by the acid air of large towns and also by sea air. Another objection to zinc for roofing is that it blazes furiously at a red heat. Zinc is obtainable in sheets up to 8 ft × 3 ft and as soft temper strip in long lengths up to 3 ft wide.

Zinc coatings. The greatest use of zinc in plumbing work is in the application of protective coatings to pipes and tanks of steel. These coatings prevent the steel from rusting and as well as avoiding staining of water ensure much longer life for the protected items.

Zinc is less resistant to corrosion than copper or lead but steel pipes protected by zinc are cheaper than pipes of these materials. Used with hard and non-acid waters the zinc combines with chemicals in the water to form an additional protective coating and ensure long life for the plumbing installation. When waters are "soft" or acid, zinc corrodes rapidly and in these conditions is to be avoided. (See Chapter 7.)

The most usual method of applying zinc coatings is galvanising in which items to be coated are submerged in molten zinc (hot-dip galvanising), or immersed in suitable solution from or through which zinc is transferred to their surfaces by the passage of an electric current through it (electro-galvanising). Zinc coatings can be, and often are, applied by spraying articles with molten zinc and by "sherardising", placing articles to be coated in heated revolving drums containing zinc dust.

Zinc is lower on the electro-chemical scale than copper so that whenever zinc and copper or items containing copper come into contact in the presence of moisture galvanic action occurs and this results in greatly accelerated corrosion of the zinc. This is of major importance in the arrangement of plumbing installations where mixture of items of different metals often occurs. (See Chapter 5.)

Brass. Brass is an alloy composed of copper and zinc, the proportion varying according to the purpose for which the alloy is required. The best proportion for water fittings is 2 of copper to 1 of zinc.

Gunmetal. This material is suitable for high quality water fittings, and particularly so where the water is acid, such water injuriously affecting fittings of brass.

Gunmetal is an alloy of copper and tin, the best proportion for water fittings being 9 of copper to 1 of tin.

Solder. Ordinary plumbers' solder is known as soft solder, and is an alloy of tin and lead in the proportion of 1 of the former to 2 of the latter. Tinsmiths solder which is used with a copper bit (soldering iron) is 1 tin, 1 lead.

Hard solder, for use on copper, brass or gunmetal, is of different composition, consisting of copper, zinc and silver. For good ordinary work, it consists of from equal parts of copper and zinc to 2 of the former to 1 of the latter.

Fluxes. To assist solder to form a surface alloy with the metals with which it is in contact, and prevent the formation of an oxide on the surfaces of the materials which are being soldered, fluxes of various kinds are used. When using plumbers' solder for joining lead to lead, brass or copper, tallow is used, and when using fine solder (more fusible), resin and tallow. For use on brass, zinc or copper, chloride of zinc, also known as killed spirits, is used. Other fluxes are Gallipoli oil, for tin and pewter, and borax or sal ammoniac, for cast iron, malleable iron and steel.

Rust cement. This cement is particularly suitable for jointing iron pipes subjected to considerable changes of temperature. It is a mixture of fine cast-iron borings; water and sal ammoniac when required to be slow setting, or borings, water and flowers of sulphur when required to be more rapid in setting.

Limewash or whitewash. Where it is desirable to give walls a cheap sanitary coating, lime whiting is often used. It is made from pure lime mixed with water. The addition of 1 lb of pure tallow to every bushel of lime improves its quality. It will not adhere well to smooth non-porous surfaces, but is an excellent preservative for both stonework and brickwork, protecting them from attack by the acids in the air. For external work, a good whitewash can be made by adding 4 lb of sulphate of zinc and 2 lb of common salt to every bushel of lime.

Distemper. Ordinary distemper is a mixture of whiting and size, the whiting being chalk reduced to powder, and the size a thin animal glue. The distemper can be coloured by the addition of various earth pigments.

Many patent distempers, or water paints, are now obtainable, the makers in most cases claiming that their products are free from size, which is always liable to decompose and smell. Smell from ordinary distemper can, however, always be avoided by the addition of carbolic acid. In place of size, water paints contain dried soapy oils, which serve the same purpose of giving adhesiveness to the paint. They are more washable than common distemper.

APPENDIX II

Legal Notes

Purpose of the chapter. This chapter is intended to give a general idea of the legal position with regard to sanitary work. It does not profess to give qualified legal opinion upon specific points. Persons who require this should consult the statutes, the Local Bylaws or the Regulations concerned. Books written by lawyers on "Public Health Law" or on Model Building Bylaws may help still further, but if these fail to elucidate the matter reference should be made to a member of the legal profession for guidance on the matter in hand.

Differing forms of legal control. Building and sanitary work may be affected by general statutes, by Local Acts, sometimes (a little) by Common Law, whilst as regards use of materials, special sizes and types of fitting and arrangement in detail, by Local Bylaws. In some cases "orders" or "Regulations" are authorised by an Act of Parliament to provide further detailed control.

"Model bylaws" have been referred to quite a lot in the preceding chapters, but these are not actual law. As their name would suggest, they are just a specimen set of bylaws, prepared by the Ministry of Housing and Local Government as a guide to help the local authorities in the compilation of their own local building and drainage byelaws. In the case of Building and Drainage Byelaws the Public Health Act 1961 rescinded the powers given to Local Authorities, under previous statutes, to make Byelaws and made provisions for Building Regulations to cover the whole country. The duty of drafting these regulations was in the first instance given to the Ministry of Housing and Local Government and a draft for comment was published. The final drafting was subsequently passed to the Ministry of Public Building and Works and it is hoped that they will soon be brought into force. Meantime all existing byelaws remain in force although no new ones can be made.

Statute Law. The law relating to sanitary matters, broadly, is embodied in Acts of Parliament, the provisions of which are administered by local government authorities.

County and county borough councils. The oldest unit of local government in England and Wales is the parish, but the powers and duties of parish councils and parish meetings have been almost wholly transferred by statute to bodies controlling larger areas.

It is unnecessary here to trace the course by which our present local government system has been evolved and it is sufficient to say that the existing system is now defined by the Local Government Act 1933, a consolidating act, which repealed and re-enacted, with amendments, the provisions of Local Government Acts and other statutes of earlier days.

All England and Wales are divided into administrative counties and county boroughs, which are governed by county councils and county borough councils respectively. The administrative counties are not in all cases the same as the geographical counties, for some of the latter are divided into two or more counties for administrative purposes, whilst the county boroughs are excluded from the counties in which they are to be found in an atlas, and have most of the powers possessed by the administrative counties.

Only the larger of our boroughs are county boroughs. The minimum population necessary to justify the elevation of a borough to the status of a county borough was formerly 50,000, but is now 100,000.

Boroughs, urban districts and rural districts. Every administrative county is divided into county districts; these are either boroughs, urban districts or rural districts. The boroughs are those county districts which have been incorporated as boroughs by Royal Charter.

The boundaries of counties, boroughs, urban and rural districts can be changed by an order of the Boundary Commission, set up by the Local Government (Boundary Commission) Act 1945, but any such order made for a county or county borough needs confirmation by Parliament.

Little need be said here as to the powers and duties of county councils, but it will not be out of place to mention that they are responsible for the construction and upkeep of all roads in rural districts and of all classified roads in non-county boroughs (i.e. boroughs which are not county boroughs) and in urban districts; also, that they have a considerable measure of control over the county district councils and the power to make those councils perform their duties, the measure of such power being to some extent dependent on the status of the district council—whether it is urban or rural—and upon its population.

It is, however, with the county borough councils, borough councils, urban district councils and rural district councils with whom we are most concerned, for it is these bodies who make and administer building and drainage byelaws, provide schemes of main sewerage and sewage disposal, collect and dispose of refuse, cleanse streets, disinfect houses and articles, and take the necessary steps against persons who cause nuisances of a sanitary nature. These bodies we shall refer to as "local authorities".

Special law for London area. The position in London is somewhat different, for the Local Government Act 1933 does not, generally speaking, apply therein. The Local Government Act 1888, however—the Act which first established the administrative counties—made a county of London, or rather of such parts of the metropolis as were then built up, whilst the London Government Act 1899 divided the county into metropolitan boroughs. The City of London is one such borough, but, being of far more ancient origin than either the county or the other boroughs, it has some special privileges and duties.

The London County Council ceased to exist as such on April 1st 1965 and its place has been taken by the Inner and Greater London Authorities. There is already discussion on the possible effects of the outcome of this with regard to the special privileges enjoyed by the L.C.C. and to what extent these are going to be continued. Doubtless a number of cases will eventually come before the courts for ruling.

Principal statutes dealing with sanitary matters outside and inside London. The legislation which deals with streets, buildings and sanitation in the County of London differs from that in force in the remainder of the country.

Outside the metropolis all matters relating to streets are to be found in the Public Health Act 1875, its amendment Acts of 1890 and 1907, the Public Health Act of 1925, and the Private Street Works Act 1892. The Public Health Act 1936 deals with buildings, drains, sewers and sanitation generally.

Within London the most important statutes in force are: the London Building Act 1931, and its Amendment Acts of 1935 and 1939, which deal with building work and the laying out of new streets; the Metropolis Management Act 1855 and its numerous Amendment Acts (the chief of which is that of 1862), which deal with the making up of streets and similar matters; the Public Health (London) Act 1936, which deals with drains, sewers and sanitation generally.

It is with the two Acts of 1936 that we are most concerned, and it will be found that their provisions are in most respects very similar; there are, however, some important respects in which they differ and these will be noticed in due course.

Definition of "drain". In the Public Health Act 1936 a "drain" is defined as meaning a drain used for the drainage of one building, or of any buildings or yards appurtenant to buildings within the same curtilage. It may be noted that there has been much questioning as to the meaning of the word curtilage; Mr Macmorran, K.C., in his well-known work on the "Law of Sewers and Drains", defined it as the land adjoining a building and which would pass with it, on a conveyance, so far as is necessary and convenient for its use.

Definition of "sewer". The definition of "sewer" in the same Act is that it does not include a drain as defined above but, save as aforesaid, it includes all sewers and drains used for the drainage of buildings and yards appurtenant to buildings. It would seem then that, to express the matter more simply, a sewer is a pipe used for the drainage of two or more buildings not in the same curtilage; but it seems also that it may include pipes used only for the drainage of roads, for the Act does not say that a sewer *means* sewers and drains used for the drainage of buildings, but that it *includes* such sewers and drains; it therefore presumably may also include pipes not used for the drainage of buildings and it is clear from certain other sections of the Act that it is intended to do so.

Public and private sewers. Sewers may be either "public sewers" or "private sewers" under this Act. In effect a "public sewer" is a sewer which vests in (i.e. belongs to) a local authority and a private sewer is one which does not. The question, however, then arises as to what sewers belong to a local authority and the answer to this is by no means simple. The following sewers will belong to a local authority:

(*a*) Sewers which they have constructed at their own expense or have acquired, whether they are situated inside the district of the local authority or not (for it is quite common for urban authorities to construct their sewage-disposal works in an adjoining rural area and to construct an outfall sewer thereto).

(*b*) All sewers constructed to the satisfaction of the local authority as private street works, except sewers constructed only for the drainage of roads which will be repairable by the county council.

(*c*) All "combined drains" constructed prior to the 1936 Act for the joint drainage of two or more buildings under the provisions of earlier Acts. In this case, however, the local authority can recover the cost of maintenance and repair from the owners of the premises served.

(*d*) All new sewers which the local authority may declare to be vested in them. The Act provides, however, that, if the owner of any such sewer objects to its adoption by the local authority, he may appeal to the Minister of Health, who may allow or disallow the proposal; if he allows it he may direct that compensation shall be paid. Any person who was entitled to use the sewer at the date of its adoption may continue to use it afterwards.

A "private sewer" is any sewer which is not a public sewer. It will therefore include:

(*a*) Pipes laid after the commencement of this Act for the joint drainage of two or more buildings, not in the same curtilage.

(*b*) Sewers laid for the development of building estates, not yet adopted by the local authority as public sewers.

It should be noted before we pass on that the question of whether a pipe is a public sewer, private sewer or drain does not depend in any way upon whether it is placed in public or private property; public sewers can be, and often are, laid in private land, for the local authority has the power to lay a sewer in any land after reasonable notice, whilst the lower ends of private sewers and drains are usually in public streets.

In the London Act the definitions are somewhat different; for the term "drain" includes not only a drain used for the drainage of one building, or premises within the same curtilage, but also a drain for draining a group or block of houses by a combined operation under an order of a borough council or their predecessors, whilst a "sewer" means a sewer or drain of any description except a drain as defined above. In London there is no such thing as a private sewer; sewers constructed by the county council, or which belonged to them at the passing of the Act, or which they shall declare to be vested in them, shall belong to the county council, while all other sewers shall belong to the borough council in whose district they are situated. In general the main sewers will vest in the county council and subsidiary sewers in the borough council.

Duty of cleansing and repair of drains and sewers. The importance of these definitions lies, of course, mainly in the fact that the duty of cleansing and repair of any drain or sewer is upon the person or body in whom it is vested.

In the provinces (i.e. outside London) it is the duty of every local authority to provide such public sewers as will be necessary for effectually draining their district, and such sewage disposal works as are needed. It should be noted, however, that the Act does not say that the local authority must provide sewers at their own expense in anticipation of future building developments; the normal procedure in estate development is for the owner to lay the sewers which are necessary for estate drainage and for those to be adopted by the local authority as public sewers, either immediately after construction or when adopting the street as a public street, after the execution of private street works. It should be noted also that there is no obligation to provide a sewer for every house; isolated houses in rural areas are commonly drained to cesspools.

Position in London. Similarly, in London, it is the duty of the borough council to make such sewers as are necessary for draining the borough effectually and for the county council to construct such sewers as are necessary for the main drainage of the county.

Where a person proposes to construct a private sewer or drain and the local authority consider that it would be an advantage for it to form part of the general sewerage system of the district, they may require it to be formed of such materials, size, depth, gradient and direction as they may specify. The owner may appeal against the requirements to the Minister of Health and (whether he appeals or not) is entitled to be reimbursed any additional expense to which he is put. No such provision is contained in the London Act, but a borough council may contribute towards expenses incurred by an owner or occupier in constructing a sewer in the borough for the drainage of his premises; presumably they would not do so unless it were of some general use.

The local authority (in London or elsewhere) may alter or discontinue any public sewer, but if any person is thereby deprived of its lawful use he must be provided with a sewer equally effective and the local authority must do such alteration to the drains as is required at their own expense.

Every local authority, outside London, shall keep in their offices a map showing the public sewers of their district, distinguishing between surface water and foul sewers if both are in existence.

Petrol and other harmful solids or liquids. In both Acts there are clauses imposing penalties, on conviction, for putting or passing into sewers solid or liquid matters which might cause obstruction to the flow or cause danger to health. Persons allowing petrol or similar inflammable substances to pass into sewers are similarly liable to penalties.

Rights of adjoining owners and of local authorities. Owners and occupiers of premises are entitled, as a right, to branch their drains and private sewers into the appropriate public sewer, provided they give notice to the authority and comply with their regulations as to the manner of making the connection. Outside London the authority may, if they wish, themselves make the connection at the cost of the owner. In some few cases it may be more convenient to branch a drain or private sewer into a public sewer of an adjoining district; the owner of the drain or private sewer may do this, but the authority who own the public sewer may make a charge, which may be defrayed by the authority of the district in which the premises are situated. Local authorities outside London may, under the Public Health (Drainage of Trade Premises) Act 1937 impose conditions as to the nature, composition and rate of discharge of trade effluents, and may make byelaws regulating such discharge. The Public Health Act 1961 rescinded power to make byelaws, but replaced it by requiring all persons discharging trade wastes to a sewer to obtain consent of Local Authority who have power to impose conditions; i.e. Not a byelaw to suit all cases, but each judged on its merit.

Where (in the provinces) plans are deposited for the erection or extension of a building and it is proposed to build over any sewer or drain which is shown on the map of sewers, the authority shall reject the plans unless they are satisfied that they can properly consent; in London any person who knowingly builds over a sewer without consent is liable to penalties.

Law relating to house drains. The law relating to the provision of house drains differs considerably for London and the provinces.

In the provinces, where an owner wishes to erect or extend a building and submits plans in accordance with the bylaws, the authority shall reject the plans if these do not show satisfactory proposals for drainage and drainage cannot in the opinion of the authority be dispensed with. The authority can insist on the drains being connected to a sewer, rather than to a cesspool, if (*a*) the sewer is at a reasonable level, (*b*) the intervening ground is land through which the owner is entitled to lay a drain, and (*c*) the sewer is within 100 ft of the building, or the authority agree to bear the excess of cost due to the distance exceeding 100 ft.

Common or joint drains. Cases often occur where two or more buildings can be more cheaply drained by a common pipe than by separate drains. The authority will be within their rights if they insist on separate drains, but they can require combined drainage by a private sewer, constructed by the owners or by the authority on their behalf.

Where an existing building in the provinces has no satisfactory drains, or the drainage is defective, the authority may require drains to be laid, or such other work done as is necessary to meet the case. If they require the construction of drains, they can order that these shall be connected to a sewer in the same circumstances as in the case of new buildings.

House drain law in London. In London it is unlawful to erect or occupy a new building unless a drain has been provided to the satisfaction of the borough council, of such materials, size, level and gradient as the council may direct; such drain shall lead to a sewer if there is one within 100 ft of the building. It may be noted that this section of the Act says nothing about the sewer being "at a reasonable level", the intention clearly being that new buildings should be erected at such levels that drainage to a neighbouring sewer is possible from the lowest floor thereof. When a house is to be rebuilt, after it has been pulled down to the level of the ground floor, its level must be raised if this is necessary for its drainage to the sewer, unless such a proposal would be impracticable, in which case the council may allow the installation of pumping or lifting appliances, or may allow part of the building to be so constructed that drainage is not required therefrom.

If any existing building in London is without a sufficient drain, emptying into a sewer, and a sewer of sufficient size is within 100 ft of some part of the building and at a lower level than the building, the borough council can require the owner to construct such a drain to the sewer and to provide proper paved surfaces for carrying surface water to the drain, sinks, and other necessary apparatus. If, again, any building is without a sufficient drain and there is no sewer within 200 ft of the building, the council may require the owner, as a temporary measure, to construct a drain leading to a cessspool. The Act is curiously silent as to what is to be done if there is a sewer within 200 ft of the building, but not within 100 ft. The regulations of local authorities usually stipulate that work involving the disturbance of public roads and footpaths shall be done by them at the expense of the owner or occupier. Both in London and in the provinces the authority, on payment of the cost thereof, may undertake the connection of drains to sewers, or do any works of drainage on behalf of the owners of buildings.

Maintenance of drains and sewers. We now turn to the subject of the maintenance of drains and sewers. Drains and private sewers are in all cases maintainable by their owners, whilst the local authority has the duty of maintaining public sewers; there are, however, some circumstances in which a provincial local authority can recover the cost of maintaining certain public sewers from the owners whose premises are served by those sewers.

The circumstances in which this is the case are:

1. Where the sewer in question was, before the passing of the Public Health Act 1936, a "combined drain", which under earlier legislation was repairable by the owners of the premises served by that drain.
2. Where the sewer was not constructed at the expense of the authority and lies in a garden, court or yard belonging to any of the premises served by the sewer (or to any of them in common), or if it lies under a building comprised in any of those premises, or in a way used as a means of access to those premises, not being a public highway.

In any case where the authority are entitled, as stated above, to recover the cost of maintenance of a public sewer from the owners of premises served by the sewer, they must apportion the cost fairly among those owners, having regard to all the circumstances of the case, such as the benefit derived by each, the distance for which it is laid in the land of each, the point at which the work was necessary and the responsibility for any act or default which made the work necessary.

If, instead of executing works of maintenance to any such sewer as we have been referring to immediately above, the authority enlarge or otherwise improve it, so that it may serve additional premises, they may recover from the owners whose premises are now being served only such an amount as would be reasonable for maintenance and the owners are then relieved of all future liability. No person shall reconstruct, alter or repair any drain without notice to the authority, except in emergency, in which case he shall not cover up the work without notice; he shall permit an officer of the authority to have access for inspection.

If the drains of a building, outside London, are sufficient and effectual for their purpose, but are not adapted to the general sewerage system of the district, the authority may close such drains on the condition of providing, at their own expense, other drains as sufficient and effectual for the premises in question.

Sanitary accommodation. As to sanitary accommodation, it is provided in the Public Health Act 1936 that, where plans are submitted for a new building or the extension of a building, the authority shall reject the plans if these do not show sufficient and satisfactory closet accommodation and the authority do not consider it can be dispensed with; if there is a water supply and sewer available the authority can require the closets to be water-closets.

In the case of existing buildings, if it appears to the authority that there are not sufficient closets, or that those which are provided are in an unfit state and cannot be made fit without reconstruction, they can require the owner to provide water-closets, if there is a water supply and sewer, and in other cases can require him to provide earth-closets. If the present appliances are unfit, but can be made fit without reconstruction, they can order him to do what is necessary. If the present accommodation is in satisfactory condition, but is not a water-closet and a water supply and sewer are available, the authority can require it to be replaced by a water-closet but must bear half the cost of conversion. The provisions of the Public Health (London) Act 1936 in respect of this matter of sanitary accommodation are, in substance, almost the same as those of the provincial Act; the appliance must ordinarily be a water-closet, earth-closets or privies being allowed only if sewerage or a sufficient water supply is not available. There is no mention of conversion of earth-closets to water-closets, but presumably the borough council can require this to be done by the owner at his own cost if a sewer and a water supply are, or become, available.

Sanitary accommodation in factories. All factories, workshops and work-places must have sufficient sanitary accommodation with proper separation of the sexes. In connection with this, the Home Office has issued an order under the Factory Acts defining adequate accommodation as meaning one closet for every 25 women employed; for men, one for every 25 employed up to 100, and beyond that figure one for every 40 men, if in addition sufficient urinals are provided. In large works where more than 500 men are employed, the number of closets may be reduced to one for every 40 men if a proper system of control is adopted and urinals are also provided.

The Shops, Offices and Railway Premises Act of 1963 lays down a standard of accommodation for persons working in buildings coming within scope of the Act.

Powers to insist on sanitary conditions in certain cases. The following miscellaneous provisions are also to be found in the Public Health Act 1936:

No room, any part of which is over a closet (other than a water-closet or earth-closet) or over a cesspool or ashpit, shall be occupied as a living-room, sleeping-room or workroom.

The occupier of every building in which there is a water-closet shall cause the flushing apparatus to be kept supplied with water and protected from frost; in a building which has an earth-closet it shall be kept supplied with dry earth or other suitable deodorant.

When plans are deposited for the erection or extension of a building and the site has been filled in, or covered with, material impregnated by offensive animal or vegetable matter, the authority shall reject the plans unless they are satisfied that the material has been removed or has become innocuous. The person who deposited the plans has the right to appeal to a Court of Summary Jurisdiction against their rejection.

The authority may require the owner to pave and drain any court, yard or passage which gives access to any house or joint access to two or more houses.

The authority may require any leaking or overflowing cesspool to be remedied by the person in default.

Offensive pools, ditches, etc. A parish council, or a local authority, may deal with any pool, ditch, gutter or place containing filth, stagnant water or other matter likely to be prejudicial to health, by draining, cleansing or covering it, provided they do not interfere with any private right or with any public drainage, sewerage or sewage disposal works, and may execute any incidental works; they may, alternatively, contribute towards the expenses incurred by others in so doing. This power does not in any way prejudice the right of the local authority to take action if it is a statutory nuisance.

In London the borough councils have similar powers either to deal with such offensive pools, ditches, etc., themselves or to call upon the person who caused the nuisance, or the owner or occupier of the premises, to do what is necessary, in which case the council may defray all or any part of the cost; if, however, such action is prejudicial to any water rights the council must either pay compensation or acquire the rights.

If a local authority, outside London, make complaint against another local authority that a water-course or ditch, at or near the boundary between their districts, is foul and offensive, a Court of Summary Jurisdiction, of the district in which it is situated, may make an order for its cleansing and for the execution of any work; the order shall state who is to do the work and by whom the cost shall be paid.

If a provincial local authority consider that a water-course or ditch (not necessarily offensive), situated on or adjoining land laid out for building, ought to be filled or culverted, they may require the building owner to do this before or during the building operations, and to provide all necessary gulleys. Any question of the reasonableness of the authority's requirements shall be determined by a Court of Summary Jurisdiction. The building owner, however, cannot be required under this section to execute work on someone else's land unless that person consents.

Culverting of streams require approval by local authority. No person shall culvert any stream except in accordance with plans and sections approved by the authority, but such approval shall not unreasonably be withheld and there is the usual right of appeal to a Court of Summary Jurisdiction against the authority's requirements.

The owner or occupier of any land shall maintain and cleanse any culvert in such land.

The authority may, if they think fit, contribute the whole or part of the expenses incurred, on works in connection with the above-mentioned provisions relating to water-courses, culverts, etc., or may, by agreement with the owner or occupier, execute such works.

Collection and disposal of house refuse. Local authorities have responsibilities in respect of the collection and disposal of refuse, street cleansing and similar matters.

Under the Public Health Act 1936 a local authority may, and if required by the Minister shall, perform any or all of the following services:

(*a*) The removal of house refuse;

(*b*) the cleansing of earth-closets, privies, ashpits and cesspools.

If they have undertaken any of these duties and fail to perform them within seven days of a notice from the occupier of any premises, the occupier may recover a sum of five shillings per day during such default.

When an authority has undertaken the duty of removing house refuse they may make byelaws imposing duties on the occupiers for facilitating the collection, requiring the use of bins provided by the authority and regulating the use of the bins. If they have not undertaken that duty they may make byelaws requiring occupiers to remove their refuse at specified intervals and to cleanse their earth-closets, privies, ashpits and cesspools.

A local authority may, but cannot be compelled to, undertake the removal of trade refuse; if they do so they must make a charge. Where they have undertaken the duty and fail to fulfil it, after seven days' notice, the occupier may recover the sum of five shillings per day during the default.

Any dispute as to whether any particular refuse is house or trade refuse, or as to the reasonableness of their charges for removing the latter, shall be determined by a Court of Summary Jurisdiction. It may be noted here that the Superior Courts have held that the question of whether any particular refuse is house or trade refuse depends, not on the nature of the premises from which it is collected, but on the nature of the refuse itself. Thus, if the refuse is of a kind ordinarily removed from dwellings, it is house refuse even if produced on trade premises. The Public Health Act 1961 has altered this position with regard to Laundries and Catering Kitchens and a Local Authority may now consider the waste as trade waste and make a charge if the volume is excessive or requires special treatment such as more frequent collection in the case of refuse from an hotel.

An authority which undertakes the removal of house refuse, may by notice, require the owner or occupier of any buildings to provide such number of covered bins of such material, size and construction as they may approve. They cannot, however, require the replacement of any existing bin, if this is of satisfactory design and in good condition. Alternatively, the authority may provide bins and make annual charge for their use.

In London the borough councils *must* remove house refuse and cleanse earth-closets, privies and cesspools, and are liable to a fine of £20 if they fail to do so, without reasonable excuse, after 48 hours' notice from an occupier. The councils *must* also remove trade refuse if required to do so by the owner or occupier, but shall make a reasonable charge.

Street cleansing. In the country, a local authority may, and if required by the Minister of Health shall, undertake the cleansing of streets and may undertake the watering of them. In both London and the country the local authorities, having collected refuse from premises and streets, may dispose of it in such manner as they think fit.

"Nuisances" defined. The next matter to be considered is what are termed "statutory nuisances". The term "nuisances" at law means anything which causes hurt or annoyance, and a person who suffers from a nuisance committed by another may bring an action in tort; but there are certain particular kinds of nuisance in respect of which a local authority can proceed in the public interest; these are named in Acts of Parliament and hence are termed "statutory" nuisances.

The most important examples, from our point of view, under the Public Health Act 1936 are:

(*a*) Any premises in such a state as to be prejudicial to health, or a nuisance.

(*b*) Any animal kept in such a place or manner as to be prejudicial to health, or a nuisance.

(*c*) Any accumulation or deposit which is prejudicial to health, or a nuisance.

(*d*) Any well, tank cistern, or water-butt used for the supply of water for domestic purposes, if constructed or kept so that the water is liable to contamination prejudicial to health.

(*e*) Any pond, ditch, water-course, etc., so foul as to be prejudicial to health, or a nuisance.

Under the Public Health (London) Act, whilst the list is not precisely the same, it is substantially similar; but in London an occupied house without a proper and sufficient supply of water is to be dealt with as a nuisance, as also is the absence of water fittings in a house.

Abatement of nuisances. It is the duty of every local authority, under the Public Health Act 1936, to inspect their district from time to time for the detection of statutory nuisances. If they discover one they shall serve on the person who caused it an "abatement notice", or, if they cannot find that person, on the owner or occupier of the premises in which it occurs; the notice will require him to abate the nuisance and to execute any works which may be necessary for that purpose. It is provided, however, that, when the nuisance is due to structural defects, the notice shall be served on the owner; also that, when the offender cannot be found and the nuisance is clearly not caused by the act or omission of the owner or occupier, the authority may themselves abate it.

If the person on whom the notice is served does not comply with it, or if the nuisance is likely to recur, the authority shall apply for a summons for such person to appear before a Court of Summary Jurisdiction. If, on the hearing of the case, it is proved that the nuisance exists, or is likely to recur, the Court shall make a "nuisance order" directing the offender as to what he is to do; the Court also may impose a fine and may award costs to the authority. They may also prohibit the use of the building for human habitation if the nuisance is causing it to be unfit for such habitation.

If the person on whom the nuisance order is made does not comply with it he is liable to a further fine, and the authority may do what is necessary in execution of the order and may recover from him the cost of doing so.

It is provided, however, that proceedings shall not be taken if the nuisance was necessary for the effectual carrying on of a business or manufacture and the best practicable means have been taken to prevent its being prejudicial to health or an annoyance to the neighbouring inhabitants.

When a nuisance appears to be caused by two or more persons proceedings can be taken against any or all of them, and the order of the Court may be directed to any or all of those proceeded against. If some of the offenders were not proceeded against, those who were can recover from them a due share of the expense incurred and of any fine imposed.

An appeal against a nuisance order of a Court of Summary Jurisdiction and, in fact, against almost any other order of such Court under this Act, can be made to a Court of Quarter Sessions.

The procedure for requiring the abatement of nuisances in London is substantially the same as in the provinces.

Where a local authority, outside London, have reasonable grounds for believing that any sanitary convenience, drain, private sewer or cesspool is in such a condition as to be prejudicial to health or a nuisance, or that a drain or private sewer is so defective as to admit surface water, they may examine its condition and for that purpose may apply any test, other than a water test, and may open up the ground if necessary. If on examination the appliance or work is found to be in good order they must reinstate the ground as soon as possible and make good any damage. If the examination shows the appliance or work to be in bad order they have ample powers under other sections of the Act to require the matter remedied.

It may be mentioned here that an officer of the authority has the power to enter any premises, on proving his identity, for the performance of any of his duties under the Act or bylaws, but shall give 24 hours' notice to the occupier of his intention, if the premises are other than a factory, workshop or workplace. If it can be shown that admission is refused, or that the premises are unoccupied, or that the matter is urgent, or that notice of entry would defeat the object of entry, a Justice of the Peace may by warrant authorise entry, if need be by force.

Similar powers are given by the London Act, but the works which may be examined include also any water supply, sink, trap, siphon, pipe or other works or apparatus connected therewith, and in cases of urgency the officer can enter without notice without obtaining a warrant.

Local building and drainage bylaws. Detailed requirements as to the design and construction of new drainage systems and of all kinds of sanitary fittings, as well as to the construction of new buildings, will be found in the local bylaws. A bylaw is a law, of purely local application, made by a local authority under power conferred by statute and confirmed by a Government Department (the Ministry of Housing and Local Government for all building and sanitary bylaws). In order that it shall be valid a bylaw must be (1) *intra vires*, i.e. within the powers conferred by statute; (2) certain in its terms, i.e. not ambiguous; (3) not repugnant to the law of the land; and (4) reasonable. The fact that a Government Department has confirmed a bylaw will not make it valid if it is contrary to any of these four requirements.

The bylaws will to some extent vary in different districts, but in general will be very similar to the Model Bylaws issued by the Ministry of Housing and Local Government but as already stated on page 415 byelaws will cease to exist for Building and Drainage when the new Building Regulations are published. Anyone remotely connected with building law should make himself acquainted with these regulations as soon as they are published.

Definition of "Owner". These notes would not be complete without explaining what is meant by an "Owner" in the Public Health Acts.

The Public Health Act 1936 defines owner as "the person for the time being receiving the rack rent of the premises, whether on his own account or as agent or trustee for any other person, or who would so receive the same if the premises were let at a rack rent". The definition in the Public Health (London) Act 1936 is substantially the same.

The two Acts, however, have different interpretations of the words "rack rent". In the provincial Act it is a rent not less than two-thirds of the full net annual value; i.e. "a rent which is not less than two-thirds of a rent at which the property might reasonably be expected to let from year to year, free from all usual tenants' rates and taxes, and tithe rent charge (if any), and deducting therefrom the probable average annual cost of repairs, insurance and other expenses (if any) necessary to maintain the same in a state to command such rent". In the London Act rack rent is a rent not less than two-thirds of the "annual value", without any reduction for repairs and insurance.

A fact worth notice is that, under the wording of these definitions, agents and trustees rank as owners, and are therefore personally liable for the obligations of owners under the Acts.

There is, however, some protection given to them under the provincial Act; for this says that, where a council claim to recover expenses from a person as being the owner of premises and he is receiving the rent as agent or trustee for another person and has not, and since the date of service of demand has not had, sufficient money in his hands on behalf of that person, his liability is limited to the amount he has, or has had. The council can recover any excess over this only from the person on behalf of whom the agent or trustee is acting.

Another matter worth mention here is that, both in London and elsewhere, any expenses recoverable from an owner by the council may be recovered from the occupier, up to the amount of rent which is due from him to the owner, or which may become due after the expenses are demanded. In the absence of any contract to the contrary, the occupier may deduct from his rent such payments as have been recovered from him.

The Housing Acts. Finally, it is necessary to refer to certain provisions of the Housing Act 1936. Section 2 of this Act provides that in any contract, made before or after the passing of the Act, for the letting for habitation a dwelling-house, or part of a house, at a rent not exceeding in the administrative County of London £40 and elsewhere £26 per annum, there shall, notwithstanding any stipulation to the contrary, be implied a condition that the house is at the commencement of the tenancy, and an undertaking that the house will be kept by the landlord during the tenancy, in all respects reasonably fit for human habitation.

This condition and undertaking are not to apply where the house is let for a term of not less than three years upon the terms that it be put by the lessee into a condition reasonably fit for habitation, and the lease is not determinable by either party before the expiration of three years.

The foregoing shall not apply to a house situate elsewhere than in the County of London, or a borough or urban district with a population of 50,000 or upwards, the rent of which exceeds £16, if the contract was made before the 31st July 1923.

Other parts of the same Act deal with the clearance of areas in which the houses are either unfit for habitation owing to disrepair or sanitary defects, or dangerous to health owing to bad arrangement of buildings, or narrowness or bad arrangement of streets; with the redevelopment of areas which contain houses which are overcrowded, unfit for habitation or arranged in a congested manner; with the repair or demolition of individual houses which are unfit for habitation; with the remedying of overcrowding of houses, the removal of obstructive buildings and the provision of houses for the working classes. It would be going beyond the scope of a work on sanitation to describe the provisions in detail, so that readers are referred to specialised books on Housing or to the Act itself.

APPENDIX III

Study Notes for Students

Need for practical study. The student of sanitation, a subject which deals so largely with appliances and fittings in daily use in the home and other buildings, has excellent opportunities of combining practical investigations with book knowledge. His studies should however be objective for, in spite of a daily familiarity, the average adult, asked to give the height of an ordinary W.C. seat or the dimensions of an average lavatory basin or the height at which it is fixed from the floor, gives some quite surprising figures.

Use of sketch-book. The student, during his studies, should therefore not just sketch these familiar objects and arrangements from memory, or copy illustrations, but work from actual observation with a two-foot rule or tape measure and a sketch-book in his hand. Information gathered in this way and co-ordinated with text-book statements will make a lasting impression on his mind, standing him in good stead in examinations and throughout his professional career.

Some examples of sanitary work are not quite so easy to see in the daily round, but time and trouble taken in lifting off manhole covers of drains, in visiting sites of buildings in course of erection when drains are being laid, in watching fittings being fixed and connected to the drains and soil-pipes and inspecting the fixing of water-supply and waste pipes and similar matters will be well repaid.

Visits to museums and showrooms. Much practical help can be obtained in most large towns by visiting sanitary museums, makers' showrooms, "building centres" or building exhibitions.

Sketching ability. The ability to sketch freehand or with simple instruments, in such a way that sketches, without being to scale, are reasonably accurate in proportion, is a valuable asset. The architectural student generally has natural aptitude for drawing, which is fostered by his training, but many students in associated professions need to cultivate this aptitude and a few words of advice to them is offered below.

Freehand or scale. Sketches made during study and in examinations (except when scale drawings are asked for) should aim at showing the essential principles of design and the general proportions should be kept as accurate

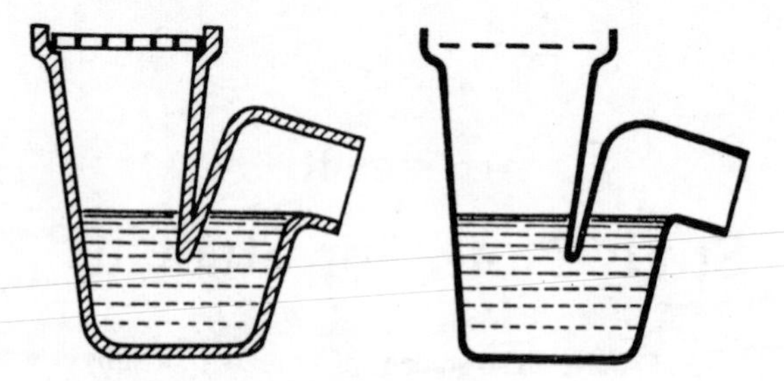

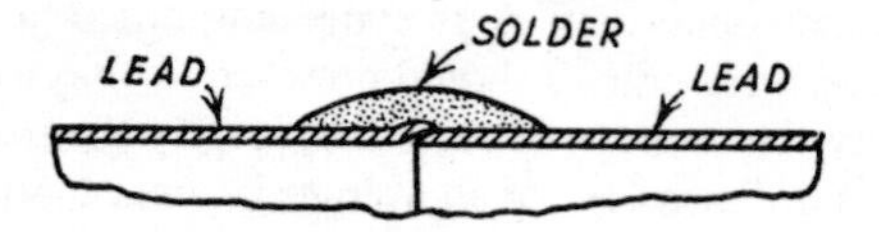
SOLDER
LEAD
LEAD

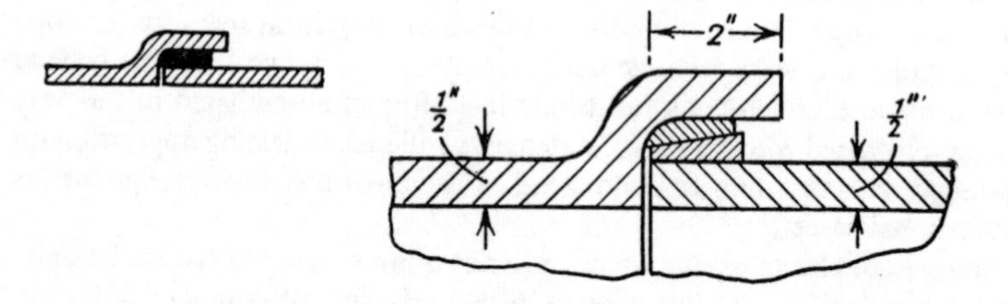
2"
1/2"
1/2"

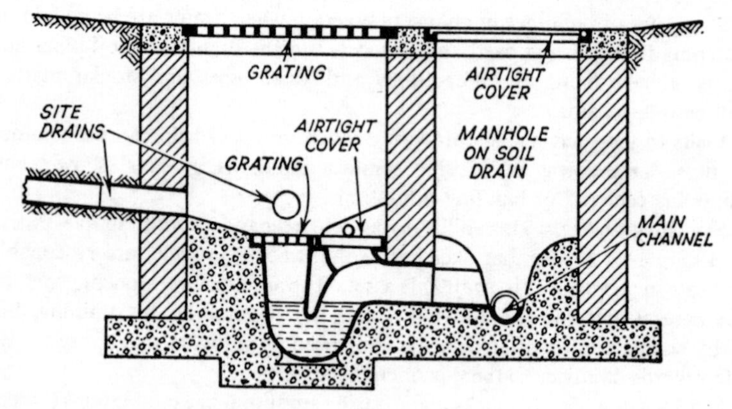
GRATING
AIRTIGHT
COVER
SITE
DRAINS
AIRTIGHT
COVER
GRATING
MANHOLE
ON SOIL
DRAIN
MAIN
CHANNEL

98

as possible, even though the work is drawn freehand and without a scale. The probability is that students will have many other subjects of study in hand at the same time, thus limiting the time available for an individual subject, and every effort should be made to simplify the work and speed up its execution. Often, a single pencil outline, drawn lightly at first and subsequently thickened, will serve to show the section of fitting, without spending time and pains in producing two parallel lines to represent the thickness of the materials of which the fitting is made. (Compare Fig. 98.) Nevertheless, when giving an enlarged detail to show how the joints between the fitting and the drains or water supply are made, it will be an advantage to show the relative thicknesses of the different materials involved (98).

Use of coloured pencils. Sometimes the use of coloured pencils or crayons will help the student to make his sketches clear to himself, either at the time or during later revision. Even in the examination room, the discriminate use of coloured pencils or crayons will help by making the students' intentions clearer and may save time by reducing the number of lines which need be drawn, but care must be taken not to make the sketches an end in themselves or to spend longer in preparing them than the questions warrant.

Size of sketches and diagrams. Size is another point to be considered. The average student starts off by making his sketches far too small. This error doubtless partly stems from the study of text-book illustrations, which are necessarily shown to a small scale for economy's sake and to keep the printed page to a convenient size. Larger diagrams are often quicker to draw and enable more information to be recorded (98).

Use of guide lines. As a help in controlling shape and proportion, the student may be referred to his schooldays, when he was probably taught to draw a symmetrical vase by the process shown in Fig. 99. The vertical line forms the backbone of a skeleton or framework, from which dimensions and proportions may be built up by the process shown.

---

98 *Simplified presentation*

(*Top*) Diagrammatic sections through a gulley trap demonstrating that simplified presentation does not necessarily mean lack of information—and *below* a detail of a wiped solder joint—a case in which retention of detail is necessary if the sketch is to impart information.

(*Centre*) Sketches to small and large scale of the STANFORD joint for stoneware drain pipes. The larger diagram gives considerably more information and is quicker and easier to draw.

(*Below*) A diagram showing clearly all necessary information without unnecessary elaboration. (The diagram illustrates the use of an accessible gulley trap to prevent foul air from a soil drain entering surface water drains connected to it. See Fig. 72, page 274.)

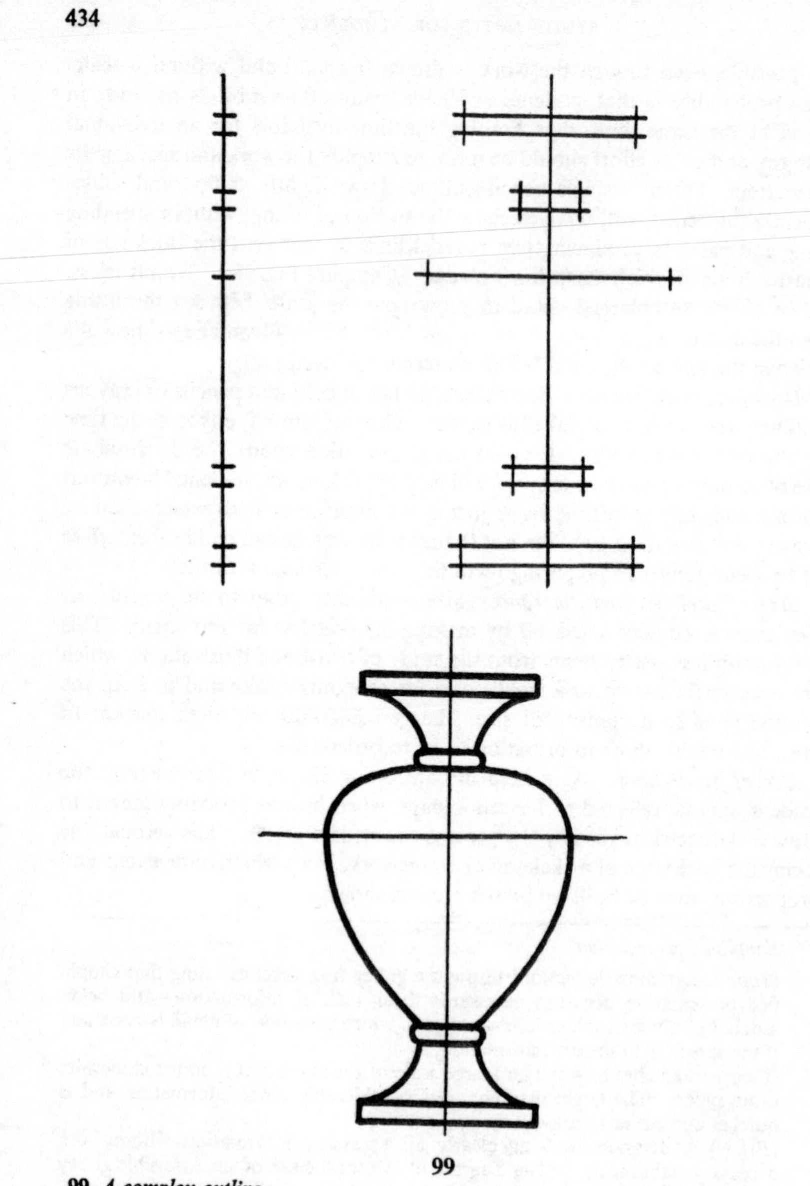

99 *A complex outline*

Stages in building up a relatively complex outline from simple guide lines.

Few items used in sanitation are symmetrical, and some base-line other than the vertical will be found more convenient in sketching them. In most trapped fittings, the water line is extremely important and the water level may well be put in first and extended to form a base-line, as in Fig. 100, which shows a useful method of sketching the common "S" trap accurately. Figure 101 shows similar principles applied to drawing an intercepting trap.

These few hints will, it is hoped, help the student in devising his own ways of keeping shapes and proportions reasonably true in his sketches.

Figuring on dimensions. A few leading dimensions on diagrams will help to preserve scale and will certainly gain marks in the examination room.

British Standard designs. The British Standards Institution exists to standardise specifications and goods in many trades for the benefit of manufacturers and consumers. The Institution has been particularly active in the Building Trade and has produced a series of standard specifications for building materials, and set sound standard designs for fittings used in buildings, so reducing the number of types and designs which the manufacturer needs to produce and the merchant to handle. These also do a great deal to simplify the work of the builder and architect.

Another reason why these standard specifications are important is that so many local authorities, in their local building and drainage bylaws, when specifying what they require for a particular case, add a note that the bylaw in question "shall be deemed to be satisfied" if the British Standard fitting is used or if the British Standard Code of Practice is followed. The student's attention is drawn to the wealth of information presented by the Institute's publications.

Unlike the manufacturer's draughtsman, who turns out working drawings in sufficient detail for the craftsman to follow, the general student will no doubt prefer to produce simplified diagrams in which general proportions are maintained but from which unwanted detail is omitted.

The architectural student who spends a good deal of his time turning out working drawings to scale in such a way that the builder or contractor can understand exactly what he is expected to put into projected buildings may sometimes find it an advantage to check his drawings by referring to the relevant British Standards.

British Standard Codes of Practice. In addition to the British Standards, there is also a series of "British Standard Codes of Practice" prepared by the Council for Codes of Practice for Building Construction and Engineering Services and which are also published by the British Standards Institution.

These are particularly helpful to students as guides to sound conventional practice.

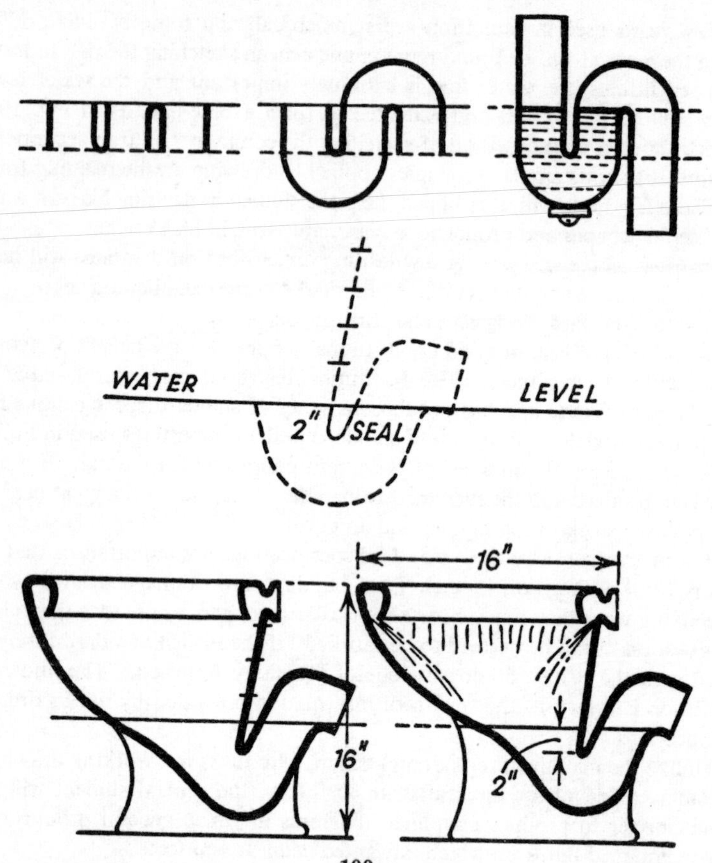

100 *Sketching traps*

(*Above*) Use of guide lines in sketching traps. Most traps are basically just bent pipes, and the diagrams simply show a longitudinal section through from back to front. The depth of the seal is important (the most usual in practice being 2 in.) and is used to set an approximate scale, so that the other proportions may be kept fairly true. A little practice will soon enable the student to draw the invert (or curved base) of the trap parallel to the seal, to form a workmanlike sketch.

(*Below*) The method applied in building up a sectional sketch from back to front of a modern washdown W.C. pan.

In this case, too, the depth of seal makes a useful guide to height of flushing rim above water level, the width of the flushing rim, the diameter of the outlet, the dimensions from front of pan to the water-supply inlet, the total height from flushing rim to floor level and so on.

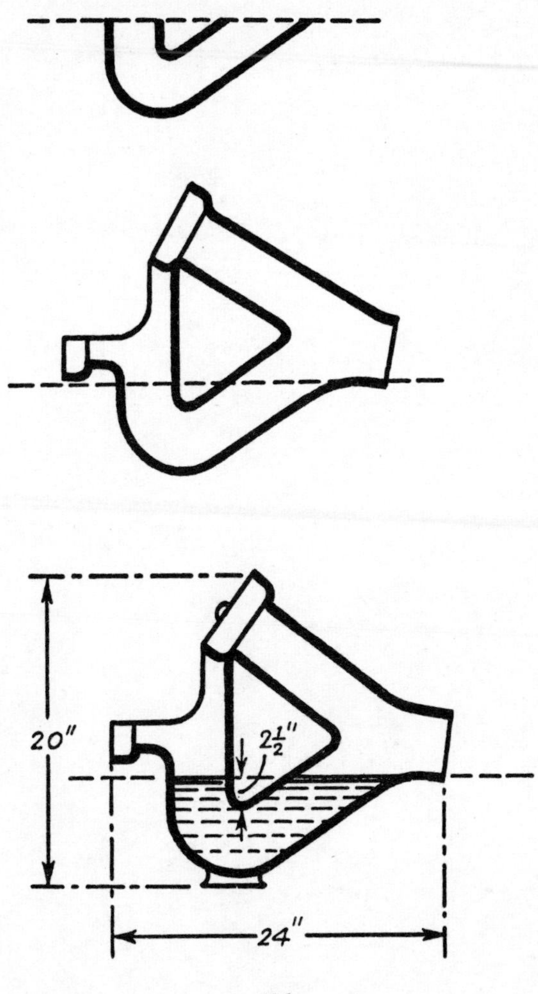

101

101 *Use of guide lines*

Many students find the intercepting trap (intercepting sewer air from house drains) very difficult to draw freehand and in correct proportions. As the diagram shows, this too responds to analysis and the use of simple guide lines. (Intercepting traps and their use are discussed in Chapter 8.)

Index